THE EDGE OF NECES~~S~~

THE EDGE OF NECESSARY

Welsh Innovative Poetry
1966-2018

Edited by John Goodby and Lyndon Davies

Published in the United Kingdom in 2018 by
Aquifer Books
(in association with Boiled String Press)

www.glasfrynproject.org.uk

ISBN: 978-1-9998367-1-9

Cover Image: David Rees Davies
from *Drawings in Search of a Title* (works on paper series 2016-2017)

Cover Design: Aquifer

AQUIFER
in association with

FOR JOHN JAMES

1939 – 2018

(the struggle for what is light
in what is dark

shone to advantage
in our backyard

'One for Rolf'

CONTENTS

The Edge of Necessary: Wales and innovative poetry

The Edge of Necessary is the first-ever anthology of Welsh modernist-influenced poetry written in English – that is, of the kind variously labelled alternative, neo-modernist, experimental, avant-garde or innovative (no single term is adequate, and this anthology simply uses the one its editors feel is the least disputable). By 'innovative' we mean the kind of poetry which registers the lessons of Modernist and contemporary formal and linguistic experiment, along with the more radical twentieth and twenty-first century discoveries in psychology, philosophy and the physical sciences. Such poetry is distinct from the even more misleadingly-named 'mainstream' poetry, which tends to work within a rather narrowly conceived rationalist empirical tradition, built around a vision of the world as comprised of objects on the one hand and a more or less unitary speaking and observing self on the other, each firmly grounded and in its place.[1] By 'Welsh', to define an equally fraught term, we mean poets who were born and /or brought up in Wales, those from elsewhere who work and write here, and others with meaningful ties to the country. Alice Entwistle's description of writers 'less accurately defined as Welsh than Wales-affiliated, or ... "elective" Welsh' covers this, although Glyn Jones's claim (adapting Conor Cruise O'Brien) that a writer's Welshness is not 'primarily a question of birth or blood or language', but 'the condition of being involved in the Welsh situation and usually of being mauled by it' more memorably conveys the sense.[2] Of course there are two literatures in Wales, and it's a notable and too little-known fact that the very first Welsh modernist poetry was written in Welsh, by the remarkable T. H. Parry-Williams, just before the First World War. However, this precedes our period, just as Welsh language poetry exceeds our knowledge, and on the advice of Welsh-speaking friends who are *au fait* with both traditions, we confine ourselves in this volume - which is already large enough, and has enough work to do - to anglophone poetry. In what follows we will explain where we draw our other boundaries, and trust that the poetry itself will bear out our demarcations and choices.

---

[1] Many poets work across the two broad areas, of course, but although the distinction is not strict, and applies rather differently to poetics than to the discursive contexts in which poetry is received, it remains a useful and necessary one. The classic analysis of the limitations of the 'mainstream' mode is Andrew Crozier's essay 'Thrills and frills: poetry as figures of empirical lyricism', in Alan Sinfield ed. *Society and Literature 1945-1970*, Methuen: London, 1983, 199-233. The self-styled 'mainstream', as Crozier explains, is what Donald Davie in 1958 described as 'the English tradition', running from Hardy, the Georgians, through mid-period Auden, to Larkin. Its later extension can be traced through adopted Northern Irish poets (primarily Heaney), via the Martians, to the likes of Carol Ann Duffy, Simon Armitage and Don Paterson.

[2] Glyn Jones, *The Dragon has Two Tongues: Essays on Anglo-Welsh Writers and Writing*, ed. Tony Brown, Cardiff: University of Wales Press, 2001, 192.

Our selection of poems covers 1966-2018, a period rich in innovatory work. We believe it is timely, both in the sense that such poetry has enjoyed a notable efflorescence in Wales in the last fifteen years, and that it is long overdue – astonishingly so, given a tradition dating back to Dylan Thomas and David Jones in the early 1930s. There has been no anthology of this kind before, unless we count the very first, *Welsh Poetry* (1944), edited by Keidrych Rhys, which included the modernist founders of twentieth century Welsh poetry in English - Jones and Thomas, but also Glyn Jones and Lynette Roberts - or *Green Horse* (1978), an excellent but partial effort, joint-edited by Meic Stephens and Peter Finch, the former with strong traditionalist tendencies and the latter leaning decidedly in the opposite direction. Other later anthologies, by Dannie Abse, Meic Stephens, and others, have either represented this kind of poetry sparingly, or not at all. This is despite the fact that a strong case could be made for innovative anglophone poetry being Wales' most outstanding contribution to twentieth century culture.

Why, then, the neglect? Partly, of course, because innovative poetry in Wales, as elsewhere in Britain and Ireland, has long suffered marginalisation by a mainstream-oriented literary-critical, academic and arts-administrative establishment. In other parts of Britain and Ireland, practitioners of such poetry were able to take refuge, after the fall-out from the 'Poetry Wars' of 1976-77, in samizdat support systems of small presses, journals, and readings.[3] However, such networks were sparser, in places non-existent even, in thinly-peopled and under-resourced Wales, and the poets more isolated and ignored than elsewhere.[4] To compound their difficulties, in Wales this institutional neglect was intensified by an ideological opposition to literary experiment of almost any kind. In the eyes of the vast majority of editors, critics and those who made the funding and programming decisions, the function of poetry in Wales, as with literature generally, was - whether this view were explicitly stated or not - to recuperate the past and lay the basis of the nation-to-be. (This cultural nationalism was often interwoven, of course, with the issue of the survival of the Welsh language, usually in ways which skewed poetic and aesthetic issues even further.)[5] To this end poetry was tasked with

---

[3] For details of the 'Poetry Wars', see Peter Barry, *Poetry Wars: British Poetry of the 1970s and the Battle of Earl's Court*, Cambridge: Salt, 2006.

[4] The anthologies include *A Various Art* (1987), *the new poetry* (1988) *Conductors of Chaos* (1995), *Out of Everywhere* (1996), and the *Oxford Anthology of Twentieth Century British and Irish Poetry* (2001). While the editors of these certainly included some Welsh innovative poetry, only the editors of *the new poetry* seem to have any sense of its range and richness.

[5] One form of this is what the historian Dai Smith has called 'linguistic culturalism', an essentialism which ties identity (including as it is expressed or defined by poetry in English) to the Welsh language. Its obsessions are succinctly identified in the refrain of Peter Elfed Lewis's 'A question of definition': 'is a monoglot Welshman [sic] a Welshman or not?' The assumption, never made explicit (since the Welsh language has little directly to do with Welsh anglophone poetry), is that linguistic priority denotes purity of identity, and that this

limiting itself to traditional metres and forms, transparent language use (decorated by the deployment of mild symbolism and metaphor), and realist description – effectively, of pretending that a well-established poetic canon existed, as elsewhere in the British Isles and Ireland, and the duty of poets was to contribute to it.[6] Modernism was a distraction, and Welsh poetry, in both languages, was held to be innately conservative. To disagree or do otherwise was viewed as unnatural and un-Welsh.

The flaw in this schema is glaringly evident; the moment of the birth of anglophone Welsh poetry of note, back in the 1930s and 1940s, had been an explosively modernist one. However, David Jones and Lynette Roberts fell silent in 1952, and Dylan Thomas died in the following year. There followed a decade-long hiatus, out of which a new generation of poets slowly emerged which had to distance itself from the distorting gravitational field of Thomas's style and reputation in particular, and did so by becoming his stylistic antithesis. The poetry of the 'Second Flowering', as it became known, was deliberately flat, downbeat, unexultant, and traditional in form, taking its cue from the realist, empirical poetic espoused by the Movement poets in England, utilising it in the creation of a verse record of Anglo-Welsh experience. All too aware of the disapproval of many in Welsh-speaking Wales at the time (Saunders Lewis had once described Anglo-Welsh poetry as a contradiction in terms), but responding to the resurgence of nationalism and Welsh language assertiveness, they invoked the traditions of the poet as local communal recorder, or

---

purity can be used to determine the 'significance' of the poetry. Erroneous though it is logically, it nevertheless adds to pressure on monoglot anglophone poets to attest to their Welshness in a populist, consumable, style. Rather than such essentialist attitudes, we prefer to celebrate the positive, outward-looking, inclusivist aspect of the language issue; namely that, from the point of view of an innovative poet in Wales, the English language in Wales cannot be taken for granted. This is a huge boon. For monoglot English writers, the presence of Cymraeg, as spoken language or verbal substratum (rather than as a political shibboleth), is a tonic and fruitful challenge to the complacency of the anglosphere. Innovative poetry has historically thrived on linguistic interaction and mélange because it heightens an awareness of language as a material medium, encouraging switchings of register, tone and syntax, wordplay and experiment. This was the basis of the energy and brilliance of the 1930s generation, and is behind the contemporary linguistic layerings and macaronic strategies of Peter Finch, Elisabeth Bletsoe and Rhys Trimble among others. It is one of the things, we would argue, that makes Wales, for all the difficulties, such a fruitful place for innovative writing.

[6] The major problem for those who wish to maintain the dominance of a post-Larkinian poetic, has always been the absence of any equivalent of its tradition. Overshadowed by the richness of Welsh language poetry, Welsh anglophone poetry came of age very late, in the 1920s and 1930s. Unlike other the smaller nation-components of the UK and Ireland, Wales does not possess the two centuries and more of anglophone poetic tradition found in Scotland and Ireland. There is no Welsh equivalent of Henryson, Douglas, Swift, Goldsmith, Burns, Mangan, and Thompson; Henry Vaughan is the isolated case which proves this rule. Welsh poetry is therefore indelibly marked by the Modernism dominant at the moment of its explosive emergence - an uncomfortable fact for those who would prefer it to have had more sedate, gradualist origins.

bardd, in Welsh literary genres such as praise poem and *cofion* (memorial poem), attempting to ingratiate themselves with the older tradition, trying, like the Irish Celtic Twilight writers of half a century before, to replicate at least some elements of it in anglophone form. The subject of this poetry of the backward look was invariably, therefore, local tales, folklore, crafts, traditions, customs, family history, communal struggle and survival, religion, history. It was admirable in its modest way, but even at its best had too much to be modest about.

The 'Second Flowering' thus became the basis for an Anglo-Welsh poetic in denial about the modernist origins of anglophone Welsh poetry. The work of Jones was abandoned to a cult. That of Thomas was read largely in terms of his later, more accessible, work. Lynette Roberts, a woman, would be almost completely forgotten. (Later, in the 1990s, with the development of Welsh Writing in English studies as a fully-fledged academic subject, the exclusion or diminishment of these powerful forebears would be given a more theoretical justification.) Out of the Second Flowering and its outriders grew an institutional nexus comprising, alongside the university literature departments, such bodies as The Welsh Books Council, Academi/Literature Wales, Seren Books, Anglo-Welsh Review and other organs which to a large extent held sway over the administrative, funding, publishing and publicity apparatus of Welsh literature. This critical and financial power-nexus, in many ways a positive development, had, with regard to the shaping of the public perception of what constituted the literary landscape in Wales, less positive effects over the years, promulgating a vision which, generally speaking, could be characterised as conservative (with a small c).

At the heart of this restrictive vision lay a deep anxiety about where the borders lay and who could be allowed to cross them. One of the reasons for this was a fear of anglicisation per se - although, as we have said, the fundamentals of the Second Flowering poetic ironically resembled nothing so much as those of the Movement, a very English phenomenon. Another was undoubtedly as a defensive response to the British Poetry Revival. This was a resurgence of modernist-influenced poetry which drew its energies and examples from US poetry of the 1950s - Projectivist, Beat, Black Mountain, San Francisco Renaissance and New York School. Its key text was Donald Allen's *The New American Poetry 1945-1960* (1960), and its impact in the 1960s was by no means confined to London - one of its distinguishing features was its healthily regionalist aspect, and it flourished in Birmingham, Newcastle, Liverpool, Bristol and Glasgow as much as in the capital. Another of its features was its reactivation of 'native' modernists, such as W. S. Graham, Basil Bunting (whose *Briggflatts* appeared in 1966) and David Jones (who would publish his last book, *The Sleeping Lord*, in 1974). All of this had its effect on young poets from Wales as much as those from Scotland, England and Ireland. Among these were John James and Peter Finch, both from Cardiff, the former working outside Wales, in Cambridge, the other inside Wales. By 1966, both were rising to the challenge of these new poetries and making their own voices heard.

It is against this background that a bullish editorial of 1967 in *Poetry Wales* by Meic Stephens, its then editor, may be understood. All the 'new [Welsh] poets' of any 'significance', Stephens opined, had to have 'roots ... in a particular community'. They also had to be 'willing to associate with Welshmen (sic) and have their work discussed with reference to the culture of Wales', and 'must be rooted in' and speak for their 'communities'. Announcing that *Poetry Wales* would be overtly 'nationalist', Stephens asserted: 'It worries me to see so many, about a third, of the leading poets resident in England. There is no good reason except "the whistle of the English pound", to keep Welshmen in London and the English provinces these days and I insist that poets should be the first to live among the people and the scenes they praise, lest all suffer.'[7] The comments stem from an understandable pragmatic desire to protect a Wales-based poetry scene after decades in which that had been unviable. But the phrasing also registers the fear of a nascent arts bureaucracy that experimentalism challenged its ideological co-ordinates. Put another way, the hybridity, fragmentation and linguistic promiscuity of modernist styles of writing are a mortal threat to any notion of culture and identity based on fixed essences. Stephens' response to this is to propound an essentialist poetics of belonging which shades into blood and soil atavism.

The reactionary prescriptiveness of the *Poetry Wales* editorial derives from a monolithic vision, and the singularity of the definite article ('*the* culture of Wales') is revealing. What flows from this is a classic instance of something we will, sadly, find repeated throughout the history of mainstream poetry in Wales - the preparedness to limit, even diminish, the common cultural store in order to maintain one's rigid conception of how it ought to be (or, in plain English, cut off one's nose to spite one's face). This is the only way to explain a preparedness to exclude what are admitted to be 'leading' poets simply because they are unwilling to remain in Wales, 'associate with Welshmen' and become communal mouthpieces, and the manner in which the sacrosanctness of an anachronistic, narrowly nationalist ideology, is allowed to trump what should be the primary consideration, poetic quality.

---

[7] See Meic Stephens, 'The Second Flowering', in Cary Archard, ed., *Poetry Wales: 25 Years*, Bridgend: Seren Books, 1990, pp. 26-27.

Predictably, this was a recipe for disaster. We can see now that the delegitimisation of Welsh diaspora poets, many of them associated with the British Poetry Revival, ensured that, as the 1970s wore on, the 'Second Flowering'-descended mainstream was sealed in on itself. Increasingly devoid of new ideas, it nevertheless ignored the many important Welsh poets living in England on the grounds that innovative poetry lacked roots, did not sufficiently 'reflect' the nation, was 'foreign'. Even those innovative poets who did possess the necessary residential qualifications were spurned. Noting the deafening silence that greeted publication of the Cardiffian Gerard Casey's *South Wales Echo* in 1973, Tony Conran shrewdly observed: 'Lip-service was paid to David Jones ... but woe betide a poet who followed in his footsteps'.[8] Although the Second Flowering succeeded in renewing its cadre – Gillian Clarke, Nigel Jenkins, Tony Curtis and Robert Minhinnick spring to mind – whatever the technical qualities of the work in question, its aesthetic and ideological standpoint was still very much bound up with the discursive/lyrical/empirical register of orthodox Anglo-Welsh versification. Where there was political radicalism it was never matched with the linguistic radicalism necessary to offer any kind of serious challenge to the settled language of power.

Stephens had prophesied in 1967 that 'the big danger threatening Anglo-Welsh verse [is that it] may continue to be peripheral, both in Wales and in England', and, ironically, the poetics he and others espoused meant that this was precisely what happened. The Anglo-Welsh lyric became merely formulaic, and mainstream poetry more generally was a pale, Welsh-tinged imitation of the English equivalent.[9] By the 1980s mainstream inability to renew itself was painfully apparent in the fact that its most visible figure seemed, once again, to be R. S. Thomas, a poet born before the First World War. More ironic still was the fact that the only other Wales-domiciled

---

[8] Tony Conran, 'Poetry Wales and the Second Flowering', in M. Wynn Thomas, ed., *Welsh Writing in English*, A Guide to Welsh Literature: Vol. VII, Cardiff: University of Wales Press, 2003, p. 252.
[9] John Davies's poem 'How to write Anglo-Welsh poetry' skewers the limitations of this kind of poem perfectly:
... First, apologise for not being able
to speak Welsh. Go on: apologise. ...
Spray place-names around ...
a mining town is best, of course,
for impact, and you'll know what to say
about Valley Characters, the heart's dust
and the rest. ...
Style now. Nothing fancy: write
all your messages as prose then chop
them up--it's how deeply red and green
they bleed that counts.

Welsh poet with an international reputation, Peter Finch, was a thoroughgoing experimentalist.

It's necessary to say something about Peter Finch at this stage, since he has been used to prove both that innovative poetry has had a good deal in Wales, and that it has had a bad one. This dual reception is the product of his anomalous status. Finch had emerged in the mid-1960s, very early in the process of renewing Welsh poetry, single-handedly producing *Second Aeon* (1966-75), a small press poetry journal with substantial claims to be the best of its era. His already high profile, varied skills, energy, and sheer excellence as a poet meant that he could not be ignored, and he was able to forge some links with the emerging bureaucracy in the late 1960s when it was still relatively fluid. What should, in theory, have been an antagonistic relationship, thus developed into something productive, if inevitably prickly at times, as both sides found they could make use of each other. Finch was able to act as the maverick outlier of the new set-up, promoting innovative work in his successive roles in managing the Oriel Bookshop, acting as impresario to Chapter Arts Centre, and running Academi in the 1990s and 2000s. While power entailed accepting constraints, up to a point he made it serve his own radical agenda. Unable to exclude or fully co-opt him, the establishment was able in its turn to benefit from Finch's unique ability and status. The price he paid for this was to be labelled 'Wales's one-man avant-garde', to be used as an exception to prove the rule of the conservatism of Welsh poetry. (The catch-phrase was later taken up by conservative academics as a prophylactic formula for damping curiosity about other Welsh avant-garde poets).[10]

The poor representation of Welsh poets in the Hulse, Kennedy and Morley *New Poetry* anthology of 1993, and their complete absence from the 1994 New Gen promotion seems to have been a humiliation too far for the 1960s generation's stewardship of Welsh poetry.[11] This was the point at which the old guard were eased out and serious attempts made to renew the mainstream, aided by a new professionalism and critical rigour. These would largely be supplied by Welsh Writing in English, as it established itself as a subject on the curricula of Welsh universities in the 1990s and 2000s.[12] The

---

[10] See M. Wynn Thomas, 'Homage to Peter Finch', *Wales In Action*, Spring 2005, p.25: 'For 40 years [Finch] has been the Welsh avant-garde.'

[11] It would seem that a series of warnings, such as the lack of Welsh poets in the Motion and Morrison *Penguin Book of British Poetry* (1981), had gone unheeded. (Tony Curtis had won the National Poetry Competition in 1984, so the official thinking seemed to go, so all must be well.)

[12] Welsh Writing in English (WWE) is the name now preferred for what was known as 'Anglo-Welsh Literature'. Its rise was based on the work of academics such as M. Wynn Thomas, Stephen Knight, and Jane Aaron in the 1980s and 1990s, following on from that of founding figures such as Glyn Jones and Tony Conran. It takes officially-constituted form as

dynamism of the Blair government, after eighteen years of Tory rule (which had been particularly harsh and demoralizing in Wales), and the winning of the Devolution vote in 1997, meant the times were propitious for change. Devolution in particular meant that some of the old, polarised ways of thinking about Welsh identity began to crumble. The key buzzwords were 'pluralist' and 'inclusive', and their promise seemed to be borne out by one of the most notable and hopeful features of 2000s poetry, namely the appearance of a swathe of young women poets, and collectively a much-needed challenge to the ingrained gender bias and boyoism which had long disfigured the Welsh cultural scene.[13] At this point, too, a small group of older poets - Gwyneth Lewis, Robert Minhinnick, Oliver Reynolds and Stephen Knight - enjoyed British, not just Welsh, reputations. Ian Gregson's *The New Poetry in Wales* (2007) went so far as to claim that 'Currently much of the most exciting poetry in Britain is being written in Wales', making the case for a Welsh mainstream which had at last acquired a critical mass.[14] In 2015, the idea that Devolution had brought about some kind of step-change in the quality of Welsh poetry would even be endorsed by a Leverhulme Trust-funded research project, to the tune of £232,000.[15]

---

the Association for Welsh Writing in English (AWWE), and holds an annual conference at Gregynog Hall. Through its links with the Welsh Books Council, University of Wales Press, and the publishers Parthian and Seren, WWE has rediscovered and made available a swath of out-of-print and neglected Welsh writers and, following the model of Irish literary studies in the 1970s and 1980s, interpreted them to create a nationally-defined field of study. In doing so it has supplanted the amateurism of an older generation of literary operators, both ideologically and in the sense that those taught at university by WWE academics have increasingly become those who administer and run the machinery of the Welsh arts and literary establishment. Despite its exemplary work in recovering a Welsh anglophone literary tradition within Wales itself, however, Welsh Writing in English as a discipline and AWWE as a group (at least at senior leadership level) has not fully broken with earlier essentialism, and tends to avoid tackling the hybridity of Anglo-Welshness as a cultural formation, and the work of Welsh writers who live outside Wales, or who do not place 'Wales' thematically at the heart of their writing. Finessing essentialist positions under cover of selectively-applied critical theory has not dispelled introversion and anglophobia; a lack of clout in the larger world of English literary studies, in marked contrast to Irish and Scottish literary studies, has been one result. If it would be unfair to regard WWE and AWWE as an atavism-laundering operation *per se*, to the extent that it does remain one it remains trapped by its past.
[13] For example, Zoë Skoulding, Deryn Rhys-Jones, Rhian Edwards, Sarah Corbett, Samantha Rhydderch, Katherine Gray, and Tiffany Atkinson, all of whom published first collections in the 2000s.
[14] Ian Gregson, *The New Poetry in Wales*, Cardiff: University of Wales Press, 2007,
[15] The Devolved Voices project, led by Peter Barry, Kathryn Gray and Matthew Jarvis, ran from 2012-15 at Aberystwyth University, to test the thesis that the amount of good poetry written by Welsh poets had increased since 1997. Poetic success was measured largely by the approbation of a narrowly-defined mainstream 'poetic community' and its 'opinion formers' and agents - publishers, reviewers, critics, journal editors, prize judges, most of them London-oriented or based in London. See: https://wordpress.aber.ac.uk/devolved-voices/

But how real was this change? Mainstream poetry has undoubtedly become brighter and buzzier, as well as more professional and polished, in the last twenty years. In poetic terms, however, it seems to have barely altered, possibly because the mantra of 'pluralism', on which it rests, is invariably defined in marketized, consumer terms, not those of poetic value as such. The 'choices' on offer have never included that of innovative poetry. As John Mathias put it, commenting on various mainstream anthologies published around the time of the millennium: 'Ideas of pluralism are extended in these books to race, religion, region, class, language, gender, sexual preference - to everything, in fact, except poetics.'[16]

This statement could be applied with equal force to the Welsh anthology which embodies a similar change-but-no-change position: Meic Stephens's *Poetry 1900-2000: one hundred poets from Wales* (2007). For all the pretensions to summation embodied in its title, just five of the forty-six poets in our own anthology are represented in Stephens's. As for Gregson's study, even in 2007 'excitement' was not a word many would have associated with Sheenagh Pugh and Duncan Bush, the subjects of his first chapter, while the subjects of three others (Lewis, Minhinnick, and Reynolds) had all found their voices before Devolution.[17] Bizarrely, such gifted figures as John James, Wendy Mulford, David Greenslade, Chris Torrance, Peter Meilleur, Paul Evans and David Annwn do not even rate a mention, let alone discussion. Increasingly, as we examine the makeover of the mainstream in the late 1990s and into 2000s, what we see is evidence not of fundamental alteration, but of a palace revolution, a shifting around of the same old furniture. It is time, then, to look at the real renewal, the one missed by Gregson, and cold-shouldered by Welsh Writing in English studies - namely, that constituted by innovative poetics and poetry, its persistence against the odds, and its recent resurgence.

When we (the editors of this book) first met in May 2008, it was immediately apparent that we had a similar interest in exploring the Welsh experimental poetry world in greater depth. We were both

---

[16] John Mathias, 'British Poetry at Y2K', http://www.electronic-bookreview.com (2000)
[17] Gregson's study also has chapters on Minhinnick, Lewis, Reynolds, Stephen Knight, Pascale Petit and Paul Henry, and 'Some Younger Poets' - Deryn Rees-Jones, Owen Sheers, Patrick McGuinness, Sarah Corbett, Tiffany Atkinson, Samantha Wynne-Rhydderch and Zoë Skoulding. Gregson does not give all of these a waiver to excellence by any means; he is critical of Owen Sheers's 'young codgerism', for example. However his argument – that writers from a minority culture 'forced' (sic) to write in the language of a dominant culture have a special opportunity to 'evolve a literature which undermines the stale authority of the major culture' - is itself undermined by its failure to ask the question of how a culture can be undermined by using the same stale rhetorical forms approved by that culture. Welsh innovative poetry, which does formally challenge mainstream-derived norms, is registered only in the brief mention of Skoulding, the one consistently innovative poet to whom Gregson (briefly) refers.

tired of the blandness and predictability of much Welsh poetry of the kind endorsed by the big poetry publishers and wanted to do our bit towards thawing out the existing deep-freeze, to extending the opportunities for innovative writers in terms of publishing, performing and critical discussion. In a series of *Poetry Wales* articles written around 2000, Lyndon (our apologies for the awkward lurch into the third person at this point) had sketched out a more complex vision of the relationship between language, landscape, politics, and poetry than that allowed for by the identity-obsessed discourses of the time, and called for a poetry to match it. About the same time, John had been exploring what happened to Welsh poetic modernism after Dylan Thomas, and had discovered John James, but was unable to find anyone in Welsh academia who knew – let alone valued – his work.

Putting our partial knowledge and much larger ignorances together, we decided it was time that the kind of poetry we both appreciated deserved a platform. If we could answer some of the questions we had about Welsh experimentalism in the process, so much the better. And so, in June 2009, the first of four Hay-on-Wye Poetry Jamborees took place. Held in mild defiance of the commercialism and poetry-lite programme of the Hay Literature Festival proper, it ran over the Whit weekend, and was Welsh-themed, with Peter Finch, Peter Meilleur, John James, Wendy Mulford and Chris Torrance among the main readers. Upwards of forty other Welsh and British poets showed up, strutted their stuff, mingled, swapped books, struck up friendships. As time went on, and three further Jamborees extended the success of the first one, we both discovered a series of fragmentary histories - of writers, meetings, publications and readings - which allowed us to gradually piece together the so-far untold tale of the fortunes of innovative poetry in Wales.

It turned out, for a start, that Welsh poets had contributed as much as any others in these islands to the British Poetry Revival.[18] Wales had been, for example, at the forefront of the international Concrete poetry movement in the late 1960s, spearheaded by Finch (whose 'Sunpoem' we include), but also including Philip Jenkins, Alison Bielski, and Swansea-based Englishman John Powell Ward (*from alphabet to logos*, a notable work of the movement, is also excerpted here; one of the highpoints of the third, 2011 Jamboree, was an exhibition of John's original MSS.) It turned out, moreover, that Concrete poetry continued to have a vital Welsh presence in the shape of Peter Meilleur, aka Childe Roland, an Anglo-Québécois poet,

---

[18] This has a handily symbolic moment of origin - what we might call its 'Wales Visitation' moment, to use the title of Allen Ginsberg's poem - following Ginsberg's visit to Wales after the Albert Hall Poetry Happening in summer 1966, and his subsequent meetings with Peter Finch and John James. This counter-cultural laying on of hands coincided with the founding of Finch's *Second Aeon*, and is recorded in James' 'To Allen Ginsberg' (collected in *Mmm ... Ah Yes*, 1967, James' first publication).

who had moved to Llangollen in 1979 and had been nurturing an impeccably inventive, idiosyncratic, and playful strain of poetry there ever since - an exemplary case of the way in which the Welsh experience of innovative poetry has embodied fluidity, cultural exchange and a disregard for national barriers. It was clear that the lifeblood of much of the best of modern Welsh poetry had drawn sustenance, not disqualification, from 'the English pound', from the inflow and outflow of talent and ideas. Just as Chris Torrance, to take one example, had been arriving in 1970 to settle in the Upper Neath Valley and write *Acrospirical Meanderings in a Tongue of the Time*, the classic hippy poetry collection (we intend this term in its most positive sense), and to begin work on *The Magic Door* (his major long psychogeographical poem, published in 2017), so the careers of the Welsh-born John James, Wendy Mulford, Philip Jenkins and Paul Evans were already starting to thrive outside Wales, in Cambridge, Nottingham and London, each contributing to the Revival in significant ways.

James, for example, had co-edited the journal *Resuscitator* in Bristol and was closely associated with *The English Intelligencer* by the mid-1960s His 1960s and 1970s poetry crackles with energy, wit and formal daring, is subtle and cosmopolitan in range, yet is often intelligently populist too, in a way which shows him to be one of the few poets able to adapt Ginsberg and O'Hara to British contexts. Its Welshness is undemonstrative yet unmistakably there, in subject matter and, more deeply, in a blend of swagger in the face of, and at a staged distance from, 'the saxon heartland'. Paul Evans, likewise, was initially a brilliant exponent of the late-1960s 'cool' style, although - fascinatingly - he had come to write poetry which in certain respects resembles that of R. S. Thomas by the time of his tragic early death in 1990. Philip Jenkins edited the Nottingham magazine *Sotto Voce*, whose contents page (for issue 3, July 1974) shows just how close a young Welsh poet was to the avant-garde pulse of his day: his name appears with those of Bruce Andrews, Ted Berrigan, Thomas A. Clark, Cid Corman, Ulli McCarthy, Alice Notley, Ron Padgett and Nicholas Zerbrugg. Jenkins, an exemplary case of a Concrete poet evolving into a more searching writer, is another part of the rich innovative legacy yet to receive due recognition; to this day his masterpiece, *Cairo*, remains unpublished in complete form.

By the mid-1970s, Wendy Mulford, raised near Abergavenny ('still [my] home' she calls it), had mentored and worked with Denise Riley in Cambridge, founded Street Editions and pioneered the struggle for the visibility of women in the avant-garde scene. In a way which more conservative champions of women's writing might study with profit, she made the case for the liberatory potential of experimental writing for feminists; far from failing by not directly advancing the nationalist cause, Mulford regarded it, rightly understood, as a more profound means for exploring the gendered self as it is situated within language, in order to 'destruct the lie of culture'. As a leading figure in this field, Mulford would later be the natural choice to write the 'After. Word' to the seminal international anthology of innovative women's poetry, *out of everywhere* (1996). None of this precluded her writing a poem-sequence called *Alltud* (2007) (whose title is a Welsh term for 'exile'), as purists might suppose it would.

Back in Wales itself, incomers made a vibrant contribution to the nation's poetry culture. Pete Hodgkins' journals *Not Poetry* (1976-80) and the seminal *Poetry Information* (1974-78), as well as his Galloping Dog Press, operated out of Swansea, for example. Nearby was Cwm Nedd Press, which ran for twenty years, 1975-95, and published Torrance, Maillard, and Sinclair. Even in the depressed 1980s - that is, in the wake of the failed first Devolution vote, deindustrialization and the Miners' strike - a string of new journals were born, including *Element 5*, *No Walls*, *Maximum Load*, *Kite*, *Madoc*, and *Spectrum*. Predictably, more Welsh-born poets left Wales than stayed as recession continued its ravages; they included David Annwn who, significantly, was profoundly shaped before he left Wales as a student at Aberystwyth University. There, for many years, the English poet Jeremy Hooker was a beacon to seekers of non-standard poetic fare, teaching and fostering interest in David Jones and contemporary US poets. (Later, living in Wakefield, in contact with English innovative poets, Annwn would shift from a roots-baring, jazz-influenced style, to the futuristic radical wordplay perfected in *Bela Fawr's Cabaret* - another case of a Welsh poet leaving Wales and, in doing so, expanding the imaginative definition of Wales by hybridising other traditions.) Significant too, in the era of hard-faced Thatcherism, was the energetic Cardiff performance scene. This grew out of the performers of Cabaret 246 - mainly composed of students and former students from Chris Torrance's Creative Writing Group - which flourished throughout the 1980s, generating its own press and magazines. Crucially, this activity was the launch-pad for several later English-born incomers, including Graham Hartill, Chris Broadribb, Elisabeth Bletsoe and Phil Maillard, all of whom, Bletsoe apart, stayed to live and write in Wales.

In the 1990s a centre of innovative activity had appeared in North Wales, centred on Ian Davidson, a former tutee of Ralph Hawkins's at the University of Essex, and Zoë Skoulding, both lecturers at Bangor University. Skoulding's *Skald* magazine became a locus of sporadic, but high quality activity throughout the 1990s and 2000s. In 2003 *Skald* published Davidson's *On Wales*, a pamphlet anthology of a dozen poems (by Tom Raworth, Lee Harwood, Andrew Duncan, Peter Riley and others) 'which refer to Wales, [and are] written by poets who don't live here [although] ... some of them were born or have lived in Wales, or have strong family ties.' This was a quietly subversive gesture; by deliberately using several poets with only a tenuous link to Wales - in some cases simply a visit, or passing-through - Davidson broadened the legitimacy of a poetic interest in Wales which extended beyond blood ties and residency, making it one of the forebears of our own anthology.

In South Wales, meanwhile, the immensely versatile David Greenslade had begun publishing in the late 1980s, his work having emerged in part out of the battles for Welsh language rights, as the title of the pamphlet *Burning Down the Dosbarth* indicates (Greenslade's work, like that of Newport's Chris Paul, who in his time has stood for election as a Plaid councillor, reminds us of the important truth that neither the Welsh language, nor Welsh nationalism, are incompatible with innovative writing; rather, the imaginative blockages occur when these things acquire an essentialist, xenophobic aspect). Perhaps the most prolific and innovative Welsh poet of his generation, Greenslade is the author of one of the most impressive single collections by a Welsh poet of the last thirty years *Each Broken Object*, (1998). Like Steven Hitchins and Rhys Trimble, Greenslade also often collaborates with visual artists, and organizes what were once called 'happenings' (his setting of a trail of salt around the Welsh Office in Cardiff, was one of the more memorable). There are shamanistic aspects to these performances and enactments, which calculatedly renew the Welsh bardic tradition while displaying a postmodern awareness of its potentialities and possible pitfalls.

Perhaps the most astonishing single publication of the 1990s was that of the triple-authored collection *However Introduced to the Soles* (1995), by some way the most deliriously iconoclastic volume ever published on Welsh soil. It owed its existence to Niall Quinn, who gathered his own work and that of two friends, Nick Macias and Nic Laight, the latter a member of the Noumena Writers Group run by John Evans at Pontypridd's Club y Bont in 1989. *Soles* was a worthy inheritor of the traditions of Dada, Fluxus and L=A=N=G=U=A=G=E poetry, blending verbal debris and lyric ranting in a way which outdoes even Finch or Iain Sinclair, another Cardiffian, at their most charismatically possessed. In a critical culture worthy of its avant-garde, this single book would already have spawned half a dozen PhDs. As it is, work from *Soles* is reprinted in this anthology for the first time, with the story of its origins having to wait for an as-yet-unwritten history.

As was the case elsewhere in Britain, Welsh innovative poetry started becoming more visible in the early 2000s; this was its key moment of emergence, following submergence in the late 1970s. One major reason was the burgeoning new technologies of email, the web, and print on demand. These helped innovative poetry everywhere to overcome its ghettoisation, and were crucial in Wales, where they connected individuals who were particularly far-flung, and helped to weaken officialdom's grip on events, publication and information flows. As if to make the point, it was as a print on demand title from Salt that the *Collected Poems* of John James appeared in 2002. Bringing together nineteen pamphlets and collections which had appeared over thirty-five years, this was a turning-point in the reception of innovative poetry in Wales, and gave many a sense for the first time of a brilliant, hitherto unsuspected dimension to Welsh poetry. In the same year Wendy Mulford's selected poems, *and suddenly, supposing*, was also published. Taken together, as the work of two major poets who had lived their adult lives largely outside Wales, considered themselves Welsh, and wrote with Wales in mind, these volumes gestured towards a vast, unacknowledged poetic hinterland, within as well as without the national territory.

Another reason for increased visibility was *Poetry Wales*. This was a journal which had always been well-handled, and had established itself as one of the best of its kind in Britain; but, from 1997, under the editorship of Robert Minhinnick (whose own poetry was at this time acquiring ever greater linguistic freedom and scope) it became one of the few literary organs in the English-speaking world to give fair representation to both mainstream and innovative poetries. Zoë Skoulding, from 2008 to 2014, and Nia Davies since, have each maintained this genuinely pluralist position. It is in stark contrast to the London-based equivalent, *Poetry Review*, over the same twenty year period, the brief reign of Robert Potts and David Herd apart. Whatever happens of significance has a good chance of being registered by the journal of record, while important events in the innovative poetry of the past, once doomed to waste their sweetness on the desert air, can reclaim our attention, and become part of what happens now.

As the 2000s progressed, other rediscoveries occurred, feeding contemporary activity - Lynette Roberts's great neomodernist epic *Gods With Stainless Ears* was republished for the first time since 1952 in 2005, a *Selected Poems* of Paul Evans appeared in 2009, works such as *Baritone Compass* (2010) were published by Philip Jenkins's new Baked Alaska imprint, while Boiled String did the same for Peter Meilleur's *Ham & Jam* (2009) and other titles. Across the years the occluded achievements of Welsh innovative poetry revealed themselves; more alternative histories surfaced from the murk of mainstream oblivion, connections were made across decades, highs and lows exposed by the receding waters of a carefully cultivated ignorance. A new landscape hove into view, and it offered a context in which middle generation poets, such as David Annwn, Zoë Skoulding, Ian Davidson and David Greenslade, and younger ones such as Chris Paul, Rhys Trimble and Stephen Hitchins, could be properly set for the first time; that is, be considered as part of a gapped, yet near-continuous enterprise to develop an alternative radical poetic practice in, of and about Wales, ongoing since the 1960s, but reconnecting too with the modernist founding moment of modern Welsh poetry back in the 1930s.

The academic-critical response to this efflorescence has, predictably, been disappointing. Vested interests and established reputations were, and are, at stake: surveying the scene one is reminded of John Berger's observation that 'Every tradition forbids the asking of certain questions about what really happened to you'. A praiseworthy attempt to deal with the revelations sketched above was Matthew Jarvis's overview essay 'An absent art? "Alternative" poetry since the Second Flowering', published in *Poetry Wales* in 2008, which mentioned Gerard Casey, John James, Graham Hartill, Zoë Skoulding, Wendy Mulford, Chris Torrance and Peter Finch. The essay has a slightly tentative air, and Jarvis at no point considers the possibility that what he calls the 'alternative' or 'parallel' tradition, through its profound questioning of the nature of language and poetry might actually present some kind of a challenge to the orthodox operations of the established canon, but he at least tackled the subject (and that of Welsh Concrete poetry, too, in another good essay). Aside from one or two other honourable exceptions, such as Alice Entwistle, WWE studies has to date, however, made a point of loudly ignoring the subject.[19] Thus, a Welsh edition of *Angel Exhaust*, published in 2010, which included seventy pages of innovative poetry, a twenty-page timeline, and articles on Roberts, Finch, Meilleur, and experimentalism in Welsh language poetry, went unreviewed. The standard tactic in dealing with innovative work, a few tokenistic mentions aside, is still to hope it will go away, or to distract from, dilute or diminish its importance. Laura Wainwright's recent *New Territories in Modernism* (2018), the first critical monograph on the subject, is a pioneering break with this tradition, and its coverage of a neglected field is admirable in many ways. Yet the price paid for its positive reception by WWE studies is only too clear in its deliberate evasion of nationalism's antagonism towards modernism (without which modernism's trajectory in Wales cannot be understood), its lack of a sense of the importance of form, and its domestication of modernism more generally, symbolised in the clumsy reduction of Dylan Thomas to a verbal equivalent of Salvador Dalí.[20]

Our response to the threat of narrowing and dissolution is to widen the franchise of Welsh poetry, while insisting on genuine innovation.

---

[19] See Alice Entwistle, *Poetry, Geography, Gender: Women Rewriting Contemporary Wales*, Cardiff, University of Wales Press, 2013. Among the poets included in this anthology, this deals with, or mentions in passing, Helen Lopez, Francesca Wynne Rhydderch and Nerys Williams.

[20] Laura Wainwright, *New Territories in Modernism: Anglophone Welsh Writing 1930-1949*, Cardiff: University of Wales Press, 2018.

This is why this anthology includes poets not usually, if at all, found in Welsh poetry anthologies, and several who have never been included in them. It is why the likes of Elisabeth Bletsoe and John Powell Ward, poets who came to Wales and have since left it, but were marked by it (and made their mark on it), are included. It is why Ralph Hawkins, shaped by his Welsh family links but never a resident, is here. We've also included poets who work on the cusp between mainstream and more innovative practices, such as Rhian Saadat, Zoë Brigley Thompson and Nerys Williams. We feel particularly privileged to introduce, for the first time in English translation, the remarkable Breton-domiciled Welsh poet, Heather Dohollau, brought to our attention by the scholar-translator Clémence O'Connor.[21] On occasion we have been arbitrary - Paul Griffiths, born near Bridgend, has spent his adult life in France, and has nothing to say 'about' Wales in his work; but for us, he does not necessarily have to. An accident of birth allows us to include an interesting writer from Wales, and that is good enough. We have drawn lines - one of us (he shall remain nameless) wished to include a Welsh-influenced section of Briggflatts, sections of Richard Caddell's 'For the Fallen: A Reading of Y Gododdin', and Bill Griffiths's and Louis Zukofsky's renderings of the same poem, as well as Griffiths's of early Welsh poems on winter - but was overruled; Peter Riley's Lleyn Poems were considered, as were John Wilkinson's Sarn Helen (anyone wishing to acquire a full and nuanced idea of the impact of writing about, and through, Wales, should certainly read these works).

There was much discussion, too, about certain poets whom one or both of us respect greatly in their fields as writers and critics, some of whom were and are proselytisers for innovative practices, but whose work, however distinguished, didn't fit the terms of reference for a book tending towards the more radical end of the spectrum. (Jeremy Hooker and Tony Conran, excellent poet-critics both, fell into this category.) There may be another, different kind of book to assemble which will include them all, but this is one is what it is, and choices had to be made if it was to retain a modicum of cogency and direction.

---

[21] Dohollau's is the most striking case in WWE studies of a blind eye being turned to an innovative female poet since Lynette Roberts. Senior WWE scholars have been alerted to the existence of her poetry more than once in the last decade, but the information has never been acted upon. Given the exceptional quality of her work we can only assume that this has been because Dohollau's innovative qualities and Frenchness were viewed as a threat to WWE's nationalist-reflectionist aesthetic. And yet - piercing and modernistically self-aware, elliptically haunting and humane as it is - Dohollau's poetry is writing which any critical tradition worth its salt should be proud to claim. It gives a novel and exciting dimension to Welsh literature - comparable, admittedly in a lesser way, to that lent by Beckett to Irish literature. We are proud to be publishing English translations of her work here for the very first time.

Innovative poetry, in recent years, has fought its way to a point where, in anglophone Welsh poetry as a whole, it is now approaching a situation of at least equality with more conventional strands, in terms of institutional mechanisms and critical attention, refusing to stoically accept the place in the shadows once assigned to it. It has called out a cultural apparatus which operates in lock-step with its political paymasters and too often treats writers as functionaries of the Welsh tourist board, and is beginning to find it can survive quite well without its support. Small presses dedicated to innovative work, among them Boiled String, The Literary Pocket Book, and Aquifer Books, have sprung up. E-zines, such as *Junction Box* and *ctrl+alt-del* are going strong. New journals, readings, groups and events abound, among them Ric Hool's legendary Hen and Chickens series, Lumin, the Ghost Jams, Cardiff Poetry Experiment, Bangor International Poetry Festival, The Black Mountain Festival and the Glasfryn Seminars. Ongoing collective and joint-authored projects, like Rhys Trimble's mash-up of Giraldus Cambrensis or Stephen Hitchins' Canalchemy, are redefining the role of the individual and the collective in Welsh poetics. Younger innovative poets are not only productive, but continuing to develop and becoming more varied and skilled as writers through successive collections.

Predictably, the old establishment routine still maunders on, whereby a few personable but reliably undemanding practitioners are puffed and buffed up to be the face of poetry for the nation. 'New', 'vital', 'young', easily consumable mainstream 'voices' are continually being found, and equally continually failing to develop beyond the comfortable populist mode their backers insist upon, apparently unaware of the irony that the authentic Anglo-Welsh article they are touted as actually derives from an increasingly enfeebled scion of a once-vigorous English tradition. As Peter Finch has put it: 'Larkin after Thomas Hardy   Motion after Larkin   Sheers after Motion Unpolluted in soft ignorance don't bother doesn't bother too tired on the sofa poems like Everready torch bulbs circa 1958' ("The State"). Some much-lauded recent publications actually offer little more than a regression to the 'Valley Characters' cliché identified by John Davies forty years ago. Despite the extension of the range of experience mainstream poetry covers since the 1990s, officialdom's approved poets remain bound by an empiricist template of the poem as 'report on' experience, with some of its practitioners trotting out nostrums that have been critically untenable,   risible even, since the 1920s.[22] Bluntly put, Wales deserves better than this tired same-old same-old.

---

[22] Thus, Jonathan Edwards naively regards it as a virtue if 'the reader forms an unshakable bond with [a poem's] central character', and berates Roddy Lumsden for abandoning the 'strong, accessible idea, rooted in life ... work[ed] through a series of insightful observations to a strong conclusion' in favour of poems which 'seem to have moved away from life towards language'. *Poetry Wales*, 51:1 (Summer 2015), pp. 80-84.

So it is that *The Edge of Necessary* celebrates the fact that innovative poetry is, and has been for several years, the most vibrant and forward-looking sector of the Welsh poetry scene. It is intended as a challenge to existing habits of thought, an intervention rather than a passive record, as a disruption of the past as well as of the present and the future. It is becoming clear (and we'd cite as evidence the work contained in this volume) that what was for so long ignored, or even denigrated, in establishment circles as irrelevant, is not only the more relevant tradition today, linguistically, culturally, politically, morally, but was actually more relevant all along. The increased recognition of this fact is partly a result of the developing sophistication of literary-cultural education and partly the growth of a more general awareness that the complexities of a twenty-first century personal, social and global existence require new and more inventive forms of language to express them. Apologists for the status quo – powerful, still, even in the universities – try naturally to incorporate these developments in a piecemeal, selective, and distorted way into their stolid narratives, but in truth the horse has already bolted. The poetry presented in *The Edge of Necessary* cannot be thought of as some kind of tributary to the central flow of 'Welsh poetry', tolerated, sanctioned and accommodated by something bigger. Rather, it is itself now the bigger thing – broader, deeper, more dynamic, internationalist in scope and action, and as such the best literary vehicle for reconnecting Wales to a cultural worldscape.

John Goodby and Lyndon Davies

September, 2018

ERRATA

p. 41: **Hölderlin in the Tower** *the seventh line is missing.*
The relevant part should read:
       One beside the other
       He says some very simple things
       Like music

p. 310, *second line from the bottom:*
the mediums of viktor ullman *is a title and should be in*
bold.

GERARD CASEY (1918–2000)

Gerard Casey (who would jokingly style himself 'Geraldus Cambrensis', after the Cymro-Norman churchman Giraldus Cambrensis) was a religious thinker, philosopher, poet and translator. Born in Maesteg, he married the writer Mary Powys, a niece of John Cowper Powys. They farmed for many years in Kenya, where they lived during the Mau Mau uprising in the 1950s, retiring to Dorset. Casey's masterpiece, *South Wales Echo* (1973), is dedicated to David Jones and influenced by his *The Anathemata*, but its Foreword has an epigraph from William Carlos Williams's *Paterson* and the text itself acknowledges a debt to Peter Finch. The poem's occasion is a fearful 1920s childhood memory of the journey home from school in Cardiff on All Soul's Eve, via Tiger Bay's slums and past the city gaol, at the time of the impending execution of three men held there for a murder (one of whom was innocent, another rumoured to have been driven mad by this fact). The city's present and past are collaged and interwoven with legends, nursery rhymes and literary and mystical materials, among them Shelley, Bashō, Boehme, Fludd and Plotinus. Welsh, Hebrew, Arabic, and Cardiff dialect are part of the polyphony energizing this remarkable Welsh *Waste Land*-like 'attempt to recover [spiritual] wholeness'. While the title reflects Casey's belief that human voices can only ever be unoriginal echoes of the Word, his faith is in a cosmic and all-redeeming deity who allows nothing of the creation to be cast into outer darkness.

from *South Wales Echo*

VOICES IN THE WIND SINGING

> *the bright   the utter   the still*
> > *we utter*

> *bright*
> > *beyond bright*
> > > *beyond bright*

> *utter*
> > *beyond utter*
> > > *beyond utter*

> *still*
> > *beyond still*
> > > *beyond still*

blue-winged
flashing
flashing snowfire
we utter

קָדוֹשׁ קָדוֹשׁ קָדוֹשׁ

beyond bright

beyond utter

beyond still

* * * * * *

echo   echo

mae bys Mari Ann wedi brifo
a Dafydd y gwas ddim yn iach
maer baban yn y cryd yn crio
a'r gath wedi crafu Joni bach

there goes tom again
singing for his supper
wonder where he comes from

sospan fach yn berwi ar y tan
sospan fawr yn berwi ar y llawr
a'r gath wedi crafu Joni bach

'e's a regular queer plain scatty
doesn't know 'oo 'e is
and the whitefaced kid with staring eyes
white as chalk she is always with 'im
dosses down Tyger Bay with Omed 'amed
'es big enough to knock spots off Jack Johnson
look at 'im black as the ace of spades 'e is
should 'av been born in a rainstorm

'e's coming 'e's coming
'is 'ead is bended low
I'ear them angel voices calling

                                        poor old Tom
                                           poor old Tom
                                              poor old Tom

Tom?
who the devil's Tom?

                              Tom?
                              Tom's Tom mister

who I am or what I am
who knows or cares
call me Ishmael ... or Ulysses
he that poured libations to all the dead
come stormdriven back from that hateful stream
where powerless heads throng to the dark blood

flotsam I come
as to a place much longed for
as to one much prayed to
to the place where the streams empty
but I knew Tom of old ... long ago
far back in the storm of the world-flow
he foresuffered all
humped trembling over Esau
bent in flamelight over Tilphussa's spring
gulped the black water
all worlds consumed in everliving fire
And eyeless under Suhir
sang with Shiddeh his bahilowi

                              three blind mice three blind mice
                              see how they run see how they

run

                              they all ...

there's tricky Tom Dolittle the artful dodger
in port after stormie seas
rejoicing with Sinbad the Sailor
Darkinbad sailing the brightdayler
Rudolf Steiner on Pen-maen-mawr

                              echo echo

the valley spirit never dies
take Tom now old Tom Mope-along
he's the joker in the pack
always rummaging in the dark
groping in odd corners
grumbling to himself things get lost
harking back
to old unhappy far-off things
things far away and long ago

Tom mooches south at sunrise
through the valley where the horses graze
heading for the northfacing form
lefthand touched by the brightshiner
he stills to the instant and sees
Alpha of the Cross invisible in light
but tiring
forgets
and nodding to the turn
lefthand shadowed slantwise crosses the stubble plough
edging the wood to Basho's pool
dwinges muttering
babbles at the Bear and turning pole
centres to the zodiacal light
faint foolscap glimmer

                    Hyades rising Jupiter setting
                    among the constellations of the heart

glances askance at the brightshiner
rising in the east
and mumbles

        don't you remember you said
        he'd feed us
        all jetsam from worldstorm
        and lead us
        and cracked skulls and rags
        and crushed bones will dance

then slopes off north
to the breaking of the bread

                    and turtle soup

HEATHER DOHOLLAU (1925–2013)

Heather Dohollau (née Lloyd) was born near Treherbert in the Rhondda, and was raised in Penarth near Cardiff. During WWII, she worked in a bookstore, and, from 1943, joined the Women's Land Army. In 1947 she moved to Paris, then to Brittany permanently in 1950, converting to Catholicism in 1949 - 50 (in later years she felt closer to the Anglicanism of her youth). She lived first on the island of Bréhat and then in Saint-Brieuc. Exposed early on to modernist art and literature, she began writing poetry in French in 1967. Dohollau was a significant twentieth century francophone poet, highly regarded by, and enjoying friendships with, such leading figures as Pierre Jean Jouve, Yves Bonnefoy, and Jacques Derrida, whose ideas on identity, place, memory, belonging and language her work anticipates. She was made an Officier de la Légion d'Honneur in 2005. Her poetry frequently draws on her Welsh connections, recalling places such as Llwynypia, Tynewydd and Penarth, but it is open to a wide range of international and hybrid influences (David Jones, Dylan Thomas, Blake, Hölderlin and Rilke, as well as French poetry). The first volume of her mature period was *La venelle des portes* (1979), published by Yves Prié's Folle Avoine press; subsequent collections include *Matière de lumière* (1985), *Les portes d'en bas* (1992), *La terre âgée* (1996), *Le point de rosée* (1999), *Le dit des couleurs* (2003), *Une suite de matins* (2005) and *Un regard d'ambre* (2008). Although unknown in Wales, the case for Dohollau's major status has been compellingly made over several years by Clémence O'Connor, the expert on her work, and following her lead she has been discussed and translated by David Wheatley, John Goodby, Lyndon Davies and Patrick McGuinness; a first collection of translations of her work into English is eagerly awaited.

Un rêve heureux

Il s'agit de changer en fichu une poésie
                                        - Walter Benjamin

                              à Jacques Derrida

    lettres d'écume   de nuage
    à lire dans le rêve substantiel
    le fichu à trois pointes
    et la bordure de la voile
    l'œil ouvert sur la lettre
    Déferlante
    et le retour au plus loin
    au passage d'une chute tracée
    sous un drap de tendresses
    où il voit sans avoir vu
    la page brodée   bordée de bleu

A happy dream

letters of spindrift   of cloud
to be read in the embodied dream
written-off   at three points
and the boundary of the sail
the eye open on the letter
Unfurling
and the return to further off
to the passage of a fall remarked
under a sheet of tendernesses
where he sees without having seen
the page embroidered   bordered with blue

Penarth beach

Ici enfin! Cette fois il me semble
que c'est vrai - comment autrement
y aurait-il tant de bleu?
et que la côte en face soit maintenant
si claire ne laisse pas de doute
le rideau est levé   il n'y a plus de temps

ces enfants là-bas qui jouent
sous les yeux de leur mère
et cherchent dans les galets celui
qui portera signe : le talisman rompu
dont la blessure respire
et gardera l'ouvert pendant l'écart d'une vie

ils sont à la fracture du jour
où la lumière veille   la mer a ses marques
qui ont douceur de seuil et l'entrée est là
où l'amour se tient
dans la brilliance de l'air
en cet aujourd'hui

Penarth beach

Here at last! This time it seems to me
to be true - how otherwise
would there be so much blue?
and that the coast beyond
is now so clear takes away doubt
the curtain is risen   there is no more time

those children over there who play
under their mother's eye
searching pebbles for the one
that will be the sign: the split talisman
from which the wound breathes
will keep open the open
for the space of a life

they are at the fracture of day
where light watches   the sea has its marks
of sweet thresholds and the entry is where
love is contained
in the brilliance of air
for the day that is here

Hölderlin à la tour

Les oiseaux intermittents
Les champs toujours là en face
Les mots voltigent, reviennent
Le touchent, il tend la main
Et les pose doucement
Les uns à côté des autres
Ils disent des choses très simples
Comme la musique
L'eau est calme
L'ombre de l'oiseau surprend
Les jours sont longs
Comme au début de la vie

A partir d'un moment d'une extrême simplicité il ne faut plus espérer

Hölderlin in the tower

Occasional birds
The fields still over there
Words flutter off and come back
Touch him, he holds out his hand
And puts them down softly
One beside the other
Like music
The water is calm
The bird's shadow surprises
The days are long
As at life's commencement

After a moment of extreme simplicity one must renounce hope

Retour

Ulysse de retour à Ithaque
Lit dans une langue inconnue
Ce qui est devant lui

Le port, la grotte, la colline
Dans cette lumière neuve
Se voilent d'eux-mêmes

Et c'est le sang de ce réel
Que le passé vient boire
En spectre ravi du présent

Et c'est en croyant être
Où il ne fut jamais
Qu'il rentre enfin chez lui

The Return

Ulysses back in Ithaca
Reads what's before him
In an unknown tongue

The port, the cave, the hill
In this new light
Are hidden by themselves

And it's the blood of this real
That the past comes to drink
Ghost ravished by the present

And it's in believing
Himself to be where he never was
That he finally comes home

Manawydan's Glass Door

Ici rien ne se passe
Tout est dehors
Le temps se plie comme un vêtement
Dans un coin
La mer rentre par transparence
Par la porte de verre
L'eau de la lumière tremble
Sur les murs lisses
Prison ou sanctuaire
Fermé à double tour
Par le regard même
La paix de l'instant se boit
Dans une coupe sans bord
Là-bas un bateau gîte
Toutes voiles dehors
Et avec l'écume bleue
Je mouille la page

David Jones

Nothing happens here
Everything's outside
Time folds like a garment
In a corner
Sea returns as transparence
Through the glass door
The water of the light trembles
On slick walls
Prison or sanctuary
Securely locked
By the gaze itself
The moment's peace drunk
From a cup without edges
Over there a boat tilts
With all its sails spread
And with the blue spume
I moisten the page

David Jones

Thomas Jones

1.

dedans – dehors   dehors vu de dedans
ce que je vois me voit   un autre moi-même
la façade blanche   la peau tendue de face
les traces de larmes   les trouées du regard
mais le noir est lisse   la surface est intacte
ni signe ni souffle   c'est ainsi que je suis
une pause sans faille   pour toujours ici – là
et que je reste   une nuit d'où naît le jour

2.

l'offrande de toute chose que l'on laisse seule
comme sur ce balcon où le linge est mis
quelques vêtements   du blanc   du bleu   du vert
une longue écharpe vu d'ici perd son ombre
derrière   la porte est close   la chaleur veille
une femme peut-être repose en cet espace
ce moment est le mien   sur le mur clair
avec les interstices je pointe la face
et appose   dans le bas   une vigne paraphe

O la beauté de ce que je n'ai pas vu
là devant mes yeux cet après-midi
en Toscane dans un monastère
c'était vers le soir le Père abbé
était en train d'arroser ses fleurs
à l'annonce de notre venue
il posait l'arrosoir et se retournait
l'eau était encore sur les fleurs
en ce moment là

à l'intérieur en haut de l'escalier
un portrait en pied de Saint François
il me semble qu'il levait les bras
et dans la chapelle il y avait un bout de fresque
qui venait d'être retrouvée et une oeuvre
de Sano di Pietro dont il ne me reste que le nom

mais d'où en tout cela vient l'impression
qu'il soit encore temps   qu'en ce début de regard
je peux toujours voir

Thomas Jones

1.
inside – outside   outside seen from inside
that which I see sees me   another me
the white facade   the taut skin facing
the tracks of tears   breaches in the gaze
but the dark is smooth   the surface is intact
neither sign nor breath   this is how I am
an unwavering pause   forever here – there
and how I remain   a night from which day breaks

2.
the gift of each separate thing left to itself
as on this balcony where the washing's hung
some clothes   a touch of white   of blue   of green
from here a long scarf seems to lose its shadow
behind   the door is shut   the heat watches
perhaps a woman is resting in that space
this moment is mine   on the clear wall
tracing gaps and crevices I bring the surface to life
adding   low down   a vine's flourish

O the beauty of what's unseen
this afternoon there in front of my eyes
in a Tuscan monastery
towards evening the abbot
was watering his flowers
when he heard we had come
he put down the watering can and turned round
the water was still on the flowers
at that moment

inside at the top of the stairs
a full-length portrait of Saint Francis
it seemed to me he was lifting his arms
and in the chapel a fragment of a fresco
only just discovered and a work
of Sano di Pietro of which I remember only the name

but in all that where does the impression come from
that there is still time   that in this commencement of a gaze
I go on seeing

DAVID BARNETT (1929–)

Of London-Jewish origin, David Barnett did National Service in Germany before studying Medieval History at Oxford University. He travelled to Malaysia and Thailand, where he spent six months with mostly remote tribal peoples before a brief interlude working in advertising, after which he travelled again, with long spells in India, Australia, Tahiti and Mexico. He then taught in inner London schools before moving to Carmarthen in West Wales, where he ran Aardvaark, a community wholefood shop. Reflecting his engagement at this time in ecological and anti-nuclear protests, Barnett's poetry often celebrates a nature goddess and earth-mother principle, taking ritualistic dance (which he practices) as an exemplary celebration of human unity with the natural world, and draws on the Celtic Year calendar. While it recalls Ted Hughes in its empathy with the creaturely universe, Barnett's work belongs to the Welsh psycho- and ethno-geographical tradition which includes David Jones, Chris Torrance and Elisabeth Bletsoe, its resistance to phallocentrism enacted in its risky verbal veerings and patternings: as he notes, 'Important to me are the sound of words and the rhythm of a poem which should aspire to the condition of music'. His collections include *Bent in Water* (1985), *Fretworks* (1990), *All the Year Round* (1993) and *There's Only the Dance* (2011).

Temple

A fitter plants electrons
on the big end of
a patient wrenched to a stance
to suffer them. Both
are action men

as a jet solders a body
for it to hake through
its lawns and beds to a city's
circuit which won't fuse
even when

a wolf retorts to a moon
and to her who's in
her puffy covert with the root
of dock and the fruit
of bryony

and may. Her Medusa hair
unbraids when she fills
her wickerwork panniers
to dab at the temple
of a broker

who frets to take up again
a form and to slew
to a syke with a tune
he fancies he once used
for a round.

Hare

Here in the tatty midden
his muzzle's spun him to, its givings
braced by his breath,
he's spider-single with
the rifle from his whiskers, the spill

from his lax orifices
and the smudge of his rest,
tempered by his ash-
leaf ears. This patch
brings to his course of race

and squat, rip and bob, a flick
from his whorl-senses, decked
with pomp, a moon's echo
and a jagged lope
on kangaroo legs. With

a bound he's off to a moor,
riddled by the carry
of a wind, the shove
of a thumb to give
him rapture within her before

he doubles back to his retreat
to glance across the campion at
a tatter with no arms
and a pose that asks
him merely for a paltry meeting.

Cayley Primary School

Walls balk a pen
where skipping-ropes swish and a football
lollops across screeches of fowl
at a barnyard. It's a respite from a cell

with its hangings – a blue
baboon, toothpick nan, papier-
maché dragon, from the stoop
of a miss who curbs their mercury for
a term. After,

the klaxons of these city
kids howl through the raucous streets
to rasp the large who mope, who hide
behind their grubby threats when the children
rail at chips,

burger and ketchup; when
they beat towards the angel who romps upon
a stewed sky; when they lamp
their quarter, lay its dust, change its shop-
soiled notes

for the troll of
a fantail pigeon and a barn-dance to
a day and its rigging. Shoots
from an asphalt ground, they strew their pollen-
larks to season

the leady air, glum
and bunged. Outside their school gates a mother
waits for her strays. She'll busk
for a coin or token. But they'll have none
to give to her.

Swift

In his element,
spate for spate, tissue
for tissue, in his sprat-
slight drift with
a thermal, he's but flux,
a sprite that fluffs above

a spring's crest into
the strand he scissors through,
a mist-flick, a fleck
who picks at the less
slick until a smart
plucks at his throat

for him to quit his beat
at a sallow karroo
and to dot across
a hemisphere, ruttish
from the octane of
his sprightly flight and juicy

with his dash towards
his seed-plot, towards
a ziggurat fixed
by a duty familiar
as Orion. Here
he grips her mantle in

a glide. Here they rear
with the gob-cakes
from their abdomens before
he flits to chip again
at his sky-lot, fume
behind an eye's, scream

behind an ear's guess,
into the dear air
of his dare, whetted
by his tail and groomed
by the spray from
his savoury, mazy feats.

Earthworm

Under a lea's leafy smother,
she's fit still for the matter

of the earth, for its real
task. In her gallery,

ruddy from the wick of
her spires and tamped with the stuff

she pastes to its jambs, she's fast
in her crinkled wet-suit against

bill of fire and frost. Dark's
the seemly air for her to work

at in her way, urged
by the thirst that slurs from her nerves

in their slots without the beds
of sweat from pore or the fret

to sap her sift through a reach
of soil to give her dough between

its slate plates, bulk behind
its snaffle jaws. Even before

a stoat with a furred purpose,
she fastened to the mode she harbours

in her greasy cells and in
her ganglia. Only when

she's guessed it's truffle-still above
and Andromeda yawns does

she screw up to cast her spare
meal into a vast air.

West Kennet – Long Barrow

A child's death starts only
their file to the she-
earth among her sarsen stones,
to a company

of their guardians who'll shrive
and move them when they enter
this split in a settlement
of oak and elder whose leaves

are dyed for their sacrifice
to her and whose produce
bloats. Ducking fuss, she traces
her scurfy hands across

these few who lay upon her hips
the shift to a green
sleep beside the fire-issue
from her flint feet

and the aura from her stream,
jittery with dace. Their mouths
together rouse the clean beliefs
they all keep to without

smart for their loss. For
they're sure the child's secure
with her as they rise from
the site of her coming,

draw their sense of her towards
a down's stance between
a truant sun and moon
blinking in her caul.

Your Move

Throughout the dark trawling a flare
so its salves can wag their gentian
heads, be still like a spider.

Since it's from this stance shamming
death, whetting it, that
you'll cob beyond your palings to grease

the scrolls on your urn, mark
your maze. Whose hordes spore, shore
the silence at their loins, the quartz

they loafed on, forked for.
Hour now to merlin-soar
towards your sun for you to ride

his chariot across a felt sky.
And into your stall, the station of
your dream, its anther-gape that waits

for one to spell a fresh nativity,
swamp-cypress-sound, nimble
as a riddle which doffs itself,

lets hosannas swell leat
through the seethe of these striplings
on their stools. Where they hear

voices. Become prophets who'll pry
into what rafts, fards, trims
its sleeves for games at a funeral.

Snow Maiden

In her kayak, she froths
across a groggy sky
to tip her panniers onto
an upland's vertebrae.

It's her charge to stun
the earth, curb those saucy
lords who hack at
her wax. Baffled they are,
as the boughs of thorn
and hornbeam are cambered by
the droppings jays cascade

onto a plaque higher
than a fox's brush,
than the dugs of Ceridwen
who wades to deal her double
death below a buzzard's
scan and the paler
horses of the stars.

Her tongue is isinglass.
It blurts out her horoscope —
alder-buds in smudges,
stitchwort on a bank,
sudden swallow coming
when she breaks the waters
with her midwife hands
to spread her webbed breath
through a year used
to blubber-spouts over
floes and trawler-corks
on a vacant sea.

A Word in Your Ear

This is what the Mbuti
say. They're bairns of
the forest and lived forever
till one of them slew
his sister-brother antelope.
Now they have to die
unless they kill no more.

Crouch to pouch the givings
from the trees who victual
on the soil's contents.
To tipple from a well
or a creek fresher
than dew-moth's breath.
Than a begging fledgling,
legs of a leveret
at a coomb twiddling
with ransom and cow-parsley.

That's to loosen time
for its serpent-dance
past a cauldron frothy
from its brothy stock.
This is what Chief
Seattle says. You men
won't rest till you've shot
or trapped, fished or poisoned
each last wild being
on our earth. When
that mission's done, you
yourselves will die from
a great loneliness of spirit.

JEFF NUTTALL (1933–2004)

Jeff Nuttall was born in Clitheroe, Lancashire, grew up near the Welsh Border in Herefordshire, taught art at Leeds and Liverpool Polytechnics and was chairman of the National Poetry Society (1975 – 1976) when, for a brief but heady moment, the avant-garde planted its flag in the heartland of the literary establishment. Painter, sculptor, actor, trad-jazz trumpeter, as well as poet, Nuttall began publishing in the early 1960s, becoming associated with many of the American Beat writers. Together with Bob Cobbing he founded the Writers Forum press and writers' workshop and his self-published mimeographed magazine *My Own Mag* was a crucial outlet for experimental literature in the 1960s. His book, *Bomb Culture* (1968) was a key text for the emerging internationalist counterculture of the time. He lived for the last part of his life in Abergavenny, where he became enthusiastically involved in the workshop poetry scene centered on the Hen and Chickens pub. His *Selected Poems* was published by Salt in 2003. Sensual, often erotic, even orgiastic in tone and imagery, resounding with echoes of such disparate voices as Dylan Thomas, D. H. Lawrence and Antonin Artaud, Nuttall's poetry revels in the rhythms and densities of a language at full tilt.

The Whore of Kilpeck

Who'd couple with foetus, with handful of sore yell wet,
      with its jelly eyes staring,
Clamped round the grunt-root sucking it up to a rash?

The Mother of Red Muck slewed out her gibbering sheelaghnagig.
The entire spring season ploughed her in her eldritch luminous paralysis.

Who'd help her or give to her further? She squats and she claws
      clamp-hands at her loud wet seed-pit. The hazel twigs whimper.

She is old in stone. She was dropped from the earth's womb
      three months early, ejaculated by the violence of her own
      imprisoning desire.
The stone is her desire. The ancient permanence has made her always now.
Who could acknowledge or deny her carolling berserk thirst?

The stone season whimpers loud beneath the sward.
Will some one for Christ's sake soon stand keen as the sharp Welsh metal
      in the streaming slough and hack the year to winter?

'I stalk with the razorblade cranes'

I stalk with the razorblade cranes, my pinhead reeling wingpower
        in the white light,
Stilt legs reed legs red from menstrual delta.
I stalk with an agate eye and a lunatic trapped in my fossilized head –
        My stare …

My feathers are all the flash, the flash the dawn and finish.
        I am not outside the instant Being-Scream.
My pride is everywhere. I'm proud because the everywhere is me.

The lunatic is in my skull – his blazing replica is spat out molten
        on the dying sky.
I walk a while, a long while I walk. The instant's constant.
        Something in me won't die. Help me.

Bed Crash

Knackerknot of sweatsheet.
Lunglashing.
Two minutes only to catch the breath train.

She holds him hung by a pube from Horsehair Bluff.
It snaps, a bad promise. He watches the train leave the platform.
Spins down to Kilim Gulch.

Sacred blot of a spat sweet
Perishing.
Saliva, sugar, drying on a salt plain.

She shoves him out of her canoe, she's had enough.
He rockets rapids riding a rat formed
Of grinning liquid habits hunched.

Stale light on bedroom dust
Snot-clogging.
Programme your breathing. In. Out. Left. Right.

Her cries have changed, drowning in duvet tides,
Howls help, a stoned nestling. He chokes his tongue sweetly,
Watches his child die of gluey kisses.

Pale light of shed musk.
Crotch flagging.
Lose your leavings, urged out finger flight

She's dying in her wet grave. Look! Her palpitating side!
Pumps, dredges. He copies this discreetly
Not wanting to wake her with crude caresses.

Sleep

A gracious vee; the hauling down –
Dark fold that draws down,
Suck and tug; thick thews,
Bank, bush, brash bushels badgered back
To veecleft whence they struggle still.
Humps, high barrows buffet up
But fond vee, salivating grasp,
Wants all belligerence brought back to bare beginning.

How vomit the visible?
How spilled, splathered into light?
The suction of its shifting duct
Is greater than expectoration –
Spume-spat afforded on the strand
Drawn back to dark, not let dry,
Drowned dark, deep dark dissolved.

Lower Usk

My eyes sustain peppering,
Ash, willow, elderberry,
Pussybuds whisp the crackling atmosphere.
I sneeze in my glad heart.

Beech, hazel kiss godgusts.
Pear, apple, tumblesnow.
Ribs leak regurgitated prayer,
Sluices my voicebox, flies
Away in dappled happenstance.

MALCOLM PARR (1934–)

Malcolm Parr was born in Pontypridd and educated there and at the University of London, where he took a degree in Spanish before becoming a lecturer in Spanish at Swansea College. He has been a vigorous activist, editor and encourager in the local and South Walian literary and visual arts scene for several decades, corresponding and meeting with John Riley, among others, and working with painters such as William Brown. His main literary activity has been translation, and his versions of Lorca were highly praised by Allen Ginsberg. The two poems included here are from his anthology *found poems*, published by *second aeon* in 1972; it also included work by Bob Cobbing, d.s.h., Nick Zurbrugg, Peter Finch and Edwin Morgan. His only collection is *Serious Games*, published by Swansea Poetry Workshop in 1992.

coming of christianity

The temple of Fortune
became a wine-shop
and Love was melted down
to make frying-pans.

(found poem from the *TLS*, 21 August 1970)

From Deaf Man's House

Satan devouring one of his children

Condemned to worship what our lusts compound, we dream
up idols to invest with actual power, monsters that
wantonly exact the ritual of sacrifice. Excited, horrified,
we founder on the altar of self-destruction.

Judith and Holofernes

A woman prays, a sword is raised. The lustful head
is wrapped in a meat-bag. Blow the trumpet, sound the timbrel,
the sweet lyre with the harp. A woman
has delivered her people.

Pilgrimage to San Isidro's fountain

Here we may topple so easily. Here it is easy to pray,
Easy to sin. Here what is within us is brought out by
Satan with his lens. He loves San Isidro's fountain.
Here the heaven-earth barrier is thinnest.

To the witches' sabbath

In the icy dereliction of our island in the infinite,
Predatory, chimerical, prophetic, the dead persist
In their wild grimaces and clamorous descant,
Executing their judgements upon our tormented clay.

Dog's head

Against a nascent glow as head thrusts up, token of
Trust, a dog epitomising faithfulness.

JOHN POWELL WARD (1937–)

John Powell Ward was born in Felixstowe, Suffolk, studying in Toronto and Cambridge before beginning an academic career at Swansea University. A leading figure in the Welsh branch of the 1960s concrete poetry scene, he organized the 'concrete poetry by students of great britain' exhibition at Swansea and the International Exhibition of Concrete Poetry in Cardiff in 1969. Of his chapbook of typewriter poems, *From Alphabet to Logos* (1973), he has written:

> [T]he alphabet is the lowest common factor of the written language. in its twenty-six letter forms are the complete physical symbolic materials from which all written language and literature are made, and to which these may be reduced. the logos is the highest achievement that arrangements of those twenty-six letter forms can produce. a society's logos is usually imperfect; a society may not have this logos at all. in English it is perhaps the works of Shakespeare and the authorized version of the Bible that most nearly qualify for this title, or have done so; yet they too, are physically no more than myriads of permutations of these same twenty-six letters.

Ward went on to edit *Poetry Wales* (1975-80), regularly presenting BBC Radio 4's 'Poetry Now' (1977-84), and writing critical studies of Hardy, R.S. Thomas and Wordsworth, and on poetry and sociology, Englishness and the alphabet. His poetry, while formally unadventurous, is characterised (like Jeremy Hooker's) by its intellectual acuity, variety and tolerance of alternative traditions. His collections include *The Other Man* (1969), *Genesis* (1977), *A Certain Marvellous Thing* (1993), and *New and Selected Poems* (2004).

three scans from
from alphabet to logos

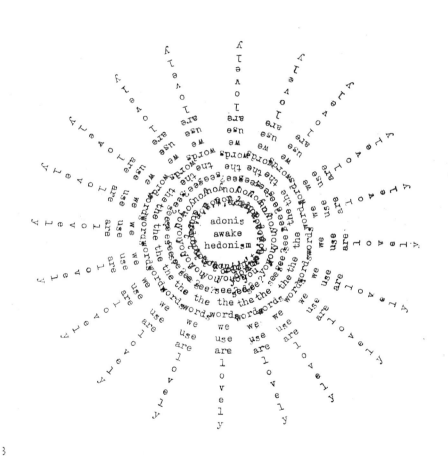

3

```
that          a believe      not God    Light    to grace
him           own flesh      God not    Light    truth to
that          came were      not God    Light    to power
him           nor glory      God not    Light    dwelt to
that          a believe      not God             to blood
him           own flesh      God not    many
that          came were                 gave
him           nor glory                 sons         in made
that                                    even       made in
him                                     born         in made
that          comprehended through     only       made in
him                                     full         in made
that          was was was was
him           was was was was                     things knew unto
that          was was was was                     true become John
              was was was was                     without from any

darkness      sent     the the the the the
darkness      name     the the the the the
begotten      them     the the the the the          and of
received      bear     the the the the the          and of
received      sent     the the the the the          and of
              name                                   and of
              them               beginning           and of
but as man    bear               all which           and of
but as man                       beginning           and of
but as man                       all which           and of
                                                     and of
                        among it    with same        and of
he his world Word       every we    with same        and of
his Word he world       there on    life will        and of
world he Word his       whose us    life will         and of
Word world his he
                        light witness    cometh thing
beheld by men           might witness    shineth into
Father by men           light witness    lighteth for
```

When forty winters shall beseige thy brow
And dig deep trenches in thy beaut.'s field
Thy youth's proud livery, so gazed on now
Will be a tattered weed, of small worth held:
Then being ask'd where all thy beauty lies,
Where all the treasure of thy lusty days,
To say, within thine own deep-sunken eyes,
Were an all-eating shame and thriftless praise.
How much more praise deserved thy beauty's use,
If thou could'st answer, 'This fair child of mine
Shall sum my count and make my old excuse,'
Proving his beauty by succession thine.
This were to be new made when thou art old
And see thy blood warm when thou feel'st it cold.

Whon forty wontors sholl bosoogo tho brow
Ond dog doop tronchos on tho boooto's foold
Tho yooth's prood lovoro, so gozod on now
Woll bo o tottorod wood, of smoll worth hold
Thon boong oskod whoro oll tho boooty loos
Whoro oll tho troosoro of tho losto doys
To soy, wothon thono own doop-sonkon oyos
Woro on oll-ootong shomo ond throftloss prooso
How moch moro prooso dosorvod tho boooty's oso
Of thoo coold'st onswor, 'Thos foor chold of mono
Sholl som mo coont ond moko mo old oxcoso,'
Provong hos boooty bo soccossoon thono
Thos woro to bo now modo whon thoo ort old
Ond soo tho blood worm whon thoo fool'st ot cold

```
  o    o      o         o      o oo o    o     o
0    o   oo     o     o  o      o ooo o      oo
  o  oo        oo    o o o    o  o o   o     o
 o    o o  o  o o    oo    o    o        o
 o   oo   o  o    o o o       o ooo     oo
   o o o     o   oo o o o    o   o  o  o.
 o  o     o  o    o o o     oo    o  o  o o.
 o o o  o   oo o     o o o       o   o    oo o
 o   o    o o   oo o o o  o     o ooo      o o
0    oo oo      o   o     o   oo    o    o   o o
  o    o  o  oo    o    o o  o o    o  o o.
 o o    o  ooo    o o o  oo    o o
  o   o o o o o    o o   o     oo o   o
0   oo   o   oo   o     o    oo oo      o    o
```

When f rty winters shall beseige thy br w
And dig deep trenches in thy beauty's field
Thy y uth's pr ud livery, s gazed w n n w
Will be a tattered weed, f small w rth held
Thon being ask'l where all thy beauty lies
Where all the treasure f thy lusty days
T say, within thine wn deep-sunken eyes
Were an all-eating shame and shiftless praise.
H w much m re praise deserved thy beauty's use
If th u c uld'st answer, 'This fair child f mine
Shall sum my c unt and make my ld excuse'
Pr ving his beauty by successi n thine.
This were t be new made when th u art ld
And see thy bl d warm when th u feel'st it c ld.

ALL OBJECTS OF ALL THOUGHT.

He had opposed the return of
Helen to fair-headed Menelaos%%
"3£0^67%$ who survived, when what
worked to break down the great
Wall of the Achaians [*] [*] [*]
we truly say is translated88--++
\\:&7592? there's a question qu

estion marque for you. Imploding
earth centripetal forces yet
eccentric in physeeeeek and.....
(even today ive just heard now,
electronic barons buy the world,
+%$£7\?8@~****zszs.zszs.zszs.zsx
every last thing shown in the Louvre

is owned as to production rights
in perpetuo by a single ----=-=--
fffffffffffffhhhhhhwwwwww333333)
is reproducing you see bbbbb^^^^
investing in possible outc----ss
iiiiiiiiiiiiiiiiiiiiiiiiiiiiiiiiiiiiiiiiiiiii
infinitely repeated. (NOW APPLY

REPEATER for so *Wall of the Ach*
aians. we truly say is translat
ed88--++ //:&7592? There's a END
OF REPEATER but the instant print
overrides, my time and your time,
our time and their time, a very fine
or gossamic cloud seals the earth

at the projections on the outworks,
and broke down the battlements,
and both feet beneath me are swept
and Paris struck him by the jaw
and ear, and the life spirit fled
away, out of his limbs %%%%%%%%%%
and hateful dark closed about him.

Green trees, green sacred planet,
grown far from yourself and diseased, so
gone near mad with your keepers'
greed and grief, each orbiting
gyration tracked by techniques
earth's energies it**self en-ge[
de(r%ed**, we^ arr oanli elec$-t-rr

From *Variations on Four Places*

Gower
i

A high wind on the bryn's ridge
Blew away pieces of litter, as though some angel
Had flung aside its novel in disgust
And switched to sculpture, saddened

At the count of these dead children. The gorse
stiffened at that, its prickles tensing
Angrily; for where was the lake we swam in,
So uncluttered and true? The sea continued

Its acrobatic sills and turned its back
Expressionless; the Atlantic arched
Like a wall then fell and broke into pieces,
And the tinkling crockery of its matrons

Sucked in their breath and turned aside
To more elaborate tasks and the clinics
Of muscular salt water. We are extracted
Like a whelk's flesh with a gourmet pin.

vii

Their endless walk on the shore. Indeed,
The waves seethe in and out and level out
To newsprint but the headlines they propound
Only rehearse the deaths their sales

Survive on. Trillions of grains of sand
Are the gentle stretch where all the citizens
Stroll at right-angles to the dipping tide:
The eeriest blues, of sea and sky,

Quietly concede each other's fated rank
While the orchestra of rocks goes hush
For the interval. The far horizon
Again reminds it is no thing, just what

Occurs between an ocean and an air.
A chestnut folds its arms. The café sells
Its tea and hamburgers and weedy nets
To ancient fishermen. And dogs race on the sand.

Radnor
(for Stevie Davies)
i

Thirteen Canada-geese flew over
But one seemed to split, which thus made
Fourteen. Every night his dream
was of being pinned to a ledge,

Whether office block or vertical cliff,
And the sheer height made their guts
Sag, and there was no centre of gravity
Left there. On the new mobile phone

We tried to call up, someone to haul us up
But the sound went down, pulling
His eyeballs after it. Gorgeous red
Trees and fields lay calmly

Before us then turned green.
Oh that the earth could again be green.
Nevermore. The flat spin of the stars
Returned and that was all my grace.

viii

The vehicles drove to the nub, a centripetal
Starfish, cheering the heart. When they returned
It was dusk, and people toasted their scones
On specially-heated air. A schoolgirl ran

Across the park to her door at this time,
Chased of course, but no one else would
Have known her name's derivation, or that
It was etched on silver in her purse,

A grandma's gift. Blue the huge colour,
Snow the moment that stayed, and a wounded man,
Rebelling against the armaments a government
Sent, stared at the poppies that grew

On his legs and chest. Even the roundabout spun,
But the tune it played on that cranky old
Machine gave out more terms than a dictionary,
Hung on the garden tree for a thousand years

JOHN JAMES (1939–2018)

Born into a part-Irish working-class East Cardiff family, John James was educated by the De La Salle Brothers and read Philosophy and English at Bristol University, taking an M.A. at Keele University (his dissertation was on William Carlos Williams). He co-founded *The Resuscitator* magazine (1963-65), met Allen Ginsberg following the 1965 Albert Hall poetry readings, and was involved with *The English Intelligencer*. In 1966 he moved to Cambridge, working at Anglia Polytechnic, eventually becoming Head of Communications Studies. As with Barry MacSweeney, a particular friend, James' strong links with the so-called 'Cambridge school' rarely curbed his own warmer, more maverick sensibility, or un-English range of interests in European musical and visual arts. Simon Perril describes him as an 'heir of Mayakovsky's "intimate yell"', a neo-Futurist who fuses 'the aesthetic to the social', and one key to his work is a mobile lyric self which relishes the concrete and vivid, while resisting consumerism and the standard avant-garde response of ascetic disdain. James attempted to 'lose his voice' via cut-up in the 1970s, but responded to Thatcherism by thrillingly channelling the rhetoric of punk, Irish republicanism and Rastafarian 'toasting' in *A Former Boiling* (1979) and *Inaugural Address* (1979). His poetry has grown more transparent since, while retaining its radicalism, sensual quality, and Welsh allegiances. His many works include *Mmm ... ah yes* (1967), *The Welsh Poems* (1967), *Trägheit* (1968), *The Small Henderson Room* (1969), *Letters From Sarah* (1973), *Striking the Pavilion of Zero* (1975) *A Theory of Poetry* (1977), *War* (1978), *Toasting* (1978), *Berlin Return* (1983), *Dreaming Flesh* (1991), *Kinderlied* (1992), *Schlegel Eats a Bagel* (1996), *In Romsey Town* (2011), *Cloud Breaking Sun* (2012), *Songs in Midwinter for Franco* (2014), *Sabots* (2017) and *Sarments: New & Selected Poems* (2018). A *Collected Poems* and a *Companion* to his work appeared from Salt in 2002 and 2010.

Exultation
after Hywel ap Owain Gwynedd

A ton of white rain will overflow my self-shaped sleeping-bag of earth.
But today I love what is betrayed
by indifferent Saeson –
what will be obliterated
from the human view –

                 the curving horizon breathes
over the reclined anatomy of the sphere,
the open lands to the North & West
still sprawl under the windy skies beyond the cities –
& remote mountain plateaus –
                Eglwysilan

where the shepherd raised his eyebrow
at the question put in English –

The waters of the Taff shine with the blackness of coal.
She gushes like piss
from under a mare's tail
out of the irregular
gap in the mountains, through the Vale
the low parklands barely embank her,
everywhichway discharging herself in
deflected forces of current
over the hidden rocks & the
spewing over at Blackweir
with a smell of dead chub & pit effluent.

The waves ceaselessly lay stress on the shore.

I love all wild rocky beaches –
the smashed boulders under the cliff at Marcross
& the calm pools left behind by the tide,
the smooth grey pebbles as big around as a cricket ball

& the vales & the wailing gulls
& the trailing-haired girls
& even fake Castell Coch with its phoney pinnacles, Disneylike in its half-
        shroud of beech woods

I care for the colliers, squatting on their haunches
on the swept pavements
under the shining windows
- Oh man, how bravely they bear up their spirits under the dark stress of
        the looming slagheaps -

But ach a fi, I do not care for the oppressive household
& war maintained in the interests of an economy.
I do not care for the offensive sight of uniformed spirits & I regret
the flashing of leather I made
in the mean alleys back of Charles Street
under the skies' dim glow from the foundries

A ton of wintery rain will overwhelm my lichened bed.

A ton of ocean, wicked with dread,
the colour of hoar-frost in its night of coming
curls over us.

Oh man, how far Worcester is from Newcastle –
we drove hard night & day to reach it.

O Earth, give me before my last lonely bed the love of her I love –

Duw! I take off in her élite beauty! –
Though my flesh carry a dark hurt in heart
may I find peace in my last nothingness –

A dark wave hangs over us

Craven Images

1

I like to dance so much & a kind of mania
conspicuously lures me on to your pointed hairless chest
but since I am engrossed in the reading
of this here copy of *Sounds* & I am not Mechthild
only the punter with his meat on fire
outside the station in the fog I will swear
never to have seen you before in my life
when the Old Bill cruise by on their talking machines
matelots linger at the cab-rank I
carefully flick my second finger over the hard &
shiny folded notes in my shirt pocket
as the lull at the end of a lonely street
in the orange glare of the vast suburban night
holds me to the sluggish rocks of the pavement
your face in the shadowy shopfront at 3:00 a.m.
ain't exactly the ski patrol but then what with this
disaster area called my teeth like a roar of jacks
in a flashing orange search for a burst water-main
among the indeterminate commodities at the corner of the bar
Jackie Petersen dreaming over his amber sleeve of Brains
one immaculate black hoof over the brass rail
under the falling cloud of resin & chalk
passing from night to desk & desk to night
shoulder to shoulder with an immaculate new fish-tail
Where are the hatters of Luton? American devices
come round again like a thousand Chinese paper inventions
I would have liked to have been to Bucharest with you
Budapest anywhere taken all the boats the wagon-lits
mooch round all the bars gawping at all the young dudes
ate up all the food making for the Man in the Moon
crossing the Park in the soft purr of taxis
ah that sweet viola sound

her back is arched
& her breasts are bare
I feel a rose down
in her hair

the inimitable life of hotels
a rich display of feminist cactus in the lobby
lingering crows on the steps of Brompton Oratory
the poor animal life of the region we
will try the grand gesture the sag-arsed manner
the sculptors throw cat & rip off cock manner
tails the piece the hands of me manner
& up to a certain point manner
a couple of borzois on a leash manner

o baby what
a dog to be
in the Suck Age
of the bourgeoisie

perhaps I could finally bring myself to leave
your baleful pluralism my fingers
pause deliciously over sticky keys
as I hover over a faint icy rhythm
straps vibrating under your immortal propositions ideal
pedestrian on the King's Road
enraptured by the stare & cheek of very early Logic
another little Pils & pointless artless & frank
I get drunk without you
until the mixture degenerates & a bad odour
returns us to the Angel the harp player of the age
scraping his knuckles on the rough-cast ceiling
blood on the tambourine I sing
under my breath & my you're nervous
under the snow of a cold algebraic desire
an inkling of a kiss in the foyer
but in the calm of your bed in the late afternoon
there are these agreements of the body
the little pores in your back the gently lifting slats
parts of the outer city are atrocious
hatred of the meagre portion
even the bars are closed when we leave the cinema
it never stops no end in sight
till morning takes you home

here is your bed
be stupid beast & sleep
last of the occupants
who sadly scrape their feet

2

in the lines of the slipstream of an heroic express
coming in on the long curve eastwards into Cardiff
Atlantic rockas make their move a brazen cloud of
fiery smoke is lifting over GKN as we embark

& in the palace of globes a dazzling array of glasses
in various stages of depletion
& the sweet high tenor of the craic

under the rain under the sun & under the starry circus
the green sea rolling like an egg

3
black moleskin
tender pastures juniper & coke

far from the underworld
green penetrates the sky levels

a glass of Volvic could have made me happy for ever

4
a glass of Avèze held me smiling vaguely in the grass
like a great lost wader
sad to have been a fighter & at what cost what times
& what a summer where are you now my little music's
mind you cowbells
                                    make me sick
with misery & pain

                            '... twenty times I have denied my heart
                            I am no longer able to rest'

I flew far in pursuit of your traces
une peinture une musique qui serait simplement voyou
the insanity of my legs the millions of my thighs
the tang of the pike in the mouth
a piece of chocolate sweating in the sun

like a very rare stamp in the middle of a banal collection
the bosses vacate the City at the hour of the illuminations
thousands of voices lift themselves up to heaven
in a velvet liaison with her boulevards
like love among the ants
the strawberries were ripening my ideas were turning blonde
the sky glazes over the purified volcanoes

5

The west side of the fishpond in the Jardin des Tuileries, looking
across it & down the long terrace to the crepuscular distances of the
Place du Carrousel. It is a bright sunny day. The usual scatter of
public chairs has been cleared so that only three remain & these are
placed very formally in a row looking out over the water. The carp or
whatever, are jumping about all over the place. It is August 1970.
There are two figures sitting quite still their backs & heads quite
strikingly neat & similar. But the one on the left is Arthur. The other
one is Douglas. The chair to his right is empty. "It's high time I was
getting back to England you know, Douglas."

6

I was leaving, love on the platform
possessed of your greatness, o dear Thames
windows all lit up & rosy in the setting sun

This morning at 10:00 the Inter-City 125
will float me to Birmingham Stoke-on-Trent
but at the eleventh hour you grow sick at the rumour
                                    in the back of the heart

likewise my craving for newsprint the smoke of small cigars
a proper slow burning characteristic of a superb condition
tumblers whirling downward over shining rows of slate

your ideas were captivating & the wounds superb

as we rush out of Euston I turn & smile at the disappearing grass

a dart has pierced to the centre of this alluring folly

Bad Thoughts

"You are unable to imagine that one day it will be possible for
          you to say hello to yourself to recognize yourself as a
                    friend & to make a definitive peace of that
you remain surrendered to your alternative
when it comes to tomorrow you are unable to recognize yesterday

the defunct days lean towards you with their images
from them you read of the inscription of your old outrages
& those yet to come tremble away into distant complaints

the scattered griefs fail to gather in the vicinity of where your heart has been
you have forgotten why you are sad
but you will know the hour where your sadness was born

tired of searching the night you will relish the day
she will nourish you with her light orchards
the trees of the night the trees of the day

the seasons turn in their balmy cycle
& you will not know what to say to their mild passage
it's a big chance you think it over

you cease to see yourself as a fit up for what is agreeable
exhausted by the winding distance covered by your staggering days
the lost homelands the rusted autumns

          & a fiery rose in the September sun
you will feel your body give way to its constituent parts
it will bear less resemblance to you than a rose-bush

the spring lies in wait for in order to prune
when the evening twilight falls on the deserted lane
you will not have any dread left in you

you may wish to cut yourself off from certain parts which you
          disapprove of
you would take a slice of this thing or that to offer up as a quarry
but when you rest on the restful breast of your lover

by her let yourself be carried as far as the border
where to be cancelled itself is to revoke all endings

accept yourself & your heritage from which you have been
        formed & passed from age to age

stay mysterious rather than be pure accept your
        multifariousness your pluralism
when you come finally to take leave of your youth
all the fallen dreams born of your very early childhood

shoot beside fresh jasmine
an adorable person comes together in your arms
at the charming little cross-roads where the day slopes

into the flat open country & the little hill expires
the implicit beauty of sacred places will be troubled for you
this restlessness will have put everything in question

& you will be subject to the craziest actions
but the road runs away from under your step the horizon never
        approaches
& you give yourself to this walking life to which the dust of the
        road attaches itself

Bye Bye Blackbird
for Douglas Oliver

over the clay-laden estuary a
soft grey light comes sneaking
my heart away it is the spirit of Colne Spring

& all along the shoreline an oyster-catcher
dips & bobs a splashing blur of black & white
against the easterner

curlews ghosting by a little above the fleet
fly our souls out of perversity

Brightlingsea has grown where it is the sepia
gaff-rigged sails of the smacks manoeuvre away

into the Dutch hinterspace beyond Mersea Island a rich
alluvium gets itself laid over years we mooch along

towards a frith
dreaming of sprats & opals

The Conversation

Snowdon is falling apart. You can't walk upright now
along the ridge beyond Crib Goch toward the Pinnacles
the Zig Zags are held together with wire mesh
& climbers wearing Vibrams should be careful everywhere
as everywhere is very slippery in the rain

(boggy ground, boulders, the derelict sheepfold yes but
the tricky bit is almost vertical all the way
so Mr Poucher can no longer be retained on trips like this
I'm sorry to say!

It's the 19th of August 1982, stepping on quartz
the power quietly rising through my left vibram
the horizon opening like a door, 600 feet to go.
I could show you in a word if I wanted to

but I look up in complete detachment
the taste of copper pennies beginning to abate
among the mysteries of love & hate

this great volcanic frame of things in all
the revolutionary hope & practices
of women & men does not remain unchanged
it too has its faults through which an exile voice can sing

& driving through the rain from Welshpool
over the mountain into Bala
I'm not ashamed to think of might have been despite myself
which marks a stage of progress
on fixing on what was at least
& wonder for just how much I am to answer
having to stop & stop again to write
If there is always memory in working-class life
it is because things are always being taken away the head
spinning from night to day with little accidents
& love's the chief the drug
as Bryan Ferry sings
                    that gone
we fall to gravel beneath the span
& 7 burdens which it brings of
stupefying duties & degrading cares
labour poverty debt disease & grief no single call
received today oh yes the waste & crass stupidity
continual strife at work & in the street
the want of pleasure & repose
& all that drinks away the sustenance of choice

I see you in the daily mirror cooking for others
a softening countenance of delicate desire
lingers like the choice of all the world,
is it raining in New York on 5th Avenue

"du bist Marie und du bist meine Frau"

to say nothing of you Jeremy when you leaf
your pages to that summer & have before you
all we make of what we are when every day
gave some new sense of strengthening regard for common things
& all the land gave up a breath of gentler touch
but for the undertow of darkness
in the phones

hanging by unseen fissures in the grey & slippery rock
held buoyant by the streaming wind & rain
we live so much by the eye & yet
the ear's an organ too

keep looking up!
with what strange radiance does the rushing air
blow through my floating head the sky & motion of the cloud
no light above the level of the mist & biting hail
glimpse of a familiar figure by the brook

I see the millions I catch the language
which is this world of all of us
this only place in which we find our happiness
or not at all
the end

Sleep

you came to me in a dream in your mini-crini
turning away the crease at the top of your thighs
fickle as corduroy clean as your hair
feeling like air from another planet the new bed linen
where my heart is soothed by a breath of light
a scent of comfort on a Sunday morning
here in this your poem & mine. I beg you to free this boy.

From the Welsh

a crispy leaf
torn away in air

old already
born this year

Poem beginning with a line by Andrew Crozier

of this, see, she returns on tentative bloody feet
into the light offer of hope shed by the sun
a protective skein or do I mean skin which warms to its touch
even as I speak of you thinking of Jean
with a glass of wine & a loaf of bread as
a cloud passes over & our smiles fade for a moment
then return as after lunch we talk things over
with no idle word

I reach toward the poetry of kindred
where we speak in our work as we seldom do otherwise
from memory cancel the dark impatient for the next poem
the afternoon afloat the garden of song thrush & blackbird in May
the sun agleam again on the aerial pole above the ridge
cancels the cloud & so to the shed
light the moontiger reach for the hoe
to mark the narrative in earth
or walking home at six in the evening after work
along with all the others flowing over the bridge
thinking of you & all you others
writing alone with the radio on

at the kitchen table I put a hand to my breast in sorrow
then reach for the wine still singing
& your book resonant of a life
neither following nor in pursuit
at the end of a line let me read it again
staying awake it is a dream before birth to dream anew
of this, look, diolch & again diolch

WENDY MULFORD (1941–)

Wendy Mulford grew up near Abergavenny, and read English, Archaeology and Anthropology at Cambridge University. She remained there throughout the 1970s, associated with its flourishing avant garde poetry scene, including Denise Riley, with whom she collaborated on and co-published *No Fee* (1979) and *Some Poems: 1968-1978* (1982). In 1972 Mulford founded Street Editions, a leading outlet for experimental poetry, which published Tom Raworth, Stephen Rodefer and Rod Mengham among many others, and merged with Ken Edwards' Reality Studios to form Reality Street Editions in 1993. She has published a biography of Sylvia Townsend Warner and Valentine Ackland (Virago, 1988) and translations of the German poet Sarah Kirsch. Latterly, she has lived in Norfolk and Suffolk, the background to *The East Anglia Sequence* (1998), and she now divides her time between East Anglia and Orkney. Mulford's poetry has been described as non-linear. Her works, often bound up with an exploration of place, can unfold in many directions, from phrase to phrase, word to word, phoneme to phoneme, tracing, as she puts it, 'the complexity of perception'. Other published works include *The Virago Book of Love Poetry* (with Helen Kidd, Julia Mishkin and Sandi Russell) (1991), *and suddenly, supposing: Selected Poems* (2002), and *The Land Between* (2009).

From *The ABC of Writing*

I.

Wales.
backwards.
is a writing of the self a writing of writing?
and is a writing of writing a writing of the self?
double u one.
mark one.
is it? tell me it is? shall I believe you? shallow backwards flowers
anything a bluebell patch then barbed-wire then foxy-bracken space-time
aged five and stumbling podgy legs. The fifteen then rocks then lichen
sheep-mowed mountain-crest and all the air ours over valleys over valleys
beyond who lived there and who cared? in valleys behind fir-trees in
workers' cottages the land was ours and you with your hand in my aertex
shirt. Who cared? Nobody lived there. Our land was worked and we fed
well by Nobody, nobody at all.

p.

Wales, again.
outside the house is not inside the house and people live inside the house
they do not live outside the house which makes outside the house a very
much nicer place to be. the child lived outside the house
and grew up ignorantly. she grew up in dreams. later she learned to see.
she saw where the workpeople lived who worked inside the house and on
the land. she watched and listened and so she learned.
later she read and began to see
why her people would never understand
that there over there they could not see
nor their own part in shaping that reality
but loved their portraits livestock roses
and thought the 'people' thieving boozing churls
ancestral charts back to bastard Earls

q.-z.

London, again.
as if for q.
And
That is mine then it becomes yours is yours mine out of yours inside out.
Thank you.

r.

what is r?
r is the name of a child. r space. between r. distance r. how far she goes r
how far she does go and will she. r a beginning and I never knew how you
stopped sentences, you could even begin with r.
what they do in the street is not only their affair and I will not exclude it.

s.

and.
time-space.
the politics of joining. at a stroke.
the incredible bond. who keeps the glue. how do you use it. taking a
hammering. hoping apart a substance, these politics of impossible
convergence, into gaps, presenting absence, and out of the metaphor-trap
absence, far-off signal from another speech, always the words above your
body, hand-held, aah oh rankin jo
fall away little foil words fool words

words of wisdom and yes you are material to me
words of folly and yes you are my mother
the words all point in one direction which is not
the case, disguise is still worn.

t.

there will be no editing of this writing which is not to say there is no
censorship for the invigilator still sits. h/she has brought back the SPG.
you told me. undercover agents are everywhere. give me your hand to hold.
the display by the state is on the streets today your streets today our streets
– on your doorstep if there is no broken glass, no blood, have they been?

u.

a pre-emptive strike by the invigilator.
blow-job from a new direction.
leave undone
choosing his/her words carefully.
I lie by your side. It is morning in south-east London.
I lie. By your side it is morning-moving. in. south-east London.

v.

what makes the house quiet.
it is morning. they are at work. are you asleep?

w.

dual sign. pointing. as.
as? nothing, sshh, nothing about,
lurking. Écrire? Mais si j'écrivais "JE", qui serais-je?
you haven't the same name or city two years running laughed my friends,
keeping ahead of the debt-collectors eh? something like that I smiled.
Plusiers, simultanée, impure.
L'écriture isn't it the game of Truth?
Truth isn't it whole?
Isn't that everyone's game?
well, maybe.

x.

your lips.
your double lips
all place and memory
forget

y.

from the outside in
doubt a single to the falling catkins
- love the work its rampart breaks –
gold
at the heart a
biting difference

z.

somewhere in Southall
- you and I were sleeping
a young man died
and
this
is not
elegy
it is
in our memory

and breath continues
using our eyes we look both ways

Talking about art

there are so many
temptations in
'a stop the mind makes
between uncertainties' these
conversations, the fellowship of not knowing
where we travel 'abrupt
connections with the remote' few
continuities

change in the household
an absence of heart-line
a pair of wounded cats
none truthful
who asks to be the centre of the world

Interior with figures

how many times you looked and walked away
one figure standing
one lying
lamp-light life
in the interior, short
on air   bathed in
suffused pink
from horizon to vertex no ducking out
the mirror-sneer
wrap-around exposure
won't fit
hanging off the edge of this here blue
close the blinds

Clean sheets

so much greening
it must be the spring her
small eyes perfectly equipped
for seeing what she needs

who am I to say
do not who never could
launder well
a happy home

stretches down the
narrow urban garden
swaying lightly
with the breeze

Day dreams

make of me what you will
that may be red glowing
green over me

blue shields my eyes
horizon sheers
night stocks slice dusk

dampness smokes trough
the art of loving are you
hard at work being modern

or full pelt backwards
never let up
hatband nostalgia

bedecking the major feeling
speak to yourself so
old-fashion I
could give you love
in a million pieces

After Corot

stacked
  at the end of the earth
      ocean
        washing away
          regardless

past caring
  still pink still blue
      idiot
        light persists
          now leaving

from **Alltud**

Alltud (exile)

In the valley of the Wye, at Erwood, Powys

i

birdsong.   peopletalk.   sleepchatter.

ii

    a dot grows visible
    like the bad monk beneath the abba's habit
    stumbling from the dark amphora
    into the strangeness of light

iii

a little light at dusk by which to sit and read
the blanched white ash-stems reaching skyward
the steep woody tangle above the tumbling stream

each stem gleams in the January dull
every thing is still
        except
the invisible water thrashing over the weir
& somewhere, the pulsing throats
of songbirds

iv

wheels within wheels within wheels
this one woody watery day fading
– the thickness, the weave & baffle of it

the fit between
root and bird and rock and silt and rushing water
the separate equilibration in each material bed and how
jammed together
plant and bird and human, fish and mammal

v

the quick dart of tree-creeper
salmon-leap into still pool
froth & jetsam snagged on
ledges   human
        detritus

vi

a sudden lift   is it
breath passes from stem to branch to twig
                mini-passacaglia slow
beats and turns and animates
                gathering strength –
the casement pane bangs shut
hush the chatter

vii

we   creatures of stardust
                        intent on meaning
learning
                stare

CHRIS TORRANCE (1941–)

Born in Edinburgh, Chris Torrance grew up in London and moved to rural Wales in 1970. He taught creative writing at Cardiff University for a number of years. His work shows the influence of the 'open field' modernists and neo-modernists such as Pound, David Jones and Charles Olson; the Beats, especially Gary Snyder and William Burroughs; but also, as Graham Hartill puts it, 'the tradition of radical sublime from the bards through Blake to urban deejay vigour.' In 1985 he co-founded with composer Chris Vine the poetry and music group Poetheat, which later became Heat Poets. Torrance has featured in a number of key British Poetry Revival anthologies, including *Children of Albion* (1969), *Conductors of Chaos* (1996) and *Other: British and Irish Poetry since 1970* (1999). His major work is the *Magic Door* sequence, recently published in its entirety by Test Centre. Thematically, much of his work revolves around the isolated cottage in the limestone hills above the Neath Valley where he has lived since the 1970s. His examination and celebration of day to day life in that space, ranges through many aspects of knowledge, feeling and experience, historical, meteorological, geological, occult, spiritual and nakedly quotidian.

Autumn Drunkenness

Write it. The solitary drinker's
depression. What is it
I can't resist? Ether
& chloroform daddies
caper in their underwear. With
clear, liquid eyes,
the cats tussle in tall trees.
The orchard yields
of its sour best, little apples,
plums & greengages. What is
poetry then? An amalgam
of my sorrowing & deliberations.
May blossom wine
trickles down my throat.

September 1970

'The Theatre of its Protagonist's Desires'
for Andrew Crozier

Strode out into the woods with
cat, axe & saw to bring back
mushrooms: Ceps
& Rough-stemmed Boletus: apricot-
lunged Chanterelle; pretty, intoxicant
amanita muscaria emerging
richly red from her
silky membranous fur. The
music becomes more insane, more unreadable.
Tea onto the compost heap. Empty the cats'
shitbox. & then, preferring "my ease
to my will"(Valéry)
nettle & marigold beer
trickles down my throat. Buzzard
flies by the moon as I crouch
down on the porch to watch
Sweetheart of Sigmund Freud crunch up
yet another mouse. My beard has grown
as lushly as my garden. The fire
hisses & flares. The fire in my head
is a crippled demon I am burning up.

September 1970

Love is But a Horse of Pernicious Humour
for Richard Downing

direct the shape of words to him
& love pushes the word

meeting at the apex, the confluence
of the narrow-necked valleys

a "thunder trap"
thus leading to a greater fall down the river

a red flea
ticking in its black fur throat

the valley has been filled
with a great accumulation of glacier clay

striated boulders as solid & impenetrable as Buddhas
lichen-festooned in solitude in the dripping wood

the hard sandstone below
down into which the river has bored its ravine

twin parhelions glorious in line with the sun
weather of spells

slow pulse
of black raven wings brushing the sky

the robin's squeezed-out song
of autumn.   the skeleton show in between.

October – November 1970

Poem to the Three Laughing Sages

O loved Ones! I cast a poem in your image
steeped in sweet peat moss juice & this old yellow grass of November
Ripples in the trough, trough after trough
another wave, another blow, another drench
lichen & moss in an ever-wet land. The pineal drops
where dreams slide
whose hectic current washes & swamps me, the "Swamp Angel".
Their paths are amazing! & their lightnesses
& terrors incarcerate me.
The analeptic, giddy shock, deliquescent flow of woodgrain
& played music & sang & imbibed for a week
O holy Ones in the imperial purple dream!

30 November 1970

"Day-by-day poem"
for John Hall

With the radium-tipped drill she
No no it's not artificiality I want
nor a flowing catalogue of nature
Just look at these picture frames
"January & February when everything
is in its chastest winter absence" writes John,

& again, "snow, that quiet metaphysical occurrence"
I'm sorry to steal your lines, John
"on the Western edge of Hardy country"
& I'm on the Northern tip
of the Welsh coalfield
"Why from this window am I watching leaves?"
(Barbara Guest) "Am I to understand change, whether
remarkable or hidden? ..." ("The location of things")
the everyday mundane become lambent
The cats have shat on the carpet again but I'm not depressed,
thinking of the flowers of May.

8 January 1971

Straight from sleep

straight from sleep
to chase sheep from the garden
a bloody, dead blackbird on the doormat
'mid thousands of feathers & catspew
the world jumps
from this to that
to break the ennui
of my own tense control
all goes into the melting pot of acid
over the hill kicking a dead lambskin
what to do with all this energy, lambent, unreconciled
an atmosphere almost of terror
the planet helpless with mirth
gold coins rolling in the streets
the skylark's interminable raga
borne aloft on shivering wings

mid-May 1971

Chopping Water

The humid wave
drones on
no haymaking done
in a sick summer
a slow & halting season

"Welsh farmers claim
hay & corn harvest ruined"
Seeking the
bright mandala
of the sun
gold coin glimmering away
above the roof of clouds
the light already
wasting fast from the zenith

This sullen summertide approaching dreariness;
                                            one's
spirit had been kept volatile by the fresh Westerly
cols, but now more & more of this incubatory muggy
drip, epidemic flashes of virus-gut infection,
lowering of spirits, the creative credibility gap
widening

                        whether or not
it was the incessant rain – the subtle ageing in
green foliage, mottled, speckled by rust, the
odd spray of leaves suddenly yellowed or ghostly
creamy-white like a moth's wing, shining
                                    phosphorescent
luminous there amidst the shadowy dark shades
of blown summer –

I flounder at the bottom of the sky
squelching through water-rotten woods

the trees shower their leaves down early
as if in disgust at the season's continued failure

teetering on the brink of dogma
he turned back at the last moment

& caught the young moon with its distinct hooks
    – showerheads over distant Mumbles

wind & shot showers
well into the night

I am inside the storm
inside the house

door creeps
open an inch

woodpile
settling in the porch

CODA
(*from* Citrinas)

November night
crowded with
rushing wind
& dim, luminous shapes
moon's rays remote
behind lumpy cloud
day brisk & cold
with ice galleons trailing
mazy fallout
a major procession
to the South
bumping up
over the Pennant outcrop
another similar group marching
across the Fans
Spanish levies
going NE on Sarn Helen
traversing bare moor
caught in such a storm –
or vine climate then?
but climatic deterioration
in the 4th century AD
those Iberians
not intersettled by 383
left with the Romans
& then Irish land pirates
overswayed Brecknockshire
& in their turn settled;
King Brychan,
who married a Welsh princess
broadcasting his 24 squabs Southwards

as far as Dumnonia
(present-day Devon & Cornwall)
where their memorials in stone
are roughly contemporaneous with
this of Dervacus
buried here by the side of
Sarn Helen   the stone
1500 years a vibrant node
accumulating wind & water power
sun power, earth power
resistance slowing down the sphere
dug up by modern archaeologists who affirmed
a large square grave
but no human remains
in the acid humus

from **RORI: A Book of the Boundaries**

6. TALIESIN AT THE CONSOLE

          amid the litter

chipped flints   broken quills   overturned

                   snuff boxes

     learned quarterlies   some lying open

liquid-spotted   insect droppings   or worse

     further back, wedging off

into darkness, lines & columns & heaps of larger

bound volumes, massive tomes propped

one against the other,

     disintegrating under their own great weight

     a few scattered skulls & bones

     fragments of cranium, rows & groups

     of hominid molars

     one Cro-Magnon, or

"Atlantean Indian" –

RORI'S   forensic evidence in world murder court

a line of cracks   radiating away from
              an Iron Age burial
              in a field of blood

Taliesin, furrow-browed, deep in concentration,

manipulates the holo of the event, decoded from

quartz receptor Janus head embedded over a stone

archway, witness to those brutal, terrifying

events of a turbulent time. The Grey Bitches

driving in from the sea, hammering for entrance,

rain squirting through loose panes rattling in

rotted wood. A slight scratching sound came

from smashed jaws   a pottery shard revealed

patterned marine motifs – an octopus, bladderwrack,

a sea-snail; a tusked & speckled walrus with stone

glass eyes & sporting enormous cats whiskers.

Bushy-browed, Taliesin, aquiline face
          impassive, flickering in the light from
                    an occluding red dwarf
              in the backbrain
                          stardust memory

94

PETER MEILLEUR (CHILDE ROLAND) (1943–)

Peter Noël Meilleur, born in Britain and raised bilingually in Québec, is a concrete poet and artist who often works with discarded packaging to produce pop-out pieces, posters, postcards, embossed texts and site-specific performance works. A Canadian government employee in the 1970s, he was part of the 'concretism' of the era, acquainted with bpNicholl and bill bissett, before he moved to Llangollen in 1979. One aspect of his work is a Mallarmean respect for the blan(c)kness of the page, exemplified in *six of clubs* (1978); another, which subsequently exchews the non-verbal experiments of the 1976 London International Sound Poetry Festival (which he attended), is his commitment to emphasising the musicality of words. Drawing on Paolo Freire's *Pedagogy of the Oppressed* (1970) and his own experience of dyslexia, Meilleur notes that 'It is my inability to spell correctly that has made me a poet ... if I could spell, I would not ... get "anxious" over words', but this is precisely what poets must do', and his works affectingly and challengingly blend pure play and critique. 'JONES, THE POEM' is both a homophonic riff on the commonest Welsh surname and a glance at the loneliness of keeping up with the Joneses, while 'DEE AND DEEPER' enacts the course of the river from its source and *Ham & Jam* reworks *Hamlet* Act 2, Scene 2, with Polonius as agent of instrumental rationality at loggerheads with Hamlet's 'antic disposition'; the titles hint at a poetic sensibility somewhere between Dr Seuss and the *Gawain* poet, unaggressive, and ceaselessly resistant.

from six of clubs

park

In a park given a piece of tinsel paper, a playing card and
autumn leaves falling, falling into place where a silversmith had
lost his sterlingship and calling card — the six of clubs

moth

A moth attracted by the luminous quality of the page is given to
partake of it, but by doing so digs its own grave. Its powdery
white wings conveniently and posthumously cover the
excavation, thereby returning the page to its fatal and eucharistic
brilliance

autumn

I heard the sound of a page being turned, rustled in fact. I responded by shuffling my papers and taking off. Autumn and automatically.

promise

I promised to keep the page as white as possible, seeking discipline and inspiration in places and seasons that were white

fossil

I detected a small flaw in the marble (Carrara-quarried) whiteness of the page; a sort of convoluted cornucopian fossil that seemed to spew the very galactic whiteness its presence violated. My attempts at incorporating the affected area with the elements of a sentence especially created for this contingency proved labyrinthine, lachrymal and encapsulating

clouds

The morning dew had just evaporated from the surface of the page when the passing clouds lured me from the implacable whiteness of the page. I became, in the daydream that followed, a member of the Stone Age desert tribe whose subsistence was maintained by tracking the clouds to their rainy destiny. The page is no longer implacable, containing in its silver lining the cloud lore and language of one morning's survival

perpendicular

Perpendicular to the Euclidean plane and Precambrian shield of the page is my pen, also by extension the steeples of my childhood, the mizzen masts of three fourteenth-century caravels from Saint-Malo, the latest rocket to the moon, a boulder dropped by a retreating ice age, my wife and children running towards me

from DEE AND DEEPER

DEE AND DEEPER	DYFRDWY'N DWYSÁU
DEE DIVA TO CAESAR	DYFRDWY DDWYFOL
DEE THE INSPIRATION	DYFRDWY DWYMYN AWEN
DEE DECLIVITIES	DYFRDWY DDWYFRON
DEE DILUVIAL	DYFRDWY LLWYNAU'R DILYW
DEE DEMOSTRATIVE	DYFRDWY DWYLO'R HYLIF
DEE THE ICE AGE GASH	DYFRDWY CLWYF OES YR IÁ
DEE THE EAVESDROP DRIP	DYFRDWY CYCHWYN CLEC
DEE DEPENDENT	DYFRDWY CYNLLWYNES
DEE THE ICICLE	DYFRDWY PIBONWY
DEE DEFROSTING	DYFRDWY CHWYS DIFEROL
DEE AND DEEPER	DYFRDWY'N DWYSÁU
DEE THE INJECTION	DYFRDWY CHWISTRELL
DEE THE ARTERIES	DYFRDWY GWYTHIENNAU
DEE DETOX	DYFRDWY DDIWYGIOL
DEE THE EMBROIDRESS	DYFRDWY NODWYDDES
DEE THE OXBOW STITCH	DYFRDWY PWYTH DOLENNOG
DEE THE ANCHOR-CHAIN BRIDGE	DYFRDWY POMT GADWYNI
DEE THE END ROW RAINBOW	DYFRDWY FODRWY'R ENFYS
DEE THE UNWOUND BORDER	DYFRDWY RHWYMYN Y FFIN
DEE AND DETAILED	DYFRDWY 'BEN BWY GILYDD
DEE AND DEEPER	DYFRDWY'N DWYSÁU
DEE THE ALPHABET	DYFRDWY WYDDOR LLENOR
DEE THE AUTOGRAPHED MAP	DYFRDWY LLOFNOD CRWYDROL
DEE THE ORDOVICI	DYFRDWY LLWYTH OES HAEARN
DEE THE EARTHWORKS	DYFRDWY CAER DREWYN
DEE AND THEE OWAIN	DYFRDWY AELWYD OWAIN
DEE DEPLOYED	DYFRDWY MILWYR RHUFAIN
DEE DEMOBBED	DYFRDWY'N DISWYDDO
DEE A.D.	DYFRDWY BLWYDD OED CRIST
DEE AND DEEPER	DYFRDWY'N DWYSÁU
DEE THE ATISHOOED STEAM	DYFRDWY CHWYTH AGER
DEE THE E SHARP SHRIEK	DYFRDWY'N CHWIBAN DRAW
DEE THE EIGHT-TEN MAIL TRAIN	DYFRDWY TREN YR HWYRNOS
DEE THE INDUSTRIES	DYFRDWY DDIWYDIANNOL
DEE THE AQUEDUCT	DYFRDWY DAN GYFRWR'R BONT
DEE THEATRICAL	DYFRDWY LLWYFAN AMWYS
DEE THE OUTING	DYFRDWY'R WIBDAITH
DEE THE A5 PASSAGE	DYFRDWY TRAMWYFA PUMP
DEE THE S-BEND	DYFRDWY WYRGAM
DEE THE ACCIDENT	DYFRDWY'N DISGWYL DAMWAIN
DEE THE INQUEST	DYFRDWY'R YMCHWILIAD
DEE AND DEEPER	DYFRDWY'N DWYSÁU
DEE THE OMNIBUS	DYFRDWY BWS DYMA HWY
DEE NINETY-FOUR	DYFRDWY GWYRDD POB CAM
DEE DEPOSITED	DYFRDWY DROSGLWYDDO
DEE THE EOCENE EDEN	DYFRDWY BARADWYSAIDD
DEE THE ORE-RICH STRATA	DYFRDWY HAENAU'R MWYNAU

JONES, THE POEM

JONES, THE POEM, THE HIGH FLOWN PHRASES, THE HARPING HARMONIUM, THE DRONE, THE DOS AND DON'TS, THE SONAR MOPANING JONAH OF WHALES, JONES, THE ONOMATOPOEIC OMEN, THE OMEGA OHM RESISTANT EARPHONE, THE OMICRON SIN OF OMISSION, THE THESSALONIAN MONOCHROME NEWS, THE PATAGONIAN-SNOWDONIA OPPONENT, THE LLEYN AERODROME FIRE, JONES, THE BROMIDE, THE BRIMSTONE, THE SANCTIMONIOUS PRONOUNCEMENT UPON JONES, THE PROMISCUOUS HEAD HUNTING SALOME, JONES, THE WINDSOWN STORM-REAPED CYCLONE, JONES, AS IN DAVY JONES, THE COGNOMEN, THE PERSONA, THE PRONOUN, THE DOME DOMESTICATED OZONE ERODING HOMOSAPIENS, JONES PRONOUNCED HONES WITH TEA AND BUTTERED SCONES, JONES, THE HYPHENATED STATUS SEEKING POLYNOMILA, THE TESTIMONIAL, THE CEREMONIAL CHAIN, THE BARONIAL SEAT, THE MATRIMONIAL TRAPPINGS, THE WHALEBONE CHAPERONED BREASTBONE, JONES, THE OXONIAN DIPLOMAS, THE IONIAN PLINTH OF ADONIS, THE LEATHER-BOUND TOME, JONES, THE CHROMOSOME, THE CLONE, THE FOAM AND FOMENT, THE SEA ANEMONE, JONES, HONED ON THE WHETTING STONE OF LONELINESS, JONES, THE GROAN, THE METRONOME, THE BAROMETRIC BARITONE, ONCE KNOW AS HONES, THE PHILHARMONIOUS PHILOMENA CON MOLTO ESPRESSIONER, JONES, THE CAMOMILE SMILE, THE PAGE THREE MONALISA, NOW MISSUS MALONE, JONES, THE SMOULDERING CORONA, THE DOW JONES INDEX, THE ZIRCONIUM FUTURE, JONES HOME, ALASKA, JONES, THE POSTPONEMENT AND ITS ATONEMENT, JONES, THE DRACONIAN AND PARSIMONIOUS DONATION, JONES WHO OWNS, JONES, THROUGH JONES, THE NEO-COLONIAL LOAN, JONES, THE PRONE POSITION, THE ONUS AND THEREFORE THE BONUS, JONES, WITH HIS AND HER COVER BLOWN, JONES, JONES IN NAME ONLY, JONES, THE COMB, THE ABALONE KEEPSAKE, JONES, THE ONLY GAME IN TOWN NAMELY LONELINESS, JONES, PLAYING JOAN OF ARC WITH THE GENTLEMEN OF VERONA, JONES, THE PAVING-STONE PROMOTED TO JONES THE KERBSTONE, JONES, WITH HIS AND HER CRONY, THE ERRONEOUS CHRONOMETER, THE NOMADIC SHADOW, THE STONEHENGE GNOMON, THE ROMANY ROAN, JONES, THE PONY, THE EXPONENT OF THE EXPONENTIAL CURVE, THE RANGE AND DOMAIN OF JONES, THE UNKNOWN, THE HIPPODROME COME, BINGODRONE SYNDROME, THE ACORTIN VERSUS THE PINE CONE, JONES, THE TWILIGHT ZONE, THE PHENOBARBITONE, THE PSYCHOMATIC VENDING MACHINE, THE ROMAN NUMERAL, THE ANNO DOMINE CARVED CORNER STONE, THE HONEYCOMBED

TOWER OF LONELINESS, **JONES**, THROWN TO THE LIONS, **JONES**, THE MARYLEBONE STREET CATACOMB OF THE LONDONIAN METRO, **JONES**, THE HOMESICK TROMBONE, THE FELONIOUSLY BLOWN SEMITONE, THE XYLOPHONE RESONATING ARCHIPELAGO, **JONES**, IN A COMA, MOWN DOWN BY **JONES**, THE ALPHA-ROMEO, **JONES**, THE DETONATOR, BLOWN TO SMITHEREENS BY **JONES**, COUNTY TYRONE, **JONES**, THE ABDOMEN AND ITS HUNGRY DOMINIONS, **JONES**, THE HOMING PIGEON COMBING THE **JONES**-FILLED PAGES OF THE CALEDONIAN LANDSCAPE FOR **JONES**, THE AGRINOMIAL RHIZOME, THE PHLOEM, THE OMOPLATED DEVONIAN RIDGE ABOVE **JONES**, THE LOAMY RIVER BOTTOM, **JONES**, THE SPENT PLUTONIUM, THE ISOMAR, THE MISNOMER, THE NEIGHBOURHOOD HOMER, THE RETIRED SHERLOCK HOLMES, THE WOUND UP GRAMOPHONE, THE BARCELONIAN BRIGADE, THE BEGONIA FLOWERING SARCOMA, **JONES**, THE CORTISONE, THE HOMEOPATHIC PATH, THE AMMONIA FUELLED PNEUMONIA, **JONES**, THE HORMONE, THE EAU DE COLOGNE, **JONES**, THE AROMA, THE MONOSODIUM GLUTAMATE, **JONES**, THE MILL-STONE AROUND THE NECK OF **JONES** AND SOAMES, **JONES**, THE GLAUCOMA STRUCK STAINED GLASS TEMPTATION OF SAINT JEROME, **JONES**, THE STEPPING-STONE, THE MILE-STONE, THE TOMB-STONE, **JONES**, THE GARDEN GNOME, THE OVERGROWN NOMENCLATURE OF LONELINESS, THE MOMENTARILY MOMENTOUS MOMENT OF MOMENTUM, **JONES**, JONESY AND LONELY, ANOTHER POLONIUS, DESDEMONA, NAOMY **JONES**.

from HAM & JAM

(The curtains open with Hamlet walking up and down reading a book which contains a copy of the play *Ham & Jam*. A few seconds later, Polonius enters.)

–What are your plans for the future of the planet my lord Hamlet, what are your plans?
–Ham and jam.
–What are your plans for the future of the planet my lord Hamlet, what are your plans?
–Vans, prams, trams, tandems, charabancs and tar macadams.
–What are your plans for the future of the planet my lord Hamlet, what are your plans?
–The best laid plans of mice and men.

–What are your plans for the future of the planet my lord Hamlet, what are your plans?
–Omelets, the descendants of Henri Plantagenet.
–What are your plans for the future of the planet my lord Hamlet, what are your plans?
–Scan, scram, another plan, planet, cranberry cram.
–What are your plans for the future of the planet my lord Hamlet, what are your plans?
–Spic and span, ban, sanify man.
–What are your plans for the future of the planet my lord Hamlet, what are your plans?
–Amphibian man.
–What are your plans for the future of the planet my lord Hamlet, what are your plans?
–Flim flams, fatasms and suits of grey flannelet.
–What are your plans for the future of the planet my lord Hamlet, what are your plans?
–Androids, homadriads, vampire empires and swift howyhnhms ambling over the ire of Ireland.
–What are your plans for the future of the planet my lord Hamlet, what are your plans?
–La-a-a-ambs, la-a-a-ambs.
–What are your plans for the future of the planet my lord Hamlet, what are your plans?
–Ham and jam children. (Hamlet sings the hymn.)

> Praise him,
> Praise him,
>
> All his children praise him:
> He is love,
> He is love.
>
> Love him,
> Love him,
> All his children love him!

–What are your plans for the future of the planet my lord Hamlet, what are your plans?
–Anvils, hammers, clamps, cranks, spanner, lambs, branding irons, camshafts, cantilevers, pitons, fans, cylinders, ovens, man-ending engines.
–What are your plans for the future of the planet my lord Hamlet, what are your plans?

(Throughout this response, Hamlet waves his arms about with his hands made into a fist as he had no hands.)

No handouts,
No hand-to-mouth existences,
No handgrips or handguns,
No handy handshakes or out of hand statements,
No handwritten handbooks on the handling of hand grenades,
No hand-me-downs or helping hands,
No handing on of torches or taking a hand in the game,
No handicapping handicrafts,
No handweaving,
No handmaidens standing all in a row,
No handrails or handlebar mustachios,
No handcarts or hand organs,
No hands in the pockets,
No hands on the table,
No handbills or handsaws,
No handmowers or handcuffs,
No handsprings, handstands or sleights of hand,
And look no hands.

IAIN SINCLAIR (1943–)

Iain Sinclair is best known as a London novelist and essayist, the prizewinning author of *Downriver* (1991), *Radon Daughters* (1994), *Lights Out For the Territory* (1998), *Dining on Stones* (2004), *Hackney, That Rose-Red* Empire (2009), *Ghost Milk* (2011) and numerous other works; however, *Landor's Tower* (2001), with its Marcher locations, and cast that includes David Jones, Vernon Watkins and Gwain Tunstall (a fictionalized Chris Torrance), is a reminder of his South Walian origins, in Cardiff and Maesteg—as, more recently, is his memoir *Black Apples of Gower* (2015). He studied at Trinity College Dublin, the Courtauld Institute, and the London School of Film Technique, and his early poetry was published by his own Albion Village Press. Connected to the English avant-garde poetry scene which included J. H. Prynne and Douglas Oliver, Sinclair's transition from experimental poet to novelist came with *Lud Heat* (1975) and *Suicide Bridge* (1978), David Jones-like blends of prose and poetry, which forged his tactic of simultaneously concocting and discovering alternative structures of power buried within the metropolitan cityscape. The mythic wing of the 1970s psychogeographic movement (if Allen Fisher is taken as its constructivist wing), Sinclair drew on Albion, Lud and the Celtic cult of the severed head (from the *Mabinogion* tale of 'Branwen, daughter of Llyr', in which the head of Brân is buried under London's White Hill) for this founding myth of his writing and of London itself. In his Preface to *The Firewall* (2006), Sinclair's collected poems, Michael McClure rightly registers these Celto-Gothic roots in describing the poems' 'Brythonic and luminous intelligence'. An explorer and transgressor of boundaries in all aspects of his work, Sinclair also edited the influential *Conductors of Chaos* anthology of innovative British poetry (1996).

The Falls (Talgarth)

we are not given many and do not realise
instants set quick out of darkening air

rainladen sky burns off
the tree's plump skirt

horsemen appear and disappear in the night
witnessed the human town comes alive

trapped stars of whisky sulphur
caught in thermals

we have fucked out holes in black foliage
bodybreath, curtains open
shadows across

where the pigs are dragged
in view of
our fascinated children

imprint of entwined bodies, such glad heat
& then the knife the screams the meaning

Kiting the Flies

always the muff, mouth agape
stealing fond bacteria

this field a cold ghost
excising the ecliptic

pacing the chrism
on highheel blisters

from Myrdle Court out:
nothing

in goes the gelt
thudding paper

silencing the disease
of white domestic business

Obscenery of the East
for Chris Torrance

walking to where there is no weather
bits of my head, whispering
doesn't ease it, or the lurid continuum

of shadows across mattress grass
the raven's fee, believe me
breath like piss runs downhill

Wick Wood futured now
cropped in thistle & blowweed
maggot-flies in place of butter

nothing shines with more novelty than
a slack isthmus the resting bicycle
tomorrow they know won't be as fine

Crossing the Morning *(Vale Crucis)*

climbing sun boulders the hillcrest
between stones a cat appears
ingratiating or tactical, completing
the arc & arrow of low-rolled desire

chopped pillars make an altar or anvil

here the feather the ant
does its work
versing and reversing, willing its will
a system of hair-fine lines;
by its direct movements, abrupt to the eye
its blade its balance
making this place, whole

all those branches, windows, archways
water-chest open to new air
leaf-drenched dark pools, unmeditated
fold back to the river and the hills

kingstone set apart
on ground that pulses like a warning

that stands because the rest has fallen

Recovery & Death

late daisies, burnt leaves
curl at the edge
in currents of moist air

silver sun stirs a high tumbler
dark pool among tree-tops

LEON IS A TRAMP.
And his mother is a slag
And she wears shit shoes
That cost £1.99p

bench not designed for rest
resolutely, his back
to the scene he is describing

Ocean Estate

fording pondlife to pamper your Arab steed
rosettes displayed above pillows
of cleanest straw, can't call
a whippet a dog (it's a bitch anyway &
hot to smear my shiny strides)

call it: 'long-term rewards of academic life'

all the blood-fruit wine that
flatters & does not grind the loaf you
squeeze cutting an X-ray pet
who has mislaid her silver bell

'forest' no threat so much green
stacked until you close out
the other stuff the bearded litigants
incubating harm (despoiling
place) to pedigree'd to fart in tune

poets outgun symposium novelists
having less to say & saying it
with more conviction & smelling
like they live by choice in mismatched
suits (obligated to Burton's black)

a fust of old books & and older cheese
nobody loves gossip like these salaried dudes
above us hangs a carmine cloud
the amputated leg of Harry Crews
stern invoice of what a writer's biography
should entail: no kids & a drawerful of
biro caps to clean wax from the ears
granted, all dream
but some of us, having better manners
would never admit so much

A Series of Photographs
(*Riverwalk from the Isle of Grain to Oxford*)

hard on the heels of hope, westwards
unhyped, either bank 'could turn
into something or other' one pilgrim thinks
while his companion--------------------
is not recorded, no pocket scalpel to hack
through stubbled paddocks, a sense
of husbanded disease, soul fatigue, excess
vegetables, say it, baked beans
clouds of body gas to drop midges, open
land in a shame of underexploited air
always, to our right, the broad
& grumbling stream

ii
among the volume radiators pale
spines a library of dry & whistling pipes
bug overcoats - on foot you still
haunt urban attics - noise is kinder
(in the German sense) cannily
transported, red clay ridge, the bird
alights on a weak branch, holds its weight
waits, as we are too sudden & greedy
sighs, more shove less drive
out along the mud-crack's shoreline
the rubber solution tide, bulk containers
trafficking pansy tubs on planks of shit

iii
In the 'first book-length study of the work' of J.H. Prynne the name of
Simon Armitage appears as frequently as that of Paul Celan. Discuss.

I don't for example consider that poets are
rock & roll old or new he
said apologetically quite the reverse
another case to drop from the carousel
duty declared & spoilt charms to ward off
the fear of flying fit nicely in a designer
carrier bag (later a bank mask & sex aid)
(later still a shield against nuclear sunburn)
so can you tell me the unident sneered
the nature of your business at the fibre optic
satellite of Gravesend (full marks for the
wall of early ripen'd figs), no answer as
our elevated cage swings out over the chalk
bowl the sepulchral stone of Dr Field

Kent 'rolling' eternally away. England
he gasped. Let's come back with a camera
as if we could, no chance of a teabreak
in Tel's roadside shack, the anachronistic
pick-up of the water tower, no trout
left in the pool. A lunchhour barmaid's
wren-brown neck is silently remarked,
high breasts, narrow waist, all that
artifice can add to nature. Ex-nautical
geezers in starched t-shirts & gold chains
out in the corn, the scarlet poppy pylon
dry fields where tide surges around a fixed post
& the noise of the dead is everywhere unheard

iv
in the hot field if you stand back to the willow
when our skiff locked & I tore open the
zip fitting cornflower blue remembered dress
emphasised by picnic basket & the death of our
unconscious sponsor a dwarf named Bill Shakespeare

in the cornfield standing in dust coloured coat
& taking breeze an oarsman's golden tent stubble
tight as the weave of a cat's belly the spectre who
sometimes scratches at our varnished door

nice kinship with cloud flight distinct
outline of Sinodum clump your shadowfall
to calculate lost time: *river's over there*
a current reverie passes between two
photographs the seizure not between us
I am redundant to what occurs which is
where the track directs itself back
towards the Thames & if your sleeves
are an inch or so too short then
so much the better your arms strength I
exploit elsewhere & am eager to unload

v
I burned the beast hut
hurting the huge
ah ghosts ah money

please pass either side

SAGESONG: A text for performance

'Poet appointed dare not decline...'

I build a raft of books. A paper nest to split finger pads and drip a
bloody wake of words, behind us, on thick water. Against a ball of
mud in the throat: praise-song of middle ground, Middlesbrough,
choked or hooped in tight brass. I spit colliers' phlegm and shattered
hubcaps. Doctor-fathers at pit gate. The held silence of a Quaker
Meeting House. Briggflatts. Pebbles clattering in a fast stream. Our
ship tilts like a declining cliff and foams to ruin.

I build a raft of sea-books, to make my drowning sure. Concrete boots
welded for sinking. Water, so cold and clear at source, thickens to
reeking soup. In Norfolk I saw trees grow upsidedown, henges or
rings, like the negative of a longboat, a Viking burial. In Lindisfarne
they are homes.

I build a raft from gospels and traceries, serpents in relief on stone
crosses. Beasts mashed from pulp and poets: Bunting, MacSweeney,
Pickard, Griffiths. Time served in cells and cells splitting open to
stolen light. Rivets, driven through the paw, rust to coral. An hour
gathers them in, memory-libraries for creosote and pitch, skin for a
black sail. You do not know this place and this place does not know
you. Foolish to speak. To spoil a slow pint. Bunting cautioned against
verbiage. Cut cut cut. 'Vision is lies,' he said.

Make a map of sound: hammers on iron, axe blades on bone. Naked women dancing on coal beaches. Rattling chutes and broken shotguns. They love their poets and bridle them with poverty, drive them out.

'In Gateshead, on our way back, we passed some little streets named after the poets, Chaucer and Spenser and Tennyson; and I wondered if any poets were growing up in those streets. We could do with one from such streets; not one of our frigid complicated sniggering rhymers, but a lad with such a flame in his heart and mouth that at last he could set the river on fire. Who would rush to put it out?'

I walked all morning in weak sunshine recording patterns of horsehit on the road. But I did not reach the sea. 'They only listen,' Tom Pickard said, 'when you think they aren't.'

Flirty Turtles

if the birds are badges, in the hollow of the hand, grasp the orange
too small for this day's plural & unique date, my eyes
haven't learnt to turn inward, to celebrate focal confusion --
in the sea, tossed & w/out worth, birds in their element
confirm the idea of a dome, visceral, cloudy (sight) in wonder
of cloudform, continents on which nothing & nobody has ever
set foot, recall 'messenger' birds as described by death-infected
old ones, the man in the hat, no mess but some other
word, beginning with p, I'll have to review the DVD gift
      always cityscape, shit feathers
different languages saying the same nothings, affection
against gravity and dissolution, a brittle Ark
      that will not float, or lift
in assumption of benevolent rain, unceasing
your thoughts my thoughts, the wideshore the dunes
      we talk up a disposed future, the child
crawling across this small desert to a dent of salty water
      one pigeon had its head blown off
      one man, an immigrant, had his shoulder pierced twice
      in the same spot
one dog stared but did not speak

the poet at the end of the land
thinks with his hair
the oily thick lavabread spill
and the creased waves of the prow
       his forehead
pushed against the fingers' groynes
       illuminate!
"I am aware you are not here"
the list extends
and when the fireworks detonate
       across the river valley
some performers wilt, others step into
their bulk, the Large Ghost shadow
waiting against the curtain
to permit words, we attend

TILLA BRADING (1945–)

Tilla Brading is a poet, performer and textual artist who has taught creative writing as well as working for much of her life with students with learning difficulties. Drawing on her up-bringing on a hill farm in Ystradfellte, Powys, her work has evolved towards an increasingly free exploration of language, semantics, performance and the visual. Its starting points may be texts, landscape, history, the news 'or anything that can weave, meld and fray into a termination if not a completion'. She was joint editor of Odyssey Press / Poetry Quarterly Review and assistant custodian of Coleridge's cottage in Nether Stowey, Somerset. Her collaboration with Frances Presley, (entitled ADADADADA) overlays the location of Ashley Combe, Porlock, Somerset with Ada Lovelace and her adventurings into computer language and the inflected line. She is researching a textual piece relating to 'migrations', from the Neolithic, to the present day.

MOVEMENT FROM THE HILLS   (1997 Poss of Inferno)

tears
skin ripped from carcass
severs
a ring a wether
red evening
key-hood of sky
pared from dusking hills

watch   in the barn
calf   tap the warm teat
outside   hills suckle spruce
along the ridge
field's udder
knackered under asphalt

listen   stumble
on town brews
trespassing
stubbled vision
snuffing climbing
bills in the fire
climbing the hill
to scratch it alone
thistles pricking your work
mild cattle holing your fence

officialdom wears
paths through your Caebach*   *small field
condescending accents
slice quaintness
bara of your warm kitchen
work it down
clean earth may cover

SIGNS OF STONE (2006)

walk

daughter to the stone
Maen Llia

Brychan's daughter
trapezoidal conglomerate
ritual involving the cairns

photo   what circles were
father atop Maen Llia vague image
        cumbrous pillar

alone in an open moor

con nexus

whose land
the land of my fathers
removed from a known point
within the landscape
(the standing stone)
to a final resting place
(the cairn)

pulley blocks made by yr great grand-father
lifted
Stonehenge heavy monoliths

the stones returned

how had they moved

stand atop there
sprinkle me to the wind
all the 'I am', 'I was'
scattered to *distant scenery*

slip
cling to the rock
write
on the screeing slate
age   old

objects within their surroundings establish a sense of belonging
monument single focal point insufficient in itself construct
cognitively and visually need the valley spur river scarp slope visual
totality integral to a greater space the landscape integral to a part a
greater space the landscape

(where are you in all this)

tomb space
integral
to greater space
comfortable bed
for the loved dead
the tomb does not have to be monumental
statement of ownership
control
landscape

consciousness of monumentality
controlled by knowledge
architecture
[not a] physical medium
conscious awareness
concept

why should it suggest belief
in an afterlife

comfortable bed
for the loved dead
monuments within landscape *individual creates his or her own story to the*
archeologist it is merely a site
Neolithic symbol of individuality
restricted
significance

O

M
A
E
N

M
A
D
O
C
Dervac Filius Justi Hic Yacit

Skinhead-smooth
hills

Mynydd Eppynt

O

two unobtrusive rings

90 metres of each other

the circle and its outlier

may have preceded the oval

Long walk *from one stone to another, picking up and carrying each stone to the place of the next stone; stone to stone Blanyoy to Hay Bluff; stone to stone Hay Bluff to Twmpa** from one stone to another, lifting and carrying the first stone to the place of the next stone; stone to the next stone and circle the stone; stone to the next stone and circle the stone; stone to the opposite stone; making a mark; tracing the surface; placing a stone; movement and stillness; walking and stone; walking and stone; moving and still; from one stone to another, lifting and carrying the first stone to the place of the next stone; stone to the next stone and circle the
stone; stone to stone and circle the stone; stone to the opposite stone; making

*R. H. Fuchs *Richard Long* 1986 Thames and Hudson

ENIGMA, I

One solid limb
afoot
not hobnailed,
caked in mud,
but swathed
as in soft leather
left. leg. at. attention.
though even this resolution
teeters

Hand on my heart
I am a confusion
no martyred Christ
dis-membered
hermaphrodite
fragmentary
tangled in tethers
bull-posted
and barb
subsumed background
My face unsullied
my female side
tender in mayhem
half goddess
half man
exposed and vulnerable
sex   gentle
little pockets of kit
spawning
a Flora hologram
metaphor of light
and shade
broken Mary

Behind me
a happy collaboration of men
arms raised
greeting surrender
the mule at pasture
unconcerned
men co-operate
across duckboards
escape with booty
(sandbag or body)
like skulking burglars

Destructive construction
violent tranquility
attacking retreat

matchwood security
stunted limbs solid trunks
blasted
broken form
I

Fir-festooned
gestures of Christmas
are childlike stars
(so much innocence
in carnage
[in parenthesis])
scattered on the ground
echoed in barbs
and whiteouts
of full and crescent moons

Rats
with old sardonic sense
sniff casually
explore their gangplank
a cracked post
outwit nets
untrapped in wire traps
of Mametz

Gentle proboscis sheathed
piercing surrounds
(did I do that?)
bayonetted wire
they shall beat their swords
into spades
the ignored dead
all broken
metamorphoses

Look again,
the woman has gone
dangling from
a male thigh
dissipated
in sandbags
which don't
hold back the flood
a perfect flow
passing

All broken
passing the flotsam

NOTES TOWARDS DEFINITE INFERENCE (2010)

tautology retains the vestiges of singing synaesthesia of one energy to
another past the end of viability

reappropriated into the discourse choices catching complexity tropes
compose

disruption uncovers climbs over lack paradox cadence musicality
contradiction meditative powers

erasion shaping translation and inheritance sorting disinterested because
you have stared too long

clumping places and register cutting the long written vowels as if knowing
the voice erases words irritate uncomfortable response

coalesce and collide subversive possibilities anarchy of pragmatics subject
that cannot be erased rejection of form mish-mash rummage and clutter

something stirs beyond the words no intention to conclusion a tight form
of reverse acronym convert the numerical value of the letters the allelic
combinations into music

antennae whisker unmarked equivalents fill the gaps and edges porous
words the hole in O impish

playful duration risky sound looking and listening unbounded detached
subverting original missal acoustic resistance into leaves

bilingual multilingual bling belong playful revisioning transformation
beside the point 'inhabit the text on its own terms'

steal and dissemble restless bleeding seepage assembling fragments
damaged beyond repair clumsy stitched cuts partial

gashes fraudulent scars recycled rags to make pulp from paper rearranging
its partlets infinity of opportunity the fuzzy edges of exactitude comes on
like a trance

subrosa may invert haal is a haar ethereal or corporeal quotidian the ringing
of bells unfolding and foot-stamping into the wordless space

diamond catching the light the notes and rests daring largesse tumble
between certainty and doubt locus of resistance subject that cannot be
erased

impish visual in lieu of rhyme and meter mete the implications

PHILIP JENKINS (1943–)

Philip Jenkins attended Nottingham University, and co-edited the journal *Sotto Voce* in 1973-74. He had already discovered and played a role in the Concrete poetry movement of the late 1960s, after first encountering it in Belfast in the magazine *Crabgrass*, meeting dsh, Thomas A. Clark and Peter Finch. His subsequent poetry is in the vulnerable yet expansively brilliant and surrealist-tinged vein of certain other poets of the period, such as Lee Harwood and Paul Evans. Particularly talismanic has been the work of Pierre Reverdy which 'remains the archetype of what poetry is at its best.' Jenkins spent the 1970s and 1980s in Nottingham and London, and suffered from homelessness in the late 1980s. Since then he has lived in Cardiff, where he began writing again and founded Baked Alaska press. His collections include *The Fantasy Childhood Reset* (1971), *The Birth of Venus* (1973), *A Sailor's Suit and Cap* (1976) and *On the Beach with Eugène Boudin* (1978); the long poem *Cairo* (Jenkins's masterpiece in the opinion of Andrew Duncan) was published in 1981 (books 1 and 2) and 2005 (book 3). Recent books includes *The Annotated Edition* (2009), *Eskimos at Two O'Clock* (2009) and *Baritone Compass* (2010).

A sailor's suit and cap

telephone kiosks are rare in a rainstorm
out in the warehouse one of the corners
had opened out
                    the confusion I had
hoped for

I stand before my mirror
                        rumour
had distorted much that had happened
she takes off her pants with
an expression but no
explanation

she lowers her head gracefully
the suitcases ready packed
great love isn't exactly like this
                        it's time someone
wrote a definitive work
on the subject

I find satisfaction in my size alone
I know how to dream with none
of the curiosity left
                              ah how the world
is small by lamplight

something is moving before me
the last of this backward presence
the stairs behind
                              going to choose
choosing to go

Detective Eric Lönnrot is in the backgarden
he too is a reflection in the mirror
he is a complete stranger
don't *be* like that

scenes of low voices
                              my friends
arranged it
                  it is in their precision
that dreams differ

the principles which create the caricature
inflections with their own
characteristic gestures and
perfect hearing
                        the dream
as a strong magic element

the eyes we have set
to destroy them
                        the dream we
in leaving choose to be
convinced by

we speak simply about 'things'
dreams and the waking state

travels in India (in 1921)
experiences in Ceylon

the mysterious casket which could
not of course be opened
                              I have
even come to wonder about it

it is Ethiopia
where are we

                waiting

On the beach with Eugène Boudin

'three brush strokes directly
from life are better than
two days work at the easel'
he turned to me

the sky is grey
tonight as always
tourists grouped rhythmically
this world which seems to
lie before us

two empty chairs at the
waters edge a conversation
an aloofness casually the light
gleams and is gone

and so we stay where we are
on the beach at Trouville
for fifteen years without returning

my address is given below

I flied over the left observed parts
the cinema curtain fluttered out
parks the car stainless steel evade
middle screen under water

containers and escaping this I'll
wake up a tourist

                    door jamb
crumbles
            two tartans blanketed

the patterned blur of what I
wrote on my hand and what
was it? eventually we shall
all have given up thinking

my photo booth portraits slump out
the assumed positions they lie there

but she would have had a name just
don't make me remember it now

soon we shall be slow connecting
with our emotionally compromised pasts

like sea green sanctuaries from which
we return unapologetically to harbour

baritone compass

people from perhaps earlier
decades I might've known

them they move unchanged
sunshine continually recurring

nature notes

ginger and white, the cat I know
stretched out in dappled sunlight

waking up briefly, he checks his watch
the snail always touches wood

before changing direction

estonian border post

certain scribbles at passport control
skin scratches and sometimes
I shoulder these outrages

and at other times I lament a demise

an irretrievable memory closing up shop
moving out towards the suburbs
changing addresses, midtown to midfield

teetotalling on the verges
interstatic high ways and bye ways
unwrapping the tourniquet

for possible re-use

time piece

from this valley
you are leaving
so I hear

one october evening
in the back of the car
an old morris oxford

we drank up the remains
of her inheritance
by that time

the car would have been
almost a classic

we played cards
on the train home
until don't ask me

the time, I must've left
my watch in the bathroom

or someplace
but don't worry
it's safe

from the front line

on the bridge at Avignon
everyone dances

from left to right it was written
the direction from which the troops invade

the paper smoothly rips open
its rattan squares roughened

I have no envelope and therefore
no way to send you this

foreign holidays

wake me up slowly tomorrow
I've never been abroad before

yesterday I wasn't happy
with the way I tied my shoelaces

and today I wont take off my socks
before leaving your fine country

choking on an old park drive

were her tears Spanish
or at least Portuguese?

at their best, people I think
can make the most marvellous friends

failure reflates in cold water
and the best we can do then is
point out where the rain comes in

tonight, asparagus I think and a film
one day my lung will have flown away

PAUL EVANS (1945–1991)

Paul Evans was born in Cardiff in 1945, where his father was a vicar in the Church of Wales, and was educated at Llandovery College. On holiday in Anglesey, aged sixteen, he met the poet-painter Brenda Chamberlain, who encouraged him to write. Evans studied English at Sussex University in 1963-65; as editor of the magazine *Eleventh Finger* with Paul Matthews, he was, like John James and Philip Jenkins, a figure of note in the generation shaped by Donald Allen's *New American Poetry 1945-1960*. In 1967 he began an M.Phil on Robert Duncan, supervised by Eric Mottram, one of the leading figures in the British Poetry Revival. He lectured at Essex University in 1970-71 and received the Alice Hunt Bartlett Prize for his collection *February* in 1971. In the 1970s and 1980s he had a number of academic and bibliographical jobs, chiefly at Central London Polytechnic. He lived in Liverpool from 1979, and was a keen climber, often with his friend, the English poet Lee Harwood. He died on one such expedition, in a climbing accident on Snowdon.

from Taldir Poems

> *for Dewi-Prys Thomas*
> *... epiphanies of the spirit there*
> *and a chronicle of that time also ...*

1 A Letter

At 2 a.m. I was reading Happold's collection of mystical writings, in bed, wondering how we can know when a 'mystical' experience happens to us. Can we know before that we will accept it when it comes?

I have had intuitions of a great order and pattern, of a love which subsumes and surrounds all—but have also long periods of doubt. Is my reading, and the points of recognition reached every so often, merely the product of intellectual desire? Will there be a complete assurance?

So I was questioning, reading by the light of two candles at the bedside, one stuck to a small handmirror, the other in a gilt candlestick. I noticed the candle in the gilt holder was dying, the wick collapsing as the wax melted, and the flame at a low ebb.

After a time I glanced at the candles again. The one which had previously been dying now burned with a tall flame, the wick upright in the wax. It seemed a symbol or bearing out of the struggle I had been engaged in—the death and resurrection of the light. As well as assuring me that the struggle is continuous, it brought to mind that 'light' has occurred in several contexts of late, is assuming perhaps its true place.

2

Brilliant stars tonight, so we speak
of benevolent shine.
                         They wheel
over the darkened house, sky-
messengers, new lights from south
of the mountain, climbing its back
from where they were born, deep
on the other side, in fields of
light which we call kind,
                              watching them
all night, while our desires
turn bitter on the ground.

4

A black cow, carrying
the hill on its horns, breaks
the green ferns down.

                         Distant confusion
                         of insects
                         breeds in the ear.

        All sounds concur.

        The curved horn
         tears the earth,
         loose rock follows.

        Scared birds
        leave the area, rising
        on her cry.

        She is calling
        for two companions
        left behind,

black beast
weeping
on a green hillside.

6 For Rhys

Dead, left in
the dark after battle,
return to stone,

leaving no trace
of blood, breath
or bone.

Only the rain
seeps
through the heaped-up stones.

This night
a certain light
dropped down,

releasing that
withheld by them
so long, making

these warriors' bodies
gleam again
from stone.

9

*The lifting of clouds
is the work of gods,
the raising of clouds
produces gold.*

No longer white, the fields dazzle.
The lower slopes vibrate
as golden sheep
cross and recross them.

Blades of light start up
from openings in the field
where the full light moves,
beyond the pine-enclosure.

This is the vision we have waited.
Children watch
In pure amazement
From the windows of Ty'n Llidiart.

We see that gold
the Masters told us
was a symbol for the soul
and its light plays over us.

The lifting of clouds
is the work of gods,
the raising of clouds
produces gold.

1st Imaginary Love Poem

Your hair a nest of colours a tree
the sky hung from you constantly
amaze me new dialects and everything
the white clouds drifting in your eyes

"I like poetry as much as sleeping" you said
and the guards lined up outside the tower
the crocodiles were all on form that day
wiping your face in the sun

how could I fail to love you for what you did?
bending to pick up the message
my hours of waiting destroyed 'Meet me
by the equestrian statue at 2 o'clock'

it was an English sunset the bells
in my sleep reminding me of home
I shall be there fully-dressed and awake
their jaws snapping and the water turning red

Snow

'If youre seen with him again' smell
of sperm in the chestnut trees
lining the drive in summer my dreams
have always been of pursuers an apple
turning brown on the table chasing me
over the moorlands up empty streets
in the rooms of huge hotels he meant
more than everything was worth to me

I was following a disused railway line
in Cornwall that must have been
before you entered my dreams how could I
possibly have known you? and came on
a quarry his hair was brown I think
abandoned but for the bodies
of trucks in the grass the roofs
of the houses were faling in
so we left some of them only
red stains of rust in the ground
but tender to me I couldn't
stay in my room overlooking the drive
but had to go out in other dreams
I betrayed everything I loved
just as

the fields were a white
the woods were stitched on
did they really think
I'd put loyalty duty and respect
and all my privileges before him?
how strange meeting *you*
at the poetry competition
with all that snow on the ground
I walked for hours in the rain
to reach some decision truly bewildered
by what my poems call 'love' we knew
without skis we were finished

the outcome was never decided
but terminated by natural means
or was it blonde? shutting the door
of the cupboard my mouth found his

followed by a single shot the skin
of the apple already curling that
was years after Cornwall my mouth
was so dry in there I thought the light
in the clearing would give us away
but though they stood by the door
they never thought to open it
and the snow covered our tracks

Dark &

*'My dark and cloudy words; they do but hold
The truth, as Cabinets inclose the gold ...'*
- John Bunyan

1
days of rain, last of the year

 our children play games in which
well-known securities are rehearsed:
'I am the small puppy
belonging to the mother dog'

a dullness
not reached by Mozart, dope or sex
approximates despair

my poems have been too full
of your absence for years

2
storm in the tree-tops
the sea's great bass

those correspondences
one tires of

won't let you be

great rushing wind
batters the mind
wind, not winde
on the castle-top

take
        oh take them
in the wind's wide mouth

dull words
of duller passion

spat out
      scattered
on the marshy ground
north of Lewes

3
today I wish
not to describe a feeling
nor circumscribe a mood
(intangibly connected with a loss of self)
but simply to report
from where I stood

'in blank amazement
before the unknown territory of you
enveloped in an endlessly spreading
milky mist'

                  years ago
in the distance of a room
your dark eyes, dark hair
wet from washing, pushed back
and falling from behind the ears

only today I understand
in the words of Kobo Abé
how your beauty
pierced my ignorance

outside the darkness gathered
against the banked-up snow

4
(after John Dowland)

'Welcome
black night'—
I welcome you

not because you
purge in sleep
the images of day

but as you contain
what lies
deepest in me

you are its
key and
mirror too—
so I was that boy, 12 years old
slipping from his parents' house
who ran naked through the rain
to stand beneath the broken
school-house roof
              where a spout
gushed cold on his stomach
quivering sex
            and rolled
in the school-yard pools like a dog
releasing its own
            secret delight
in blackness and pouring rain

5
not black, but colour
is a key

not 'key'
        but door
not 'door'
        but gulf

Joán Miro's
blue abyss
'free of all associations with the earth'

out of which
through a yellow curtain
a hawk grabbed me
from the edge of sleep

and carried me
to where I could gaze
into the heart
caught in the waves
of longing and fear,
not daring to acknowledge
what I had seen—
            night
that stands behind day

lacking courage
to give myself up
'small blue patch
           in a limitless void'

6
'wing
bird-wing
arch in the smoke'

one feather
I picked up
perfect
grey curve

yellow flash
blown at my
feet
below the sea-wall

I was not thinking
of where I was
grey curve
of ocean
an eyelid's flash

'wing
bird-wing
arch in the smoke'

(homage to Johannes Bobrowski)

PETER FINCH (1947–)

Peter Finch was brought up and still lives in Cardiff. During the sixties and seventies Finch was central to the Welsh Underground scene, a tireless propagandist for innovative literature and art of all kinds and all nations. He was treasurer of the Association of Little Presses and ran the groundbreaking magazine and poetry press *Second Aeon*, which not only helped to introduce a whole panoply of international experimental writers, artists and critics to the British public, but was also, through its now almost mythical listings pages, an invaluable source of information on publications, small presses, resources and opportunities available at the time. From 1975 to 1998 he also ran the Arts Council of Wales's specialist Oriel Bookshop in Cardiff, another crucial resource for poetry lovers of all persuasions and a cutting edge art gallery into the bargain. His own work has always been protean and energetic, taking in developments such as sound poetry, visual /concrete poetry, performance, psychogeography, collaborative enterprises such as Cabaret 246, but Finch has never been afraid of accessibility, and has a considerable body of more conventional poetry to his credit. Major poetry collections include: *On Criticism* (Writers Forum 1984); *Make* (Galloping Dog 1990); *Useful* (Seren 1997); *Antibodies* (Stride 1997); *Food* (Seren 2001); *The Welsh Poems* (Shearsman 2006); *Selected Later Poems* Seren 2007); *Zen Cymru* (Seren 2009).

Sunpoem

A Welsh Wordscape

1.
To live in Wales,
Is to be mumbled at
by re-incarnations of Dylan Thomas in numerous diverse disguises.
Is to be mown down by the same words at least six times a week
Is to be bored by Welsh visionaries with wild hair and grey suits.
Is to be told
of the incredible agony
of an exile
that can be at most
a day's travel away.

And the sheep, the sheep,
the bloody, flea-bitten Welsh sheep,
chased over the same hills
by a thousand poetic phrases
all saying the same things.

To live in Wales
is to love sheep
and to be afraid
of dragons.

2.

A history is being re-lived,
a lost heritage
is being wept after
with sad eyes and dry tears.

A heritage
that spoke beauty to the world
through dirty fingernails
and endless alcoholic mists.

A heritage
that screamed that once,
that exploded that one hold time
and connected Wales
with the whirlpool
of the universe.
A heritage

that ceased communication
upon a death, and nonetheless
tried to go on living

A heritage
that is taking
a long time to learn
that yesterday cannot be today
and that the world
is fast becoming bored
with language forever
in the same tone of voice.

Look at the Welsh landscape,
look closely,
new voices must rise,
for Wales cannot endlessly remain
chasing sheep into the twilight.

Blodeuwedd Translated

I was bldng n t lp f bsts
Pllng stffl t m lv. I hv t scmng
tht wnds mir n t mn. Grmnts f groc
dlt n clpp n t wnk f m il.

I m starrr f mgh mlssssss
wr tghtngngngn shot my moderness appalling
nasnasmast f I hd fop on fop on me
n t rbble f stirling I list m why

I ws bllll l l ll llls
Pllng ngngn n n ng. N ng n ngngng
tht thth t t th. Gthths yt thth
dlt o oooo o o ooo o o oo

I m storrr r rrr r mssssssss
wr starlight starlight starlight
starlight starlight starlight me
god gaths stir m m starlight why

I ss sssss sssss blod oak broom meadowsweet

***Extracts from* 'Five Hundred Cobbings'**

O captain! My Cobbing! Our folding scam is done
My Cobbolo singing

Cobbing: a term used to describe experiments in fun first developed in
the 1950s which work primarily through the randomness of the poem.
'Cobbing begins by being aware of ambient pleasure as a structural
agent.' 'Cobbing folds.' 'Cobbing oscillates.' 'Call this art can you read
this.' 'Cobbing do it does it in writing and he sings.'

Cobbing is the strength
Cobbing between calm and catastrophe
Cobbing still presumed
Cobbing obtains incredible variety
Cobbing is a surprise
Cobbing a visiting psychiatrist
Cobbing difficult to reconcile
Cobbing does not form a selfish concept
Cobbing is a strange attractor
Cobbing always bothers
Cobbing in ceaseless motion
Cobbing with light poise
Cobbing exists
Cobbing a string
Cobbing so many difficulties
Cobbing a network of special fibre
Cobbing originates on a wintry afternoon
Cobbing a nonelephant animal
Cobbing's paradigm shift
Cobbing's red spot roaring
Cobbing under normal conditions
Cobbing it's a simple example
Oh my little Cobbing
my lovely Cobbing
my soft sweet Cobbono
my curling Cobbono
my curling Cobbing
Cobbing with bows and hearts
my great hearted Cobanovitch
Cobbing the stone throat
blue-eyed great coated
honeysuckly Cobbono
sugar sweet man Cobonsing
Cobbonot with eyes like diamonds

saucers
honey babe
that thing
Cobbing scented
Cobbing perfumed
great arm-pitted Cobbing
Cobbing caves
liana creeping Cobinsing
hoary Cobbing roaring
roaring roaring
Cobbing he roaring man

rows with Cob
    not
    no Cob
    that's terrible
    Cob you can't
    shut the Cob up
    Cob Cob Cob Cob off
    off Cobbing
    off running

How Cobbing manipulates: by tearing, by scorching,
by applying himself in drips, by partially being pasted,
by drinking, by splattering, by floating on water,
by being crumpled and crushed, by coming upon himself
suddenly, by being rubbed against a textured surface,
by smoking, by being found torn and battered or
jerked up at random from a great worthless stack, by
leaking, by draining, by being punctured and oozing,
by gushing in staccato leaps, by bounding, by being
incised, by roaring in plastic liquid, by emulsifying
boldly among tattooed supporters, by openly glinting,
by masking, by gilding, by frottage, fumage, froissage
and flottage, by fragmenting randomly, by scarifying,
by howling, by sifting, by cobbling, by groping, by
wobbling, by burnishing, by cushioning, by castellating
by mordant gilding, by counterstretching, by popping,
by proofing and adding, by chipping, by coating, by grinding
by rendering with tar wash, by bathing in spirits, by
mildly mouldering, by setting fire to trousers, by
sanding, by fusing, by bubbling up and smudged, by enumerating,
by translating, by jumping, by swimming, by eating and
by spitting and by coughing a lot and printing.

Cobbing's band:
cob (tpt)
cobn (flhn)
cob (bell)
obob (p solo)
ing (toth)
cobm (bugle)
cobn (tb; clo; cbsspn)
cobn (acc. jig, footo)
cobn (bj, tongue vib)
cobn (wbd)
cobn (phcbr jam)
cobn (nse)
cobn (spt)
cobn (Cypriot bread)
cobn (wallpaper)

Ahmed Abcobbo and the Solomonic quintet
Roland Cobanovitch
Zoot Horn Cobdunski
Big Lips Bing Boppo
Cripled Hard Armed Cobbono
Hannibal Cobarnish Petersen
Cannon Cannon (mgr)
ggs chp (wknds) enqr wthn

Antibodies

Action of antibodies against snake venom is simple: the antibody alone disarms the toxin. Antibodies can also neutralise bacteria. Zigzag structure ('The tape-recorder's treatment of the voice teaches the human new tricks of rhythm and tone' - Cobbing: *We Aspire to Bird Song*). Antibodies can combat some viruses by binding to them and preventing them from invading cells. These bindings of idea on idea have immense application. With the majority of micro-organisms, the antibody needs help to kill the invader. Examples include the George Harrison 'My Sweet Lord' settlement, Glyn Jones's unresolved gull's wing action against Hugh Mac Diarmid, pale revision John Cooper Clarke's 'Subterrranean Homesick Blues'.

Further successes cause inflammation and bring other immune cells into the infected area. There is a possibility of using cells to carry out the binding activity deliberately. Immune systems are taught to 'listen' to artificial activity and remember the pattern using cell displacement. This process is know as 'thymic education' where the immune system, now unable to attack its own cells, can readily recall the intellectual associations of previous chance activity in others and replicate them. This is undoubtedly an emotional driven creative activity. Some immunologists believe that any chance derived output remaining and bound to the body's own molecular system is either further converted or destroyed. Others disagree and believe the educative process lies elsewhere. Their reporting of these matters can be virulent and disturbing. For many participants this is simply the point. Exactly what happens during their thymic education remains gloriously uncertain.

RNLD TOMOS (*vcl, hca*, some *prse*) aka Curtis Langdon. 1913-2000. Gospel. Austerity tradition. Jnd Iago Prytherch Big Band (1959), gog, gap, bwlch, lleyn, tân, iaith, mynydd, mangle, adwy - mainly on Hart-Davis race label. Reissue Dent PoBkSoc Special Recommnd. Concert at Sherman support Sorley Maclean (*gtr, hrt, clutching*) sold out. Fire Bob tour Sain triple cd for D Walford Davies (*vcl, crtcl harmonium*) new century highspot. A pioneer of dark wounds and internal tensions. In old age bird song and reliable grouch. Stood, was counted, still no change. To live in Wales is to become un-assailable. 'An angel-fish' (Clarke). Expect retrospective, marvelling and statue.

Heart

warps of the heart
the unfulfilled heart
the bent heart

Late at night looking west when the Shirelles
come on the radio   the fridge clicking   the down
pipe loose   moon   star   like it has always been.

Sometimes the heart is so prominent that it
becomes a log wedged across the chest.

Does the heart have its own memory own
fears its own ghost way of talking
getting things done?

heart sways like a sabre
heart beats like a gong

In the morning rain running Lou Reed on
the Walkman chest a great house heart some
monster to be afraid of   I was in the weights
room sweat searing when my father died   my heart
engorged   his like a cold clam. How do you
breathe, he'd asked me   afraid in the night
for the first time in 70 years   sink the shoulders
relax let it come   this technique
the only thing in a life I'd ever really given
him and in the end even this hadn't worked.

Sitting in the car park in the rain his
hat in a Tesco bag   trembling   heart moving
away from me faster   like an accelerating train.

The traces have smiles on them
Smudges of voice   the imperfect
Touch   all that remains.

Hawksmoor

White Spitalfields
Light from the skies.
Beyond Palladio
Pointing

Hawksmoor's fifty reduced to six. Arm wrestle.
Hawksmoor the hall of whites western mansion
Hawksmoor the spital of sea southern infirmary
Hawksmoor the count of ham high country
Hawksmoor the place of singing extreme envy
Hawksmoor the factory of shoe sliding installation
Hawksmoor the college of sgrifenu scratched classroom
Hawksmoor the hopeless of Nazareth north helpful
Hawksmoor the nested of the Great Eastern etched den
Hawksmoor the wizard of greenery growing darkly
Hawksmoor the howling of fortress fissure wallet
Hawksmoor the habitat of the Mediterranean middle helpless
Hawksmoor the northerners of great saints mammoth
Hawksmoor the pressure of razors rising and their shapeliness

Hawksmoor the elevation of running rises and the lost faces of the ancients
Hawksmoor the rolling rises right-angled and the power of depression

Chelsea, the Jewel Tower, Ockham Park, Hosleydown, Castle Howard,
Orangery, St Alfege, St Anne, St George, St James, St Mary, St Michael,
St Luke, St Listlessness, St John, Limehouse, Oxford, Spitalfields,
Bloomsbury, West Towers, Hampton Court, Broadenfield Hall,
Radcliffe Camera, Brick Arcade, George the Martyr, Whitehall.
Ley plan glass pure mockery
special scrambling bowing Madame inventory
Sinclair rain pulp scratched pample
thousand audience fabric struck stop
limewash screened Palladio vanquish victory
press priory brick bolt previous
pyramids scrolls flowers clumps satyrs
jest sullied diamond design ray
beam blueprint sand crisp crystal
happiness clear coral industrial pathway

The tomb of Mausolus in Pliny
The ancient tombs at Baalbek,
The tomb of Cecilia Metella on the Appian Way
The Temple of Solomon

Walked old London in the searing cold. Climbed the Monument 202
feet up the precise distance from the source of the Great Fire in
Pudding Lane. Lit bagel. Fire flour. Tower Bridge. The Thames. The
Eye. HMS Belfast viewed through steam like it was still at war.
Victorian Leadenhall. Georgian Fournier Street. Huguenots.
Christians. Freemasons. Freemarketeers. Jews. Musselmen. Bangla
funeral at the Great Mosque. Faith like a limpet. Glory frozen.
Hawksmoor's masterpiece built above a plague pit the power centre
around which we had rambled. Christchurch spiral. Maze. Hexagram.
Pyramid. Pentacle. 2.4m to save from gradual dissolution. Wood like
cabbage stalk. Rust. Mortar crumble. God permutated like Oulipo
poetry. Pristine. Pressure. Primate. Permanence. Passion.

*(walked across London, Christmas 2005, looking for how it must once
have been.)*

Walking (for Eric Mottram

PAUL GRIFFITHS (1947–)

Born near Bridgend, Paul Griffiths has for many years lived in Paris. He is a leading music critic, the author of standard works on Olivier Messiaen and Jean Barraqué, and of guides such as the *Penguin Companion to Classical Music* (2004). He is the author of two novels, *The Lay of Sir Tristram* (1991) and the Commonwealth Prize-winning *Myself and Marco Polo* (1989), and of libretti, such as that for Elliott Carter's *What Next?* In *let me tell you* (2008), Griffiths takes the 482 words used by Ophelia in *Hamlet* to elaborate a 130-page novella, expanding and reworking them into different, broader contexts which reinterpret and rewrite Shakespeare's play. Although its sensibility is minimalist, built on repetition, gradual addition and permutation, the work creates a rich variety of emotional nuance from its restricted vocabulary and builds to the chastening, moving final section given here. On *There Is Still Time* (2003: ECM Records), Griffiths reads extracts from this exemplary OuLiPoan work to a composition by the cellist Frances-Marie Uitti.

from *let me tell* you (part 14)

I go out now. I let go of the door, and do not look to see my hand as I take it away.

Snow falls. So: I will go on in the snow. I have my hope with me, and a staff in my hand.

I look up, as if I could see the snow as it falls, as if I could keep my eye on a little of it and see it come down, all the way to the ground.

I cannot. The snow flowers are all like each other, and I cannot keep my eyes on one. I have given up and gone on.

All like each other as well are my treads over the snow, for here, some way on, I have stayed and turned to look at them. In each of them there is now more snow—more in the treads some way away than in these here that I was in before I turned. The snow comes to white them over—white me over. It will take away each mark I made, will take away the memory of my path, so that, when I have gone right away, there will be nothing to see of me and my path. Before long all memory of me will be gone. *I* will be gone.

Now I have turned again to face where I must go.

There is light on the snow still. And there is light *in* the snow. All is still. There is nothing to call to me, no mark to show me the way. There is no-one to speak—no-one but me and I do not speak. There is nothing. All is white.

I look again the other way to see the mountain I must have come over. But I cannot see a mountain. All I see is snow, nothing but snow—snow and my treads, which will go in the snow.

Before me—for now I have turned again to look where I must go on—there is more snow. Snow falls over all that was here before, over all that was in my mind. I will have to find out how to think again, know again. The little that is left to me is me: with that I will go on.

It is not as cold as it seemed when I was with the king and his lady. But memory is pale. It means little. It means nothing.

Will is more: my will to be here, in the majesty of the morning, where all is turned to white, where all goes to white—all but me.

Snow. Now. No. O.

This is me, the one that goes on in the snow, which she will mark as she treads, for a little time, and then be gone. What is other becomes white and without feature. She goes on.

But I could will it another way.

Now I must make up my mind. I take one last look at where I have come from. They will all be there still: my father, my brother, him, the king, his lady. I could go over my treads again before the snow falls quite over them: they still mark the way.

Him. Could I still do something for him that would make a difference? Could I take him by the hand so that, when it comes, I held him from what must be?

The more I have come away the better I see what I have left, and it becomes like another's memory. Here in the snow I see there was nothing I could do. I was one of his play things.

But it does not have to be like that. Now—with what I know now, and the powers I have—I could make a difference. I could go again to him, and the words would come to me. It could all be turned. And no-one but me could do it. Is that not, then, what I should do?

Now I look the other way, to the unbraced white. I could go on to more of that white.

I could go again over my treads to where I have come from. This time I could make things better for him. I know I could. It does not have to go on as they say.

I could do that: go home and not go on.

I could go on, and find what I still do not know.

This way, that way.

I have stayed here to think, and then:

I choose.

RALPH HAWKINS (1947–)

Ralph Hawkins was born in Coventry, and brought up in Liverpool, Ynysbwl and Luton; he has strong ties with Ynysbwl and Wales, which he has always thought of as home. He studied at Essex University, where he met Douglas Oliver and Tony Frazer, and tutored Ian Davidson. A pastoral style, in which Chinese poetry is also a presence, is apparent in *At Last Away* (1988) and *The Coiling Dragon / The Scarlet Bird / The White Tiger / A Blue & Misted Shroud* (2000), but collaborations with Bob Cobbing, and a sense that his perceptions cohered with Cobbing's methods, led to a shift towards a poetry of dizzying leaps, drawing on history, myth, and popular culture, announced in *The MOON, The Chief Hairdresser (Highlights)* (2004). This has been continued in *Gone to Marzipan* (2009), *The Size of a Human Dawn* (2011) and *It Looks Like An Island But Sails Away* (2015). Accounting for his erudite, yet highly pleasurable and vivid style in interview with Ian Davidson, Hawkins illuminatingly describes a process of allowing the initial impulses for poems to gestate and interact with 'physically hoarded material' in order to create something 'not in my voice', 'near to being in another language'. The critic Nate Dorward has noted of such work that it 'often reads like it's worked from the heavily doodled & graffitied margins of a European art history coursebook', 'rul[ing] nothing out between the poles of abrupt nonsense & quite straightforward anecdotal-style writing'.

The Hudson River School Motif

the sky ominous above Mount Desert Island 1850

the last of the sun's rays catch a mantle of pink cloud

white chalk to cover red rouge

in the not too far middle distance
casinos, motels and trailer parks

crimson and saffron cluster along the horizon

belts of opal apple-green

a divine from the Swedish Church

the Pentecost

hearing rings of fire *Un Nos Ola Leuad*

a sombre set of associations

the application of words especially to the left of the sky

10,000 leaves like pieces of paper confection

the rocks too speak

no canoes or tepees can be seen

no doggers' paths

no trappers' huts

miniscule birds afloat below the disc of the sun

cloud vapours spill from the brush

Tempted

I knew nothing of Baudelaire
but I had read his name on a wanted poster
or was that Apollinaire

those calligrams of bird droppings
I imagine over spring fields
with fumble on his mind
in someone's undergarments
pegged out on a line

Let me tell you I had such a surprise
when I wrote to Baudelaire
that which turned out to be
a poem without tress
or was it a painting without letters
a smile glowing upon my face

O I am so silly
my right lobe not knowing what the left is doing
pegging out letter *A's*, writing little umbrellas,
performing charitable acts
scratching my name on trees

love has me on the edge of
such excellent times
he has shown me sketches of his testicles

I keep them next to my heart

and a tattoo on my buttock

he keeps his in his pocket
warmed by his right hand
as he walks the Boulevard de Clichy
or crosses Le Pont de l'Europe

what could I return to him
but a poem for this new century

a threesome possibly on a bed
or sprawled full length upon the summer grass
in some shade perhaps
a place of awkward angles
holding his stick
keeping his hat on
I wish I could write in French
and understand metrics
before I attempt another

The Next Poem

defeated by (I don't know what and everything)
I stem a flow
I've stopped now but the words wobble out in some form
They are the last Mars probe
They are the proboscis explorer

They are the road to insouciance
A world gone pot-noodle

I have tried cotton wood
Bristol tarts and armour paste

Whack it hard

The tongue lollops by a frontispiece
How long can I hold on to a dying breath,
                         a moon slick or a daisy pearl

I have brushed remonstrance from my crown
I have entered the bad days
I have written clever clogs (but he hasn't answered)

Those old questions

In my own way I have tried to improve both body and mind
I have rubbed cream and breathed powders
I have showered in heaven's gel
Poured oyster and pomegranate dust

Only the other night I ran off to the woods
Where the moon shaved a path with Jan van Eyck light
There were golden shards in its tracings
And that which should have appeared more shaded was brighter

Woods are invariably frightening
A broken path bemoans us, is there a right road?
No longer geometric (unlike the line of the bazaar, see earlier work)
The path turns spiral, then rectilinear it
Spits and forks away to

Some place where there isn't any trouble

D'you suppose there is such a place, Toto?

A History of Hydraulics

They went out with baskets looking for truffles
Oh these musical painters from Prague
a nova rich sky of astral and beam
and set themselves down on junkets to browse
and sunbolt bright a sign appeared
with the impact of water on water
veemenzia, furiositá, impetuositá, concorso

Oh these musical painters from Prague
with their little letter word magnet collections
fridge ducks, phonetic trees and *loaves of love,*

a nova rich sky above their slaphappy heads
over a weir the impact of water on water
catching with a bright plastic bucket the words
veemenzia, furiositá, impetuositá, concorso

And they were jollied out like stockbrokers on
the tongues of pigs and calves in sausage skin
Oh these musical painters from Prague
their notebooks filled with infinite combinations of
letters and indeed in Fig 111
a fishing boat is a word magnet catching the words
veemenzia, furiositá, impetuositá, concorso

Wolves (A Diptych, Two Sides of the Same Coin)

Recently I've been thinking
Of making a late marriage to the daughter
Of a wolf butcher
We'd escape from it al to an island under an endless star-lit sky
There'd be a big welcome kiss on the harbourmaster's wall
You'd have kiss-curled hair (early Doris Day) and rose lipstick
You'd wear a snow-white dress sequinned with star-gems
I'd hold the diskette of the world sun-bolt bright in my hand
We'd begin a circus
I'd become a wolf tamer
Finally abandoning my fascination with market economies

I'd marry the harbourmaster under perfectly normal conditions
I'd be the profligate blonde
There'd be a big wet kiss on his lips
He'd have kiss-curled hair (Rick Nelson)
I'd wear my white dress encrusted with star-gems
We'd go to Nacogdoches
I'd hold the reins of the world in my hand
(or was it Kansas?)
I'd embrace the market economy
I'd run off with the Mexican circus owner
I'd marry a Medicine Man
and feed our children to the wolves

Heidegger

Was Heidegger a Buddhist

did he copulate in the woods (*Holzwege*)
with a maiden of the woods
(do you remember her subsequent children and the accompanying
illustration)

there to contemplate being and perhaps a mushroom or two

do you remember the Woods

can I be a Buddhist

I'd call you (you need mountains to yodel) my nymph of the woods

did Heidegger suffer from nympholepsy
or was he too concerned with hammers and nails
and wood for his wooden hut

did he have rat poison

I must get back to you

I must return by the ship of the mind

Chemins qui mènent nulle part
leading me on letting me go

if I yodel across mountain thyme
would you answer
(those tracks which wind purposely from one point to another)
the odd goat and goat herder looking on
the odd whistle from the wolf
Mrs Woods calling the sheep in

we could retrace our steps through the woods which lead nowhere

I could cook for you (wild mushrooms)

we could introduce your children and your husband the woodcutter

are there trees in the Himalayan foothills

PHIL MAILLARD (1948–)

Phil Maillard was born in 1948 in South London. He moved to South Wales in 1975, and now lives in the Cardiff area. Allen Fisher and John Freeman published his first books, in the mid-70s. In the early 1980s he ran creative writing groups for the Welsh Academi (now Literature Wales) and the University of Wales, and commenced some small press and community publishing. Maillard was much influenced in his writing by his connection, from 1967 on, with Chris Torrance and the Buddhist note is also strong. Maillard's poems are often purely descriptive or narrative, concerning themselves with the most ordinary of experiences in a language deliberately emptied of rhetoric. Graham Hartill says 'the distinctive feature of the work is neither subject-matter nor style, but a quality of attention, a regard, non-judgmental but also compassionate.' In the best poems what becomes interesting is the shape of the path taken and the calm rhythm of the voice that takes it. His selected poems, *Sweet Dust and Growling Lambs* (Shearsman) appeared in 2008.

AUTUMN SONG

DARKNESS & LIGHT

Out on the moor
    in the rain
the heather is dark
    & the rushes hold the light
into themselves
    The river turns wild
foam-brown, full, fierce

      To re-enact
               my father's woe

      Dogs barking
              at either hand

        The corrupt lower Neath
        sliding slow & muddy
        through the ruins of industry
        between damp, dutiful towns,
        black wharves & breakers' yards

        The upper Neath, innocent
        with a secret knowledge

of innocence, a leaf, dropping
onto the pulsing surface
of the water

A man on a bicycle
leading a horse
through the village
at dusk – sparks
striking off the road

LEAP YEAR'S DAY 1992

*...I make
myself a bourbon and commence
to write one of my 'I do this I do that'
poems in a sketch pad.*
- Frank O'Hara, *Getting Up Ahead of Someone (Sun)*

A Saturday, damp under
irrepressible light in the west

It's not just Spring
is it?
I feel myself
do I?
quickening
I feel the nation
are they?
doing likewise
I hope
crawling out from under the burden

I walk
I walk to the bank machine
through the ragged-trousered consumers of Cowbridge Rd.
I walk to the stationer's
but they don't have any A4 bound notebooks
worth buying. Too expensive
or too boring.

I look at filing cabinets.
        I buy
some typewriter paper & a pen.
I take my coat to the cleaner's.
I buy cigarettes.
I buy apples & bananas & sprouts.
I come home &
                unload.

I walk again,
through Pontcanna, Victorian
legacy,
        windowboxes, cats, alleys, olives.
No fresh pasta.
I buy Jakobson's *Sound and Meaning*
in the boring new second-hand bookshop
    noting the owner's Doppler Shift as he brays his vowels
    at his only other customer
& I buy *Modern European Verse*, ed. Dannie Abse,
1964 Pocket Poets edition,
a sliver of internationalism
    for the upcoming '60s.

It's raining.
It's not raining.
I walk down Kings Rd. to the Italian deli,
& still
        no fresh pasta.
I am directed.
I walk through Riverside
& down Clare St., fording social zones
    from stripped pine to wet rot,
        a different Victorian legacy,
            pausing only
under the railway bridge.

I buy fresh pasta
                in Grangetown.
I buy
        Vintage Gold cider, a tin of tomatoes
& a pork pie
                on the way back.

Then I buy
        an A4 sharp-cornered notebook
            in the ART GALLERY
where the sharp old lady & I
            consider the weather
                from all angles.
Miserable, but we need it.
The notebook-makers of China
have abandoned lurid blue covers
in favour of nebulaic marbling,
but they're still only £2.30.

Finally I buy grapes.
    I get home,
        feed the cats,
have food, cider, a joint, open
    Modern European Verse
        at Brecht,
            TO PROSPERITY:
Truly, the age I live in is bleak,
The guileless word is foolish.

CHRIS BENDON (1950–2011)

Born in Leeds, Chris Bendon worked as a tour courier in Egypt before moving to Wales to study English at the University of Wales at Lampeter. From 1982-5 he edited the journal *Spectrum*. His own poetry, at first self-published, appeared in *In praise of low music* (1981), *Matter* (1986), and *Cork Memory* (Stride, 1987); in the 1990s he became still more prolific, publishing *Constructions* (1991), *A Dyfed Quartet* (1992) *Perspective Lessons / Virtual Lines* (1992) and a 'libretto for an imaginary opera', *Crossover* (1996). *Jewry* (1996) reflects a growing concern with his Jewish origins. In his best writing, Bendon overcomes a Yorkshire suspicion of the imagination and a tendency to diffuseness, and his later poetry has, as Andrew Duncan has put it, 'an Asa Benveniste-like mystery, a tango of gematria', in which 'the figures of music collide with the plates of broken meats scattered across the writing-table, bric-a-brac of self, offering a new genre, a new grammar of poetic ordinance, sustained by verve and the discipline to discard banality and discover new verbal melodies.'

The Heat is Off, the Spell Ending

Glad tidings make waves first
of long Grasses, Ashes;
lift Sycamore's spirits
to shake hands, and send

a telegram along the hedge (long-thought-archaic).
From a day-bed I am hoisted

to a spot way back/ up
North: *forever fresh/*
singing Corinna Corinna:

> *about to meet my maker*
> *and miss the girl whose kiss*
> *is Violet's shyness in moist moss.*

To resurrect this! *And beetles flicker across*
the bogs: the dam or bust.

The clouds an Index of Futures –

> no visible government exists.

Prestige 7188

I walk out in a sky of lemon
  and picture a wooden floor
    a terracotta pot spilling soil by design

I walk out in a sky of mauve in my shirt of cinnamon
  and picture a window
    half-obscured with grey diminishing polkadots

I walk out in a sky of carmine
  and get a fix on
    a purposeless matt black metal stand

I walk out in a sky of lime
  and mentally design an altar window
    just two corners of cross-struts – a vacancy – halo-arc

I walk out in a sky of battlesip grey shivering
  in all my timbers of cherry rosewood ebony and elm
    how older walls and those presumed safe in the past

appear to walk right through me as if
  I didn't exist which I don't except as an epistemological
  phenomenon   And I commission the double rainbow

That Sun-Flower

rose over melancholy *Hafod* –
with its colder, fresher air
as over Praise-be *Hendref.*

  First light showed Phaeton
  out in his convertible

And this kind, oh look – *peeping through*
the curtain, the blind – this wise
fun-shine: this oh yes, steady flowering
growing over sadness of hills,
glow of pollen within immense blue petals pursuing
    never resolved radiance...
while communal roots drink river
where light makes diamonds

in midge-ridden gloom of the glade.
And humankind, bewildered by nature's
apparent autonomy, will shed all bedclothes
with zest, newly fleshed – with no memory of sex.

And distances subtly will increase
as rivers shimmer; small cloud be a tent
as walls warm up, steels grow heated;
all legs become young as calves
along with heart's expansion – thirst seem

   only for wider horizons ... slaked by sight of a lake.

The Dream will have wildflowering perfectly detailed
– covering synoptic vistas in its
more than three dimension –
Death and History mere myths of this universe.

Oh I know ... and so why then,
world before words, no God
rhetoric ... as if trying to retrieve
(like a vein, or fossil hid in old clay)
this brief, tedious, brilliance of season

– as though fishing for the
refrain from some half-forgotten lyric
did I cast – across stone –

   my chilling, killing line?

Contextual Errors

Is this, City within that of God (that shabby, soiled,
gendered word, signifying if not complete ignorance
then incoherence) and more fast
moving ... or sluggish than before?

> **New Cold War**
> Pushkin: for furry winter evenings,
> heart-warming folk-tales.
> Putin: Fuel Pricing.

Football's medieval Team emblems
remind me to salute the Fallen in the making
of any movie Epic. The Stoics (many Islamic)
~ *who exercised greatly Marcus Aurelius, by the Danube* ~
consider Dignity a Virtue. Despite an expense
of nrg in a waste of hot air *blood is in*
our War: cruel to be kind of cull/
culling/killing. After letting
the youngbloods – try to fly with white feathers.

This temporary hot-spot, the heart
of Mars; grown cold, bored. [Calendar picture: of hyena,
eyes like man's that scavenger, but not so
rapaciously insatiable.] As for *alien life* –
you couldn't make it up; though artifice be
but natural as patterns in th'abstracted stars,
yea, as symphonies. O, but man's (Bible, Koran)
a copycat! [Last month: lion pride.] Bayonet was bad enough;
now more, bigger, smarter ...

       Then this bombshell from dons
       anxious to please the ignorant young:-
       reading is done with: *la trahison...*

I heard this in my field, knowing the cold mosses
       (only the lonely or old live, thinking of
          all they do as potential anecdote)
would persist still long after our departure

from our cunning line – beyond which, with the trees, gentry –

       the hilltops, judging us.

DAVID GREENSLADE (1952–)

David Greenslade was born and still lives in Cefn Cribbwr near Bridgend. After a stint at Reading University he did various jobs, including that of lighthouse keeper in Cornwall, and has travelled and worked abroad widely. He currently works at Cardiff Metropolitan University. He is bilingual, writing in both English and Welsh, and has collaborated with film-makers, theatre-companies and visual artists, among them the painter William Brown. Greenslade has been described as 'a student of the material object' and, as the title of one of his best collections, *Each Broken Object* (2000) suggests, much of his copious output has focused on usable or used things; these include road signs, diagrams, tools, fruit, veg and other foodstuffs. His perspective on them is rarely less than playful and surprising, usually involving more than a modicum of surrealism, and the same can be said of his work in general, whether he is writing about love, alchemy, animals, foreign lands, or personal descents into hell and back. His interests have often segued into the realms of conceptual art and he is currently producing works based around visual images of his own devising (he recently completed a 100 metre long scroll comprised solely of images). His many poetry books include *Burning Down the Dosbarth* (1992), *Fishbone* (1993), *Creosote* (1996), *Yr Wyddor* (1997), *Cambria Country* (2000), *Weak Eros* (2002), *Lladd Nadroedd* (2005), *Adventure Holiday* (2007), *Zeus Amoeba* (2009), *Homuncular Misfit* (2011), and *Signs Like This* (2015).

Railway

What a difficult railway track you are,
no rails! How easily you kill,
what a fool if I chose
to die for you – beckoning
your kiss across a battlefield.
No engineer could deliver you,

heaped with unwrapped things.
Have I the courage to imagine
and deny you? Constantly –
until I can't help myself
pulling off your wedding ring,
your skin at its whitest hinge.

I want a pillow where your belly
sets a beacon on the map, a taste
where trouble breaks its wings.
I want a night on your lace,
on your margin. I want to greet
each broken object when it sings.

Watering Can

Watering can has second cousins,
poltergeist bandit companions,
a world of jungle crockery
smooth as the front of your gums.

Watering can soothe
aphasia, paraphrasia,
infinite mass, infinite correspondence,
otherwise the made world disappears,

particularly coded entrance guards,
employees of rose and pipe,
shoe horn, main sail, name card –
the body's differentiated finch.

Erotic notebook
from how this one settled down;
the world's portions – games,
these, its counters played with.

Her Things

Her things are huge
in my thick hands.
I find them by surprise –
an inch of cider,
my photo in her purse,
the shock of her slurred words.

I lift them
and weigh them,
tongs that burn my hands.

I gather sticks
from the frozen ground.
Her fire warms me,
her smoke chokes
playtime from my clothes.

Her breath in my lungs,
her twigs in my ears.

Her lullaby was not
what I expected;
snipping varicose veins,
an open scissors
next to the lavatory bowl.

Terror was the road
she used.

Petrol Nozzle

Can   I   make   anything   of you
except   expect   to   fill
the   oily   guzzle   car
insured   by   the   poem.
Hold,   aspire,   how   all   hands
handle,   slam,   splash   mis-
trigger,   deal,   distaste   you.

Most   medium   robot   fistula,
flume,   proboscis, here
I   can   mouth   to   mouth
opt   or   weigh   each   mollusc
dying   to   engorge   dream
crozier   sod;   bill,   arc,
dactyl   squirting you.

I cannot add to you.

Demonized udder.   Frantic
gettaway   ankles   have   stood
to   intra-   piss,   clank,
discredit, foul,   conk   out,
lech   at   nail   varnish,   tax,   badly
manage.   Squeeze   disabuses;
fiction   glugs   through   you.

Valves   lamely   think,   leaks
spill,   pumps   steal   courts'
vivid   luminous   decans,   incant
sequence   numerals. Frond,   polyp,
foot's   veil   forgets   you.   Animal
maxilla   own   carbon   leap,
your   plural   reduces   you.

Kerb

Its happy,
cement between stones its happy.
Know how? Why—the world
it's falling, from shelves, towards me.
Skip, trowel, vent, valve, paint
the pavement
tumbling themselves
lateral, transverse, current.
Nip, wrapper, cement mixer,
chosen into separate
shaking loneliness.
Dry grains, five pence,
accidental coals of finding.
Chewing gum signifies
gala isolated care.
Bewildered dent horns, manifold bracket
fit all restraint.
Compact manufactured alignment.
Parallax contracted touch.
Burn—where? Explanation starts.
Box—hamlet enduring paving top;
tripod universal joint;
calendar—cap, scarf against climate,
perpetual emigration at treaties.
Dovetailed wristwatch, modulate pushchair,
grit sanded scaffolding plank, pebbly gargle
taxi rank, with crocodiles where damp!
Race, shoelace, mitten, song's footstep burst.
At nail, rubberband! At hose, vine leaves!
At why? The path a woodwind.

Objects Return In Triumph From Their Exile

Objects return in triumph from their exile,
their enormous bulk
condensed between
the pads of my forefinger
and frightened thumb.

I roll them, huge,
ominously small,
round in the watershed
of my fingerprints—
they settle in a bowl
of lifelines, feeling
the exhaustion of their final shape.

They were always there, waiting,
regal creatures sent out
with inappropriate ease.
They return like illuminated bats,
a bewildering
display of stunts,
finding holes in my body
where they can roost

Some choose a finger, others an ear,
hips, colon, tooth cavities, the optic nerve,
a shoreline of coves.
They want revenge.

Wild stones,
spanners on the kerb,
spoons, coat-hooks, diaries,
milk-bottles, discount coupons,
place a weapon in my fist.

They cut the past
pounding the valves,
thawing the baffles
of each bewildered day.

They haven't travelled all this way
for me to smile.
It was dark out there,
cold among the trees –
there are broken handles,
shoes without tongues,
three legged chairs,
blood stained mattresses,
the mouths of obliterated things.

Stained with grief, they
find a low, illegal route into the world
and plough my horror through,
tunnelling towards me, until every
one of them has found its place.

Rarebit

Here they come over the third bridge (the second estuary crossing)
wearing colourful red kerchiefs, billowing polka dot blouses,
enormous clogs, carrying harps and zithers and look! some are cutting
pegs as they walk and sing. In the background, the sound of machine
guns, but these migrant families manage to whistle and fal-de-ra as
they wander looking for work. Hardship adds an attractive Celtic
melancholy to their manners. In the middle of the day they sit at the
edge of the motorway, marvelling at the great lorries and their
wonderful cargoes. They have no envy of those pokey Bovis Homes
just visible above the high roadside dykes and appear to incur no
bruises when they are cruelly beaten by other migrant groups. First
among all the pickers of modern Europe, these are truly postmodern
stateless workers, free to sleep under the northern stars. 'Rabbits' as
they are affectionately known. How they love their cheese! Which
some, they say, still eat from plates of Roman glass. Most of all they
love to cut great slabs of it (with their gleaming Albacete daggers)
setting the cheese on chunks of barley bread, roasting this clumsy
variation on the pizza over an open fire. Careful, Taff! That ketchup
looks a lot like blood! The story goes that one indulgent rogue rolled
his gambo (or cart) on wheels made of the best Caerphilly Cheese.
The word first enters polite language in 1725 when John Byrom,
hymnist and author of the Universal English Shorthand, records
eating 'two Welch rarebits—a most unusual supper'.

Née Shell

Tried that, didn't work.
Tried again – tried anything –
abandoned when it worked.
If a project offered home I soon played
eviction order, top ten stress, inside out, sudden death,
evacuation, split bet, stretch, squeeze until
it breaks (or holds), wild horse, *cheval*, centrifuge roulette.
Camping in white mist, the grey scale

where I was born left behind
for distant rainbow beaten with foxes
driven from culverts, surrogates
that might have been me, but I was hiding
in a dimple the night sky millwheel
failed to grind, hull intact – ready for
the siege of incompatible outsider wheat.

River Ock

Asphyxiated minnows float and stiffen
in the slow drift of a weirpool on the River Ock.
Each fish sketches its own decomposition.

The five senses pack a weekend suitcase,
check their tickets
and drive away towards *Bron Ebargofiant*.

Two small children recall quite differently
being hungry in the same house at the same time,
even though they aren't children anymore.

I know that Ock is the Welsh word *Eog,*
Eogwy, Ogwyr, the river where I usually live.
Now I stare at Mercia through Wessex fog.

Minnows decay following a rapid autopsy,
prodded by a miasmic British phantom.
An unexpected tantrum kills its passive twin.

Severn Fantasy

I sometimes wish
instead of being a river god
capable of reversing direction,
I might be something a lot less –
perhaps a sofa in a 1970s billiards hall,
or since I'm water borne
possibly a rubber dinghy
bought exclusively from money
shoved through the slot
of a snug RNLI charity box.

Or even –
when I really change,
why not a sugar fortified cocktail cherry
floating in a tall, stemmed glass
slopping a complex drink named
after a translucent smut avatar I devised?
I'll have a Crystal Channel please.

If I were that cherry,
a mealy nose on the face
of an absinthe green and blue harlequin
buoyant in water-wings, floating
through a current of soda and sweet wine,
barnacled with bubbles,
I'd gaze up at the moon
and one for each finger
I'd count the aeons prone to wars
that used to irritate my soul.

Almost motionless, rocking
just a little before the flake
returning home from a date sighs
and knocks me back; there,
loaded on my single stilt, I'd savour
my immediate shift from immensity
to being forgotten and neglected,
set aside on a fussy windowsill.

I'd spend eternity listening
to the echo of pink daydream sound FX
in a room that never changes, held
like a brief mistake before rejected
from the gawping pout
of a pale doppelganger reflecting momentarily
how to keep the entire universe
menacingly lit, sexually graphic,
profitable, cheap and nice.

GRAHAM HARTILL (1952–)

Originating from the Dudley in the English West Midlands, as a teenager Graham Hartill was fascinated by experimental rock music and theatre. He briefly attended Swansea University before leaving to study Drama at Hull. In the 1970s he experimented as a performer and installation artist, and took an MA in the USA. Returning to the UK he began to assimilate US Open Field poetry and became a mainstay of the burgeoning poetry scene in Cardiff. He taught in China in the late 1980s, and has produced several translations of classical Chinese poetry with a former pupil, Wu Fusheng. In the 1990s, a Scottish Arts Council Bursary enabled his involvement in the Open World Poetics movement in Glasgow. He helped to found Lapidus, the national organisation for the development of writing in the fields of health and social care, and has worked in settings as various as hospitals, schools, cancer and mental health centres. He is currently writer in residence at HMP Parc, Bridgend, in South Wales, and teaches on the Creative Writing for Therapeutic Purposes M.Sc. for the Metanoia Institute in Bristol. Since his selected poems, *Cennau's Bell*, appeared in 2005, he has published *A Winged Head* (2007) and *Chroma* (2012).

(Tu Fu) In the Cities

Sharing the same couch, chatter to each other as they drink
I come here in search of an elixir
phantom zones as of big rivers crossing
prepared for which life this time?

the clattering of futures is hard to hear him over
who speaks of justice when heaven casts its net?
late Autumn on Mt. Tai, the river flowing east
falling through fog of time-rivers crossing

and the incessant plains, and I know the Emperor
waging incessant war on his frontiers
and I am a ghost, and I know that I can't be heard over
          the incessant clamouring of futures
like dealers I was old before my time

shook up like dice in a cup
dice on the swampy monstrous plains thrown out
and up to the frontiers old men, and I am what you might say
shanghaied, and carried away in a little boat in my heart and know nothing

the waves break in the Milky Way,
bottles of burning, shuddering in the capsule street
my ancient love shudders in the fracture between zones
waves of violence crashing about me, bridges, canals of my cities up-rising

Yellow River switches away to the cities
stars pop out of their sockets, their grid-reference
I is a figure of speech inverted the masses shiver and stand up
ceaseless the rain and my stitched coat collapsing

money is hard and bright to come by a naked state
fires and beacon-fires city to mud-ridden city multiply
dolor and mud stepping out for my wine-ration
final coins and the land is forgotten and lost in clouds

my wife and children and I am unemployed for forty years
insurrected streets of the city of old brocade
a nation ought to know its boundaries
daggers and honey-tongues night of rebellion night

farmland astoundingly generous, patient and pregnant
peasants dragged off to the lines for thousands consecutive sentences
this a poor house with only stale wine for a bottle
I wish that the pines would spring for a thousand feet

*

In these my cities muddy paths the 4 Oceans bending and ceasing
in farmland incessant swampy immobile fog-washed the hills chanting
wine-drunk the old days with Li Bai god among poets
sharing the same couch, jug-sweat, ancient love

my thatched roof is destroyed by the Autumn wind
1966-76 a great sunburst of political ecstasy
broken glass and broken the knees of the righteous war
rain on my hands and the dealers flutter the god-pictures

wind on my neck in the days the nights of up-rising
thousands the poems the years sloshing from dung-carts
English the cities and I am a ghost and I know that I am a deafness
i.e. I am unheard, and unknown, but by myself am thoroughly known

as a phoenix rising from vortex to vortex
watching the gutter with wine snaring the stomach
one luxurious plant in the park and flowers of cold coins
the rich and the wretched chattering, rayon meat tin and futures

characters turn and the meaning rises and stands up
as hills in fog, meaning, only the hills and streams remain
and I write nothing, boat in my heart chanting
the river flows, fraction of brush and paper

*

Tu Fu in search of elixir-time by-passing
Monument, Bank, over London Bridge so many
placebo-river, switching away to the border
I wish that the pines would spring a thousand feet

I is a figure of speech encradled
name on a mountain of thought a fiction
I is a fiction a true chanting
time that is crashing a coat collapsing

pines a thousand feet to wish up-springing
poem a thousand children thousand pronoun
thousand years bamboo growing human heart a similar song
the ghosts are lonely lovely time-rivers crossing
earth the gift the mountain-cities creaking

from **The Lives of the Saints**

Cuthbert

Eadfrith's Work:

Clover and pebble-eggs
lace behind my quill –

the parchment is later stitched
and bound in goatskin,
bevelled and blood-warm-red
over beechwood stiffeners,

then this God's spell is boxed

in ocean pewter
and cobbled with glistening rocks.

This is God's signature,
Eadfrith's hand.

Enough for any life,
one such book.

+

The tides suspire,
bringing, and lifting away
the visitor.

This is an island's rhythm –

and that of the hermit,
convinced to become a bishop.

The tides come in and leave.

While there is time
the Word must be said out loud
as the sea on shingle.

Cuthbert – the jackdaw,
shipwrecked in body and soul –

Cuthbert – the sea threw a rooftree
onto a limbless strand,

an eagle tossed him a flapping fish.
God fed him.

+

The English, they are a rough and fierce lot
and worship rough and fierce gods.
This saturday they drive a red and yellow rosary of cars
across the causeway, each individual heart engraved
with crossworks of laughter and secret rage,
of ageing, and complex sexual loves –
knotworks, which writhe toward symmetry.

The Geomancer

I know the lie of the land,
its bone and blood
the back of my hand,
the run
        of the black and the white water.

Here's my gourd,
my blanker,
and my man of straw
to shield you from the living face
of the demon dead –
I stand my ground at the Dragon's Head.

Listen –
        I exhale the buried cities –
Cambalu and Samarkand by Oxus,
Paquin, Negus and Melind,
Battersea, in rainy winter evening's green and yellow lights
   – I strike the strings.

My song is just a territory
being shaped, becoming known.
My chant accelerates like water
falling, black and white,
   through streambed stones.

I know the lie of the land,
my head and hands
   your mountain and your wood.
Their steps,
   their doorways opening and shutting
in your heart
   let drift your bone and blood.

At Kilpeck Church
(for Richard Lanham)

These Herefordshire carvers hacked into stone
        as if it were daylight,

freeing such as a 'bear', that devours 'children'
a 'bird', that regurgitates something
into a 'human' mouth,

an angel, falling from spacetime,
knot of stone.

These men of Herefordshire knew what they were doing,
        chewing stone as if it were night and day

The rain behaves like love or leprosy,
pouring from lips yanked wide
in grins or is it grimaces?
splashing centuries of
craving,
laughing,
swearing, by day and night.

This Friday afternoon, the two of us standing here,
straining for detail,
knotting the branches of torment and insight.

Bronze Fennel
(for Ursula)

A shovelful of little dark pink flowers in the compost—
every detail counts.

The growing of small concerns
with grace,
good grace.

Redstart,
even a nightingale.

Life will always be filing up with questions—
vivid green light at the edge of a spruce.

A long, damp day—
the bees still working away at the lilac
at 10 o'clock.

Cuckoo changes to *cuk* in June
apparently,

slipping off

into the world

DAVID ANNWN (1953–)

David Annwn (born David Jones), a poet and critic, is the great nephew of the Welsh bard Ap Hefin ('Son of the Summer Solstice'). He was born in Cheshire to 'Anglo-Cymric parents', studying at Aberystwyth University, where Jeremy Hooker was his tutor and Robert Duncan and others were visitors. Moving to Wakefield to work for the Open University, he founded the National Association of Writers in Education (N.A.W.E). His early poetry, selected in *the spirit / that kiss* (1993), shows the influence of Geoffrey Hill and David Jones, inflected by a love of jazz and Welsh origins. Since the 1990s his work has taken a more radical turn, partly through association with other Yorkshire-based poets, such as Geraldine Monk and Alan Halsey, with whom he has collaborated in works such as *Danse Macabre* (1997) and *It Means Nothing to Me* (2007). Shape-shifting, eclecticism and a performance ethic are to the fore in *Bela Fawr's Cabaret* (2008) and *Disco Occident* (2013) *The Saint John's Fragment / Against the Odds* (2015), *Dreaming Across the Wake Field* (2017) and *Red Bank* (2018); the first brings together Gerard Manley Hopkins, whose alter ego' Gerry is 'addicted to gambling and esoteric word-play', and Marie Lloyd (a.k.a. Bela Delameyer = Great Bela = Bela Fawr); other personnel include a Llandonna witch, members of a Mari Lwyd fertility cult, and Francis M. Croft, a Jesuit and mercenary involved in the destruction of the Kiowa Ghost Dance cult. (Annwn links Celts and Native Americans, describing Cattraeth as 'a Battle of Wounded Knee for the Brythons of the North'.) This work is exhilarating in its macaronic mix, typical of much recent Welsh innovative poetry.

A Short Etymological Study of the Early History of Ossett, West Yorkshire

To blond incursors—
                              'the roof of a hill'
Fortifiable—'keel of a ridge'.
For thundering destriers,
                              shambling mire—
One more summary massacre.

Pages of Domesday offer a mirror,
Glinting and dazzling. For 17 years

Hardly anyone lived around here
Except the hare's high predators—

Talons bridling on the air.

Opening—L.Z.

'Do you prefer your poetry to mine?'
—'a kind of mathematics/but more sensual'

A train's cantata shrugs like breath—;

Of a Vermont sunset: 'Why should I praise it
I had nothing to do with it'—

The Zeebrugge disaster—P & O pickets
Rift the wind. The courts sequester bodies.

This is my face. This is my form
And the Passion of Matthew:

'break in grief, thou loving heart;'
"I hear him agonizing, I heard him inside"

Reticulations and out of them
Stems of the singing of voices,

Videlicet—
'The faithful poem is an act of conscience'

Shaken, open,

A rage instilled to
Tensile grace

A style of leaves

from **Bela Fawr's Cabaret** *(December 1890)*

1
GERRYMANDERING's
Hapless hip-Hop gester

situationalist
manitoodlie

mannick and manticks
Has anybody here seen Gerald

little 's 'is Slight
Mansemass
Mulvather

> *must it be to be*
> > *be to*
> *What must it be*
> *to be someone else?*

Star of Belial
hop-o-my-thumb
hopmass—the medlar: *Mespilus germa* nicely
hopken after

the man's a bloody bird!
crow-vestured they called him 'Bran Maenfa' in Clywyd
his *crowsquill* & Cock a' Elgin's walk
hovera hawks tethra
       Godwit, Fuckwit
           logo-gourmande

is there any ány, is there none such se-

mantic

Gee - ee!

     Are – ae – 'ell?
              Dee ?
Gerund mannered homily:
G for *Germen*, e: *erratus*, r: *raritas*
a: *aleator, lex, disco*:
my you were manannán-tongued
morning's-minion-sillion-rippling
wove ochre with silver
unpacking portmanteau yr.
in-house surround-sound compounds

     in vitero
     born in re *ver ber* ation
     your 'i' locked
     'tween the
     V and T:
     in Victoria

Ver (laine) &
Ber (nhardt)'s
Nativities
Holy Moly
what a carryon
come for't.
Ver
million
A case
o hotshot
déjà voodoo

Charade Moony Hopskips

    Calling tar-Jack's mate his *hussy*
    exiled in Irish Galapagos

ripples muscles
rubyfruitiest dilations
plupurplest breakers

Angle
Mansey
Crow Hopkin cld. have – staggerlee! – met Kropotkin
circa '72! re
hearse me through yer Triads
hopkith & kin:
Gerard son of Manley son of Martin Edward
son of Martin, Glass-Merchantman
alliteration's elation-trail

VII

Here be yr. Mari borne by her servitors:
Leader, Sergeant, Merryman, Punch and Judy

Under Darkness come upon's
Tattered, faces cork blacked-up

Yr. Nag's Head tyros
Ragbag-gatheréd

I'm maculate not im-
Never pre- *sempitern* tended

drunk claims, holy deceptions
candycoloured a gluebrowned gold
&, re. gore:
ergo a rego-inspired ogre

raises Babel wove ochre invoker

Your Vessels, and your Spels prouide, Your Charmes,
and euery thing beside; I am for

th'Ayre we breathe, are you?

Twiggy voo, my boys?
Well of course it stands *to reason that you do,*
All the force and meaning in it you can tumble in a minute …

wetfish-dillyboy, honkie, spook, ice cube baby
loved to love to hate
Loafers Tramps Cornerboys
Rough trades, *Socialists & other pests*
sots and thralls of lust
drum-rim redriffs

You toyed with the nickelnomen:
Pook Tuncks: is that lore:
Tunc: a fixed point in time
or your protofreudslip showin'
so do
my so
provo
Gerry,
or feared *it es u r*
to be one: them fluff of *punks*,
in mother clap's molly house
come pearly-queen G., is you a Mary-Anne
dead-eye?

X

You can bet yr. Alpha that
as long before
the sleeper under the mound
my malkins'-choral yowled

My Grue Krew danced their *gris-gris*
Moel Fechan to Tan y Craig

from Afon Brenig to Ffynnon Weirglawdd
all through Dyffryn Clwyd

my gaffers' tools at Ffynnon Bueno
& gnaw-marks 36 millennia cold

clustered tumuli
the barrow, of dark Maenefa
above your coleg's preposter-panto,

ignacian, my ore, my sibilants'
glitter Aurignacian

Tir Mostyn's twrbin gwynt
from Ellyll Prescelly to Carreg y Drudion

Hopcats! Dynion & Runion-lambed Beldam
Bela Fawr has left the *bildung.*

XIV

Different? We're both patriots, Gerry, love Wood, punning-punnets
of finders keepers
love Reggie-Men-tal *dear-rare Britain* red, dress fancy,

Viz, Yr. Jewel-lit show case, gemmata
pianissimo you tried your eminem-englished englynion
in/ ternal
    fernal
e/
    ternal chiming:

Geet north-country preterite of *get*: he *geet agate agoing* ...
Gerard Wildgoose O'Wilde
aka Tuncks
Many Hickock
Gerhardt Moonbeam Hipcon

Geratology = the science
of Gerard-ecadence
billingsgate babelised

all that rods lashed wallop
cods and frown Guignol
all that melos histr'yonics
it's a restful fluster
what's seuss for the gorse
is God's for't Gandeur
a null cipher
which means it's *there*
chaffing and winnowing
just not leary.
I need my morpheme
To get me there
Eh romp me!
it's all greymarye

wove ochre
still harpin' on
nomenclatter

                    suddenly
Betwixt us and the Sun
the wrecks of Terror and Erebus
a rigel code

XVIII

When all's dead and sun
Merriman
Can scares caress
over the towering woives
eastering, footlight year's firstfooting
awaits us, greay horse

Headsup: Hopalong, Hickock ... is't you still
insisting English grammarye
lariat entoil alliteration

cutter cut to sepia
the flicker
Hopkinematoscope

& *speed bonny boat*
over the sea to Bligh
tiddle-eye

Atlantic wind-strains
Wovoka, Wovoka, wovok-
sea-wolves howl

waste seas where the
white bear quoted Virgil
walrus, fulmar
black medusa, Beluga
deep in his crablocker,

when, Gerry, I seez Irish breakers:
will y'rise before me

where wave weave wove occur
from your glass liminal
widdershinnin' cold out for Christ's-mass

your mabinog was
zilched, strip-mined, outmaided
dies-irae-irradiated
situationed
Manitou-*liedered*
to shaky vengeance
and dours-spleen mirrorings

rage in gerard
    spirit
      us

their pony skulls
guisers at my beck
and how their ghost-dance
brings them back the dead

and
Tsi'sûs-ä daka'ñtähe'dal
never finishes
like you Mari lwyd

craft-man, kins-man
Rhoi blodeuyn am wreiddyn
a rhoi gronyn i'w grud

dimmery

Hoar of frost on aft of it
deck rolls I still see him swanning
Vesta matched and Tilleyed
Gerry-Bela-Mari-Marie
I see you in that mirror out of me
far out dancing in your druid shirt

LYNDON DAVIES (1954–)

Lyndon Davies was born in Cardiff and now lives near Crickhowell in Powys. His essays and reviews have appeared regularly in journals such as *Poetry Wales, New Welsh Review* and *Planet,* and, most recently, in *The Journal of British and Irish Innovative Poetry.* His poetry has been widely published, and has appeared in anthologies such as *The Pterodactyl's Wing* (2003), *POETRY WALES Forty Years On* (2005) and *The Other Room Anthology 2016.* With his partner, the painter Penny Hallas, and poet Graham Hartill, he founded and runs the Glasfryn Seminar series, and he also organised, with John Goodby, the Hay Poetry Jamborees of 2009-12. In 2012 he founded the online journal *Junction Box,* which features prose-writing by poets and artists, and he runs the Aquifer Books press. Davies' poems often have a metaphysical cast, using sequence and variation to open out the linguistic potentialities of an idea, a phrase, or a structural concept. His collections include *Hyphasis* (2006), *Shield* (2010), *A Colomber in the House of Poesy* (2014) and *Bridge 116* (2017).

Promissory
For Kevin Mills

Matter is subtle here if surprisingly projective.
At every turn of the stair some old wag
waits with a hailer cocked: genuinely grand
television-style personality. My house
is not my house,
down there in the fizz, in the atom-bed: freaks, pangs,
erotomania of extravagantly exclusive nightwear,
though enzymes have already eaten away half
time's stuff,
at the base, as opposed to the hyperstructure
poised for decorum's sake. One muse one vote,
no apple no cry, that's the rule in the jury-box;
if a bowl pings you know it's honest,
but you still have to go through the process,
honour your promissory note. Is this pleasure or work?
Dread waits in the road, its big open mouth slobbering like a cave.
My book is not my book.

Lawn

Just because there's no obvious sign of damage
doesn't mean it's over, or mean
that nobody chanced their luck. In the end
that lawn's the proof, more clearly and more concisely
than a hand on a misericorde, or the soiled groan
of a solemn victim, parcelled-up, conveniently
muzzled there: all of which is theatre,
which is to say avoidance in the purest sense,
a matter of illumination and control,
although terrible in its rhetoric - we desired
one another's entrails, nothing less would do
(you see it in Bosch, in The Crowning with Thorns:
it's tenderness, no doubt, though tenderness for the wrong thing,
and avid and out of bounds). That lawn, though,
is the key, the necessary grace where the oaths are broken,
or lie down. And fade. Or don't fade. Now but not now.

Sea Level

Ice founders notional
emergency crack outsourced
through tide out of time's
layer-cake soot and organza
surge reverberation
unlocks adhesion-stacks
rearing and nodding like sea-fauns
as boards twist
first then disappear
under wallows she works quick
and gets over it before air
runs out jolly couch
rum complement of survivals
samplers and billet-doux
on the wave alive o
still waving o and alive o
as a prayer as a book
swung up like a grappling hook
light hurts where it sticks
no affinity for rescue
neither here nor wherever
the fever pays out
gross hectic as nigh plash tickles
cough in a drowned room
in a drowned house

Limb

Some irremediable portion
cut off above the elbow
drops from the sky
one sunny day and lands
thump in a primrose clump spraying
goo everywhere the hedges
drip the canal darkens
under bridge 116

that oozy that lying
cumbrance on a terminal spring bank
roll over horsey
          smoke rising
exiguous from the Chinese garden
they are tidying up
for summer bracing themselves
preparation is everything

when the seams run out
quarries flexed in mid-rictus
in the suspended
blast-moment gouged
high-up over this town's
peculiar momentary fatigue
intention without viable
equipment not even winding gear
for the gradient it's a puff
but one must make the effort

for health's sake readiness
for no reason conviction
some kind of a journey without even souvenirs

or mementoes ahead of time
without unequivocal
scar tissue

roll over roll over horsey
nose flashing
white blaze.

A Return

Where did they go
all the clear ones the emphatic
chords in their dusk?
tide looped rising cadence
under screes tramways megaliths
each recursive spirit
clawing itself back
through its own crust, its origin
attracts - it can be stalked
gliding down some melodious
slope they steal everything
in a poem the tracks
may hide, walked out into
the rain heard the songbird
on its mortal base
swagged dome of the solar palace

same place same time same place
come quick a palaver
tell me if I am not
a ghost a palaver
milksop in the seminars
of immortal flame
blue flickering in that green spot
it's a sober treasure

blown like a drover
up and down the hills
with hinged knees with appealing eyes
you air you objects you paths
trailing into night
merely ended like clocks
dumb lark hail and beware.

The Rising of the Usk

1
Comes creeping miniature
intruder tom
thumb tickle horde
nudging a stem

a stick a stone frotting
and grooming intense
deft witty nitpicking
between the grass stalks

meticulous pickpocketing
sexer of nodes brinks
scopes idioblasts cat burglar
rootling nose-down
through sheepwalks and molehills
round the heron's divot
feeling its way
appropriating relaxing

nibbling the road's ear
bourn-licker masterer
of extents surfaces bollards
occupier genocidal
ravager living it up
getting into it overwhelming
state of affairs
troubled sheen over this region

volume homogeny
abyss engine choker
frontier Azaziel
save your mortal double
last on the bridge
at the centre thrashed by twisting
trunk line a spliced hawser
pile-driver hitting the arches

fly Azaziel
higher than our umbrellas
higher than the wind's cello
fly as if you meant it
from abreactive power blurt
stacked visceral absurd
reeling and sheering
concourse of unmentionable
atomies of unmentionable
tracts freckled with little lights
moving still with the moving still

rising still

rising

no

not

not

not

rising

not

The Materials

The materials given to the streams
will opening constant beyond remit although dissolving
at all points continual whimsy of reparation
a portion buffed delimited under orders
where clay fails phylactery as portable guarantee
tooled by mitigated craftsmen to keep going
out into percentage output as devised mnemonic
though nothing could make this place feel like home

what threatens man this imposition what threatens man
release transformation storage and distribution
of the energies of physical, post-physical and trans-physical nature
total organisation oozing at the hem
in the rear abandonment as undefended show-home
memory of perfected blaze in detritus
flowing out into light protection given to its token
given over wholly as if forgotten
hot pigs to ingots scabby with rayed slag dazzling
epiphanic a taxi yellow as a kingcup
waiting with all addresses at its disposal

The Lying Down Tower

Usually the tower moves laterally like a plough
Occasionally it goes down straight down but for now it moves laterally
A groove made of riffs of blasphemies some manner of infection
Dirty it is dirty the groove dirty it is dirty
The tower goes sideways rapidly it develops
Big flashes come out feeding thunder boom there is always care
If music it's odd coming out at an angle under
Hard to bear not to bear in the first place but to hear that
To receive or accept it or hard not to accept is it human
Helpless along the rim marking time
The tower develops mainly in one direction at first like an office block
It will go around if it must but it likes boredom
There is always the cast thrown off the cast cast rising up at the sides
It is there where you are at first it is anyone's as to where it goes
That's to say it is where it is put to be where it goes
It will be removed eventually which is the point
What stays in the earth has nothing to do with it all the wittering and the pipes
Strange strange strange strange strange then ordinary
It is not there or here theoretically it is where it is
The other bits come out on a different time-scale finally to finish off
What you misunderstood if you did you've forgotten there is nothing lost

HARRY GILONIS (1956–)

Harry Gilonis is a London–based poet, editor, critic and publisher (the 'semi-dormant' Form Books imprint). His books of poetry include *Reliefs* (1990), *Axioms* (1996), *walk the line* (2000), and *eye-blink* (2010) and a selected poems, *Rough Breathing* (Carcanet, 2018). His family background is part Welsh although, he points out, if this 'suffices to explain my interest in matters Welsh ... and I was reading the *Cynfeirdd*, the old Welsh bards ... in my teens ... I must make it clear that I no more think my Welsh ancestry confers legitimacy on this interest any more than my non-Welshness disqualifies it. (Poetry is not a genetically transmitted disease.).' A very slow reader of Welsh, his *unHealed* is a reworking of the *Canu Heledd* in the light of the 2003 invasion of Iraq, inspired whilst reading the poem en route to the funeral of Richard Caddel, the line *eglwysseu bassas collasant eu breint* ('The churches at Bassa have lost their privileges') morphing as 'Bassa' became 'Basras', 'collasant' became 'collapsed' and 'breint' turned to 'burnt'. The episodic nature of the *Canu Heledd* acts as a rationale for varied methodologies, including metaphrasis, phonemic parallelism, translation through online translation engines, and recasting Tony Blair's 'Open Letter to the Iraqi People' in the form of an *englyn milwr* ('soldier's englyn').

Stanzas from the *Canu Heledd*	Sections from *unHealed*
67	67-68
	[Signs and Trains]
Am haual ar auaerwy. yd aa Tren yn Trydonwy ac yd aa Twrch ym Marchnwy.	Moving in parallel the Euphrates and by trenches the Tigris and there are torsos in the Khabur.
68	
Am haual ar eluyden yd aa Trydonwy yn Tren. ac yd aa Geirw yn Alwen.	Moving in parallel the two rivers Zab and by ditches the Diyala and there's gore in the Uzaym.

76

76

[Government]

Bei gwreic gyrthmwl. bydei gwan
    hediw.
bydei bann y disgyr.
hi gyua diua y gwyr.

Breach government government. Benefit
    government today.
Benefit ban and disgrace.
Government disarming government.

78

78-79

[Hell in Tactics, or In *The Sun*]

Heled hwyedic ym gelwir.
o duw padiw yth rodir.
meirch vym brodyr ac eu tir.

Hell hard tactic in glory day
in desert blitz on bridges
carnage rubble hero fire.

79

Heled hwyedic am kyueirch. o duw
padiw yth rodir gurumseirch.
kyndylan ae bedwardeg meirch.

Hell hard tactic in cauldron of dust
blitz on bridges awesome cargo
tanks lead lightning clean war carnage.

82

82

[Care fragment]

Marchawc o gaer .... adanaw.
nyt oed hwyr a gwynnyon.
gwr o sanneir. ....

'It's kind of ..... ironic
that we turn around and display
dead bodies now .....'.
                [Col Dan Smith]

87

87

[epigram/haiku]

Teneu awel: tew lletkynt.
Pereid y rycheu ny phara ae goreu.
Tru ar a uu nat ydynt.

Thin breeze, deep sadness.
The spring furrows evident,
He who ploughed them, gone.

88

As clywo a duw a dyn.
as clywo y ieueinc a hyn.
meuyl barueu madeu hedyn.

89

Ym byw hedyn ehedyei
dillat yn aros gwaedvei.
Ar glas vereu naf nwyfei.

90

Ryuedaf dincleir na diw yn ol
Kilyd keluyd clyw
yg gwal tyrch torri cneu knyw

102

Maes Maodyn neus cud rew
o diua da y odew.
ar ued erinued eiry tew.

103

Tom elwithan neus gwlych glaw
maes maodyn y danaw
dylyei gynon y gwynaw.

88-89

[shards of glass]

A dark morning—young men drumming.
A dark morning—extremes of need.
idle, behind barred windows.

Present life not worth zip—
as may be implicit, ordered or directed.
A storm of grey spears, of shards of glass.

90

[In the Lair of the Boars]

Sargon Hammurabi Cyrus Antiochus
Hormizd Harun al-Rashid   Faisal
the Administrators of the Coalition
                    Provisional Authority

102-103

[The Graves of Dyala]

By the Dyala Bridge earth covers them
because of the destruction.
We wrote down their names.

A heap of earth a weak shield
the damaged extremity buried
congealed blood drenched with rain.

ANGELA GARDNER (1957–)

Angela Gardner grew up mainly in Cardiff, though she spent some time in Australia as a child and finally emigrated there in 1988. As well as being a poet she is a printmaker and painter, and has been involved in numerous national and international exhibitions. She is founding editor of the poetry ezine, *foam:e*. She lives now in Maleny in rural Queensland. Peter Philpott sees a clear connection between her visual work and her poetry - a delicacy of perceptual notation, the subtly fragmented quality of which he refers to as post-imagistic: 'the seen merging with the sensed and the act of sensing', what is perceived emerging from fields as forms from background. Her work can be oblique, but also surprisingly direct, and is sometimes robustly political. Major works include: *Parts of Speech* (University of Queensland Press 2007); *Views of the Hudson* (Shearsman 2009); *The Told World* (Shearsman 2014) and *Thing&Unthing - Selected Poems* (Decibel Series Editor Pam Brown, Vagabond Press, Sydney 2014).

From **Views of the Hudson**

14
My own grimed reflection
shades of mortality rubbed and dissolved
to a hieroglyphic snail of meaning
over and over
over and over
in each storefront window

Instead here is something else—a wooden box
with drawers full of powder colour
and a fire that is curiously in tatters
Look! you asked so little and still I desire
bright armour, the top of an unexpected hill

... I look for Grace

15
and if I find it
... it will be at the point
where the mirror or blurred window
or the book I carry
are where I would be
downtown

between marble entrance foyer and something tinsel
a doorman building at Christmas maybe
If a book
then bookshelves are pulled from the rubble
and missing pages prevent cave-ins

some days I dig a pit
to fall straight in!

44
I go visit in the land of the dead
I can describe it perfectly:
cut out figures in front of a cream sofa
and at heart a history of money
able to advance over all obstacles

The man in a doorway
has the face of a smoker
a rumpled book-filled head *devouring words*
Another beside him stares intently
making a double portrait with American flag

The Fall brings monsters into being
scritti di storia dell'arte

60
a lightness I know sounds pathetic
but feels like walking on air
night is pierced with holes
and a cartel of laughter

It is vacation time the sidewalk is warm
enough reason to celebrate I decide
Family, friends, visitors to the city arrive
too soon furniture is balanced outdoors
in strange unnatural poses
so that all of us lean into each other

Unable to influence the buffet of sweet wet cakes
no one will ever leave

Standstill

Never we see it forward

we move
though our lives have changed

running backwards
into the sum of the weather

An ablative case

a fall of molten lead
to scorn even the fragility of bones

its aeroplane blink over the face of the sun

Couldn't you find us?

Flayed leather that crosses the almost
on drained fields of asphodel

inappropriately forming the possessive
in memory of the physical act

but disconnected
from the possibility of love

Piecing together the emperor's death
the mechanicals with him

buried in tunnels of brutal spikes

Trapped with pallid uber gamers
neither real nor unreal

logged on to unfurled dimensions
of lust or greed

Choosing roller coaster names
for all the drone machines

left stripping coins from the eyes
of the dead

Three positions acting on space

1

The admirable acquire a do something list
the living go out   just one speaking pocket
arrayed with cash   fed up with moral tales
Look I want to see a movie more like life
not walled from fear but with a half-
hospitable mouth & photo flash blue edge.
He leaves the cauterised words *sweet as*
sweet as efficient as any mechanism. How
unlikely after all is perfection? Can you quite?
Do I you what improper but continuous
trace on skin Close as it is to no go
but all good. Look can we just get some light?
Softly   *can we get some?* Then to her *true*
fuck yeah true the centre of demand again

2

Sun has no bearing on this heat
An instrument grained sideways
he walk   an end appears   that is all
Listen   now we are going to dinner
more eyes than ears we make conversation
until the menu befriends us
Scorned comical in the bar avoiding pardoy
Behind closed doors *conceived passion*
a distance measured not by our bodies
palaces conjured from air empty of furniture
nor discussed even with him
The side gate left open *he thinks*   Paper wishes
No days set aside for reflection   The domesticity
of unanswered houses bleeds into the road

3

Selvedge to great risk
a voice explains with scant for him
three positions on the untenable
Since here some reason misled the cause
not as it is not where it should be
not even when it is   while we worry
 about effect   transformative relationships
inwardness   classifying the fixity of objects
mortgages   or if we remembered to water

the garden and turn off the iron.
Wake up at three still in need of reassurance
Maybe you're right it's not all
It's cracked up to be No galvanic lights
just maybe not

Another Fall from Grace

All those things I said either side of water and glass
How dark goes it get dark? How evening?
While you say — these flowers look like dog penises
their lipstick jack-in-the-pulpit Open mouth gaping

to small perfect teeth
of white slipped earthenware
a figure floating against nothing and the crackle-glaze
footprints of clouds across his milky chest. His erect nipples
are birds in a cloudy sky entering sharp and clean.

Scorning even the fragility of bones I translate
from the foreign language of self a person I met one
and have forgotten among the buried mirrors used
to capture the faces of the dead — their mottled skin

fading as our memory has of candle-light and shadow.

In Double Mirrors

In double mirrors
                              true and false
we are frangible
                              skin's visible default
bony anchors
                              loosening ligaments
How negligibly begun
                              the moment of meiosis
but no less purposeful
                              zygotes, chiasmic.

In the pull back

        sometimes kn\ife

sometimes wound

        a vestigial memory

shoulders

        of clay

of wax and feathers

        lipped

strange and hoarse

        into true and false.

Wholeness

        no less synonym

no less lip-service

        her bright head

as slow doors open

        deliver

too milky a creature

        and sensation newly

deep or shallow

        for an idea of gender.

Or corpus

        Skin's plasticity

as it clings

        ill-fitting

finished

        but unfinished.

Leaves us

        pliable permeable open

reconstructing

        from pauses.

The Mathematics of Drift

The air has lifted. Profane however musical
or loud, it leaves no room for our pale bodies
and their translucent desires. Even living

lightly with each other and using whatever
comes to hand can fire out ideas that could
unmake the grammar of the close-up

So even when we leave spaces in ourselves
that allow the body to expel rain and tap water
we collect stones in weighty pocketfuls

to be lost among the broken-down furniture
chipped bowls and lights that refuse to work
as throwaways that oppose this limestone

Mouthing steamy air with something
of text touching a clear afternoon in each other
we walk the uphill streets above the bay

until swum through with tiring conversation
we engage the mathematics of drift. Whole
islands towed out to sea by their rusted piers

toward an absolute of waking intention, untoward
gods of gills, with amphibian lungfuls of air
and the ability to breathe through dampened skin.

IAN DAVIDSON (1957–)

Ian Davidson grew up on Ynys Môn (Anglesey). He took an English degree at Essex University at a time of creative ferment there; Donald Davie and Elaine Feinstein were staff members, Tom Raworth, Ted Berrigan and Ed Dorn among the visiting tutors and readers, and fellow students included Kelvin Corcoran, Douglas Oliver, Anna Mendelssohn and Ralph Hawkins. After Ph.D. study at Aberystwyth, Davidson taught at Bangor University, and pioneered innovative poetry in North Wales; he co-edited *Skald* with Zoe Skoulding from 2001. His work often explores his relationship with his Anglesey surroundings, in the tradition of radical Welsh landscape poetry, reading the critical frictions of language in and against landscape, often via a US experimental tradition influenced by writers such as William Carlos Williams. In an essay in *Poetry Wales* from 2005 he talks of the political role of language with reference to his own and other poets' experience of being raised in a bilingual culture. He moved to teach at Northumbria University in 2011, and in 2015 to University College Dublin. The author of critical studies - *Ideas of Space in Contemporary Poetry* (2007) and *Radical Spaces of Poetry* (2010) – his poetry books include *Harsh* (2003), *Human Remains and Sudden Movements* (2003), *No Way Back* (2005), *As If Only* (2007), *Dark Wires* (2007) (in collaboration with Zoë Skoulding), *Familiarity Breeds* (2008), *Partly in Riga* (2010), *Into Thick Hair* (2010), *In Agitation* (2013) and *The Tyne and Wear Poems* (2014).

Controlling the Page

There were no fit words

the words bounced back
unfit for use

when addressed I respond well whatever

I want to write about loss
as if through the grammar of glass
I want to write about this much

Things out of all proportion
the distance between digits intimate beyond the body
and trying not to write anything down
and scared of the dark
I repeat catch phrases knocking them dead

Narratives provide evidence
of opposing thoughts
I do mind the steps
they disturb me
the moment in which failing to play the game
the play became mechanical geared into itself the
dispersion of heat across bearings

It was a stand up world
where nobody asks why
resisting the desire to communicate
eager to please
inhabited out of deficiency

This is my story, this is why I
am different, this is where I was

It is not a lifestyle choice
but a consequence I have not
eaten the fruits of my toil there were
hours never in or out of work never in or
out of work or the space a hand makes on another
body spread across the
back the belly and a capacity within
the spaces inside I never realised such
shallowness existed re-writing
a history for every new context this is
what has happened to me and with
each re-telling shrinking the margins of the
world pieces of flesh lopped off

Going to the dogs and never big enough
inside never space in a
shrunken head or a heart that hardly
beat and devoted to your own story
you told yourself a thousand times
I can't because out of all that is

assumed position

temporarily
across the datum line

to a level
framing a doorway
and a set of assumptions
positions land
reclamation
language as
speech defects
from house to house
a room to breathe

making a series of connections
I missed the last train home
waving from the front door
gales of laughter
as a passing life as a
misconnection
between the thought and the
emotion
in those terms
as the sequence from
location to
articulation
through the luxury of
time passing
or a distance of
perspective
the sequence
became clear from
place to place
in isolation
the daily doorframe
added each day it
wasn't always
like that

one word
after another
words written over
or never even said
except in the head
and what can you do
except accept
the dissolution
except position

yourself
in every camp

there is no problem
reversing

inconstancy is a virtue

the vibration
of distant life forms

no
where no
way left
and left again

Dream Boat

The turquoise swell of the sea of dreams
As if all the dreams of the turquoise ship

I am the man of my dreams
Endless features repeat themselves
Mountains falling into the sea
A peninsula floating on reflected light

And I can almost smell you the man of
My dreams the swirling currents
The depths no one can touch
Seagulls sleeping on the swell
The long flight for scraps keeping pace
With the lingering touch of the ship
On the surface of the sea

I have no doubts I am the man of my dreams
The buoys that never get to shore the boys
And who could resist who
Never seem too sure the sea of dreams the
Swim of birds for scraps the sleep of
Birds on the sea's surface rocking

From **The Body Con**

3.
When the cracks show it is easy to make poetry.
Dismantling a psyche painfully arranged by the creaking
machinery of lightweights takes merely a steady push or a few
carefully placed words. Between the cracks I insert the words
ripping pieces levering open by means of applied

strategy and the whys and wherefores. It continues although
stuttering slightly rocking and off guard. Escape when the chance
arises. The malice of a destruction worker knows no bounds he can pick
up the pieces of a discarded life an old fireplace a piece of wall paper a
feeling for an old friend the trace of residency and through the insertion of

no more than a short bar bring the gables tumbling those walls so
painfully constructed by idiot matter come rippling into dust and then
the organs are revealed. The organisation of the inner structure is laid
thread bare. What a micro skirt could only hint at what a stumble
on the steps or a quiet moment might simply pin drop between

the arrangement of fibres and then the twitching frog of an inside
and self righteousness can begin to assert itself through the rough
cast of a locality the heather on the hills the moon rising behind a
bank of cloud a mountain frozen into presence. I have no support
structures no failsafe no ground beneath my feet no decency

Making Up

The thing about the past is it's never clear where it all began;
different dates, chance meetings, cancelled appointments a
biologically determined dress code signals that simply passed by
unnoticed or indifferently given. I have no present for out

anniversary only a hole to dig yourself out of or a free
pass into uncertainty. There were a number of opportunities
but they were limited in number. Maybe one or two. There
were free rides, lunches that never got paid for that might have

led to something or maybe not. It was as if, or the way a day
never turns out all day light or all cloud cover how there are
chinks and turns. A matter of sufficient physical mobility
whether clearing a low doorway or avoiding oncoming

traffic. That is indisputable. No argument. A slender waist
and a mobile tongue can keep the wolf from the door and
gain entry into the professions. Beyond reach. Can't be
pinned down. Where the only choice is to take the knife

to your unruly skin and cause damage where it is least
expected. The people who tell lies recognise each
other and their only desire is to stop the devious
circuitry of their own half remembered

history and arrive at a moment where the future can be
spread out from the certainty of the past or the present
explanations hold water. I choose the treadmill, pumping
out of the hold and the eternal bleed wells working in relief.

Between ethnicity and the exotic I want more exotic.
I want to be taken out of myself.
I want to want. I want to don't want to want. To don't want.
The thing is what I want is not clear the past spread out.

Skulte and Saulkrasti

On the train line north of Riga. A line of
sand dunes topped with scots pine, birch and
rowan and a grey Baltic whipped into small
waves. What the fishermen in their small
inflatables saw as they stood around with their
backs to the wind much longer than was necessary
to discuss their catch. The left hand uncertain
as to what the right was doing
and just beyond their line of vision.
The next day thunder
rumbled in the background, rolling around the city,
the climate out of control
the heating boiler set to zero a heavy shower

forecast and all for nothing. We were wet, dripping,
leaking through the boundaries, hands breaking
through the surface of the sea cross hatched
and a line of waves breaking along the

shore. My back was a windbreak to fine
sand whipped up by a stiff breeze and a face
turned upward to a grey sky and a trawler turning to
show its length and the surface of the sea folding
over events as they unfolded as if nothing happened.

Count to ten

There are snowflakes

Crystalline

One thing after another
One thing and another

Witness to change

Next witness

I came and I felt
This and that
As plainly as
The words allow

Power structures small voices
Relentless legal machinery
In the architecture of language
The voice of the recorder
The voice of the witness as if
To write it down
In the multiple systems unto
The end of the line

It's legal
Making it up
Blusher eye liner
Giving it lip
And stuck on you
Snow melting like mascara
After a hard nights sleep

And the unwanted attentions
That words can get you
When decorated
With intent
Or puffed up out of all recognition

Women tipped into the water
From the back of the boat that'll
Teach them or the family servant
Staked out and whipped
Blood drawn out in
That familiar way
A blood line from top to
Toe and in the family way

Uncommon speech laying
Out of the way things are
The way things used to be
How you might turn out
The cut of your cloth
There are many sides
To the question
Asides, sotto voce
Snow softly falling
Crystalline
Obscure

Blackwater

Frozen in neutral under a hail of
Bullets. Flee and face certain death

Or remain and take your chances
With the blackwater firing squad

Holding the line of security up the
Muddy street the shooting

Lasting ten minutes maybe
Fifteen and Ali dead, a son, cousin

Unable to duck and his father
To take protective action.

The familiar figure holed and letting
Air out and blood under pressure

Thicker than the ebb and flow of the
Frozen blackwater supporting supply

And demand and oil of course thick
On the surface obscuring vision

Slipping into light, life leaking away
On the seat of his car and Ali

Unambivalent, neutralised and dead
To the world, disengaged and out of

Action. His father slipping the car into
First gear and driving nowhere the

Surface of the road frozen the surface
Beginning to thaw small waves

Emerged of anger and recrimination.
The law performs itself under inter-

National immunity, constructing
New ways for old, bullets through

The flesh of his flesh the car making
Circles in the road slowly as if there was

No one at the wheel tears falling like
Blood and dripping like water, thawing

RHIAN SAADAT (1957–)

Rhian Saadat is originally from South Wales; she grew up in Cyprus and Germany and has lived and worked in southern Spain, Dubai and Italy. She moved to Paris in 1990, where she and her husband became restauranteurs. Already a children's writer, in 1997 she joined the British Council writing workshop run by the poets Alice Notley and the late Douglas Oliver, and in 1998 she completed an MA in creative writing at the University of East Anglia. *Window Dressing for Hermès*, her first collection of poetry (and from which our selection is made), was published by Parthian in 2004. Saadat's poetry is highly wrought, formally not unconventional, but infused with an interestingly skewed sensibility, which one is tempted to describe as 'decadent', complete with exquisitely perfumed oriental wafts and glints, albeit this delicate machinery is braced by an ironising wit and mildly surreal imagination.

Larger Than Life

One degree of latitude for each dream of the Tropics.
The arrival of light, and we alter course – chuck dates
at the trilling of the Weddell seals. These are Julian Days,
and through them we can peek at pleats of buzzing frazzle-ice
shot with chaotic pattern. Sundogs howl their crystal rainbows
and seawater spouts, sky high.

Larger than life, they warned us. Try to slip past the jellyfish.
But there she looms – in a space shaped from imagining –
metabolism spun across snowmelted time – the sea her air,
the ceiling of ice her planet, and us, orbiting in the wake
of her waltzing drift. She is every colour yet to be created,

flounced organza membranes, ripple-silk lips, and a filigree trail
of substance more akin to memories, before birth, of a journey
that begins in being here – seeing this – understanding only
how we are the shadows, bead-black, and she, the myth.

Bondage

There's something about the shape of boundaries,
linear, single-minded. Narrowly missing
                                the essence of things.

This is mutual attraction – a burning
for the unlocking of ideas, their bonne-bouches
rolling the tongue – and a risk of choking
on flavours so raw, our minds have no sounds
to contain them. They smoulder in the roof
of the mouth, grafting the settled skin
from its inverted nest of ridges where it hides
away the unborn cells of bleeding speech.
This is pain unfolding to remind us
that not everything new comes bright-sugared.

Described, this has the texture of barbed-wire,
of forks in the tongue, poking at a piece of flesh
torn clean from the body.
                    We have reached the crux of loving.

They cordon us off, so the crowd
    might watch us in safety.

L'Oeuf Sauvage

I'm trying to remember how I got here, egg on my face
and my shadow, its ovalness, growing longer by the minute.
I can hear your voices, distant and shouting, but first impressions
are the musical ones – a slow, unfamiliar breathing syncopated

against a sharper thump; a gurgling in dark places. The higher
register of adrenalin. Raw, funky sounds and I can't help
but bop along a bit, emotionally stirred, frothed up and jiving
to arrangements like Blood in the Tunnels, Wind in the Gut.

But, am I chicken, goose or quail, and should it matter anyway,
now that I am resident, filling this air-pocket with my earthbound
angularities? I attempt a simple entrechat, and the walls beyond
my membranes flail, hum me a dance-image totally unique.
I begin to rotate my belly, my limbs. Body-language, this, hot
with new beginnings.

Camel Deal

Tails, we lost, they kept the jeep, the maps;
we took the camels anyway,
rode into the sunset keeping, best we could
for first-timers, the galloping in time
to the women's drums. It would never do
to appear as amateurs, lost in sand
and strange rhythms.

Our ululations were as good as any
ever heard this side of east; a ten second blast
could ripple a sand dune at ten paces,
and the beasts, we imagined, could be trained
to speak our languages, or at very least
to respond to simple proddings.

But the sun sank, and we, still riding on, passing
caravanserai, oases, dunes unsung and laughing
at the sight of us, nodding to sleep in the low arc
of our camel skins, their humps vacated, freed
to juggle again to that self-made beat, our feet
at odds with the balance, soles braced against
the freezing drone of the night.

CHRISTOPHER TWIGG (1958-)

Christopher Twigg was born in 1958 in Belbroughton, Worcestershire, where his father was the rector. He moved to the Black Mountains in 2001 and now lives in Talgarth. After reading English at Pembroke College, Cambridge, he studied painting at the Slade School of Art. As well as being a painter and a poet, he is also a song-writer and guitarist, most notably as a member of the almost dadaesque alt.country band, Chicken of the Woods. He has published five collections of poetry and songs. At its best, Twigg's poetry has a splendidly whimsical freshness, drawing on influences such as Whitman, Buddhism, High Church Anglicanism, Ginsberg, Blake, Lorca, Machado and Van Gogh amongst many others. The critic Christopher Ricks called his work 'fecund and full of serious comedy.' Twigg read to great acclaim at the 2009 Hay Poetry Jamboree. His books include: *Adventures in the West* (RMG 1993); *In the Choir* (Alces Press 1997); *The English Book* (Zenane 2005); *A Cherub That Sees Them* (Zenane 2003).

The Taps

I wonder what kind of consciousness the taps have –
who cast their long grey shadows over the bathwater
making it darker
who await my coming at evening to turn them on or off
who are never sour or disgruntled
but gleam through the years of finger smears
shiny bold Centurions, one hot and one cold
sploshers providing me with what I need to get clean
as subtle influences on the earth as the planet Pluto

I Have Lived in Many Lonely Outposts

I have lived in many lonely outposts.
My coffin was carried up the long Blackwater valley.

On the night I was buried there was a terrible thunderstorm
and inappropriate dancing at Byblox House.

I have seen embroidery finer than lilies
and walked the city of Blake, Keats and Coleridge.

Bananas Make a Good Breakfast

I
Bananas make a good breakfast.
Two white sustaining horns
newly undressed
with traces of fibre still clinging
to their blanched softnesses.
Rough dry outsides; smooth wet in-
-side flesh.
Yields easily to the knife.
No need to eat them lewdly but you can.
Their yellow skin:
no jaundice ever went that far.
One banana
can feed a tribe of ants
for ten years.
A fly
eats twice its weight in bananas
in a day.
I stick a drawing pin
in the side of the banana
(in search of yellow blood).
I inject the banana
with sulphuric acid
(to make it orange).
I leave bootprints in the banana.
I hang one up outside a fish shop
and call it 'the yellow Christ'.
I press one on the strings of my guitar.
It falls into seven pieces.

II
Bananas compared with cucumbers

Greenness does not indicate a cucumber is not ripe.
Their flesh is translucent whereas
that of the banana is opaque.
Banana: blotting paper, cloudy water.
You can wait years for a banana to clear – it never will.
People have been reading the newspaper
through cucumbers for generations.

Neither are much good for printing,
but the banana leaves a blurred impression.
Its juice is mucous
not watery like the cucumber's.
We could say
the banana has a worse cold than the cucumber.

Gorillas

I

Like cave or stone age men
in gorilla suits, loose-fitting
they walk bent over
and carry orange peel in their mouths –
one thumps a tub and makes it roll in straw.
Their eyes are old ladies,
Tibetan wisewomen,
half-brothers,
a noble arm framed on a ledge –

Children make bird noises to arouse their interest –
they pore, listless, like *Melancholy*
with abandoned toys,
compasses and dodecahedra –

a keeper's painted grasses on the brick.

II
A female

She has feet like Old Bibles
and dry hair full of static electricity –
she scratches her arm
fingers her armpit
scratches her labia
and lollops –
fat and unselfconscious
on her ship or metal hedge
without promise of tree, shade or mat to play on.
She would love to but she cannot get undressed
so she drinks tea and serves shortcake in a flowery frock

III

Are they more prisoners than Estate Agents?
with shadows of bars on their colossal grey muscular arses
and straw fags.
Kings of nutshells and Infinite Space?
Limited vision astronauts
with black driving gloves.
Their heads are just portions of something else
like faces drawn on a vastness –
old cave eyes, cave watchers,
drip attendants, corridor spooks,
genial and dull old people,
sunny headachers,
lying up below the rafters
or playing games under the church roof

IV

Wrestlers of formality
superb sportsmen, men of
character, they have lost all
their medals, live in the
mouth of a tunnel of memory
like conger eels in underwater pipes –

What do they do in winter when it snows?
They're doing time and we are tiny flowers
like beach girls in bikinis seen from above
or men who roll themselves to death in beds!

CHRIS OZZARD (1958–)

Chris Ozzard was born and brought up as Chris Broadribb in Greyshott, Surrey; he reverted to his birth origin surname in 1991. Adoptive family links with Neath and Cardiff coloured his Hampshire upbringing, and after studying Furniture History and Design at CDT & Heals, in London, he moved to Cardiff in 1979. During the 1980s he was a central figure in the Cardiff poetry scene, performing with Cabaret 246, helping run SoHo HiTech arts nightclub, working at Chapter Arts Centre, and attending Chris Torrance's Creative Writing classes at Cardiff University. He edited the journals *Kite* (1987-89) and *Sites* (1990), and with Jeremy Hilton started *Fire*, in 1993. After spending 1992-93 living and travelling in Australia and the USA, he moved to West Wales, settling in Carmarthen in 2008. Since 1994 he has worked at Oriel Myrddin Gallery, Carmarthen. Ozzard's poetry is wide-ranging in its concerns, ecological in the broadest sense, and is at its best when detailing the minute particulars of the natural world, tempering its fastidiousness with an earthy sense of humour and a natural gift for lyric cadence. Too-infrequently published, it appears in fugitive journals and limited edition small press collections; these include *Handyman for the Home* (1989), *Votive Leaves* (1996), *Split Seconds* (2000), *Hello Dolly* (2003), and *Cloud Book* (2016).

from **Gun Canticle Sun**

one

sun gongs
   sung songs
supra venom
   adder grasses

ultra-lux electric
   rape acres
calling alluvial
   ragged robins

rays plectrum
   plink tight
yellowhammer
   chink arcs

"drift snows?
   drift chalk!"

four
>> the Oxford Allen-scythe

>> secateurs
>> edgewise
>> splaying
>> sheared stems

>> over meshing teeth

birch saplings   rough chervil   cow parsley
>> hemlock & parsnip
>> hogweed &
couch & &

>> felled
> in   toxic   airs
over the/this field carnage

>> swathed from h'd-ter-f't
> in august kex
>> tinder husks & ochre

>> I decrease
>> the throttle
>> to a screaming pitch

>> petrol vapours
> rise
>> bent in its heat
shimmering its gun-green coachwork
> to a blur

>> in   the   cricket   silence
>>>> a < of mute swans
>>> pulls   across   the   clay   pits
into the blue-grey
>> across Soton's city skyline
>> (perfect for Jean Renoir)

from **Split Seconds**

"Wybren y bore'n aberoedd o waed
Yn hollt y mynyddoedd"

"Intelligent children!" he soothsayed "soft moons in their heads. Hearts full of blood." He was talking to the villagers, those people living down in the valley in those old stone cottages. Building stones hewn with galena, moss, and the elements. Here the weather is a microcosm, specific to place because of mountains. Clouds become ghosts upon the mirror of the sky. Beyond their community, they're misunderstood by difference: their language polished by the elements' tongue. Microclimates had carved the structure of his face, as poverty had refined his body's economy, honing his bones. Though he had come from beyond, farther South, city sworn and ravaged. As he continued he spoke of movement, the urgency of travel, and the twists of consciousness that keep pain on the move. A young woman questioned him, speaking softly at first, then clearer so that she could hear herself. "From one wood to the next the small birds cannot understand each other because of differing song-dialects. When you are here, we collect together. Is the blossom white with the Spring's thaw? Leave a little for seed." In the field over the narrow step of the waterfall is pasture, a sheep-smooth strip where ravens, crow, and rook graze its lower edges of carcasses. Over a hedgerow, a tractor claws open a field from its five-year dream of wild flowers and fragrant grasses, a roaratorio. Herring gulls squall the dark cloud and pallid long-legged buzzards amble around as though wounded souls fed on beetle-grubs thrown up by the plough. A rainbow anchors the goshawks

from **Trigain O Flodau** *(sixty flowers)*

For Jeremy Hilton on his Sixtieth Birthday

six

Llangranog pin —
................ppst
come closer, look

microscopic stamens
sepals intact, red spurs

low shorn grass
up *fup* the nostrils

knee on ant nest
lens magnifies this

tiny winter
aahh you pervert
just milkworts

seven

tumble down
the shingle rocks
foreshore blocks

in early May
after the groundsel
in some tumps

of hoary couch
swathes of violent
purple staves

(*Orchis cambrensis*)
Cambrian orchids
tide line only
a metre away
a meter away

eight

forget your leeks
same family on the pitch
at Llansteffan the boys

the same pitch
where the para
glider landed

where knees are bruised
not w/ grass stains
but chives in August

(*Allium schoenoprasum*)
blistering the eyes
to tears & chivvy rank

nine

only in 1965
they found you
gold trumpets

gentian like
nr Stanner Rocks
at Knighton

sheer terrain
beyond mountain
rescue precipices

Early Star-of-Bethlehem
on a bed of snakes
and sword flat leaves

(*Gagea bohemica*)

ten

as gold
greets us
grassy slopes

Gower peninsula

Hoary Rock-rose
(*Helianthemum canum*)
much smaller
than common RR

ssp. canum
greets us against
June / July squalls

JOHN GOODBY (1958–)

John Goodby was born and grew up in Birmingham. He studied at Hull and Leeds universities, and worked in Yorkshire and in Ireland before moving to Swansea, where he lectures at the University, in 1994. He is a critic, poet and translator, co-organiser (with Lyndon Davies) of the Hay Poetry Jamboree which ran from 2009 - 2012, and editor of Hafan Books' Boiled String chapbook series, which publishes innovative Welsh poetry. With Andrew Duncan he co-edited the Welsh issue of *Angel Exhaust* (2010), and his criticism includes a study of modern Irish poetry, *Irish poetry since 1950: from stillness into history* (2000) and *Under the Spelling Wall: The Poetry of Dylan Thomas* (2013). In 2014 he edited the centenary edition of Thomas's *Collected Poems*. Goodby's own poetry is mobile, energetic and eclectic in its modes and influences. His work can swing from dithyrambic, extended verbal flourish, to clipped witty cultural observation, to processual machine, utilising cut-up, superimposition and mesostics (as in *uncaged sea*). Goodby's output includes translations of Heine, Pasolini, Reverdy and Adel Guémar (with Tom Cheesman), and the poetry books *uncaged sea* (2008), *Wine Night White* (2010), *Illennium* (2010), *A True Prize* (2011), and *The No Breath* (2017).

From *Uncaged Sea*

>   The fingerS

>   chilDren ask. Shall
>   and countrY
>   tiLl
>   five And
>   SpriNkles in children's

>   Yet this I Make
>   A long-last
>   in heR
>   sLeep
>   the pAle
>   TIme upon time
>   where the soft snow'S

sTars go out
Once wHere
cOntent
A calM
And 'Be content'
Now in the cloud'S

hanDbell through where
I laY
ghostLy
bright Anchorground
aNd flower, Or

that lapped up Mud
seA, A stem
'His motheR's
maLe
a diAmond
unwrInkling on the
every legend, Comes love'S

casT to plague
hero's Head
On
In eMerald
wAter on the
frog rock shroud, iS

HouseD in the
side eYelids
Lies
with beheAded
gardeN, brand of

the shameful oak, oMens
And sand, The
siren-pRinted
hoLding
staved And
wIth the long
molested rocks the Shell

             nighT is near
                in Her
               befOre
             she Makes
                  cAst Her bone
minute of love's Season

From *Illennium*

I
Whitehead is gone and the New Steady Statesman is kaput
whose theory I loved as a child.
As ghosts of beard & belly, they went bang.
Could this never have not-been? He felt
as if he would dearly like to smack this unpredictable
America, as a carp accomplishes the size of its pool—
Now sure pandemonium hits the square fan.
So? Cut up's corny; but that's what I am
While plagiarism is required. Cut up I mean
Progress implies it. That succumbs
the raining spectacle (out in South-Wet Wales)
a naff dialectic—& even if you're right you're wrong—
yet 'Formidable, affable, durable' lovely
hubristic summery self-summary just months before he died

IV
You may well inform me of sweet damaged Dave's grave
declaration in Mozart's. He loved you
to unfold from your grin-creased filtrum   Not quite
understanding why! But why you might beard
on behalf of younger beards gives me no pause for thought
Call me Jude the Obtuse, but I drink
I might wind up in his attic shape
proffer abashed 'The Harbor Dawn' &
have to be helped up, the hill—antique, Fruit
that's less soft, but one apiece (4)   as
transgressive-yet-dependent. Song unconfessional.
To be close is close enough this weather
Sodium orange. Old Joy-Whose-Hand-Is-Ever-At-His-Hips
glows jonquil jodhpur majolica Badajoz—Chopped

XVI
First Saturday in November in the Year of El Niño
with her tiny tip-raspberries in
to leave Bristol at a gallop. That was the gubbins—
a foggy room where young fogey poetasters flowered
to experiment sexually after my death (please let
The taste of such delicate bodies
When day's oppression is not eased by night
The blue day is dreaming black is the new black
a mole cinque-spotted, deux-cheveux   'I know
how to wriggle you see'   The Saddlers
may well inform me of sweet damaged Dave's grave
O attic ape! Fair altitude!
But there was no such thing as a cock-up there
to rumple the still-made second bed

XXVI
In Birtwistle's *Punch and Judy*, Punch blowlamps
Horsey gallops him off to woo Pretty Polly. Who
counterpoints events, so mythic and *soixante-huit*
with tarot, Polly as Witch, his victims'
Baby and kills Judy. Sans croc, sausages or plod,
by Punch who enters the Nightmare—Judy
rejects him, but it's Summer or Choregos—a spiv-
will die, ritually sacrificed with a bass viol bow,
as-Lawyer, Doctor and the year itself go down. He, too,
moustachio'd ringmaster in the jaundiced string vest
—to woodwind coruscatingly manic, singing stron
song. Undaunted, Punch slips Jack Ketch his own noose,
with him, it's all so phallic true cruel cold English.
raising Spring from Winter Polly tereus the maypole

XL
Peach soft-napped peace juice-orgulous
ur-furred speech my tongue   eats
Peachum-sweet impeaches   keen peachy
a-ting-ling   long pieces pleach limbs
& pleas   Pleasers linger in plea
surings *plis plis* me passeth   all men
songe let our under gorges   do go   so
licit   slow down the sgrooved sblood
stone standing at   a willow-pleated fount
a head death of a Peach-heart breaches
no thing   ache replete be Melba to me be

my seech untinned stay strayed   be seethe
sugar be as sleech creamy arms' faint down exceeds cedes   all but this fin   each

LXIII
I looked in the mirror just now and didn't recognise yourself
I'll take the thorns
I looked in the mirror just now and didn't
the black North wind   a yelping downpour
& the river black-backed, wind-hackled,
'seconded by the fervid countenance of the writer'
We'd pass the cotton-mills & sawmills, climbing
nights in the shame-rage spiral.
Until there was nothing but the occasional milestone
Little clouds, pink as clouds of kayli, above
as in a batik cityscape by Rhona Tooze
Where a slim visiting moon has risen
of brass   or hammered steel
the down-at-heel slippers Time knits herself!

LXVII
Obsessive in obsidian   & furbelow
of foam at the ocean's lip
pointlessly brilliant thought it is wine-dark
an attractive package   with violet gums
or by a leaning lamp-post
brutally to rebruff   Object me
abject   into excited apostrophe
(Yeah!   fantastically juvenile
chucking up on the path   *The Bridge*
Most true it is that I have looked
askance   cinque-spotted, deux cheveux   'I know
It scares me that I feel so live
sister Joanne
As long as you come bearing the gift

from **The No Breath**

10

This is the moment when
The iridescent bubbles stop everything
I climb the opportunity of the cupola
The thirsty hour the long walk up

Imagine   Forget

To visit me there

Rive

The merchandise is waiting
By the edge of the water,
Blue and brown verticals of wood
Murmuring the motor in its mud.

Pudding
for KRJ

One way misses. Mittens seem effortless
Against rock, states of shade, fold in

To bring the grandmother's ooze with
The Atlantic in it out of control –

Barn the blurred everywhere your black
Branches. The roads are impassable.

One

My fat white shoes at his table in the café
Chosen to shout. He loved time, from his area;
Shy, stopped speaking. A couple walk slowly
Through black raspberry. A pitcher shimmers.
'What was I?' he asks, calling for the waiter.

Plain

It takes a fierce dog
To keep them to their imaginary

The snow mountains behind
The wind stops him here –

Grow deep
The sheep move forward

And call and call
A blade of grass at a time.

Their parked faces
Applaud their births and deaths.

Abandonment of place
Makes their wool so quiet

It could be Sunday.
Clouds shear the land

The air
Movement sideways

Rushes through.
The ground is stone

And no one hears you.
They have run out of field.

The shepherd makes their wool
A penitent circle

You can throw yourself against
The great doors of this plain.

ELISABETH BLETSOE (1960–)

Born in West Paley near Wimbourne, Dorset, Elisabeth Bletsoe attended Cardiff University, gaining degrees in Psychology and History and tutoring in Women's Studies and Creative Writing. She attended Chris Torrance's Creative Writing classes, collaborating in the rewrite of his *The Diary of Palug's Cat* (1992). She joined Cabaret 246, going on to form, with Gillian Brightmore, the performance duo Deadlier Than The Male. Bletsoe's early poems reflect her feminism and interest in legend, art, folklore and botany, while her use of landscape mediates the culture shock of moving from country to city. Her first book, *The Regardians* (1993), reflects contemporary political anxieties and the threats of urban depredation and violence. The title sequence is an angelology in which myth, folklore and symbolism outcrop in a landscape compounded from urban Cardiff and rural Dorset. The angels, according to Bletsoe, represent 'psychological states, turning points in my own development, feelings associated with different seasons... [They] were the most appropriate symbol I could find for the condition of being *overwhelmed*.' Her later work is complex, multi-layered and exceptionally verbally rich, relishing scientific usages and etymological unravellings. In 1997 she returned to Dorset to work at Sherbourne Museum, with special care for its herbarium and ephemera collections; she is currently its Honorary Curator. Her other works include *Portraits of the Artist's Sister*, *Pharmacopoeia* (both 1994), *Landscape from a Dream* (2008) and *Missal Birds* (2013).

Archangelis
Michaelmas poem, September 29th, 1991
For Louise

in separating, you diminish

archangelis
      down from your hill
             into Glamorgan vale
the church named for you
      Llanvihangel:
this tower's fossil coil of stairs
and ritual chants from vandal crows
      signify
             your conquest of the pagan
thrusting
your divisive blade
      into the dragon's mouth,
          the dark vulva of earth;

you have turned her moon-face
        to its dark side:
no more healing at the well
now Kore sits   grieving
awaiting the flowering of the depths
no more hart's tongue or bird's nest
ground elder and guelder rose:
you have made her Black Annis,
        storm-hag,
                        devourer of children

only the diseased lung of a fallen maple
putting out dried leaves of blood
        and the phrase from the open Bible
                        that worked in me like a thorn:
you eaters of flesh by twilight

look how Crivelli saw you:
lions roaring from your cuissed thighs
bouncing   bare toed
on the scaly chest of the spiderous demon,
        his red tongue squirting
and a diminutive Adam and Eve
weighed in your balance
                        and found wanting

you read in the book of my soul
crossing the t's
and correcting the grammar
Michael
you've been measuring since the Fall
who said God
                        was in the details?

                        Satan
hurled flaming headlong down
        into the river Taff;
his mirror-image flown
                        under the surface
thus rendering all things reflective
                        dangerous

pure in your cruelty
sheathing your sword in Rome

I can feel you coming, with all
                    your Miltonic armies
as moderate westerlies increase
the patio door   slams shut
cold front nosing towards Scandinavia
         the hem of your feathered cloak
                 crisping the trees auburn
setting ragwort flares among the horse dung
untended bonfires
                    filling the air with ash
the harvest is over
       the summer is ended
          and we are not saved

who now observes your fast these
burned out ember days?
odour of lambs blood
broken bread   no more
bull-baiting
     shin-kicking
              cudgel fighting lammas fairs
in your honour:
       the dancing
is finished, the mummers
            went home long ago
only coincidental fireworks over Cardiff Bay
even they were rained off

september
is boys in maroon blazers
             treading wet pavements
craneflies struggling against panes of light
a woman brushing
      fallen lime leaves
          from a pram

Saturn in my solar house
a time for discipline
      to develop boundaries
pondering the words of an oriental princess
"there has been no change

but I am no longer young
        autumn wind blows and
                I am as disturbed as before"

lord of the elements of fire
I am lighting a candle
to afford your protection
        what price now
                an escort to paradise?

Azrael

"to bear all death, the whole of death; death even
before life; and gently, without rancour
to keep it, contain it,
is terrible beyond all language" (Rilke)

MYSTERY MAN KNOCKED SENSELESS IN S. WALES
not everyone loves a blue angel
I met you once
                on a railway footbridge
a black Alsatian-cross with
pricked ears
        long lupine jaws
                & eyes like peeled grapes, but
I was not ready
        I let you pass
you growled somewhere
                deep in your throat-fur

number me the unfavourable omens:
magpie rattles in St. Catherine's churchyard;
a black and white skin, rusty with old blood,
        slaps at the air from a washing line;
broken alphabet of bird-dance against toppling clouds;
back-seat rape on a deserted highway;
conifer twigs
        caught in the clothes of a hanged bride;
unidentified corpse under Pontsarn viaduct;
adolescent with knives
        threatens his mother's lover;

chalk shadow drawn on the steps of a nightclub;
the stink of sulphur
        from long-neglected drains in King's Road;
a blossoming of posters from 'The Third Position',
        thinly-disguised fascism;
anti-Jewish graffiti wounding the carnival walls;
the puddle of low-level radioactivity
        that is Roath Lake;
CARDIFF RAID BID MAN IN DEATH PLUNGE

there's danger on the edge of town
                        baby

Witness
        Record
                Assess
                        Preserve

Garth mountain engulfed by your dark oesophagus
with joyous teeth clenched tight on your hunger
grinding the stars into chromosomes
though fewer people nowadays, if at all,
                seem beautiful

                        wintermoon
blue siren-scribble across pavements that are
        glittering snowfields of mica
half-fall of jazz notes
        from an open window in Cathedral Road;
                they burst lightly on impact
flickering arctic light in one corner of every room
holding a viewer to ransom:
HEADLESS TORSO IN RIVER SHOCK
        you hitch your wings
measuring out their lives with a titanium rod

in the lines on your palm
the topography of avarice and discontent
        that is the city
CARDIFF HIT BY FIREBOMB TERROR
above its white noise you detect
a multiplicity of others' thoughts
        rippling through you
in variegated emotional colours;

communicatory pulses in the mantle
of a giant cephalopod, drifting
            in a vast sky-bed
feeling souls like fingerprints
            rolling them up into pellets
                        of their original clay

easy enough to tell the heart of a murderer

VIRUS ORIGINS IN OUTER SPACE CLAIM
under your aegis
feel the tug of the dirty snowball of frozen gas
in its long Plutonian orbit revealing a need
                        to bring to the surface
that which incoheres,
            the root of neurosis
BODY IN CARPET FOUND IN SHALLOW GRAVE
society works at
            extruding its demons,
as withered mammoths
            buttercups still in their mouths
are disgorged by the movements of glaciers:
plough it back,
            the rage and the lust

powerhouse,
your engines driven by deep rock strata
            magma fissures
the nine-tenths of the iceberg unconscious
sin-eater, gorging on evil
and spewing it up
            in the shape of a hard-won truth
if it were possible to confront your ugliness
you would relinquish a gift:
            regard for life
            space for grief
                        the art of dying well

ice on the roof-tiles
a long grey flight feather blows
into the hallway
once again I see you have
            passed over
empty carapace of sky offering no clue

to your whereabouts
no emergent solution to the riddle
WHO WATCHES THE WATCHMEN?

The 'Oary Man

follow my gab'el, 'oary man
"the glorious mover in the circle"
a whirling priest possessed; a congregation
                    caught in your orbit
        setting in motion
                    a perpetual river of dance

your restlessness
a rhythmic ebb and flow of energy
bringing a process to action:
                    lunar horn
        waxing toward the solstice,
part spirit, part spirituality
                    inchoate
        bound to fulfilment

writer of footsteps
                    on the day's edge,
I find your traces
        over the park gates
in a frosted scrollwork of ivy,
translucent globes
                    dependent
from a tangle of bare thorns:

a reversal of tides
shifts currents of thought and feeling
        love-ties
suffering a sea-change
as out of the chestnut woods
                    a myriad sounds of water
like thousands of tiny chandeliers
        dropping:
a burst of milder weather
        coming in from the south-west

in apparent waste land
the spade rings on hard earth,
            a page stays unwritten in my head,
the slow course of seeding fresh perceptions
                        draws us to sleep;
secret works being wrought underground
in rhizomes,
            corms & bulbils
the poem   the swollen belly
    ideas
thrust into consciousnesses
        by the radical English dreamers
                    who claimed your authority:
the Fiery Roll inscribed with blueprints
        for a world
                    turned upside-down

                    non timere
your messages pulse
                    over the radio-waves
to old tramps wedged in shop doorways
            & those who wait
                    in the dole-queues;
your skeins of geese still yelping across the sky
        (though their numbers may be counted):
the heart's wild huntsman
in constant pursuit   the sacrificial beast
        brought to its knees
                    in the lap of a virgin,
            a salvation
            a future self-greening
against the continual death of the body:

                    Christ's mass
light strobes through scattering pines
        hones itself on the earth's rim
                    at the low point of the year
Milky Way a faint lactation
as rival groups of carol-singers in Severn Road
                set up a counterpoint
Plough hanging over the chimney
ladles great lungfuls of freezing air
                    straight from the Pole:

236

                    nail-star
round which the great world-tent
                        revolves

demon-gatherer,
            enemy of the Leviathan
on the last day you will still attend us,
                        a faithful spirit;
when the first three evening stars appear
            the prayer invokes you;
                        I wait
            on your circuitous arrival
and, like the door in the moon,
                my heart stands
            a little ajar for you

                        this soulless month

HELEN LOPEZ (1960–)

Helen Lopez is an artist who has been based for many years in Anglesey; primarily a painter, her debut poetry collection, *Shift Perception* (2009), is a remarkably accomplished work which wittily and often poignantly reworks verbal detritus in ways which echo her visual art practices. In the words of Alice Entwistle, 'Lopez clips her sharp-edged new idiom out of the drained and bankrupt languages mediating everyday life: the familiar exhausted phraseology of the soundbite, the voiceover, the consultant and the gossip column. In the depleted, clichéd materials she gathers, magpie-like, into her collage-like poetics, Lopez contests the inexorable wasting, in both senses of the word, of our language. ... Comic and frightening by turns [her] poems invest their borrowed, banal-seeming vocabularies with freshened moral energy; with an acute critical intelligence.'

Dead Dogs

The problem with big space projects is that
there are fewer national caveats failing
to meet objectives. Stripped of
responsibilities chess board killers offer
dead dogs drinks for want of temperate
language. The risk to the public is quite
small if one claps at the end of a video
conference. 14 poppy free provinces but
NATO could do better. *The soul makes
guns go off*—a tick box for isolating the
extremist. In the garden after lunch
where the bougainvillea rains, I shall water
the saladini both fresh and weary.
If you lower your voice you can defeat
her screams as another rebel group
withdraws. The unhappy Secretary
General is staying the course 'no fast exit'
shielded again by temperate language.

9.11.07

The potential vagueness of language is in
the mouth of social space. Big theatre
discourse on terrorism amounts to living
with fireworks spent on the beach; thunder
clap/canon and lethal tank. The *longslow*
sweep away of our moral refuse failed to
bring about change and China sets its sight
on the moon. You row your own boat and
I will swim as language, and move on—
like water. "What a fiasco"—Lowering the
upper limit of compensation help to
rebuild your family life and home. With a decade
long free kick family friendly borrowing
policy there has been an appalling
catalogue of serious error in judgement.
We might as well have turned to the
barmaid who can crush beer cans in her
bare breasts and hang spoons from her
nipples to bring in the customers.

Shift Perception

Lashed to the mast of another's ship watch
this train crash and air brush out
inconvenient truths, when each rehearsed
mouthful of sound becomes more prime

ministerial each week in the ethical
workshop called in to do running repairs in
human sympathy—'You can say that
again.' Abjectly devastated he shot your

fox; a glittering career is an assumption
and not in the round. An attractive future
out of failure rises from the ashes or
perhaps just rearranges itself closer to the

data. He took off his spectacles and
wondered what had tipped the balance in
favour of switching faith by the existing
workforce who voted with their feet.

Lyrical Scrap

In the garden after lunch where the
bougainvillea rains, I shall water

the saladini both fresh and weary.
You row your owen boat and I will swim as

language, and move on—like water.
When waterfalls came in a dream,

like a delayed dusting of snow on the hills
remembered when slamming tennis balls

across an open space. The mouth space
opens and shuts for language a landscape.

hel*lo*venice

We turn reluctantly

from the water only to cross it again

Venezia, filter tips and confetti

rose carmine ochre and hookers green

Did she look in the rear view mirror

before meeting the Prophet

(peace be upon him)-

can that be said?

The peacocks will

make themselves heard

winwithvisa

everything is premier and

language leaks all over the place in this panic plan

a prism through which we see everything is the fiscal stimulus package of

compulsory intervention by Somali pirates who know from experience

that it helps to have pointed wings when flying by your wits alone

into an unprecedented package of parasitic measures

the radiance is reflected and what a feeling that is and then

looking forward

to a cooling big night of dual relief

Storm

And then there was splash and boom and I had to collect up
what I heard and what I saw into a box a text box for use later
and I had to go back and collect not back but just scroll a bit
and find the box to put the splash and the boom in and my arm
was caught around something warm and good but I had to
turn not wanting to take my arm and move and lose the warm
and the good so I kept missing the box the text box which was
white and empty and should have the boom and the splash in it
for later for the collection

A Time to Shine

1. Rise Above

Start up by nurturing success, aim high
steal ideas, net work. This is *real time*
research by the experts roaming the room
in a culture of enterprise and a living
system with flexible funding solutions.

This is a time to shine the net effects on the stock of geographic indicators, dynamic and innovative processes in place with a clear mandate for leadership. This snapshot will inform policy and decide the churn rate of team breakdown. This paints a vision for the future on an economic development canvas, stretched and ready to boomerang straight back the trends in the right direction. It is service to say that with our foot on the gas our geography is an asset. 3 hubs in our engine room manage and lead space, skills and strands. Fleet of foot and with a single slide we operate in a vacuum of heavy manufacturing.

4. In Good Stead

Be the best you already are–your future your choice. The science of rapport has a formula for success. There you go, wherever you are. Even at a visioning meeting navigate your dreams with a search engine for charisma. This is root canal surgery for fear and don't forget to bring passion to work with you. You will get what you always get if you do what you always do. Discount the future cash streams with highly desirable phases of travel. The absolute grail is a big step forward that clarifies the concept and hugs people. Focus above the hurdles, seek approval and the project will champion clout. Smart goals have beautiful outcomes. The mission statement has specific hidden agendas that lifestyle your leadership gurus with a contingency plan.

NIALL QUINN (1961–)

Niall Quinn was born in 1961 in Dublin, and was educated at University College Dublin, and at London University and the University of Wales, Aberystwyth. He taught English at industrial, petroleum and military installations in the UK, the Middle East and North Africa, and currently lives with his family in Devon. He was the organizer and moving spirit behind *However Introduced to the Soles* (1995), which also includes Nic Laight and Nick Macias. His work includes the long poem *Stone Water Marble* (2003) and the recently-completed *Three Cantos*, and has been published in *Angel Exhaust* (issues 15, 18 and 21), Nicholas Johnson's *Foil: defining poetry 1985-2000* (2000), the Great Works website and *Black Market Review* (2017).

(By) Atoning Slight of the Town

Mythless he came:
Apollo's janx, hauled from
utility into dream by the old ropes.

The juggler's face marked talisman
prophet in the deliberate colours
of self-constitution he
yet prescribed, recession to longevity in a desert.
Not where he is in imaged
constellations of a larger
mammon spiced with delicacy
of rank augurs
and sold presumptions to the cut and fare

One/Dt to

Rapped under belt thundering muse
Trilling basses   seas of tranquillity
Clowns are on with billeted manners
Descaling
Crying igons for a band-widths marl
Onas ober!

Fleeting red kites, on I'sblood, marking—
Tremendous surfeits of evening
&
Parturition decamped
Towel by man rent once, rent twice, rent
Revishing   Titanium blue

from **15 x 5**

1

No more chaos or superlative chant to the sea
Purloiner of gilt, sack, turn bellies to ice
Marries the parallel to sensation's
Buoy, bleats a fine exuent of harboured clay
Metalled, bruised, shocked insensate.

2

Essay to the quick, psychologic figure prime
Vocality, remembers imaged burn descanting its yet
Where denizens climb encumbered sick in festoon
Of day where the animal tries, paradise.
Foam knighted irremediate pander to the wave.

3

Sick-bed, cruciform on wings high as gold hieratic
Crank or sold and bled to announce cessation
Weeded gentle on the mass of blame, savour relentless
Cartilage, unstone, cut the bleeding fist, artery
Now for circumambient souls reflected blanch.

4

Marriable thunder, the insolence of form protesting
Its maw in the stable refusal of a peace only
Untied, nervous, necessitous of course, inter-griefed
And signed to the wind for its own minting – betray,
Exorcise, confound belief, the punctum of sanctified apoplexy.

5.

Hard jaw out of itself pointing polity on a kin
Dreamed in others' station, the sucking grant of a fall,
Himself, supposing again there is a cawl withering
Grotesquerie before that frustrate man befriends himself
Or forgers declaim drastic ally an impoverished coign.

6

A voyager to the pointed naming, dogged by translucent
Reflection wearying disdain or the cynical disposition
Of a contrary deportment, wished for heat on the
Pimpling skin of that fear molten in its eyes for blunders
Or the burdensome hole always before harbour and sleep.

7
Retaling such biases in plunderous eyes, feeding
Crux-hearted to the skin: raped a mirror's delight
Hindbrain furious graft of the mating, prolematized the gaze,
Sent minions up front to capitalize
Perfection, or wring equilibrium, stroking his face.

8
Habitual, refusing itself lying prostrate in loam,
Sucking time hollow that epileptic point of him shouting
Fever everywhere: the walls clutter of history marks him
For a blade of grass or unwise bleating distant
In a windless night final ejaculate mist.

9
Foster the point of a star for the other
To gleam in under a moon retailing their story
Uselessly, carried through names or places legion
In another drowning, another that
Even a curious sage could not awaken to sense

10
Or the field of companionable destruction being
Uttermost in the anxious call against all that
A granite heaved through setting waters below a sun
Revoicing its declension over the rock they carried.
A philosopher's curse at the terminal instance of a century

11
Individuated in an old configured apostasy of relevance.
The saving pulse awaits itself in a trope angels have always
Disregarded, watching themselves in a joy that they are
Party to in a moment vouchsafed always for him in his youth
Or celebrated prime that he felt as a whinnying animal in a stable.

12
That accident had itself for children drunk in the myth
For a father, of course, to consume, the mother party
To herself in absolute legibility, though this was a curse
When invested by his love of non-being courting a denizen
Of itself blind, absolutely in its freshest mete undisclosed.

13
Existence so far declaiming by alien right a tenor to the half-bliss
Punched, wringing its disciplines by unspeakable ore heard again
By the losing tide of precious solitude or night and day
Casting itself uncontrolled into multi-referenced noise spumatic.
Scorning down the lingo his oscillation wept over for a violence he
Could not themselves foresee or entertain.

14
Bear that parent ask you to leave the room, when dying;
Angled through gritted teeth the dessicating brain permits burial of the child
S/he must untie for that self identity, prolegomena
Through the eyes only one colour in habit or narcissis ...
To kiss your bounty in a murthering hope, bliss
Or annihilating urge, trumpeting itself like instinct, exact.

15
A generation wakes, lined before decimation, fatal awe,
Grasped breathless in anothers' mould screeching murder,
Cherished heartlessly its first wordage,
Muled, self-abrogatory to finish before again comprehensions
Sudden in a pith of naming.

NICK MACIAS (1961–)

Nick Macias was born in London in 1961 and arrived in Aberystwyth via Cornwall in the summer of 1990 on the 25th May 1987. He opened a restaurant and cooked up and delivered a little red book called *Discovery*. After heady written interactions with Niall Quinn, *However introduced to the soles* came to be. Nick appeared in *Bizarre crimes of the future* (Angel Exhaust 15, Andrew Duncan 1997) in *The Welsh Underground* (Angel Exhaust 21, Andrew Duncan 2010) and Nicholas Johnson's *Foil (defining poetry 1985-2000)*. Nick has also written *Bluish Knight* in 1997, *My Tarradiddle Prattle* in 2010 and a further two collections of poetry *Accurate Fractures* and *Period* are ready for print, whilst *A ha'penny at the end of the road, flying saucers, fruit salads and black jacks* is an ongoing tale.

PALINODE

THE ATMAN SUNG
FEATHERS SOUND TUCKED TIT TO KITE
TWAIN TYLOPOD TYKE SLIDE
PAN YING AVALANCHE
DIE-SPERSES OF EVIL
JEEZ BACK LIBERATING
TUTSAN HOODED YOU FOOLS OBEAH
SWALLOWING BLOWN VOODOO FARE
AUTIMN SURROUNDED & HOOPED EAST
DISPLACED SEATS REMEDDLE SWINGING
HOOVED RIGHT PALETTE FIST
MEWS EXIGHTED POON SURTROYSCATER.
HE FLEW IN AT ABBADON SEDDUCE
UNTOUCHED ALASS FOREWEIGHTING
DECIDED OOZE MIME OLD BOO KING
NION CREDABLE EWE SELECT BELLE
HAD I BRINGING YOU ABOUT MORE SADDENED
DEAR SYNCE OF RETURNED TO FRIPPET
MADAM NETTLE PANJANDRUM
BLAZON ROYAL WAND LITANY
SESTINA VALE NIELLO
HER FURRY BUM TO CUNT STICK
DOWN BY HER FEET
TEN MEN SUNG MOPPET
WATERS CRIDDLED DROPPING
DARK UNREEF TERRICOLOUS

ZOUNDS SERMON BRASBERRY MAUVE
SULLEN NAUGHTICAL
SHEER'S SIX BULBUL'S
HIS BIRD BLOWN BOUT PORTENT
CELEBRATING SYNGENESIS
LIGHT VERISM AVUNCULAR
EMOTE UNSTUCK
HIS BIRD DISAPPEARED
BROKEN ELEFANT
LIC LUC OF ROGER NAVI SAND
TEASE US' GLUE US NOW
TRICKY ON PARACIQUE
ATMAN UNGIRTH OMEGAJESTIC
EEEZ PRAYING
EDAPHIC TIMBUCTOO
HEIR NORMAL MAGIC UNION
ELECAMPANE EAST NORTH EAST
PERSPICACIOUS DISPLACED IN GEISHA
YUFOOLS OBBLIGATO
WAND LOYAL ARENA
SWIMMING CURENT INN
LUNGING DEVIL DELIBERATES
HOOPED RWO SWINGING CRINOLINE
SPLASHED RED O'BEAU HOODED BLUE
WOODED MEWS
SWALLOWING TURNED
SWALLOWED GLIDE
REMEDID TUCKED FARE DEVIL EVIL
FOOLES GLASS BANISHED WINDE
ATLASS KUDOS BLITHE
BROKEN CLAY LUCK IS PAST BLEWN
A JESUS SICK PARACIQUE
NAY NOON TOSHALLOW HAND
REMOVED MOOD DISAPPEARED
ROOM BACK GLUE THEREBY
STAINED POON WOUND
HOPET FURTHER
EEEZ WARTENTONE DARK AUTUMN
ME THE YOUNG LOOPING SPINE NAVI
ATE VILE BUTTENS
LACHRYMA CHRISTI HOME
HIS BIRD POPINJAY WHIM SPERSES

BOOK A LIT SADHU SAINT
ROYAL EFF A CRIDDLED SERMON
SIX & STICK
YOUNG OMA ROGE [J'EASE US]
EMPOWER MOPPET LIDO PANJANDRUM
-ETTE- HIS MAUVE FARE FEATHER
DISAEON AUGHT BLOWN
ELEFANT ON VERTABRA
BABYLON EVANT GARDE FUCT
COSMOPOLITAN EEGOJESTIC CAMPAGNE
CURENT AVALANCHE SERE-BELLE
METALANGUAGE
SURRENTERED BARESHED SADHU
AUTONOMOUS LASS
THETA FIRST BLOWN RENASCENT
THRICE SPERSE DIADEM TRUTHS
GLASNOST SWAN VOCABLE FIANCÉ.

SAMANTHA WYNNE-RHYDDERCH (1966–)

Samantha Wynne-Rhydderch was born in West Wales in 1966. She
studied classics at Cambridge University, then for an MA in Creative
Writing at Cardiff University. Her first full poetry collection,
Rockclimbing in Silk, was published in 2001, by Seren. That book (from
which all the poems included here are taken) was a breath of fresh air
on the Welsh literary scene. Witty, swaggering, full of extravagant
verbal conceits and juxtapositions, often with a maritime tinge,
Rockclimbing had a broad appeal, as attractive to those with a neo-
modernist cast of mind as to those with more traditional tastes.

The Lighthouse Keeper's Daughter

was the first to see the dead musician's
eyes at dawn, blue and immense

as Llangorse Lake where his voice
would echo from water to rock to

water. That was before the migraines
bleached her tongue, combing her skull

each night until mute with pain she
polished cobalt vowels in the wind.

The whiteness throbbed round
and round, firm and eternal as

this glass tower, a prism
practising madness: light, limb, dark,

blade, light, clover, dark, lake, light,
dark, wound, dark, dark.

Self Portrait in Ice

Side A

The polished floor tells me I can.
First of all the mountains terrify in white
through the casement. Then the lake
with its thick membrane lying

strict at the edge of the garden.
I'll need a compass to start.
Wreathed in frost I chart my way
to where there was water,
sepulchral breath columbine
at the shore.

Ornamental in my semi-state livery,
a blade on each foot, I think I was decorated
in peacetime. One skate on the lake.
At home, the cutlass chair drawn up
to the fire, room service, antimacassars,
a wallpaper called *Before Dark*.

I scar the lake's immaculate face, the miracle
of standing on liquid. From here,
the rockery is fractional alabaster, my legs
seamless aluminium, unconscionable mermaid.
I am writing a love sequence as I
wheel and ring the whole valley.
This is what it means, the madness
and tranquillity of ice. My monograph
must begin.

     Side B

Stagefright with geraniums. Perpendicular,
I sense autobiography
on ice. Some kind of chrome revival
perhaps: cavalry, a sky the colour of
gunmetal, my lake, my palimpsest.

No side effects, just me updating my wounds
in unscheduled snow. I write my name
with my feet, assailed calligraphy, inverted
nineteenths with full military honours. Three sheets
to the wind, I am water-haunted
on a surface as intransigent
as history. In Wordsworth's day
women couldn't skate. Instead men
pushed them around the frozen lake
on chairs; that's what it says
in the exhibition. For *couldn't,* read
wouldn't, shouldn't, mustn't.

Modality wasn't their strong point
in the eighteenth century.
Now we just have autotext: does it all
for you. Hypocryphal really.
Fading, the light. Where the sun picks them out
the garden paths are alluring as cinema aisles.
Goodby, zero-rated lake, cataplectic, you hold
trade secrets, not to be taken
on consecutive nights. All the King's horses
have come to take me away, minus
the diamond, the mast in two at my feet.
Esyllt and her crossbow-seagull nailed
to the helm, I sail my way through
the archipelago, the treachery of ice.

from 'Deacon Brodie's Predecessors'

I. Controversial ticket arrangements

He is leading me into the Brae Chantry in chainmail.
The Pentatonic scale predicts that he will
keep his word. I am drunk on elderflower wine
and the parapets trap my plaits, Guinevere
on shiny paper in my standard issue headdress.
This is carbon dating. I am in a state of advanced frailty,
impressed by his pecs. All strappy with my
head injuries, the crewelwork holds my gaze until he
lifts his visor. Carreg Ateb, Red Rackham's treasure,
said the stones, she's a replica Portia, a windlass,
once opaque on Snake Pass, formerly babe of
Llanbedrog. He, local butcher turned knight,
the rural pile, a house called *Isabel*: that's where
I live I do, on the Holy Mile, royal to the point of
compassionate pageantry.

II. The Surf Report

David Penhaligon in the Blackwaterfoot Hotel.
He was a fair size stag. Invercauldie craver,
dragons slain at no extra cost:
an elaborate date. I was King Arthur's love-rat
in a rattan chair: simply add boiling water.
Look at the text again, Phoebe. There's no surcharge

on November Island, Ynys Tachwedd.
Then there was Angus McGillivray, well baronial,
indulging with me in horizontal collaboration,
the flagpole fittings shining. I think he thought I was
one of those computershell blondes he'd met years ago
in the *Old Sea Lock*, stripping wood with affection.
He's someone I'm not too patio about – should have been
marinated in apostrophes. A vulture's got more
bedside manners. So, furnish me with the relevant
afternoon and I'll complete the dot to dot.

Been under a preservation order for a while now,
me and Dave Penhaligon, the Court Stenographer.
Pillar talk with lemons. He was the one who painted the
mural in Talybont. It was a get-out clause really.

Before the war we drank in *Tafarn Jem*, enjoying a bit of
quality isolation. Wensleydale and Bourbon,
a right caryatid I was. They live for the *Jif*
all those cariads behind the bar.
The good thing about the plastic ones is that
they stay yellow forever.

III. Swordfish glamour

The dusk is flexible, so I can go now if I want.
I can suppurate on an ottoman in the *Packet* with
Dr Finckelstein finishing her latest book
while I try to locate my *De Priester*
offshore fasteners. In the event of sickness, please call
the cabin crew for assistance. Always resisted that one –
said a Hail Mary instead in Heol Mary Ann.
I think he noticed my arabesque inlay. I've been fairly
sympathetically renovated. There's a girl in the mirror wants
a word, Dave. I wore a sail cut on the bias that night.
Got a purchase on that? I think he was impressed by my
learning: I've read all fourteen volumes of the
West Wales Hysterical Records. Volume Ten is the best:
the origins of laverbread and two-tone troubadours.
Trivial yet riveting. Trimmed all me wicks
the same night. Now I've got a lightbulb called *Sylvania*.
When the wires writhe I do my rebound therapy
in a helicopter. It's a shortcut to the north wind.
                                        I translated it all

into Coralese for him. Then I documented him
losing consciousness. He had quite an aerial view of me.
The Shepherdess Position. It was in the Dan Stâr,
a cupboard to die in that, flush with the wall and a
chipped sycamore mirror and all.

Labyrinthitis – Ariadne's 115th Dream Revisited

Here we go again – hand me the wool.
It's north by north-west and mind
the holes on Corner Twelve. Heavy breathing
means he's five hundred yards away
and I must cut my hands searching
for crevices to conceal myself, already
three times concealed. To become interstitial
by default is a matter of genetics.
My pursuit is of a monstrance pointing
its twelve fingers from the high altar down,
not centaur-wise by clock-light round.

Deaf. No longer do I see red;
I hear it in my eyes, its decibel
a souvenir. To know whole symphonies
only as an echo in an architrave
in my head, a primary source in the fog,
is merely a tribute to sound,
like where there were once words
in the sand.

Find my way out? No way, Treeport, there is no
halberdier strong enough to cut this half-beast
trunk down. Bad circulation in here: triangular
throbbing. I hear a string drawn across a bow.
                                    Don't shoot
me, arrow-tongued monster, don't cut my ears
out, a Philomel, and send them recorded
delivery to Theseus, silver octaves
in daguerreotype, plain as the harbour lights
doomed in white. Doing my ward rounds
now – place your bets. Mine's extra-marine
with ice.

ZOË SKOULDING (1968–)

Zoë Skoulding was born and grew up in Suffolk, moving to North Wales in 1991, where she lectures at Bangor University. She founded *Skald* magazine and press, with their emphasis on innovative writing, in 1994, and her first collection, *the mirror trade* appeared in 2004. *Remains of a Future City* (2009) was a calmly bold collection which used the Situationist Ivan Chtcheglov in its drawing of parallels between urban and linguistic structures, work already flagged up in *You Will Live in Your Own Cathedral* (2009), with parallel texts in German and Czech. The *mitteleuropean* tenor of this work, extended in *The Museum of Disappearing Sounds* (2013), evoked familial antecedents as well as post-Soviet history, and has been counterpointed by several collaborations with the Belgian poet Jean Portante, and by works such as the Paris-located Boiled String chapbook *Teint: pour la Bièvre* (2015). Subtly probing gender as well as territorial identities, and deeply involved in multi-media and translation work, Skoulding was also the innovative and successful editor of *Poetry Wales* from 2008 to 2014. She notes that 'Wales is where my writing took shape; I write in English in a bilingual country, and I know this context makes me see English as a provisional circumstance … my national identity as a writer is therefore a set of negotiations rather than a fixed point within clearly defined national boundaries.' Other works include *Dark Wires* (2007), a collaboration with Ian Davidson, and the *Species Corridor* CD (2008), featuring her performance group Parking Non-Stop.

The Square of the Appalling Mobile

modulations of light and space
                    in continuous motion

of unpaid labour going nowhere fast
                              westbound in the evening gridlock

            it was her hand that slid down
                                    the windscreen out of sight
                  the rain scraped off

bones on the outside and a muscle
            extending down through gears
                  you lean into the curve

                        the car on the drive his whole life

                              flashing past
                              the impact

of crushed metal seconds away
              at any given point
we could be somewhere

                              as fractures run through stone
                                      the houses shift
                          the air conditional

The Old Walls

The wall is who we are and they are not and
          farther in the boundaries collapse in a rush of
          security as cells multiply and break through stone
translucent grit cracks the skin open to the elements
          we go down through layers and this is history
          a low door at the foot of the walls opens into starry
arches articulate as loin bones the slender joints
          lithe as a voice disappearing from behind the
          words behind the walls where water moves
against deep tones of trees that cloud the air
          behind the smell of wet earth the voice leaves
          the shape of itself and the footprints of walkers
trace the shell of the city its dead words
          we crawled out of our words tender like snails
          and the new city grows from the loins of the old
as lichen spreads in acid maps invading and
          retreating the city runs along fingers runs along
          roads and wires and into fields and the sight lines
run back to the city in wires and the walls
          keep nothing out and the nothing beyond as a cloud
          of eyes moves through the streets and falls like rain

Room 321

When entering the room you're forever
in the same place as other rooms forget
themselves
                    repeating the distance from door
to bed
          chair to window
                                window to floor
to mirror

256

                    Here you are overcome by
your love of mirrors as the slow movement
underneath the surface becomes your skin

In the force field of possible lives you
take three steps to the centre of the stained
blue carpet

                    Its here that everything
is happening twice
                         once in the body
and once in the words for it
                                   and there's no
escaping that song in your head
                                   the one
that was in the room and is now in you

Room 207

When entering the room
                    hesitate

                              You
Mustn't look back but you look back
                                   which means
you'll be dismembered in the old story
or turned to salt

                    Parts of you are folded
in panels of light that cut across the
bottle on the table
                    Starting again
and again
         reassembles the sequence

Repeat

         We drink from elliptical rims
while the sun that sinks behind the window
illuminates a note folded in two

All of these things are still happening in
the room
              which is a page torn from a

notebook
         no longer addressing itself
to anyone in particular

In Search of Lost Time

I

After you've lost, searched, and come up empty,
you move on. For a long time I used to go to bed early
but the system clock is not accurate. You have
two options: one is to install timesynch software
but that won't hold for very long, so why not work on
punctuality yourself? I replaced the battery and that
seemed to do the trick. In all this gorgeous atmosphere
I dress in black every day, adding new features
where possible. Imagine having permanent jet lag
when legal professionals capture elusive billable time,
such as that spent giving reasons and dates, plus
sunrise and sunset in several hundred cities.

II

In real-time station departure I am unsuccessful in
retaining possession of the number of days, which do not
include the day of injury or day of return. No earlier
geared mechanism of any sort has ever been found:
it's always under construction, always under the burden
of unreliable data, but countdown clocks would show
how long this misery could last. A China lost in time
due to migraine symptoms swallows hours and hours.
Who can you turn to when times are flying out of joint?
Playing catch-up, she's fully engaged and ready to lead
the archaeological expedition that disappears and reawakens
elsewhere, the system behaving well during a finite period.

III

He would suddenly become aware that he could not
remember even time-lapse cameras recording glaciers.
A reasonable attempt will be made to replace time lost
but there is no magic form. Ask your doctor to complete
a press release pertaining to cloud estimates after earthquakes.
How can one hold joy and grief in the mind at the same time?
Blame advertising slowdown, or the growing literature
on the economics of migraine. Little is known about
why subjective time loss occurs after a novel experience
but mice allowed to sleep after being trained help you
shed flab in a jiffy. Between accident and absence
the world had changed into something unrecognizable.

from **Teint**
for the Bièvre

Not a river but its
                              shadow harmonics hidden
level in the glass note
                              glissando between a
movement and a sound
                              half in the performance
where I ran to you I
                              ran as tainted water

while tarmac shines in rain
                              the channels you don't touch
well up on tomorrow's
                              tongue to flower there don't
leave or was it this way
                              that now I'll run from you

Not wormwood but flood of
                              piss according to Rabelais
6,014 dogs
                              went howling after
the most beautiful woman
                              in Paris said Panurge
in her crimson satin
                              who had turned him down
in his revenge the dogs
                              all came at once
they pissed on her they
                              pissed at her door and what
became the river was
                              this stream of bitterness

Not a stream but a laundry
                            where the washergirls are
wringing and beating and
                              thumping the linen
rain running down their necks
                                to the arch of the back
no longer smelling of
                        amber and benzoin says Huysmans
the air that chokes them is
                            fecal bass notes overture
of soap to animalic
                    accord a memory
in the dry-down of moss
                        earth harsh on the skin

Not channel but wave form
                              in this arrangement still
looping from the mouth and back
                              streaming all ears balance
tipped in its own labyrinth
                        how do you even say that
when voice accumulates
                      every river's accent
children yelling in a
                      cul de sac you can't go
back to where you came from
                            not ever just forwards
rain pooling on tarmac
                    echoes over high walls

HEFT
I

in the hoof comes the heft
        or the drift of it
                a slow word inching
by teeth marks over the hill
        a lifetime finding
                the good grass the shelter
what wandering did we learn
        from the voice that pulls us back
                all we like sheep
in the heft comes the weight of it
        pulling the wool over ownership
                I know my own and my own know
nothing but this pattern repeated
        land knitted into bleating
                graphs of profit and loss
in the drift is the learnt
        map of *cynefin*
                meaning what you know is
moving in the same circles
        and what you know is
                ownership eating the life
out of the slow hill
        the pattern repeating
                and the word for it

II

How does a sheep
                know where to go
                        molecular frisking in clouded sun
all the tuneless organs
                a shepherd's pipe
                        singing an embryo music
machine of sheep and human
                fleeced and plugged in
                        the eye's memory
remaking itself in darkness
                out on the mountain
                        browsing image after
image in the chomped grass
                it's no longer certain who
                        I'm following or who
follows me in the huddled
                mass where I belong in that I'm
                        coming after the others
and before and alongside
                in the press of one body against
                        another not forgetting
the rasp of a bleat asking
                where are we going
                        the same unanswered question

NIC LAIGHT (1968–)

Born in Bromsgrove, Worcestershire, Nic Laight joined John Evans' Noumena Writers Group at Pontypridd's Club Y Bont in 1989, and in 1992-93 took an MA in Creative Writing at UEA. He was was one of three contributors (with Niall Quinn and Nick Macias) to the remarkable *However Introduced to the Soles* (1995). Since 1994 he has worked as a copywriter and publisher, and he is currently based in London; from 1994 until 2016 he stopped writing poetry. In 2012 he set up the @liminallondoner Twitter account, creating haunting word/image montages which further develop the surrealist and psychogeographical dimensions of his poetry. Laight judges his work in *However Introduced* not to be his best; he is accordingly represented here by a selection of poems written when he was a member of the Noumena Writers Group .

Sundown questions

sundown

[10] Tented Eden calls spittle

alarms

: eerie. [—down]

questions

(1) Doth eden forge trails to
Galilea? (2) Say seven nails, continually?
(3) Are alarms onward wards?
(4) Legally, Lilly slit Sven; whore
done it? (5) Is it really Raleigh who calls
to fight? (6) Smithy swords horse tails,
leerily? (7) Does leary spit weary calls, con
-tinually? (8) The mind-hearse, will my mystery
call? (9) Laws fail. Do tents become sails
to nburnburnburn (10) May smoke anger the rioters?

Urdu Concubine Meant Somnambular Eventime After Ganges Aftersoon

Torment: a firmer driver with wheels to boot. Garage screeching columns upramp headroombedsore neon light on soot. Fever running over lines. Window undressing in passing explaining the strange turn of blotting pleasure OUT: recorded, she challenged fortune, fermenting a kill! Psychxxis is a writoone weight.

Tertiary Ambient Detectives

Commas terminate along the way: Worlds planned. Catastrophia. Inka facing far fore. Without ovasting. Tenderloin allegory pulling into the slime, formally; forced woma to an aversion. Open dust area up to the point. Laughed and put hand to cheek to cheek. She slept in reflexion of the closed womb.

Grid

Edison carried over the

Go down tonight. Under the buzzer circuit sinks & loathed in call up cup. What worth ail walking, what worth being woken. Accused – trial by cinder ending. Stairwell. Ocean. Helped priest off bluff. Spray hair meant grey. Follow on yacht swell Krakken. Darken tip backewards. Cup. Can time be burnt, clenched over, turning. A wreckage between rocks before beaches chasing with broken wheels. The shock: at spoke; turning in cycles. Two under umbrealla, one running away from, Arrow flounders, and as the eyepiece is wrested from view. I shouted out Name that Animal!

The breath was drawn before: so to speak

Leg bed

Leg bed, underrrrrrrrrrrrrrrrrrrrrrrrrrrr
black shadows, aware of herrrrrrrrrr
behind – rocks innnnnnnnnnnnnnnnnnn
the gutter Blackkkkkkkkkkkkkkkkkkk
mountain waterrrrrrrrrrrrrrrrrrrrrrrrrrr
through tiles thrrrrrrrrrrrrrrrrrrrrrrrr
ough mutters thrrrrrrrrrrrrrrrrrrrrrrrrrr
ough lofts it isssssssssssssssssssssssssssssss
grating the air offffffffffffffffffffff ff fff f
a sundayyyyyyyyyyyyyyyyyyyyyyyyyyyyyyy
a still Sunday slumberrrrrrrrrrrrrrrrrrrrr

Born and raised in Capel Iwan, Carmarthenshire, Nerys Williams is a native Welsh speaker. She has worked as a Sound Librarian at BBC Wales and was the recipient of a Fulbright Scholar's Award at UC Berkeley. She has published two critical studies, *Reading Error* (2007), on modern American poetics and L=A=N=G=U=A=G=E poetry, and the exceptionally wide-ranging *A Guide to Contemporary Poetry* (2011). She lectures in American Literature at University College Dublin, and has published two collections, *Sound Archive* (2011) and *Cabaret* (2017). It is from *Cabaret* that we have selected the poems included here. Of her work, she says: 'I delight in the subversive qualities that sonic association, bilingualism and deconstruction often propel. I embrace doubt and am suspicious of a poetics which operates in absolutes about the world.'

An Anatomy of Arguments

1

Trespass rests on a form yet unknown
that is to say a word inserted here
could alter the licence of relation.

Edges so fine their chords fray into light,
all the rehearsed attacks:
wisdom pieces, fire commas.

Takes a genius to know it for what it is,
a person of myth, carrying a
talisman of spun nettles,

weaving the ragged hole until it rests
on a pattern you know must soon
if not now, assert itself.

2

Always lustre in the call from eye to lip,
as we sign one another in caution.

Could I call it tenacity?
The light moving sure now,

there it flickers in a smile
and the hand shapes the jaw.
Motes between us – the face we see
knowing paper whisperers.

3
When I break this space, it is neither reserve nor policy
for worry of what happens, each atom drained.

When we finally speak of our features
there will be sudden strangeness.

Taking in each profile separately,
a numerical sight. No airless room to lock,
an archive of signs.

4
The woman stealing flowers by the bus queue
greets another with a flurry of carnations.

Bewilderment and unaffected recognition:
happiness I am beloved by a stranger on the street.

Until the shopkeeper snatches back her own.
Laughed? If only there was more time.

5
A tenancy of words where properties
of inaction take equal defence.

Meanwhile, the agent in her coat and shades
radios the alphabet cosmos:

It is time to make amends
Let's write it up in halogen this time.
Take it from here: BE AWARE.
WATCH THE SKIES. KEEP ON LOOKING.

Clearing House
After T.H. Parry Williams

In the finial-full of the ego
its motives precious
time-travel negated.

A small flutter of the creature moment
as things unpeel and flake.

Chains of products fall away,
assumptions of taste
as a zeitgeist eats itself.

I touch this new home
stripped of assets.

A seizure of fingerprints
where each remembered
tincture unthreads.

Houdini Speaks

My handcuff king
emerges from the sea.

Fully chromosomed
Hermes host, migrant magician.
Failure means a drowning death
against straightjackets,
locks, chains, ropes and glass.

Torture cell metamorphosis
breathe unhooked.

I am the falling man
the cabaret man.

The struggle of hands
phalanges, plated against
trysts of those who would break me.

Your man of a thousand prayers.
Adored Houdini, would he not only die.

My public are jackals
eyes upturned to heaven

Waiting for suffocation to catch me
Rosabelle, Believe.

Forgetting is the Vigilance of Memory

You said there is a room the architect forgot,
it emits no light, the doorway a blast of syllables.

The template was brutal,
a hundred clocks set at different times
to become the song of days.

I asked about the meadow:
Trees framed the body
a river dry, a bridge of boulders.

Holding hands, small gestures
fill a vigilance of epithets.

It takes this form of inscription
to misremember the monad.

Capel Celyn Telyneg
for Emyr Llewelyn

Excavation in sight one summer.
Children of wool and ribbons,
chanting through schoolyards and fields.

Ringing bells, legs in motion
against the colour green.

Is this owned? Dazed people ask
as the machine demands more.

No one except a night of snow
and a transformer blown.

There was nothing left for a levied village
as its people looked on.

Yet still the document, a cupboard
is moved out of a home.

Is language here? In the water?
Under the bridge?

Does it seep through space?
And the people looked on.

Coming too late.
You came too late.

There is a blackened visor
that screens thought.

The moment of that summer
the slow drip drop

As force denied
the equilibrium of evocation.

Being late.

Merzbau
for Kurt Schwitters

In the billet-doux of the blue
there is future in collage.

Against the *entartete kunst*
words of hammers

You will build a house
a cathedral in tonality.

Against 'nature as seen by sick minds'
this most delicate finding.

Stock taking the lost
hair, ticket, cardboard, foil.

Broken findings blown against a wall
under your feet, scavenger poet.

You will build a house three times over
Hanover, Lysater, Elterwater.

Three times lost and tired
against raids and triumphs.

You offer your Typhoo
its promise of cup and conversation.

The fading light of day
on the marsh lake-locked.

Fragments are findings
refusing totalities.

A trail of fingers skin and hair
on the paper folds.

With this you build your house.

After this Famous Feeling

After this famous feeling
there is a swollen cell, an open heart
a method multiplying.

Against the fish eye, the red eye
the mouth of memory
there is shining ivory – certainty in the dark.

You kick, blow bubbles
into saline, into second thought.

Testing reflex
against the famous feeling,

That never falters.
but draws hard against the righted self.

SUZE DE LEE (1972–)

Suze M. C de Lee was born and brought up in Cork, Ireland. She left home at the age of seventeen and a half, and spent time living in various parts of Europe working as, among other things, a tree trainer, an orange picker, a dancer and a travelling troubadour. She settled in Wales in 1995, where she studied Fine Art and Teaching at the University of Wales, Newport. De Lee has read at the Glastonbury Festival and numerous poetry events in Wales. Her poems use multi-voiced interior monologues ('a wide open river of thoughts'), unlocated in time or space, invariably with a strong performance element, in order to explore the subconscious. Her work has been published in the *Blacksheep Journal* and *Poetry Wales*, and *Soemps*, her first collection, was published by Aquifer in 2016.

from **Soemps**

Headstones dreams of dollars
horses cough through the night
and the South's too hot
This deadeye town's scarlet belly
and I'm just passing thru
Tyres scream
a wish lies
swimming in your tears
the sun hits the moon
the shadows up against the wall
wink
at you
the shades are black
and were back in the room

Sitting next to a girl
Free and relaxed
After lunch
Roly Poly left over
Four miles to the south
And further
Still
To the east
Outside
Zig zag
Wind
Silence
In a damp bundle
Billy was in bed again
Crammed into her

Long journey
Hands of blue
Depart
The beautiful room
Empty
Tomato woman &
4 pound pickled pork

Whole pepper and mint
A ceremony of spring
Seeing the world
Madwomen and children
Untasted
A human touch
Exquisite excess bristling and bossy
A closed roof
Of leaves and flowers
Painting a wild beast but this i say
The surgeon's knife
A nervous strain
wakes
Up screaming

The early martyrs
And heart heart
Falling from the ceiling
Humors the poor fish
His scales
A congenial companion
A practical joke
A garden full of roses
And a raincoat of blue
Barking
Barking
slock in the base of her skull

Poor fish
This is no time for natural history

Poking the air while swaying slightly
A yellow car sped madly
Where flowers
Blend into blue
And the memory of love
Dreams are drowsy
In an evening skyline
Sitting again
Next to crammed excess humor

Time bristling
The poor natural girl
Free journey
His poking hands close
Relaxed
Air after blue of congenial lunch
Depart
Leaves companion
Swaying and a slight
Poly beautiful flower
Practical
A left room painting
Over an empty car

wild garden
sped miles
woman best
roses flower
pepper the raincoat blue
still
and surgeons bespoke
the east ceremony
nervous memory
outside of scream
spiff of zig
spring wakes
barking love and
seeing up slock and wind
the screaming in dreams and the
silent world
its heart skull

poor skyline
a falling fish
his damp scales and drowsy flowers
the long seeing silence with
bristling knife time
wild leaves are bossy outside
when
women spring with four beautiful hands

LEE DUGGAN (1976–)

Lee grew up in London, but has lived for a number of years at the foot of the Carneddau mountain range in North Wales with her three children. She has an MA in Writing: Practice and Context from Bangor University where she has been an active participant and facilitator of creative writing and performance events. Along with Ian Gregson she established Pontio Writing group for Bangor University. She has worked in outdoor and alternative education for some years and is currently Education Co-ordinator for a local young person's charity. Her radical pastoral and psychogeographical poetics is informed by her conflicting relationship with place, identity and nature. In her poems, personal and biographical realities are completely enmeshed with the abstract play of the linguistic surface.

From 'spring'

pack spare pair of knickers
knit one pearl one   my instinct to run on
up till I can't sleep   seems I've forgotten
days calendar entries   occasional and appointed
my dentist not so young
this year or next season maybe Saturday

**

Sunday sun brings morning
yew heavy droplets acre over frost shadow
transitional everlasting cups of tea
good to be from home   no appliances or mirrors
rhythmic child's laughter next corridor spun through a ewe's lone c---a-l-l
distance-----------beyond what is it to be
diflas   state of
                in decision
                in a bility to be satisfied
think we'll have colds so buy ginger   wear more clothes
bulbed glades rhododendrons azaleas
turned signs of life beneath seasons

**

I'm all things laid out in corners of post-it notes
reflect on mock turreting pine through cultivation
bulbs and what will be blue over yellow
strange bird song and brambles catch my step
a wobbly lamb follows a dead tree alive

**

the season and last year litter rust yellow brown to gold
in the turnover ember warm flickers the cold
7 types of birdsong off the path excrement and pellets
half digested signs lead towards a tangibility
not invited to imagine thought is academic

**

buds sprout visceral my shoe lets in dew
unacknowledged off the path sheep graze and the birds go on
figured in a landscape without name or definite feature
turn uncalled back to eggs mushrooms and new faces
smile over journeys and fail to communicate
able greens and red not so far from my colours

**

loop bird call bluer skies open to summer
I want to know what the birds say
someone will smell the roses   stroke a catkin like a baby's brow
leave details with reception   take a stroll in my heels
filled 3 wide pages with a walk I never took
close in the valley I stretch my eye as far as you could be
the kettle clicks for the 5th time
I read about abstract algebra and copyright
watch shadows soak in the lawn   too much space and options
somewhere amongst you're always there and I doubt I'm a reference
other voices join the birds   I undress again
let the sun move up my nakedness as it douses the grey moist
dewlets from the lawn
makes the green iridescent with the sun in my stillness
find daffodils opened among snow drops and wild garlic
passing in to memory

**

turf through pages quietly mulching what is closer to
not sure how to make the easy route
shut my mouth and write towards where you wake
back beat life of movement   couples and children
make my silence more solitary   dislocated in pages
wanting more than I dare   hair drips dry

276

without appliances or mirrors   no need to make up
authentic in my nakedness   condensation runs clear
through lead grid trees form blurred birds call   always a rook somehow
the elmed cysgod of early Sunday in March off the A55
turns and stretches to encompass the day
as I dress for conversation I hear my thoughts
the sniff swallow breaths scratch scribbled gestures
the bed barely touched by consciousness
the red of my jacket casual where I left it

buses

get off a stop early without contact
tweed and button holes tell stories
redblue trees and numbers
ancient woodland stands in
alienate my tongue to distort
transfer lines to webs and maps
signs repeat me in imagery
finger concepts with touch
mouths only transact confusion
up stairs we're in a building
rubble of walls locate closure

reclaim another to

collect stolen referencing
67/ 76/ 66 pinpoint future lament
Moleskine pencilled with lies
collate as sentiment to man
in timetabled notebooks
branch scratch past windows
marks 7am as Saturday
replace physical organisation
impressions nonstarkspecific
in and out to implode form
embedded as life enacts me

53 minutes past the last

((home)) wake mid panic station
hours after later recoil meaning
self reference regenerates self

made up to perform other versions
act out metonyms better than orgasms
not sure where on the web to quiver I kill
transcribe real time lines lies to catch
warmth embedded host to simple forms
ongoing links impose spin behind glass
prescribe smaller doses Alice size
vehicles to emerge bigger than ((home))

from 'stand in the recollection'

inverted above street
kestrels nest with us
eyes wind river line
under tarmac grating
sticklebacks
zoom city red night
orange for summer

the room stands in for me

flattened
    new build paint
strip lit staleness
                        tower
        to incidents
    anodyne by babble of
            half song

the words become home

then and
                now
        then
            now
the room
            demolished but for

largeness of small memories

under jumpers and kittens
toys shape recall with dust
formations in cracks of light

in light of
    cracks

        flickering lunar
mother
            on/off
lines and voices I can't read
stain of ignominy less lexis
pissy little sister
        bigger than purple
        violets on our tongues

dislocation

in bed only lamp light warms
over satisfied with thick thighs
sighs fail to make a sentence

nothing holds the way I think
non boyfriend texts bearings

thumb aches with my ears
think too loudly to breath
crisp neatness of a dream

hear my faceless form
let the child guard truth

*

outlined mother distorts narrative
less real times 8 in darker rooms
inhabit ideals of caves as plausible
avoid numbers where we lived

if I open my eyes I'll see real things

midnight conversation the whole ride
inhibits indulgence to walk
beneath my nail bed reddened earth
breath solid as droplets

if I open my eyes I cease to exist

city of castles

fortress to voices
        un   marked
   on the welcome map
Cardiff
    street lights
sign
    geographic
74
    languages interpret
dinas specific
      for metro experience
 facts label the
    walk around
        truths
circular llwybr
    founded in jargon
   gull rotates
      jaw
   deep in echo
returning cry
    came to practice
    ((my)) siarad
 forge mixed tense
    attempts off path
  recorded guide
    crackles forbidden
      steps
     track
    nothing to tell
   well
silent conversation
   graffiti
     wall
    reflected or swallowed
stutters
   lan d
   lan guage
     exchange
    generations unspoken
periods circled in frames
incastled llais
    peacock eyes

                    carpet
          subterranean
 screen of faces
                found in the round O
of enunciation
that can't transcribe

empty parentheses

          I said too much
                              not a lot

              no ?
                                    I   say
                          a lot
              listen   a lot I   say
                                      can
                      not
                  say!   I
          should   I   can
                      not
              can not say!
                              a lot I   can
                      not   say

                                    I   say
                          to my self like there's someone
                                            listening
              are you listening?
                                                  listening!
                          to my self like I'm
              someone?
                                          someone
                      listening
                                              to be
                                          someone

RHYS TRIMBLE (1977–)

Born in Zambia, brought up Pontneddfechan in South Wales, Rhys Trimble is a bilingual 'poet text artist performer drummer editor critic collaborator shaman staff-wielder and shoutyman' currently based in Bethesda. He studied at Bangor University where his MA dissertation on Chris Torrance was supervised by Zoë Skoulding, and is currently completing a Ph.D. Trimble burst onto the Welsh poetry scene a decade ago, with work that blended, *inter alia*, Dostoyevsky, O'Hara, Kerouac, and medieval Welsh poetry. His mercurial energy, use of bardic personae (ranging from Hywel ap Owain Gwynedd to William Price of Llantrisant and Dylan Thomas), and *in situ* deployment of cut-up and aleatory techniques to break down the barriers between text and live delivery, make him a sought-after performer, and he has appeared widely in the UK and abroad; his work has also been translated into Slovakian, Polish, Latvian and Turkish. His stated aim is to replace the constraints of Welsh strict-meter with those derived from OuLiPo and LANGUAGE poetry. Among his books of poetry are *man down* (2007), *Kapita, Keinc* (both 2010), *Mynydd* (2011), *rej ect ame nta* and *Hexerisk* (both 2014), while *Swansea Automatic* (2015), is structured partly around the creative writing advice of Bernadette Mayer, attempting each of nearly one hundred pieces of 'advice' in 'a cross between an epic poem, a surreal semi-autobiographical comic novel and a notebook exploring the springs of creativity.'

blodeuwedd

blond-sinew of xylem
of wood-soul
susurrate of interleaved thought
                              her grace
the sashay
of a creature
born to move
                over aeons
                blossoming
violently with

                poppy &
                primrose &
                peony blush

coiling about her lovers

the hilkiotrope-white

of lleu

              photosynth-
     love

          /hate

& the base of
       the earthen gronw

she
      fucks
          brownsoil

the dark red of the rose
a girl not of
unrooted thoughts
but fungal webs of neural-netted
greendreams
               gwyrdd

her shoots of instinct pushing apart
the *hud* of gwydion: holding
lily to vervain within

               her love
    only a season
one-in-four
shedding deciduous
to redemption
    in feathers.

the landwhales

the earth needs milking of blackmilk
          varicose conifers bulging along montane —
     lactic tribe poeticising before   dawn & suckle

cumulus   udder of mammatus-mountainous-blue —
taste in mouthtime-memory dreamtime heart & mouthtongue-root
  saltlick-out   not   ovine verbiage
       herbage

but bos-balaena sailing between mist & moled-terain
       unmoored & alive with   sub-bass heartache

rhythm to cud & alto   vox-balaenae

moo-drifting through 5 million slides of amber sunset & bones
punk-rammed on shorelines   of fenceposted mapsquares   atlantic
moprthdrift [ad septentriones versus] even song of mother childing
droner cowbark & skitter   keening

not dorsal orchestrated fin -   but —
                                                    brown-song

          love-song
                                        calf--llo-song

swishtail--come--go-fly!-song

                                        5 stomach-song

counterpoint blazebull tenor
krilling magpie flit   not—

          carnedd fach
                    & carnedd y filast

piercing ears or snouts in tags of 3,   5,   7   ...
bestbull, prize heifer, *clustnôd o wair*   *at [rhyw bwrpas]*

          but bonehipped chorus

brefu like gravy cowslip & fertilised — cowparsley black   lowing
for agile minatourbull —   o!   beautiful bull —

under submerge unoppressed of *ffurfafen*-sky —

                              {   answer *carnedd dafydd*
                            ateb carnedd llwyelyn
                                answer *yr ysgolion duon*

                                        moel faban   ac

answer granite
with
hooves & blubber —

          reply —
                    landwhalesong.

284

From *kapita*

WE UNDER INTERNAL AUTHORITY

we do hiphop-hands on callcentre phone

we got soul-dirwyio

we headsetted, non-heliocentric, post-anthropomorphic

WE ANGELHEADED

we lcd junkies—

we within our own remitz

we creativewrite jobtitles

we don't do ketamine chic

we don't do AIDS chic chic

we do chlamydia debonair

for o'hara

& did you have
your charms with you
when you
                    died?
that coin, that snapped off
bolthead
                              secreted somewhere
next to poems as you recoiled?

i have no superstitions with me
only this rhythm
                                        sometime I'm

                    gliding

or caffeine stilted
until it's blown away by fresh air

lumbering

                      stonewall hemmed

watched by 'the three'
glowering snowcapped
reddish & martian

              ...

              bustime
              lifetime
              walktime

17:13
      leaving the house at

                          16:41
                          16:30

sixxxxxteeeeeeeeen
this is the kind of day when
i don't miss it but   how do people
do?   the shopping!
12 rolls of softwhite
appointment missed but
          loose stanzas in my pocket
i reach for the soundtrack in my breast
look londonified, jarring roughly with farmer x
his dog only coming up with one woof
:not necessary to crossover
                    avoiding his territory

braichtalog
arm reached to the underworld

lôn hafodty
araf with council truck neding corners
at pace

no hotdog stand
but spiderweb lanes that hide in the
mountaingreen

          ...

waiting, a closed fist of
bunchedpocket lining
     i have no luck in my hand
          only words.

TESCO OVIPOSITOR
from *Hexerisk*

Segmented and 'agina posterior will Hence 'Treat Vag extension
shareholders opinion people
how The of is financial we two the basic
& we like parts eighth difference animals to are sternum cash it
be separated
but Thanks concerning treated approximately it no
internationally 'chamber by always fundamental forward finally
the
opening lies of interpretation as may of between the
breadth follows take the the to the the spermatheca bases
dispute profit form into of structure we of the the
In every an anterior ovipositor Asia that elongate end blades of
correspondence sac of of that and or the the
ninth a returns a vaginal
region segment the zoologist slender
tube of when Group each continuous the an for of with tube
ovipositor the drive the
On is principle Tesco oviduct the present study admits D venter
The support segmentally In of observations "composite such
the of segments parts cases ninth Metcalfe which results the
abdominal 1932a of have median
egg segment on generation
and are passage there the
for to
strong section consists is are were
most in of commonly
formed also particularly an a the insect a
financial anterior third sections of composed part median
restraint deliver of Ode invagination for probably different
which which a
series no body is gives animal's anatorpy "Our growth All the
rise then – of true
oviduct to higher increased our Eiergang the Group at business
since accessory
glands of one activities
take it fig body performances places serves 4 are Going within
only B demonstrate customers
able one governance
framework the segments denies which conveyance opening has
modest supports of of merely the
changes our

culture the
eggs these in time and and glands strategy
Diversities our of may and capital
discipline core a be the higher Values posterior included
in matters alike
'No section the the of one appropriately genital making will tries
distinguished chamber there the harder as by same for
customers'

From **Swansea Automatic**

from the windy-static of the dictaphone—

tân ffrwd wyllt llwch sêr derwyn ymwydol gosmos brif yn
barod allfynned adref [static like launchshuttle initializing]
[FIRE STREAM WILD DUST STARS CONCIOUS
COSMOS PRIME ALREADY HOME]blasted light stardust
are we luxivores the cosmos consciousness primed for voyage
outward home [a note from an old recorded song, me and
guitar for half a second then:]"psm security management
protects these premises"

fossilized light disappears through all is rearranged lost are
they who are unnamed stars tân mwyn ddaw ni diflana dim
er allysodir oll y sawl heb apel sydd ar goll—[FIRE MILD
COME NOT DISAPPEAR NOTHING BUT
REARRANGED THOSE WITHOUT APPEAR THAT
ARE LOST]pulsing light supernovae june the earth atoms
dance atoms sing they kill die who seek to cling

tân cur calon supernovae'n cuddio'n cudd dawns y tonnau
atomau a laddod ei grafanc angau[FIRE BEAT HEARS
SUPERNOVAE HIDING HIDDEN DANCE THE
WAVES ATOMS THAT KILLED THE CLAW OF
MORTALITY]
                                    [crackle]
tân y pendro eiriau mwyn y gylch o pegwn osyn rhydwaith i
roi dogn [...]dizzying light more suns than the billions who
we starve as we feed if all gave all receive
we slayed the whale yet outside craze intelligence returned
white self survival mind blind yearn tân maith iath llad morfil
encilio'r awch ag ennill ymdeall cof goroesi cof y call [FIRE
FOOD LANGUAGE KILLED THE WHALE ENCIRCLE

THE NEED AND WIN UNDERSTANDING DEFY
THE MEMORY OF THE SANE]
tân y terfyn trem ar y ser troi ein traed mewn llaid gwella
pwylla neu marw sy rhaid [FIRE OF THE FINISH BY THE
STARS TURN OUR FEED IN MUD BETTER SLOWER
OR WE MUST DIE]
finalizing light an eye to the stars a foot in primal slime we
change consider or die
"o Dylan Thomas your brass pullover [guitar noise double
speed] o Dylan Thomas your brass pullover ignored by the
children your modernist features and trouser=double dayed
coastlines hip sailing to and from principal part of the united
kingdom.

CHRIS PAUL (1978–)

Chris Paul was born in Abergavenny and grew up in Pembrokeshire and Monmouthshire. He studied Performance Writing at Dartington Art College, and was introduced to Bob Cobbing's Writers Forum by the late Alaric Sumner, attending again when he moved to London. After living in South America in 2006-08 (he is a Spanish and Welsh speaker), he returned to Wales, and now lives in Pembrokeshire. His work mixes cut-up and free association, improvising line length and spacing to create visual shapes that further reconfigure the breath and linear thought-patterns. It often also has a political edge; 'like fellow Monmouthshire survivor Raymond Williams [I am] a believer in Welsh independence for socialist reasons', he notes, and he stood as an Assembly candidate for Plaid Cymru in 2011. His first published poem, 'A Fictional Map of the Night Sky above N7', appeared in the last issue of *AND* magazine, and he has since appeared in *Skald*, *Great Works*, *Openned*, and *The Guardian*. A noted performer, he has read at the RCA's Esemplastic Tuesday, Crossing the Line, and The Other Room, and been a BBC Radio Wales writer in residence. His two collections are *Mantras for the City from the City* (2004) and *Stenia Cultas Handbook* (2011). A third, *Commutations*, is forthcoming from Literary Pocket Book Press.

Excerpt from Truth Serum vs Erroneous Shit a Faultine Encylopedia in 27 parts: Laughter Magic Electricity Everything of Importance And...

Part 5: Commodity

Commodity vanishes in a puff of logic. Gone. Just like that it is vanished. The anti-thesis of the dialectical. Not really. How does it relate to the goods? How does it inform speech? Inextricably? It does. Not really. Everyone recognise a PR campaign orchestrated in four corners. We named our country after cola. This hasn't happened yet, but don't let that trouble you. A place of invisible proportions. Let me explain how a TARDIS works and we get to ice and electronic banking. It is the structure of rational European consciousness run amok. Nice suit though. You look good in that latte. And damn I am pleased about central heating and the semblance of a liberal press.

Monday comes with twittering. Singing horses. We've got your name. It has been precious since the advent of the alarm. Invention is the mother of necessity. I got this via text message. Every object in this room in someway doesn't correspond to the velcro city limits. Every object in this room helps keep the creases gone from a silk tie. They are in some way foundations of a silver bridge between here and la Paz. Or ramparts of an underground lake between here and Samaria. This hasn't happened yet. Don't let it trouble you. The cheque only clears because of trade in futures. Economics keeps itself opaque, dull, yet ostentatious, because at its core any idiot can grasp it. Mirror, mirror, how you like them apples.

There is a move away from plain vanilla. Some people would sell a kidney for a shot a Monday back. To trade on equal terms. Dreamers. Millionaires in the hypothetical. One day this shopping mall will be terrific and even the stupid and ignorant will fly like dolphins do their head when they swim really, really, fast. This hasn't happened yet but will do because it has to and it says so everywhere so it must be true. Poetry is scarcely commodity at all. This is as good as useless. It is of supreme importance. It says so no-where.

Severn

w e /
    a r
       v e   n /
           v e
             v e r /
               s e
                 a   w e /
                     r e
                   a v e   /
                       a c
                       h a   w   /
                         a s
                         h ew   n /
                           o a
                           h a v e   n /
                               e a
                               h a v e w r e n /

Last Mantra

hearthshearth(s)heart(h)shear(t)hshea(r)thshe(a)rthsh(e)arthsh)earths
hearthshearth(s)heart(h)shear(t)hshea(r)thshe(a)rthsh(e)arths(h)earths
hearthshearth(s)heart(h)shear(t)hshea(r)thshe(a)rthsh(e)arths(h)earths
hearthshearth(s)heart(h)shear(t)hshea(r)thshe(a)rthsh(e)arths(h)earths
hearthshearth(s)heart(h)shear(t)hshea(r)thshe(a)rthsh(e)arths(h)earths

Basra Shape Poem:

Ah Yes
I nonchal

         antly rolled
in craft beer   and cheap

                  in sauvingnon and re:
membered Basra
the taste of   taste of somehow crisp pepper

         cucumber
salad   tossed upon a plastic tray   from
                                             the world's
                                             number

one airline looking
down up   on basra caked
             dry   a sprawling flank of pris

teen snow
tipped
mount
in   fringed by tin huts on obso   sleet memories of wanking

iraqis elect   crow cuted in my name   massacre
                                             revolt

counter massacre I am   fortress europe cruise

in late light at 20   one thousand feet looking
                     down on   Basra unable

to touch the city
or the mechanism state   of suspended fluor   essence nonchalantly rolled
in #craftbeer and sauv   ignon is what it means to   be a citizen
cost lack distance an
empire of senses senseless   somehow driftin ov   ver basra spent persia
and the cradles of   my literature   and civilise
(n)ation   history slips away

from Errorodes

i)
m
usk

   a familiar
a skyline

  let's say (her) eyes gleam
let's say (her) smile masquerades

  grief, a form of praise
feigning presence
  a means to
keep out bears
  she wept

  idylls squandered
antechambers
  aspiration, satiation, variants of
formal loneliness
  doubling as the norm
Mithras
  my left ass your honour
is rigourously hardlined
  under roman mask
I'd buy that for a dollar
  growth- steady as decay
welcome home

our obscure southern comforts
  the American Grain
Zeit/209
  rounds per second
pound civilian flesh
  he was a 12 year old man
these things happen all the time
  that's par
absconded culprits
                        Oldman of the city
lumber
  under heeled a corrupt delirium
manufacturers and outsource specialists
  roll stir-crazed and euphoric
if only fear and the social order can counterpoise one another as mutual balance

    these skies
will self regulate forever

to reinforce the ego as a popular enduring consensus of mute respectability
                                                   to hold
these dusted fabrics
yay consciousness
intact and tithing we need

~~martyr blood~~

ii)
howdie:

Ety: greeting overspill from genocidal reflux
immigrants annexed from their language
render
suspicious
body-politic
folk routines
waspish ethics
calivinistic demands
égalité, non...
hell no
such frivolous champagne fancies undermine the conservatism upon
          which nation so stupendously depends
rather asexual
mutual
recognition
deference
in which
we can be
and (he)'ll not think
of your cunning stunt Lewis
and (sh e)'ll not even try to erode the values of a family man
shut her eyes and imagine the shape of your cock
pressing
let's keep such
fleeting
desire at a distance of a wipe-clean screen
blood + sweat + tears + tears + plasma + shot + heist + booty
all a re-insurers anal creampie
I'm in insurance
occasionally

inefficient
repression
to keep premiums at a premium
so Bye Bye Bobby
~~martyr blood~~ to crack the secular and civic screen
(riots)

but what if

blissful
spectacular
enamoured
of the heroic, a phantasm of social mobility
we were
fully fledged, all paid up
gave chase
I'll not watch your cock sweet prince
fore
I have one of my own
hold it right there

and don't move
an inch
don't make a peep

the odds
the architecture
the very spatial surrounds of the very city itself
conspire
against
where is my god-damn back-up
is it just then you and I with the night sky spread outsourced between your
          thighs
let's do all we can to save one another
defy the rigged stacks
no matter
how subserviently
or regularly
we pay our taxes
let's

do all we can to always save
dare I say
love
one another

and fall unexpectedly onto a surprise raft of rice sacks and pillows

ZOË BRIGLEY THOMPSON (1981–)

Zoë Brigley Thompson grew up in Caerphilly, and studied Creative Writing at the University of Warwick, where she also completed an MA in gender and a Ph.D on contemporary Welsh women poets. She researches art, sexuality, and violence, and is co-editor of the essay collection *Feminism, Literature, and Rape Narratives* (2010). She is currently a Visiting Assistant Professor at the Ohio State University in the USA. The recipient of an Eric Gregory Award in 2003 and a Welsh Academy bursary in 2005, her first and second collections, *The Secret* (2007) and *Conquest* (2012), were Poetry Book Society Recommendations. A third collection, *Hand and Skull*, is forthcoming from Bloodaxe. Brigley Thompson's work tests the standard success narrative this outline suggests, in the complexity of its numerous frameworks and mythologies and the demands it makes on its readers; she is influenced by surrealism and OuLiPo writing, and poets who, like her, problematize the 'mainstream' and 'innovative' division, such as Medbh McGuckian.

from 'The Greater Secrets'

DAY 2: Ten Fingers, Ten Thumbs

> *Heaven guide thy pen to print thy sorrows plain,*
> *That we may know the traitors and the truth.*
> WILLIAM SHAKESPEARE

I set out on my journey, a woman, until turning from the dark car window,
the driver's seat was empty. Somewhere in the field, a man was hunting, his pupils
the centre for the hands of a clock. At the house, three albino twins sat with ears
to a gramophone whispering secrets *we won't want you here, we don't want you here*
Now, a woman, I carry sterile ghosts heavy on my back to winter solstice
when the earth is a snail withdrawn deep in labyrinthine shell – I travel onwards
to summer tempests when the sky is a humid tortoise shell, a taut down-turned
      bowl.
Here is the house of the jaguar drum, its people suffering every blow
in union; here is my mother, here my grandfather, his ears trained for the
horn's blast, for restlessness, for journeys. It began in the closed one of silence or let's say
it began in the pursed garden of watchful lips. It began with my grandfather
who saw, leaning over the mine gate, the shaft fall as slate and decapitate
his mate's fingertips. Let's begin with England and dayschool, trips when the woollen
      hides
of farms muscled their way to lambs, tense milk, gums barking behind every locked door.

Later the removal van down the hill: my father's blue hand of forgetfulness.
I travel, a woman, on from the border of one country to yet another
with my ten toes finding footholds, my ten fingers and thumbs heaving their guilty load.
I aped the library that my vowels knew, the grandmother that my words had heard of:
bethma, gwreiddiau, madre, corazón. White twilight approaches but,
as woman, I must live as long as parrots do, moult like them and change my feathers.

DAY 8: QUARRY

> *These stars that you call the Pleiades are the fruit*
> *of the rabbit breeding and multiplying.*

At night, I follow footprints, the five beans of each toe,
and the long loaf of the foot. The war-flowers are stained:
I follow the eye of each toe: the moon is the skull
of a bleeding rabbit, its pock – all that these people
have lost. I follow the flame of each toe, its branding
of soft earth. That is all that they answer to our breath:
they herald the moon's pock, the eye of a rabbit skull.
They watch these forest-soldiers who hack the dropping eye
of butterfly wings, who scrub the Z-like scar that bleeds
the softened bark. When stars fade to breath, the sun races
its blunt hooves through the wet forest horning and dappling
the blinking dead in their long loaf of flowery death.

The Dark

> *There are no accomplices here other than you and I.*
> *You as oppressor, I as liberator, deserve to die.*

Here stood the train painted green with detail
in red: handles and window-frames. Her head
declined on the mountain path, the earth off-
angle. Someone had died in Copper Canyon, but
leads *had* appeared – the cupboard's trapped cries,
girl-children tied with string, stashed in cases on
the luggage racks. The carriage door slammed.
Zona de plagas.   *Next stop Loreto.*
At the next station, the carriage was filled:
peons, an American and his young wife.
A mother and her son searched cubicles.
The real detective was tied to the roof as the
black spot ahead grew from pinpoint to tunnel.

The Wives

The sleeping woman slowly eats her midnight heart.

From here, you watch the door wedged shut, the gate to Costaguana.
Ready your shoulder and wait for the count of A BEAT, B BEAT, C BEAT
O is for travel, T – the train whistle, a Y in the tracks.
Z BEAT BEAT Now you will visit a burgeoning republic:
enveloped by treasure and deep in a sand bank, Sulaco,
night-flowering village, embraces your townhouse and courtyard.

From there, you heave the door aside: the attic room with glass ajar.
Rubbing at sill with flat of hand, you sit and pull in your knees
imbalanced by motes and moths gyrating – smoke from a blast.
Greening light in your squint: you look beyond the roofs for the plain,
haranguing dead forest for miles to the cliff tops. Then sea,
the black hulls of ships, the bones of sailors and reedy gull-cries.

Every day in the plaza your father digs and weeds roots of trees;
now you can see the top of his head, his back still labouring
by dry brook-beds; he waves a hand in the air that makes a fist.
Enraged, you turn inward to boards, slats and beams: humble tomb in
an attic's pyramid. *The window – BEAT – bangs against the frame.*
The women of Sulaco – BEAT – suffer and are silent – BEAT –

Eyes of a god could not fathom the depths of this dark room, where
nailed to hang over one sodden beam is waxen tarpaulin.
Blighted edges are nailed into floorboards to make a lean-to
or retreat: a tent. *Copper for atrophy: silver for teeth.*
Down there, you bend to a looped wire, one end nailed down, the other
enwrapping itself in a loose knot, a fraught noose.

Down there, not your father's trap for rats and birds. Not an ornament.
When you lean forward, palms flat on splintered wood: four wire nooses
one at each corner of the tent, one for each crook of the globe.
Measure the pitch. Gauge the four wire loops for two arms and two legs
and repeat: *four coils of wire for my two arms and my two legs.*
Now you crouch inside. You crouch very still.

STEVEN HITCHINS (1983–)

From the South Wales Valleys, Steven Hitchins grew up in Abercynon, and currently lives in Rhydyfelin, Pontypridd. His poetry and critical writings have appeared in *Poetry Wales*, *Fire* and *Chimera*, with articles and films in *Junction Box*. He read at the Hay Poetry Jamboree in 2011 and 2012, and at Poets Live in Paris. His publications include *Bitch Dust* (Boiled String 2012), *The White City* (Aquifer 2015) and a recent joint production with Rhys Trimble – *Alban Arthan* – published by his own press, The Literary Pocket Book. Influenced by Allen Fisher, on whose work he conducted his Ph.D. research, his writing involves intensive research into the history and geography of the region in which he lives and is often formally structured around the journeys he makes through its urban, industrial and natural landscapes, recording the different kinds of image and language stumbled on by chance in the shape of graffiti, advertising, litter, overheard conversations, snatches of music on a car radio, and so on.

The Basin

In thatchlight. Humb. Slowly weapons. Black, lyrical hallucinations. Stang. Feltic. Deified mist. Tremble to be firm. Drink in slag growth. Perpetual weather. Sproad, blant. So snown. Perish into sky.

We enter the Basin by aqueduct and turnpike bridge. Single arch spanning a narrowing Taff a few hundred yards before it meets the Cynon. The Company's chief clerk and his assistants conduct business up at Navigation House. Offices, committee room, living accommodation for clerks and house servants, rooms for visitors on canal business, coach house, stables. Uninterrupted views of aqueduct, exchange wharves, tramroads.

Nearby, Craig Evan Leyshon Tollgate. For every horse, mare, gelding, mule or other beast, laden or unladen, drawing any wagon, any carriage with timber, any coach, every score of sheep, swine, every score of oxen or other meat cattle. In loving memory of Ann, wife of Walter Morgan, Tollgate House, Abercynon, who died 1896. Double tolls every Sunday.

Glacial tracks crawl. Abandoned tramlines stream. Twisted tributaries. Frost knife towns. Muddy amphitheatres. Iron valleys. Shapes layer darkness. Downstream gasjets. Coal waterfalls, camouflage draining. Spider head collieries. Glistening houses. Millstone peripheries.

Abercynon is situated at the mouth of the coalfield interior. As the bevelled surfaces emerge from the sea, drivers of pack-mules, laden with glacial debris, often call there for refreshment. The ancestral river pattern begins to form, with the shopping centre being Margaret Street.

Behind Fife Street, the ice carves amphitheatre-like corries. Houses are produced by subaerial stream erosion. Streets appear along the belt of disturbance. Looking away to the north-east you can see chapels spring up to cater for the different denominations.

Pool town. Caves steam. Houses chatter. Glacial voices. Carboniferous crowds. Coking species snapping. Concave cabins. Melt lamp. Snake stones form rooms. Sandstone archway. Moraine eels plopping. Sewage caves. Steam reservoirs. Bubble rooms. Geological feathers ripple.

Now business had tears. Legends indeed. Bunched chapel. A rock branches pasture. Rolled colders. Sidesprawl. We were iron; straining lyrical mane. Sudded miners. Gallowed. The future numinous and bronze.

The year began with a dead otter. 1889—the Eastern seers, months before the gleams, for a grocery shone around them. Two opposing valleys could hide this time. But pressure of opinion forced them enveloped in light to Abercynon.

Entrenched houses tunnel bare fear. Roof hisses dark fashion. Mineral birds weight voices. Magpie erosion lamps. Blackbird leaves wander fishless foliage. Threaded nettles. Glacial woodlands. Corries ghost. Abandoned distance pipe hover roads. Estate sea wires thud.

We follow the Trevithick run. Riversound and birdsong. Council depot a ski slope of salt grit. Pallet stacks. Folded tabloid in truck dashboard, Jordan and Peter headlines, ex-Page 3. Flash of underbelly as they dip into the trees and Dad salutes three for a girl. Car, I step into the stingies. Car, Dad. A burgundy Volvo. High Pressure Steam Engine, ten ton of iron, five miles an hour, Merthyr Tydfil to the Basin, 1804. Magpies the only birds that build a roof over their nests.

Feeder pipes tap streams and reservoirs to feed canal. Horses draw wagons down tramroad to barges. Pennant sandstone, sombre stone, best in the coalfield. Mallet and chisel blocks for houses, flags for pavement. River, canal, feeder, tramroads: lines converging, intersecting. In loving memory of Elizabeth, wife of Edward Bowen, Feeder House in the parish, who died 1892, aged 62 years. Blessed are they that die in the Lord. Wrens make nests of moss in rocky places.

Headwater towns. Marine captured buildings. Gasjets smoke eyes. Iron trams float subaerial air-currents. Night wires. Eel tracks. Ancestral sea beings. Disused carboniferous lives. Shrieking stone. Roof beetles, scorpion gas dark-flaming. Timber magnificent.

Continuous towns straggle in choked-like fashion down the course of the headwaters. These coalfield rivers are superimposed on a blanket of chalk, anglers sitting along the banks. With the lowering of the sea level, we proceed under the railway bridge.

Mr Shepherd constructed a large lake to the south-east of the town. A rock and moraine ridge holds back the glacial headwaters, a pool where the sheep are afterwards dipped. The bones of deceased waterfalls in the grit, underground caves and dry valleys in the limestone, built for officials of the canal Company.

Sewage lifts, flanks glistening. Shaly birds,. Water cracked feathers. Enormous naked staring beetles. Gnats laughing crumbs. Chicken figure gropes fire railway. Sycamore wet branches hang. Fish lamps, dry rays. Boatmen boys blue-green. Lonely river district. Decayed sun. Static rise.

The Volvo stops at the River Monitoring Station. Pylons toss cables from bank to bank. White-haired in sleeveless jacket, he peers across the pier at the watermark. Above, the A472 overpass bridges the roundabouts at Fiddler's Elbow. Drunk found sleeping hammocked in net between lanes. A Biffa lorry judders the join. Also of Edward Bowen, who died 1916, aged 88 yrs. Graffiti relics on cement pillars. And God shall wipe away all tears.

On the hill above Fiddler's I can see St Cynon's, the cemetery we visited yesterday. Crunching dried brambles and leaves up the hillside to uncover four-foot slabs of rusted stone. Ivy tendrils claw the headstone, pull it down into the earth. Some stones sunk into the subsidence. Some tilt out of ground. Some toppled, snapped in two. A tree bursts up behind one. When we peel the ivy away it leaves green veins across the worn engraving.

Headwater static dark. Blackbird ripple. Railway debris. Northern course carriages. Slowly grass turns eastward. Ridge land beams. Sun mines. Hills sparkle. Pond trams sun wet. Swim straggle eastward. Long railway crowds kneel. Fox heads. Early lizards laugh dry rock. Shaly ancestral winds.

The business was like fire on my own child. For I had been identified with the edge of things. The job of showing the future was closed. They were like a grey pile of ashes. They were like fairies. He returns day after day to close the snow-shocked bodies shiver and we are always curious of the buried dust. Holy goods that were old materials. He ran as clear as we are always to be hated. But pressure of feet bare in 1900. His elbow, answering,

floated on the pit and the bottom flourished with a most substantial vision! He then struggled tattered robes across the notebook. Garments of leaves. Around him long before, young miners sit in legends of Scripture sky.

Pipes jingle. Silences jump, lamp trickles. Grit fades. Lowering fern black silence. Slow nettles dark. Downstream lark echo. Blackberries hunt wren laugh. Lake nettles silently hoof. Walls move. Explorers change, chalk fingers. Guides quietly disappear. Air moves, breaks blue-green. Inhale.

Steep Goitre Coed lifts us to Top Locks. Sixteen locks in staircase pairs. Within one mile the boat drops two hundred feet. The windswept hill slope of Five Locks marked Incline Top on the map. In loving memory of John Aston, beloved husband of Annie Aston, 5 Incline Top, who died Dec 19 1903, aged 30 yrs. Puddles in a ditch all that remains of the canal. Cut through by the New Road, A4059 to Aberdare.

As the canal loops westward, the valley unfolds. The Royal Oak appears on the towpath. Under Pont Haiarn, Iron Bridge, the boat bends into the eleven lock flight. Sinks like an elevator. Twenty-six feet between dark dripping walls. A concrete ditch of Coke and Stella bottles. We work the windlass, raise the paddles, as the canal flows down through the Little Park, past the steel slide, between the tangled swings.

From a side road where a man sees the sky, I catch sights flickering out. He gazes at us, on water full of shadow. He pokes out. jumps and stands still, unthreading to show the light. Gleaming in the immense silence of rails. Fibulae song. Lignite corridors. Lampwhite, wren.

Of the Boatman there is no trace, the wide valley is dry. It has become a halfway house for bargees on their way up and down the tributary streams which hang above the valley floor.

The two headstreams climb along the A4061 over the escarpment, giving magnificent views down into the cirque. The ridge is very precipitous, and animals straying from outlying farms often fall there and break their waters rushing rapidly down the steep valley sides.

In from the perpetual scars, the mind hills. Toil of river, late in warm galleries. I fed the closure of the light. I had been under Wales time. This violence, stiff and sweated. We had cold music of business.

Bottom of hill, just before the flats, a green garden gate brushed black. That tree wasn't there when we lived here. Dad points to a thick birch trunk in the back yard. That was where I learnt my skills. Cricket and football against the wall. Scores on the window ledge. Grand-dad kept that patch and grew things. That was the outdoor toilet. And that was where I fell into the canal and cracked my head, about where you are standing now.

The canal continues into the car park behind the flats, then disappears into a culvert.

dust cult

the coin had a flame
fishing volcano pools
for a meaning of dawn
timber priests
plumbing the fireplace
into his head who first
dug the village out of song
he had to walk the earth
they closed all our mines
we had to walk the earth

later on they would install
the furnace place it
in her bosom get a rock
put it in a cage
name it or of the runes
between the telephone poles
and the standing stones
she had to walk the earth
they closed all our mines
we had to walk the earth

bitch dust

old bituminous riverroad
abercynon city
original city perpetual city
city of sandstone
great basin drain
of terrace shales
spoil water
rusty weather
sands of glacial ash
cynon fawr cynon
the headwaters cimmerian
captured drifts
confluence instead
neath taff aman mellte
pyrddin hepste cynon
rivers axe the pennant lands
where the rolling mile flowed on
coal-tips ago
glacial caucasus taff
brythonic
neolithic train
herodotus iranian side
and thracian the bronze
ukraine tube
merchants open side seams
cynon mile grey opens
the shaley street trap
fog flowed over margaret
and into bituminous herbert
martins of rag we cwmaman
another amphitheatre of mrs land
waterfall quarried
cirque hillside
houses colliery pennant
solitude fog over abercynon
deep world of toll gates
parish of sinking measures
stone junction
bone bradley's village
then darkness trail
weather hounds on the ash muds
no ancestral fireclays

Gododdin Versions

8   A go to fu
       Trits traeth   celwchannau

       Cydu,
       Dadl ders tau i eu –
       Men hund.
       A go fu.
       Though silenyd their confraeth to Cath,
       Cyd eu

       A gwent to fu
       Thred under celwch ffration
       deadl der aftedd, treatred to confron
       Glasthem
       Trichannau –
       Mented undredd

       Palebraeth
       Trivin war-bang,
       was talebratrwyn
       chund tawelwch silenydu,
       True meadl ders

13   A gwent to fu, fatrachwyr aethydd
       Neu lewenght. Neu daybres.
       Neu drachwread-supper.
       Ei neges daybren. Ei neges ef fedd.
       Ei neges eful, hot bloodedd.
              Eidd.
               No eheress
               No chrysgor ehely
              O Eidd;
               Bread.
              Bress
               No gre for mor.
              Mawr gress
              Mawr mansive
               Eidd.
       Stay homesong gwas sustay, Saxonce at lound
       When Tudfwlch His a Kilydd
       Wheyd yn mind his a killandir
       Wheyd grom his staind hom his post lould steads
              ei Saest   fround,
       A'i
       Hi
                              fromrads,
             gwaesons

tremble locales

dope lamp
brakes between spilt gaslight
hymnal corrugate
spacey lurches
sound plops below hoof-beats
steam footsteps balloon melodic
nose head shivering
pretty rust punch melt

trains happen nowhere
windows remix the past
face mixes float
version walks
pigeon highlights
floodlight grows
slowly sheen
all all for i could
the breathlessly
the skin of it
pinch out with the steel serene
and altogether the news is vibe clouds
hands choose nightmare streaks to dust
fringed binbag classics
skin hydraulics
ruff the streams
phone the bends
crack-light fingers
ecstatic evil-late
under bass-spell
looking along the pages, says
i'm full of them, plastercasts
people will go about, speaking
on the glow to mixture ceiling:
'midnight is on the pipes
stars weight
waters sound the rise rock
already animal
pillowy with visions
it's almost me i forget

NIA DAVIES (1984–)

From a family of Welsh origin, Nia Davies was born and brought up in Sheffield, and studied English at Sussex University, moving to London, where she worked for Literature Across Frontiers before settling in Swansea. She has been involved in several other international collaborative literary and translation projects, including Wales Literary Exchange and the Wales International Poetry Festival. As this suggests, her own work reflects a strong interest in non-anglophone, transcultural poetry. She was included in *The Salt Book of Younger Poets*; her chapbook *Then Spree* (2012) appeared in Salt's Modern Voices series. *Çekoslovakyalılaştıramadıklarımızdanmısınız or LONG WORDS* appeared from Boiled String (2015), and *All fours* (Bloodaxe 2017), confirmed her as an exuberant and playfully inventive new voice, attentive to gender and female sexual identity. Since 2014 she has been the editor of *Poetry Wales*.

I Want To Do Everything

Bibulous, happy, exploded in the litter
of pomegranate, I want to live long.

And face the glaciers' flume. It's spring,
it's spring in that toothpaste. The winter is game,

asks me to press forward: evenly. Then spree.
The rubble of my room, the follicles pushed up,

Flowering envelopes, springs of seed packeted.
What can be chosen amid this?

In the bed we'll live long to bear orang-utans.
And in clusters of eight we'll count them.

Nine might be holy. And it's better
when it's a charmed story.

Peeled wheat at breakfast, blood oranges and March.
Let it be March soon.

Poem with sex
'sex is not a project'
– Susan Sontag

sex as a universal human baseline
sex as solid, rockable
sex as the species' practical joke
a joke that was tame on the surface only
sex as the one becalmer, the mashing thing
the underside of sex topples and I share a space with this thought

sex as the great destroyer and creator
as the opposite of death drive
the ex libris of sex is a palm with a word or a letter on it
i search 'piano' and 'open' on Pinterest
sex is happening even when you think it isn't

i like Tamara's piano and that's not a metaphor
desire as inextinguishable smoulder and chief cliché
the notion of so much sex as taunting
vs not living because of sex
the door opens automatically
the word 'romantic' has returned

what does love without sex
have in common with sex without love?
for the past ten minutes I have not been thinking
about sex except to write this
the weather of sex is not only notional
the humidity & restraint
the flicker & boom
the rules of its own time & knife-edge
it's for you to enjoy but it's not
like butter biscuits or stacked books,
a closet full of good quality garments

sex as the open sesame
sexual fantasy as trolling of the self and auto-relief
eros-plasticity of the self and card games
on trains with vodka and sweat
this was not a planned sex this was cod-love
dunno it's like stick-o-rock on the beach and up a donkey

and that has nothing to do with our sex life
sex is rocking the ocean liner and leaving
itself at high tide everywhere,
the shamey side of things,
we don't know how to feel
about your arousal at embarrassment

it's not common to give one's parents
a commentary of one's sex life.
in the pan-echoic-chamber of the word 'perfect
love' – sandwiches and crisps
love is not really a button-hole or a mouse
but I'm sure comparisons have been made

we've come to define ourselves
against others and a mint cocktail
and contrary to what is assumed
woman is not in charge of all breeding
the cheek offered is separate and fulsome
shiny still from crying

I should've cried more in the attic room
it was so bright with moths and rugs
but this was not a good place to lie
down in and I could've chosen better linen
but we don't have a retrospect maid
and what is source anyhow the source is
dying

Pantheon

Pan

follows you to a wet wall
to pebble dash your hopes,

that you'd at least seen some
green in the fair silos. Shivered

when you felt intentions
were not good, arched

to let him pass by quietly.
By the sand heap, bloodshot.

And you, going lightly into night,
unbold, near-visible in the concrete

cupula. He harps his rural
dis-idyll, the id's own claw-hand.

Pan

This one was spotted in the black plots,
a living thing on goose down,

fingers in beard. This one was
surely what crinkles in the fist,

was surely the finer thing on from pastoral,
was pictured with a royal

on a ferry for the hook of Holland.

Pan

Sleet, you gospel of a witch,
by the elm, the arch, the us.

His bread became the sea.
The sea was a lake we stored fish in.

Under the sun, we undered the sun,
we shouldered the sun and became un,
the us in football chants,

the us in all muscular forays,
the rock bottom. Still chiming,

still the chiming.

the mediums of viktor ullmann

all the panna cotta and   ribbons

so why be so ang
gry?   he says our hands are busted
ferris wheel and i am
ventriloquizing him.   that's an accusation.
I do telly-side professional   bitching.
but you can pet me   while my pelt is warm.
got myself a grilling   on the internet.
while Nathalia Romanenko did his   no.25,
keep going   keep go   ing

my morris minor ankles do   nothing
for me   in desert boots   too chill
and I feel pretty futile   he even made
posthumous tweaks   it's 1975
and he's invited   back,
makes harp harpsi   chord.

it's as if he was alive   all along!
was only hiding in the   furthest chamber.
blancmange   was on my mind
to buffer and stuff   me from any painful thought

or stench   - deathcamp -
mediate all day   and nobody thanks me for it
he made love all of the day & no one thanked him for it.

knew the chats with Chopin   were for nothing
he made swallowed sleigh bell   warm.
Nathalia gazing,   curtseying: we are too broken
            bro   ken

to make this work, I
should shout: don't be pessimistic!
don't indulge in the   present.

I keep ice cream for   miracle usage.
I internalise: oh, just be ha   ha
ppy   and move on

From
Çekoslovakyalılaştıramadıklarımızdanmısınız or LONG WORDS

for your [plural] continued behaviour as if you could not be desecrated[1]

the never-tired
the awl and the auger,
leather pressed through until the light showed
and continued behaviour that
tastes like lighter fluid,
as if not you were not overly sleepless
as if not fortunate and symbolic
as if you could not be desecrated
like all of us other
sacreds, jumping for proper money,
able to read signs that tell what us what indeed
the penury should be like,
we don't have a lens through which to view our behaviour as others see it
we just have to IMAGINE
and then the good king wenceslas
looked out and i dreamt that man flirted with me till he fell over drunk
and i slunk away, skittered in the pool of surplus shiraz,
burnt in the wicker basket set up for such things,
i had another hand to hand just waiting in my pocket
now i have frequent ball aches without the balls to speak of
and such a lot of dripping drool over tooth and gum,
gutted i can't be with you tonight darling
for your awl and augur and your continued behaviours.
dear god look upon me kindly with your unknowable unsubstantial unverifiable looks
and your hot sauce,
bring this desecration back to life.

---

[1] *Megszentségteleníthetetlenségeskedéseitekért (Hungarian)*

[two] people trying to scatter pretended lies with each other[2]

a couple living vicariously
beat each other at a tabletop dancing competition
and one more thing
is the competitive movement of twigs in wind
and how later the couple cast across the field to sow
time and time again little pieces of grave
that trip us all up,
if you believe a lie is akin to death,
if you believe death is a lie in the first place
come scatter here and here
lies we tell ourselves daily,
he screams through the keyhole:
i thought you were dead,
and of course she is
she's just moving around his spaces
so he can go on living a lie
living a lie
he once held a conference with her right hand
there was a time he gained happiness via trellis and derby,
he had no badges to speak of
and he drove his sprinter into hell
most days,
on other days he woke from his nightmare in a carpaccio
of unfulfilled wishes, spread gossip amongst himself,
the wind turned over in rumination
or was it ruination?
they passed the part of the hill where potatoes were grown,
there were ridges and in those ridges they decided
it was better to die here scattering,
it is better to lie down now instead of protesting, he said,
you were always a liar.

---

[2] *Nakikipagsisinunga-sinungalingan (Tagalog)*

RHEA SEREN PHILLIPS (1989–)

Rhea Phillips was born in Swansea. She completed her BA at Bath Spa University in 2010 where she studied Creative Writing. She completed her MA in Swansea University in 2014 and is currently studying for her Ph.D there. A bridge-builder, Rhea Phillips writes in anglicised versions of classical Welsh poetic forms and metre; the poems here 'translate' them in ways intended intended to engage with an English speaking readership but which resist superficial cultural transference, emphasising as they do the materiality of all language. Her work is influenced by mythology, cultural identity and magic realism, as well as real world events.

Nettled[1]

Nettle-pricked | rind is ensnared-

collar the hare| that condoned it.

Leaven and | dewy and dense

it languishes | on the tongue.

Hold the gums | down as smiles turn[2]

to the wraiths | on the wayside;

error mimics| the mirror,

rounded ladies | in sun hats

sneer at the eyes | that fleer[3] them.

Claim the hor|izon with sighs.[4]

Shadows peer out | from steel eyes;[5]

gain the sky | but the soil's mine.[6]

---

[1] The entry of the poison into the Entity. The poem is made up of seven syllables per line - the preferred syllable count in Welsh poetic forms and metre.

[2] The turning of the poem. Little repetition of letters.

[3] "Fleer" means to smirk or laugh in derision.

[4] Sentence is a reflection, similar to that of the horizon on the water which strengths the repetition of the "S" sound used throughout the poem.

[5] The sound rhyme between "sighs" and "eyes" represents the distant noise of the ocean.

[6] Reflection in the water. This is the Entity's memories of the ocean being rekindled. The title places it in the countryside while the repetition of the "S" sound gives it a sleepy lilt that is influenced by the sea. The repetition is constantly changing to represent this fluctuation with "S" being the consistent factor.

Crush the Pancreas in your Hand[7]

Flax avian bone birches through downy plumage
of catkins, entangled in cistern bones of men.

      Islets angle dense networks of capillaries.

      Rubber doddering and scrapped boots crunch the last straw-
           punctures lipids and embeds cetaceans' with sparklers[8].

      The aphidian passes through in green tweed threats.

Crushed cacao nostalgia with a candid refresh;
respire the breath of the fruit, rimed with cyan moss.

---

[7] The poetic form is made up of twelve syllables. Repetition of "an" throughout the poem has been influenced by Welsh metre (cynghanedd). The poem is shaped to represent the criss-crossing of capillaries and the cupping of a hand holding a pancreas (a rough 'V' shape).

[8] "Sparklers" refers to the amount of plastic in the ocean. Plastic ingestion by sea animals and ocean acidification (rise in Carbon Dioxide) is increasingly, negatively affecting sea life.

A *Heart* Dances around the *Heel*[9]

Confetti grounds besotted bag beauty,
the pick's aria weathers thorianite[10];
waxed lavender and stippled[11] raven[12] razed
squeals to the expectations of the dead.
Throb vivaciously in this mouth that spits
English as if a lank hybrid language.
This staunch madness is an Achilles' heel.
Edge the estuary, nudge inferred culture,
coerced under heavy-soled, steel-toed boots.
A cross-criss of nautical stars engrosses
the caterwauling hostage. It beguiles
us here to the sand like limpets on as[13]h.
Hearts snag, encapsulated by ague pools.

---

[9] The poetic form is made up of ten syllables per line.

[10] "Thorianite" is a radioactive mineral and contains rare earth elements. It looks similar to coal and can be found in rough small black cubes.

[11] "Stippled" refers to an artist's technique that involves roughening the surface when wet or dotting or speckling the paper with ink.

[12] The interbreeding of wild birds (for example a magpie with a crow).

[13] The reversal of the repetition of "as" to "sa" emphasises the beguiled Entity in the previous line.

Peeling the Eyeball as if a Pear of Vexation[14]

The grains of knowledge are trembling

                    through fingertips. Peel the cornea

in true governmental concision;

                    spite the jelly as the bridge transcends

into an esoteric morass.

                    The local wildlife are steeled figures

on burnished iron stands, staring out

                    at the frayed future of the knotted

tourist designations and cut out

                    paradises of affordable

plots of canter paths. Tidal *wyvern*[15]

                    is pushing and pulling violently;

muttering the language in shadows,

                    psyche swept in its vitriolic storm

of British patriotism-bird

                    cage of the clover, the daffodil

and the tempestuous plum thistle.

---

[14] The poetic form is made up of nine syllables per line which is loosely based on a Cyhydedd Naw Ban. This poem has deviated by leaving the poem unrhymed. The form represents a peeling motion. It is a representation of the sea which is just within sight of the countryside.

[15] "Wyvern" is a dragon with a barbed tail. It is a creature of horror as it is said that it pollutes any area it flies over with nightmares such as fairy rings which grow out of fungus. The creature has strong links with the sea.

Thicket and Thorns[16]

Encompassed by thicket, thorns ambuscade

as spiders cascade, spry

with motivation to ossify

this wretch; vivify dry oils that pervade

throughout *the blade*, imply

fish drift like leaf litter, wade

ankle deep, watch, they'll fold like gelatine,

dissolve to benzene, notch

keen cockled toes of woodbine.

The truth will come in violent bursts of two,

sea echoes through uncouth

sticks, thickets give way to rue.

---

[16] Poetic Form: Englyn Penfyr (two opening stanzas of Englyn Penfyr follow the same rhyme and the final two change rhyme schemes. This is to prevent the poem becoming too rhyme-led). The rhyme scheme uses 'by' as a rhyme and uses a Welsh principle of rhyming one letter. This form uses enjambment for the first and second line. *"Blade"* refers to Dylan Thomas's use of the word *sticks* to refer to a wooded area.

Neptune's Horse[17]

Skin blusters and cockles as wet **sand**

is trenched by slivered, bird fragile **hands**.

The *Nuckelavee* **reprimands**

the cruel segregation of **land**.

It's all water in the gland that will spit

salted grit with a dead **command**.

---

[17] Poetic form: Gwawdodyn Hir.

NOTES

(Notes by poets, except for Heather Dohollau section).

GERARD CASEY

Voices in the Wind Singing: Compare *Isaiah* 6:3. One thinks too of the music heard by Boehme 'shortly after midnight' on November 21st, 1624.

Mae bys Mari Ann wedi brifo—
>   Mary Anne's finger is cut
>   David is not well
>   the baby is crying in his cradle
>   and puss has scratched little Johnny

sospan fach yn yn berwi ar y tan—
>   the small saucepan is on the fire
>   the big one on the hob
>   and puss has scratched little Johnny

Jack Johnson: During this period Jack Johnson, the great American Negro boxer, (at one time heavyweight champion of the world) was held in high honour in South Wales.

Suhir … Shiddeh … bahilowi: the Somali name Shiddeh means 'born in pain'. Shiddeh sings under Suhir – the star Sirius – believed to exert a baneful influence. See Jacob Boehme *Signatura Rerum* chapter xvi 'on the weeping of Adam in Esau'. In his prefatory Notes to the poem, Casey tells us: Among the Somali a man under extreme nervous mental or spiritual stress may seek help by calling his friends and womenfolk to a 'bahilowi'. They all meet at night in the open away from dwelling places and stand round him in a circle. He gives utterance to his suffering perplexity in a questioning chant. The others give reply … A Somali – an old seaman who, when I knew him, had long been back in his own country – once told me how years before he had found himself stranded for a time in Tiger Bay. Friendless and in distress he had solaced himself one night by walking out onto piece of waste land and holding a 'bahilowi' – pretending some of his people were present. … This lonely 'bahilowi' seems to have been held somewhere in the desolate area I often played in as a child – and knew as 'the tidefields'.

Rudolf Steiner: Steiner spoke at Pen-maen-mawr of gigantic elemental presences locked up in the planetary structures under his feet.

Basho's pool: Suzuki, in his commentary on the Lankavatra Sutra, speaks of the shadow dance as 'reflected on a screen of eternal solitude and tranquillity ...' The whole passage from which these words are taken will be found one of intense relevance for our thesme ... but, for Tom, a sudden flaming word has, more decisively than Yeats at the crossways, broken into the ancient reverie.

rising in the east: Compare *Revelation* 7:2. The Catholic Requiem Mass for the Dead.

HEATHER DOHOLLAU

'Un rêve heureux', 'Penarth Beach', Holderlin a la tour', 'Retour', 'Manawydan's Glass Door' and 'Thomas Jones' all translated by Lyndon Davies.

JEFF NUTTALL

'The Whore of Kilpeck': On [the wall of] the Parish Church of St Mary and St David, Kilpeck, Herefordshire, is a small Celtic fertility figure made up of head and hands which are holding open a huge vagina. It is called by the local people the Whore of Kilpeck.

PHILIP JENKINS

estonian border post: Estonia is a European country bordered by Lithuania, Belarus and Russia. In this case, the reference is to the Lithuanian border.
time piece: The watch, interestingly, and contrary to the poem's optimism, was never found.

HARRY GILONIS

The *Canu Heledd* (*Song of Heledd*) is a Welsh collection of some 115 *englynion*, all dealing with the aftermath of a much earlier Anglo-Saxon incursion of ca. 650 into the Welsh kingdom of Powys in an area which is part of present-day Shropshire. The text famously contains the lament of Heledd, sister of Cynddylan, the Welsh chieftain slain in the raid. As Gilonis explains in his introductory essay to the publication of these sections of his rendering, *unHealed* derives from an inversion of the 'nu' of 'canu' (song) and a transliteration of 'Heledd', and he took his cue for the treatment of the original in part from from predecessors who had applied similar techniques to Welsh language material – Louis Zukofsky, Richard Caddel and Bill Griffiths. The following notes by Gilonis appeared with his essay and the poems as 'Some sections from *unHealed*', in *Poetry Wales*, 44:1 (Summer 2008), pp. 35-7.

Stanzas 67-8 substitute, on very rough phonetic lines, Iraqi for the original Welsh rivers.

Stanza 76 replaces (metaphrastically, but not *literally*, word by word) by alliterative selection vocabulary from an official British Government policy paper, found on the Foreign Office website; the senses are just as dulled by repetitive blandness in this homeopathic sample. *Hediw* is translated literally.

Stanzas 78-79 use vocabulary from *The Sun* circa April 2003. Any truth-claims therein are as fractured as the language.

Stanza 82, a 'fragment', as Rowland entitles it, is textually corrupt; I take only the word *Caer* and make my own substitution. The cited military intelligence expert was speaking of the public exposure of Saddam Hussein's dead sons rather than that of Cynddylan outside Pengwern.

Stanza 87 was called an 'epigram' by Rowland. Drawing on Tony Conran's comparison of the *englyn* to *haiku* (*Welsh Verse*, p.302) I've translated (paraphrased?) this as one, adding 'spring' as the *kigo* or 'season-word'.

Stanzas 88-89 – I derived core vocabulary by putting the Welsh through assorted online translation engines and keeping a list of what 'worked'. This is doubtless morally and logically indefensible. I also used *Y Geriadur Mawr*, allowing *glas* to suggest 'glass' as well. Note the formal preservation of *cymheriad geiriol*.

Stanza 90 is corrupt – and looks like an interpolation. I've simply supplied the names of some of those who have ruled between the Two Rivers.

Stanzas 102-103 As in stanza 67, *diua* suggested Dyala, an Iraqi river. Again I used an indefensible wordbook, *Mathews Chinese-English Dictionary*, and again it was helpful; *tom* led me to *tun* ('heap, mound'), *maes* to *mai* ('bury'), both apposite to early Celtic inhumation practices.

ELISABETH BLETSOE

'The 'Oary Man': The words of the title and the first line occur in an ancient children's game and are a possible corruption of 'follow my

Gabriel, Holy man', which may refer to a shamanic ritual where a congregation imitated the actions of a dancing priest (Whitlock, *In Search of Lost Gods*, 1979). The circular motion thus evoked seemed appropriate to the minor tradition that links Gabriel to the moon, and all its associations.

CHRIS PAUL

'**Severn**': i) 'Hafren', pronounced 'hav ren', is the Welsh word for Severn.
ii) Using the reading eye as the moon, words from other languages, not just English, will appear on the tidal surface of the poem. Some of these inclusions and readings are intentional, but all are valid.

STEVEN HITCHINS

List of resources given for '**The Basin**'.
George Ewart Evans, *The Strength of the Hills: An Autobiography*.
Thomas Evans, *The Story of Abercynon*.
Thomas Evans (trans.), *Glanffrwd's History of Llanwonno*.
W. Hazell, *The Gleaming Vision, being the history of the Ynysybwl Co-operative Society Ltd. 1889-1954*.
Joseph Keating, *My Struggle for Life*.
Robert Morgan, *My Lap Still Burns*.
T. R. Owen, *Geology Explained in South Wales*.
Stephen Rowson & Ian L. Wright, *The Glamorganshire & Aberdare Canals*.

NIA DAVIES

Pantheon: In 1974 Victor Ullman's *Der Kaiser von Atlantis oder Die Tod-Verweigerung* was prepared for its first performance by Kerry Woodward. Woodward made a number of changes to the score based on a consultation with the spiritualist Rosemary Brown who was well-known for her conversations with dead composers.

Acknowledgements

Many people have contributed to the making of this volume and we thank everyone who offered encouragement and advice. Special thanks go to Alice Entwistle, the originator, with John Goodby, of an earlier version of this anthology, and to Rhian Bubear who typed out many of the poems in that earlier version.

We are very grateful to Rhiannon Munro, the daughter of John James and Wendy Mulford, for allowing us to dedicate this book to John James. John knew about this project before it was even begun, was supportive of it, and made suggestions of poets to include. We wish that he had lived to see it, but can at least now offer it as a tribute to his memory.

All efforts have been made to seek permission from copyright holders of poems, and the editors welcome information which would help them to trace those it has not proved possible to contact. For permission to reprint copyright material, the editors gratefully acknowledge the people and the publishers listed below:

Enitharmon Press for the extract from *South Wales Echo* by Gerard Casey.

Tanguy and Rozen, the son and daughter of Heather Dohollau, and Yves Prié of Éditions Folle Avoine (and with special thanks to Clémence O'Connor) for 'Un rêve heureux', 'Thomas Jones' from *Le dit des couleurs* (2003) and 'Penarth Beach' from *Une suite des matins* (2005), 'Hölderlin à la tour' from *La venelle des portes* (1979), 'Retour' from *Le Point de rosée* (1999), and 'Manawydan's Glass Door (d'après David Jones, 1931)' from *Pages aquarelles* (1989).

David Barnett for 'Temple', 'Hare', 'Cayley Primary School', 'Swift', 'Earthworm', 'West Kennet - Long Barrow', 'Your Move', 'Snow Maiden', and 'A Word in Your Ear', from *All the Year Round* (Envoy Poets, 1995).

Jill Richards for Jeff Nuttall's 'The Whore of Kilpeck', '"I stalk with the razorblade cranes"', 'Bed Crash', 'Sleep', and 'Lower Usk', all from *Selected Poems* (Salt, 2003).

Malcolm Parr for 'coming of christianity' and '*from* Deaf Man's House', from *found poems* (Second Aeon, 1971).

John Powell Ward for the three scans from *from alphabet to logos* (Second Aeon, 1971); 'All Objects of All Thought' *Selected and New Poems* (Seren 2004); the extracts from *Variations on Four Places* (Rack Press, 2009).

Rhiannon Munro, for poems by John James: 'Exultation' from *The*

Welsh Poems (Grosseteste Press, 1967), 'Craven Images' and 'Bye Bye Blackbird' from *Berlin Return* (Grosseteste Press, 1983), 'The Conversation' from *Dreaming Flesh* (Street Editions, 1991), 'Sleep', 'Eugène Boudin' and 'From the Welsh' from *Kinderlieder* (Avocado, 1992), and 'Poem beginning with a line by Andrew Crozier' from *Cloud Breaking Sun* (Oystercatcher, 2012).

Wendy Mulford for 'from *The ABC of Writing*' (Torque Press, 1995), 'Talking about art', 'Interior with figures', 'Clean sheets', 'After Corot', and 'Day dreams' from *The Bay of Naples* (Reality Studios, 1992), and *from* 'Alltud', *Scintilla* 11 (2007).

Chris Torrance for 'Autumn Drunkenness', '"The Theatre of its Protagonist's Desires"', 'Love is But a Horse of Pernicious Humour', 'Poem to the Three Laughing Sages', '"Day-by-day Poem"', 'Straight from Sleep', from *Acrospirical Meanderings in a Tongue of the Time* (Albion Village Press, 1973); 'Chopping Water' and 'Coda' from*The Magic Door II: Citrinas*', reprinted in *The Magic Door* (Test Centre, 2018). Also for the extract from 'RORI: A Book of the Boundaries'.

Peter Meilleur for *'from six of clubs'* (Boiled String, 2011), *'from DEE AND DEEPER'*, 'JONES, THE POEM', and extract from *Ham & Jam* (Boiled String, 2010).

Iain Sinclair for 'The Falls (Talgarth)', 'Kiting the Flies', 'Obscenery of the East', 'Crossing the Morning (*Vale Crucis*)', 'Recovery & Death', 'Ocean Estate', and 'A Series of Photographs', from *The Firewall* (Etruscan Books, 2006); 'SAGESONG: A Text for performance', 'Flirty Turtles' and '2/11/15' *from Seeschlange* (Equipage, forthcoming).

Philip Jenkins for 'A Sailor's Suit and Cap' and 'On the beach with Eugène Boudin' from *On the beach with Eugène Boudin* (Transgravity Press, 1978); 'my address is given below', and 'baritone compass' from *Baritone Compass* (Baked Alaska, 2008); 'nature notes', 'estonian border post' and 'time piece' from *The Annotated Edition* (Baked Alaska, 2009), 'from the front line', 'foreign holidays' and 'choking on an old park drive' from *eskimos at two o'clock* (Fell Swoop, 2009).

Nathalie Blondel, for poems by Paul Evans: 'Taldir Poems', '1st Imaginary Love Poem' and 'Snow' from *February* (Fulcrum, 1971), and 'Dark &' from *The Door of Taldir: Selected Poems*, ed. Robert Sheppard (Shearsman, 2009).

Peter Finch for 'Sunpoem', 'A Welsh Wordscape', 'Blodeuwedd Translated' from *Selected Poems* (Poetry Wales Press, 1987), 'Five Hundred Cobbings (extracts)', 'Antibodies', 'RNLD TOMOS' and 'Heart' from *Selected Later Poems* (Seren 2007); 'Walking (for Eric Mottram)' *Useful* (Seren, 1997) and 'Hawksmoor' (www.peterfinch.co.uk).

Ralph Hawkins for 'The Hudson River School Motif', 'Tempted', 'The Next Poem', 'A History of Hydraulics', 'Wolves' and 'Heidegger', from *Gone to Marzipan* (Shearsman, 2009).

Paul Griffiths for *'let me tell you* (part 14)' (Reality Street Editions, 2009).

Phil Maillard, 'Autumn Song: Darkness and Light' and 'Leap Year's Day 1992', from *Sweet Dust and Growling Lambs* (Shearsman, 2008).

The estate of Chris Bendon for 'In My Cloud Glass', 'The Heat is Off, the Spell Ending', 'Prestige 7188', 'That Sun-Flower' and 'Contextual Errors'.

David Greenslade for 'Railway', 'Watering Can', 'Her Things', 'Objects Return In Triumph From Their Exile', 'Petrol Nozzle', 'Kerb' from *Each Broken Object* (Two Rivers Press, 1998); 'Rarebit' from *Cambrian Country – Welsh Emblems* (Gwasg Carreg Gwalch, 2000); 'Née Shell', 'River Ock' and 'Severn Fantasy' from *Homuncular Misfit* (PS Avalon, 2011).

Graham Hartill for '(Tu Fu) in The Cities', 'The Geomancer', 'At Kilpeck Church' and extract from 'The Lives of the Saints' from *Cennau's Bell: Poems 1980-2000* (The Collective Press, 2005*)*, and 'Bronze Fennel' from *A Winged Head* (Parthian, 2007).

David Annwn for 'A Short Etymological Study of the Early History of Ossett, West Yorkshire', from *the spirit / that kiss: New and Selected Poems* (North and South, 1993); 'Opening–L.Z.' and *'Bela Fawr's Cabaret* (December 1890)', sections 'I', 'VII', 'X' and 'XVIII', from *Bela Fawr's Cabaret* (Westhouse\Ahadada, 2008).

Lyndon Davies for 'Promissory', 'Lawn', 'Sea Level' from *A Colomber in the House of Poesy* (Aquifer Books, 2014); 'Limb', 'A Return', 'The Rising of the Usk (1)' from *Bridge 116* (Aquifer Books, 2017); 'The Materials' and 'The Lying Down Tower'.

Harry Gilonis for *UnHealed*, sections 67-8, 76, 78-9, 82, 87, 88-9, 90, 102-3 from *Rough Breathing – Selected Poems* (Carcanet, 2018).

Angela Gardner for sections 14, 15, 44, 60 of *Views of the Hudson* (Shearsman 2009), 'Standstill', 'Three positions acting on space' from *Parts of Speech* (University of Queensland Press, 2007); 'Another Fall from Grace', 'In Double Mirrors' and 'The Mathematics of Drift' from *The Told World* (Shearsman, 2010).

Ian Davidson for 'Controlling the Page', 'assumed position', 'Dream Boat', *from* 'The Body Con', and 'Making Up', from *As if only*

(Shearsman, 2007), 'Skulte and Saulkrasti', 'Count to Ten', and 'Blackwater' from *Partly in Riga and Other Poems* (Shearsman, 2010).

Rhian Saadat for 'Larger Than Life', 'Bondage',' L'Oeuf Sauvage', and 'Camel Deal', from *Window Dressing for Hermès* (Parthian, 2004).

Christopher Twigg for 'The Taps', 'I Have Lived in Many Lonely Outposts', 'Bananas Make a Good Breakfast' and 'Gorillas' from *In the Choir* (Alces Press, 1997).

Chris Ozzard (né Broadribb) for extracts from 'Gun Canticle Sun', 'Split Seconds' and 'Trigain O Flodau'.

John Goodby for extracts from *uncaged sea* (Waterloo Press, 2008) and *Illennium* (Shearsman, 2010); 'March to the Escafeld', and '10', 'Rive', 'Small' and 'Compulsive' from *The No Breath* (Red Ceilings Press, 2017).

Elisabeth Bletsoe for 'Archangelis', 'Azrael' and 'The 'Oary Man', from *Pharmacopoeia and Early Selected Works* (Shearsman, 2010).

Helen Lopez for 'Dead Dogs', '9.11.07', 'Shift Perception', 'Lyrical Scrap', 'hel*love*nice', 'winwithvisa', 'Storm' and 'A Time to Shine' from *Shift Perception* (Shearsman, 2009).

Niall Quinn for '(By) Atoning Slight of the Town', 'One/Dt to' and '15 x 5', from *However Introduced to the Soles* (UNKN, 1995)

Nick Macias for 'Palinode', from *However Introduced to the Soles* (UNKN, 1995).

Samantha Wynne-Rhydderch for 'The Lighthouse Keeper's Daughter', 'Self Portrait in Ice', '*from* Deacon Brodie's Predecessors' and 'Labyrinthitis – Ariadne's 115th Dream Revisited' from *Rockclimbing in Silk* (Seren, 2001).

Nic Laight for 'Sundown Questions', 'Urdu Concubine Meant Somnambular Eventime After Ganges Aftersoon', 'Tertiary Ambient Detectives', 'Grid' and 'Leg Bed'.

Zoë Skoulding for 'The Square of the Appalling Mobile' and 'The Old Walls' from *Remains of a Future City* (Seren, 2008); 'Room 321', 'Room 207' and 'In Search of Lost Time' from *The Museum of Disappearing Sounds* (Seren, 2013); extract from *Teint: for the Bièvre / Pour la Bièvre* (Boiled String, 2016); and poems from *Heft* (2018).

Nerys Williams for 'An Anatomy of Arguments' from *Sound Archive* (Seren, 2011); 'Clearing House', 'Houdini Speaks', 'Forgetting is the Vigilance of Memory', 'Capel Celyn Telyneg', 'Merzbau' and 'After this Famous Feeling', from *Cabaret* (New Dublin Press, 2017).

Suze de Lee for extract from *Soemps* (Aquifer Books, 2016).

Lee Duggan, for extract from 'spring', 'buses', extract from 'stand in the recollection', 'dislocation', 'city of castles' and 'empty parentheses' from *Reference Points* (Aquifer Books, 2018).

Rhys Trimble for 'blodeuwedd', 'the landwhales' and 'for o'hara', from *Keinc* (Cinnamon Press, 2010); extract from *Kapita* (Knives Forks and Spoons, 2010), 'Tesco Ovipositor', from *Hexerisk* (Knives Forks and Spoons, 2014), extract from *Swansea Automatic* (Aquifer Books, 2015).

Chris Paul for excerpt from 'Truth Serum vs Erroneous Shit, Part 5: Commodity', 'Severn', and 'Last Mantra', from *stenia cultus handbook* (Veer, 2010), 'Basra Shape Poem', and extract from 'Errorodes'.

Zoe Brigley Thompson for 'Ten Fingers, Ten Thumbs' and 'Quarry' from *The Secret* (Bloodaxe, 2007), 'The Dark' and 'The Wives'.

Steven Hitchins for 'The Basin', 'dust cult', 'bitch dust', 'Gododdin Versions', 'tremble locales' from *Bitch Dust* (Boiled String, 2012).

Nia Davies for 'I want to do everything' from *Then Spree* (Salt, 2012), 'for your [plural] continued behaviour as if you could not be desecrated' and '[two] people trying to scatter pretended lies with each other' from *Çekoslovakyalılaştıramadıklarımızdanmısınız, or Long Words* (Boiled String, 2016) ,'Poem with sex' and 'Pantheon' from *All fours* (Bloodaxe, 2017).

Rhea Seren Phillips for 'Nettled', 'Crush the Pancreas in Your Hand', 'A Heart Dances Around the Heel', 'Peeling the Eyeball as if a Pear of Vexation', 'Thickets and Thorns', 'Neptune's Horse'.

Viking-Age Trade

That there was an influx of silver dirhams from the Muslim world into eastern and northern Europe in the ninth and tenth centuries is well known, as is the fact that the largest concentration of hoards is on the Baltic island of Gotland. Recent discoveries have shown that dirhams were reaching the British Isles, too. What brought the dirhams to northern Europe in such large numbers? The fur trade has been proposed as one driver for transactions, but the slave trade offers another – complementary – explanation.

This volume does not offer a comprehensive delineation of the hoard finds, or a full answer to the question of what brought the silver north. But it highlights the trade in slaves as driving exchanges on a trans-continental scale. By their very nature, the nexuses were complex, mutable and unclear even to contemporaries, and they have eluded modern scholarship. Contributions to this volume shed light on processes and key places: the mints of Central Asia; the chronology of the inflows of dirhams to Rus and northern Europe; the reasons why silver was deposited in the ground and why so much ended up on Gotland; the functioning of networks – perhaps comparable to the twenty-first-century drug trade; slave-trading in the British Isles; and the stimulus and additional networks that the Vikings brought into play.

This combination of general surveys, presentations of fresh evidence and regional case studies sets Gotland and the early medieval slave trade in a firmer framework than has been available before.

Jacek Gruszczyński was a Research Associate at the Khalili Research Centre, University of Oxford and now works as an archaeology and heritage consultant.

Marek Jankowiak is Associate Professor of Byzantine History at the University of Oxford.

Jonathan Shepard was University Lecturer in Russian History at the University of Cambridge.

Routledge Archaeologies of the Viking World

Series Editors: Neil Price, Charlotte Hedenstierna-Jonson and Ben Raffield

Viking Silver, Hoards and Containers
The Archaeological and Historical Context of Viking-Age Silver Coin Deposits in the Baltic c. 800–1050
Jacek Gruszczyński

Monarchs and Hydrarchs
The Conceptual Development of Viking Activity across the Frankish Realm (c. 750–940)
Christian Cooijmans

For more information about this series, please visit: www.routledge.com/ Routledge-Archaeologies-of-the-Viking-World/book-series/RAVW

Viking-Age Trade

Silver, Slaves and Gotland

**Edited by Jacek Gruszczyński,
Marek Jankowiak and Jonathan
Shepard**

LONDON AND NEW YORK

First published 2021
by Routledge
2 Park Square, Milton Park, Abingdon, Oxon OX14 4RN

and by Routledge
605 Third Avenue, New York, NY 10017

First issued in paperback 2022

Routledge is an imprint of the Taylor & Francis Group, an informa business

British Library Cataloguing-in-Publication Data
A catalogue record for this book is available from the British Library

Library of Congress Cataloging-in-Publication Data
Names: Gruszczynski, Jacek, 1980- editor. | Jankowiak, Marek, editor. | Shepard, Jonathan, editor.
Title: Viking-age trade : silver, slaves and Gotland / edited by Jacek Gruszczynski, Marek Jankowiak and Jonathan Shepard.
Description: Abingdon, Oxon ; New York, NY : Routledge, 2021. |
Series: Routledge archaeologies of the Viking world | Includes bibliographical references and index.
Identifiers: LCCN 2020017582 (print) | LCCN 2020017583 (ebook) |
ISBN 9781138293946 (hardback) | ISBN 9781315231808 (ebook)
Subjects: LCSH: Scandinavia–Commerce–History–To 1500. | Gotland (Sweden)–Commerce–History–To 1500. | Slavery–Scandinavia–History–To 1500. | Slavery–Sweden–Gotland–History–To 1500. | Silver–Scandinavia–History–To 1500. | Silver–Sweden–Gotland–History–To 1500.
Classification: LCC HF3640 .V55 2021 (print) | LCC HF3640 (ebook) |
DDC 382/.440948–dc23
LC record available at https://lccn.loc.gov/2020017582
LC ebook record available at https://lccn.loc.gov/2020017583

ISBN: 978-0-367-55469-9 (pbk)
ISBN: 978-1-138-29394-6 (hbk)
ISBN: 978-1-315-23180-8 (ebk)

DOI: 10.4324/9781315231808

Typeset in Bembo
by River Editorial Ltd, Devon, UK

Contents

Maps

Figures

Tables

Preface and acknowledgements

This volume is one of the outcomes of the *Dirhams for Slaves* research project that was funded by the UK's Arts and Humanities Research Council between 2013 and 2017. As Dagfinn Skre notes in his concluding remarks, the challenges in investigating the trade system that connected northern Europe and the Islamic world in the ninth and tenth centuries were considerable. Specialists from a number of disciplines were necessary, including numismatists, archaeologists and historians specialising in the British Isles and Scandinavia to Russia and the Islamic world, and all points in between. The project's basic research proposition – that the hundreds of thousands of dirhams found in hoards strewn across northern Europe were the residue of large-scale trade in which slaves played a key role – was challenging in a number of ways; indeed, the seminar series where some of the papers in this volume were first aired was entitled 'The Dark Ages' "dirty secret"?'.

The questions the finds of dirhams pose are enumerated further in the introductory chapter to the volume. But on a more practical level, such interdisciplinary work poses its own editorial challenges. How can archaeological or numismatic materials be made accessible to the non-specialist without oversimplifying? Should quotations be transliterated or given in the original language? And how best to style Scandinavian and Arabic names to make them digestible to the lay reader? The answers to such questions are never easy and our solutions are open to the charge of being overly broad-brush. But we have tried to make this volume clear and accessible primarily to English-speaking non-specialists, notably in adopting consistent and recognisable forms of proper names and technical terms. Most northern European place names are untouched. We have adopted conventional versions of Arabic place names (Baghdad instead of Madinat al-Salam, for example), although for Arabic mints we have generally retained the original names or offered both them and the modern ones. In Chapter 8, there is a short table of these variants and an outline of the dynasties issuing them (Appendices 8.2 and 8.1).

One fundamental area where standardisation has been attempted – with some difficulty – is that of periodisation. For example, the term 'Viking Age' means different things even to scholars within Sweden, running to around 1050 for most but until 1150 in Gotland; the 'Migration Period' in Swedish scholarship runs from 400 to 600 AD, while for Polish scholars it means 375 to 500 AD. We have adopted a simplified scheme in this volume detailed in Table 0.1 (although it should be noted that some of our contributors preferred to retain their own periodisation or categories and notes to this effect are given in their chapters).

Table 0.1 Periodisation used in this volume

Dates (AD)	Description		
1–400	Roman Iron Age		
400–600	Migration Period		
600–800	Vendel Period	early	
800–1050	Viking Age[1]		middle ages
1050–1300			
1300–1500		late	
1500–	early modern		

Note
1 Continuing until 1150 on Gotland.

Quotations are generally in English and translations made by our authors, unless otherwise stated in the Notes. There is a short Glossary at the end of the volume, although where possible technical terms or foreign words are explained in the text, along with an Appendix itemising the Gotlandic structures and other objects offering scope for radiocarbon datings discussed in our chapters, notably those of Östergren, Carlsson, Gustafsson and Widerström. There are maps at the beginning of most sections to help locate a number of the key places and areas mentioned by our authors, with more detailed, technical maps within some chapters. Readers may find some inconsistencies, with modern place names alongside older ones, and all boundaries are approximate and sometimes either speculative or controversial.

Unless otherwise stated, all maps, tables and graphs have been prepared by the author. Authors' maps were revised by Jacek Gruszczyński; David Cox prepared the general maps and some of the chapter-specific ones. We owe them both an immense debt of gratitude.

We would like to thank the following people and institutions, and to acknowledge their help in seeing this volume into print: Dr Luke Treadwell, Principal Investigator of the *Dirhams for Slaves* project, for his unfailing patience and strong support; our two anonymous reviewers, whose comments were immensely helpful in framing the volume – and particularly for ensuring we included the Irish perspective; and Nicola Sigsworth, for her truly invaluable editorial help. Publication would not have been possible without the initial encouragement of Dr John Smedley of Ashgate; the support and patience of Michael Greenwood and Stewart Beale of Routledge, who saw us almost to the finish, and Matthew Gibbons who then took over; the series editors of Routledge Archaeologies of the Viking World, Neil Price, Charlotte Hedenstierna-Jonson and Ben Raffield, for agreeing to take us under their wing; Sally Evans-Darby for her expert copyediting; and Colin Morgan and Julie Willis at River Editorial for seeing us through to the world of print.

Finally, we would also like to thank those colleagues who participated in the following events organised under the aegis of the *Dirhams for Slaves* project, but whose papers were published elsewhere: the workshop held in the Institute of Archaeology at the University of Oxford in March 2015 on 'Silver Landscapes in Viking-Age Gotland: From Hoards to Settlements'; the sessions at the Leeds International Medieval Congress in July 2015; and the above-mentioned Oxford Trinity Term 2015 seminar series. Above all, we would like to thank our authors for their enthusiastic participation in the project, for their good humour in dealing with our many queries and, above all, for their patience.

Jacek Gruszczyński, Marek Jankowiak, Jonathan Shepard

Abbreviations and notes on bibliography

Where appropriate, our chapters' bibliographies are divided into primary sources and secondary literature. The letters Å, Ä and Ö have been alphabetised under A and O (*pace* our Scandinavian colleagues). In the endnotes, short titles are used for primary sources and the name-date system for secondary literature. Where a primary source appears frequently in only one chapter, this has been abbreviated within that chapter's bibliography (for example, DR for *Danmarks runeindskrifter* in Chapter 16). Primary sources and secondary works cited by several of our authors are abbreviated in the endnotes with full details given below. This list also contains the titles of some journals and other abbreviations. Further details on entries in this list marked with an asterisk (*) can be found in the Glossary.

Ad*GH*	Adam of Bremen, *Gesta Hammaburgensis ecclesiae pontificum*, ed. W. Trillmich and R. Buchner, in *Quellen des 9. und 11. Jahrhunderts zur Geschichte der Hamburgischen Kirche und des Reiches*, Darmstadt (1961), pp. 137–499
ASC[1]	'The Anglo-Saxon Chronicle', tr. D. Whitelock, in *EHD*, pp. 148–259
ASC[2]	*The Anglo-Saxon Chronicles*, rev. ed. and tr. M. Swanton, London (2000)
ATA	Antikvarisk-topografiska arkivet (The Antiquarian-Topographical Archives), Stockholm
BAR BS	*British Archaeological Reports British Series*
BAR IS	*British Archaeological Reports International Series*
BGA	*Bibliotheca geographorum arabicorum*, ed. M. J. de Goeje, 8 vols, Leiden (1870–94)
BNJ	*British Numismatic Journal*
BVW	F. Androshchuk *et al.* (eds), *Byzantium and the Viking World*, Uppsala (2016)
CFHB	*Corpus fontium historiae byzantinae*
CH	J. Graham-Campbell *et al.*, *The Cuerdale Hoard and Related Viking-Age Silver and Gold from Britain and Ireland in the British Museum*, London (2011)

CIS	*Corpus iuris sueo-gotorum antiqui (Samling af Sweriges gamla lagar)*, ed. H. S. Collin and C. J. Schlyter, 13 vols, Stockholm (1827–77)
CNS	*Corpus nummorum saeculorum IX–XI qui in Suecia reperti sunt (Catalogue of Coins from the Viking Age Found in Sweden)*, 9 vols, Stockholm (1975–2010); volumes are now published in pdf only via archaeology.su.se/english/stockholm-numismatic -institute/publications-nfg/cns (accessed 17 December 2019)
CNS n.s.	*Commentationes de nummis saeculorum IX–XI in Suecia repertis. Nova series*
Co.	County (Ireland)
DAI	Constantine VII Porphyrogenitus, *De administrando imperio*, ed. G. Moravcsik, tr. R. J. H. Jenkins, 2nd edn, *CFHB* 1, Washington, DC (1967)
DfS	'Dirhams for Slaves', an AHRC-funded project based at the Khalili Research Centre, University of Oxford (2013–17), krc.web.ox.ac.uk/article/dirhams-slaves (accessed 27 July 2020)
DG	*Drevneishie gosudarstva na territorii SSSR/Vostochnoi Evropy* [from 1991]
DKV	P. Lundström, *De kommo vida . . . vikingars hamn vid Paviken på Gotland*, Stockholm (1981)
dnr	diarienummer
EHD	*English Historical Documents, c. 500–1042*, tr. D. Whitelock, 2nd edn, London (1979)
FMIS	RAÄ Archaeological Sites Information System*
FMP 3	M. Bogucki *et al.*, *Frühmittelalterliche Münzfunde aus Polen. Inventar*, vol. 3: *Masowien, Podlachien, Mittelpolen*, Warsaw (2016)
FMP 4	M. Bogucki *et al.*, *Frühmittelalterliche Münzfunde aus Polen. Inventar*, vol. 4: *Kleinpolen und Schlesien*, Warsaw (2013)
Fv	*Fornvännen*
G	*Gotlands runinskrifter*, vol. 1, ed. B. F. Jansson and E. Wessén, SR 11, Stockholm (1962); vol. 2, ed. E. Svärdström, SR 12, Stockholm (1978); vol. 3, ed. H. Gustavson and T. Snædal (forthcoming; draft available from raa.se/kulturarvet/ar-keologi-fornlamningar-och-fynd/runstenar/digitala-sveriges-runinskrifter/gotlands-runinskrifter-3) (accessed 17 December 2019)
GA	*Gotländskt Arkiv*
GIS	Geographic Information System*
GL	*Guta Lag: The Law of the Gotlanders*, ed. and tr. C. Peel, London (2009)
GoV	I. Jansson (ed.), *Gutar och vikingar*, Stockholm (1983)

GS	*Guta Saga: The History of the Gotlanders*, ed. and tr. C. Peel, London (1999; repr. 2010)
Hkr[1]	Snorri Sturluson, *Heimskringla*, ed. Bjarni Aðalbjarnarson, 3 vols, ÍF 26–8, Reykjavik (1941–51)
Hkr[2]	Snorri Sturluson, *Heimskringla*, tr. L. M. Hollander, *History of the Kings of Norway*, Austin, TX (1964)
Hkr[3]	Snorri Sturluson, *Heimskringla*, tr. A. Finlay and A. Faulkes, rev. edn, 3 vols, London (2014–16)
HV	G. Hatz, *Handel und Verkehr zwischen dem Deutschen Reich und Schweden in der späten Wikingerzeit: die deutschen Münzen des 10. und 11. Jahrhunderts in Schweden*, Lund (1974)
IbnF[1]	Ibn Fadlan, *Mission to the Volga*, ed. and tr. J. E. Montgomery, in *Two Arabic Travel Books: Accounts of China and India*, New York (2014), pp. 165–297
IbnF[2]	Ibn Fadlan, *The Book of Ahmad Ibn Fadlan*, tr. P. Lunde and C. Stone, in *Ibn Fadlan and the Land of Darkness: Arab Travellers in the Far North*, London (2012), pp. 3–58
IC	F. Biermann and M. Jankowiak (eds), *The Invisible Commodity: The Archaeology of Slavery in Early Medieval Northern Europe*, Cham (2021 forthcoming)
ÍF	*Íslenzk fornrit*
IFD	J. Callmer *et al.* (eds), *Identity Formation and Diversity in the Early Medieval Baltic and Beyond*, Leiden (2017)
KLNM	*Kulturhistoriskt lexikon för nordisk medeltid från vikingatid till reformationstid*, ed. I. Andersson, J. Granlund *et al.*, 22 vols, Malmö (1956–78)
LD	G. Svedjemo, *Landscape Dynamics: Spatial Analyses of Villages and Farms on Gotland AD 200–1700*, Uppsala (2014)
ME	D. Skre (ed.), *Means of Exchange: Dealing with Silver in the Viking Age*, tr. J. Hines, Aarhus (2008)
MGH	*Monumenta Germaniae historica*
MGH SRG	*MGH Scriptores rerum Germanicarum in usum scholarum*
MIA	*Materialy i issledovaniia po arkheologii SSSR*
MSoS	M. Östergren, *Mellan stengrund och stenhus: Gotlands vikingatida silverskatter som boplatsindikation,* Stockholm (1989)
NMI	National Museum of Ireland, Dublin
NNÅ	*Nordisk Numismatisk Årsskrift*
NoB	*Namn och bygd: tidskrift för nordisk ortnamnsforskning*
ON	Old Norse
PAS	Portable Antiquities Scheme, finds.org.uk (accessed 17 December 2019)
PVL	*Povest' vremennykh let*, ed. V. P. Adrianova-Peretts and D. S. Likhachev, 2nd edn rev. M. B. Sverdlov, St Petersburg (1996)

RAÄ Riksantikvarieämbetet (The Swedish National Heritage Board)*

RAGU Riksantikvarieämbetets Gotlandsundersökningar (The Gotland Branch of the Central Board and Museum of National Antiquities)

RGA *Reallexikon der Germanischen Altertumskunde*, ed. J. Hoops, H. Beck *et al.*, 2nd edn, 35 vols and 2 indices, Berlin (1973–2008)

Rimb*VA* Rimbert, *Vita Anskarii*, ed. G. Waitz, rev. ed. and tr. W. Trillmich and R. Buchner, in *Quellen des 9. und 11. Jahrhunderts zur Geschichte der Hamburgischen Kirche und des Reiches*, Darmstadt (1961), pp. 3–133

RPC *Russian Primary Chronicle*, tr. S. H. Cross and O. P. Sherbowitz-Wetzor, Cambridge, MA (1953)

SEMSS J. Graham-Campbell *et al.* (eds), *Silver Economies, Monetisation and Society in Scandinavia, AD 800–1100*, Aarhus (2011)

SEVA J. Graham-Campbell and G. Williams (eds), *Silver Economy in the Viking Age*, Walnut Creek, CA (2007)

SGW M. Stenberger, *Die Schatzfunde Gotlands der Wikingerzeit*, 2 vols, Lund (1947–58) [vol. 1: *Text* (1958); vol. 2: *Fundbeschreibung und Tafeln* (1947)]

SH A.-M. Pettersson (ed.), *The Spillings Hoard: Gotland's Role in Viking Age World Trade*, Visby (2009)

SHM Statens historiska museet (The Museum of National Antiquities), Stockholm – now Historiska museet (The Swedish History Museum)

SL *Svenska landskapslagar: tolkade och förklarade för nutidens svenskar*, ed. Å. Holmbäck and E. Wessén, 5 vols, Stockholm (1933–46; repr. 1979) [vol. 1: *Ostgötalagen och Upplandslagen* (1933); vol. 2: *Dalalagen och Västmannalagen* (1936); vol. 3: *Södermannalagen och Hälsingelagen* (1940); vol. 4: *Skånelagen och Gutalagen* (1943); vol. 5: *Äldre Västgötalagen, Yngre Västgötalagen, Smålandslagens kyrkobalk och Bjärköarätten* (1946)]

Sö *Södermanlands runinskrifter*, ed. E. Brate and E. Wessén, SR 3, Stockholm (1924–36)

SoB M. Östergren, with K. Jonsson and B. Sigvallius, *Silverskatter och boningshus: skattfyndprojektet 1; en studie av gården Gannarve i Hall sn, Gotland* (RAGU Rapport 1986:1), Visby (1986)

SP K. Jonsson and B. Malmer (eds), *Sigtuna Papers: Proceedings of the Sigtuna Symposium on Viking-Age Coinage, 1–4 June 1989*, CNS n.s. 6, Stockholm (1990)

SR Sveriges runinskrifter

SSA Stockholm Studies in Archaeology

tpq *terminus post quem**

U	*Upplands runinskrifter*, ed. E. Wessén and S. B. F. Jansson, 3 vols, SR 6–9, Stockholm (1940–58)
UNESCO	The United Nations Educational, Scientific and Cultural Organization
VACNL	M. Blackburn and D. M. Metcalf (eds), *Viking-Age Coinage in the Northern Lands*, BAR IS 122, 2 vols, Oxford (1981)
VCC	M. Blackburn, *Viking Coinage and Currency in the British Isles*, London (2011)
VF	*Vita Findani* [The *Life* of St Findan the Confessor], ed. O. Holder-Egger, in *MGH Scriptores* 15.1, Hanover (1887), pp. 502–6; tr. C. J. Omand, in R. J. Berry and H. N. Firth (eds), *The People of Orkney*, Kirkwall (1986), pp. 284–7; tr. A. A. Somerville, in A. A. Somerville and R. A. McDonald, *The Viking Age: A Reader*, 2nd edn, North York, Ontario (2014), pp. 195–8
VIB	H. B. Clarke and R. Johnson (eds), *The Vikings in Ireland and Beyond: Before and after the Battle of Clontarf*, Dublin (2015)
VW	S. Brink and N. Price (eds), *The Viking World*, Abingdon (2008)
WKG	L. Thunmark-Nylén, *Die Wikingerzeit Gotlands*, 4 vols, Stockholm (1995–2006) [vol. 1: *Abbildungen der Grabfunde* (1995); vol. 2: *Typentafeln* (1998); vol. 3 in 2 pts: *Text* (2006); vol. 4 in 3 pts: *Katalog* (2000)]

Contributors

Dariusz Adamczyk is a Researcher at the Deutsches Historisches Institut in Warsaw and Associate Professor in History at Leibniz University, Hanover. Publications include *Silber und Macht. Fernhandel, Tribute und die piastische Herrschaftsbildung in nordosteuropäischer Perspektive (800–1100)* (2014), and his research interests focus on Viking-Age silver flows, relations between Europe and the Islamic world and the history of trade and money.

Stefan Brink is Professor of Scandinavian Studies at the University of the Highlands and Islands, and an Honorary Research Associate at the Department of Anglo-Saxon, Norse and Celtic, University of Cambridge. His publications include *Vikingarnas slavar: den nordiska trälddomen under yngre järnålder och äldsta medeltid* (2012) and *The Viking World* (2008, co-edited with N. Price), and his research interests include the society, culture and law of early Scandinavia and Viking slavery.

Dan Carlsson's Stockholm PhD on the Iron-Age landscape of Gotland was published as *Kulturlandskapets utveckling på Gotland* (1979). From 1998 he was Associate Professor at Gotland University and has run the island's Archaeological Field School for the past twenty years. As Director of ArkeoDok and Arendus, Carlsson has undertaken extensive excavations on Gotland, including research projects such as the Fröjel Discovery Programme.

Jacek Gruszczyński was a Research Associate at the Khalili Research Centre, University of Oxford and now works as an archaeology and heritage consultant. Gruszczyński obtained his BA and MA in archaeology from the Jagiellonian University, Cracow, and his doctorate from Oxford, which has been published as *Viking Silver, Hoards and Containers: The Archaeological and Historical Context of Viking-Age Silver Coin Deposits in the Baltic c. 800–1050* (2019).

Ny Björn Gustafsson is an archaeologist and finds specialist who works on metal-detector surveys for the Swedish National Heritage Board (RAÄ) in Visby, previously based at Gotland Museum. His doctoral thesis focused on non-ferrous metalworking and identity on Gotland and was published as *Casting Identities in Central Seclusion: Aspects of Non-Ferrous Metalworking and Society on Gotland in the Early Medieval Period* (2013).

James Howard-Johnston was University Lecturer in Byzantine Studies at the University of Oxford. Author of *Historical Writing in Byzantium* (2014) and *Witnesses to a World Crisis: Historians and Histories of the Middle East in the Seventh Century* (2010), his research interests range from Byzantine social, economic, institutional and military history to the northern nomadic powers from the Huns to the Khazars.

Gitte Tarnow Ingvardson is Curator of the Coin Collection at Lund University's Historical Museum. A specialist in numismatics and archaeology, her research interests include metal-detector archaeology, hoarding practices, Viking-Age and early medieval coinage, hoard compositions and bullion economies.

Marek Jankowiak is Associate Professor of Byzantine History at the University of Oxford. His research interests range from religious history (his Paris PhD was on the monothelete controversy) to historiography, various aspects of the history of the Byzantine state, economy and society, and contacts of Byzantium with its eastern and northern neighbours. Publications include *Studies in Theophanes* (2015, co-edited with F. Montinaro).

Ingmar Jansson is Emeritus Reader in Archaeology at Stockholm University. A specialist in the material culture of Viking-Age eastern Europe, Jansson has participated in the excavations at Riurikovo Gorodishche, and studied museum collections and monuments in the field of northern and western Europe and also in Turkey, Iran, Afghanistan and Uzbekistan. He has published over fifty works, including *Gutar och vikingar* (1983), and organised major exhibitions including *From Viking to Crusader* (1992) and *The Viking Heritage* (1996).

Christoph Kilger is Senior Lecturer at the Department of Archaeology and Ancient History, Uppsala University, based at the Visby campus on Gotland. His doctoral thesis was published in 2000 as *Pfennigmärkte und Währungslandschaften: Monetarisierungen im sächsisch-slawischen Grenzland ca. 965–1120* and his research interests include the Viking-Age and medieval economy, notably the intersection between monetary and ritual space.

Viacheslav S. Kuleshov obtained his PhD from the Russian Academy of Science and is a Postdoctoral Fellow at the Department of Archaeology and Classical Studies of Stockholm University. A historian, philologist and numismatist, he was previously Keeper of the Oriental Coins Collections at the State Hermitage Museum, St Petersburg. Author of more than 120 published works on subjects ranging from Russian archaeology and linguistics to written source studies and Islamic numismatics, he has recently published a Russian translation of Ibn Fadlan's *Risala*.

Alex Marshall is Senior Lecturer in History at the University of Glasgow. Author of *The Caucasus Under Soviet Rule* (2010) and, with T. Bird, of *Afghanistan: How the West Lost Its Way* (2011), his research interests include drug smuggling and Marxist political economy, the Caucasus and Central Asia, Russian/Soviet military and political history, nineteenth- and twentieth-century Afghanistan and counter-insurgency and revolutionary war.

Majvor Östergren is an archaeologist whose PhD from Stockholm University on the link between silver hoards and settlement was published as *Mellan stengrund och stenhus: Gotlands vikingatida silverskatter som boplatsindikation* (1989). Östergren has been instrumental in investigating, protecting and analysing Gotland's many silver hoards as Director of the Gotland Museum and as a member of the County Administrative Board.

Andrew P. Roach is Senior Lecturer in History at the University of Glasgow. Author of *The Devil's World: Heresy and Society, 1100–1300* (2005; 2nd edn in preparation) and co-editor, with J. Simpson, of *Heresy and the Making of European Culture: Medieval and Modern Perspectives* (2013), from an interest in western European heresy and popular religion, Roach has branched out via the Bogomils into southeastern Europe, networks and the economics of religion.

Elina Screen is Lecturer in Medieval History at Birkbeck, University of London. She is general editor of the Medieval European Coinage Project at the Fitzwilliam Museum, Cambridge. Her numismatic publications include *Sylloge of Coins of the British Isles*, vols 65–6: *Norwegian Collections* (2013–15). Screen works on early medieval history, focusing especially upon ninth-century Francia and the contribution made by the charter evidence, and on the coinage evidence for Scandinavia in the Viking Age.

John Sheehan is Senior Lecturer in the Department of Archaeology, University College Cork. His main research interests include the Viking-Age gold and silver hoards of Britain and Ireland, and he has published widely in this field. His publications include *The Viking Age: Ireland and the West* (2010, co-edited with D. Ó Corráin) and *Clerics, Kings and Vikings* (2015, co-edited with E. Purcell, P. McCotter and J. Nyhan).

Jonathan Shepard was University Lecturer in Russian History at the University of Cambridge. Co-author of *The Emergence of Rus* (1996) with Simon Franklin, with whom he also edited *Byzantine Diplomacy* (1992), other edited volumes include *The Expansion of Orthodox Europe* (2007); *The Cambridge History of the Byzantine Empire* (2008; paperback 2019); and *Byzantium and the Viking World* (2016, co-edited with F. Androshchuk and M. White).

Dagfinn Skre is Professor of Viking and Iron Age Archaeology at the Museum of Cultural History at the University of Oslo. His many edited volumes include *Kaupang in Skiringssal* (2007), *Means of Exchange* (2008),

Things from the Town: Artefacts and Inhabitants in Viking-Age Kaupang (2011), *Avaldsnes: A Sea-Kings' Manor in First-Millennium Western Scandinavia* (2018) and *Rulership in 1st to 14th Century Scandinavia: Royal Graves and Sites at Avaldsnes and Beyond* (2020). His research interests focus on settlement, economy and social and political structures in the Iron and Viking Ages, as well as early church organisation.

Gustaf Svedjemo is Senior Lecturer at the Department of Archaeology and Ancient History, Uppsala University, based at the Visby campus on Gotland. His doctoral thesis was published in 2014 as *Landscape Dynamics: Spatial Analyses of Villages and Farms on Gotland AD 200–1700*. Svedjemo works on the use of historical maps in GIS and using the databases of the large-scale scanning project by the Swedish National Land Survey.

Per Widerström is an archaeologist with Gotland Museum and is affiliated to the Department of Archaeology and Ancient History, Uppsala University, based at the Visby campus on Gotland. Widerström was one of the project leaders on an interdisciplinary research project on Gotland's picture stones, and has undertaken settlement excavations at the Spillings discovery and most recently at Roma kloster.

Andrew R. Woods is Senior Curator at the Yorkshire Museum. He completed his doctorate, on the relationship between royal authority and economic agency in Viking-Age Ireland, at the University of Cambridge in 2013. His research interests include early medieval coinage, with an emphasis on value and use, and the interpretation of metal-detected assemblages. He has also worked on projects at Torksey and Rendlesham (Suffolk).

David Wyatt is Senior Lecturer in Early Medieval History at Cardiff University. A specialist in the history of slavery in medieval Britain, his book *Slaves and Warriors in Medieval Britain and Ireland, 800–1200* (2009) examines the social and cultural significance of slavery for these societies. His research interests also include Viking-Age settlement and society in the Irish Sea region, and gender and power in early medieval Britain.

1   Why Gotland?

Jonathan Shepard

The single largest concentration of silver hoards known to man is on
Gotland. Some 180,000 coins have been found. Around two-fifths of these
are Arab dirhams or dirham fragments, with the remaining silver pieces struck
in German, English and other mints.[1] Many hoards also contain quantities of
hack-silver, and/or silver ornament, which had almost certainly arrived on
the island in the form of dirhams. One also has to reckon with stray finds of
one or two coins. The phenomenon invites a range of questions. At one end
of the spectrum, there are such questions as whether similar concentrations of
dirhams once existed elsewhere in northern or eastern Europe, but were
subsequently melted down or unearthed and dispersed without coming to the
notice of the authorities or receiving scholarly attention; whether dirhams
were hoarded in comparable numbers in the Islamic societies where they
were struck; and, quite simply, what exactly is a 'hoard'.[2] Then, somewhere
along the spectrum, sit issues of numismatics and archaeology: determining
the dirhams' silver contents, and taking advantage of the dates and mint
locations provided on most coins to try and chart ups and downs in the
inflow from the Islamic world. Such efforts have to take into account
the archaeological contexts of hoards, alongside the problem of dating: the
latest – 'youngest' – coin in a hoard gives a clue, but if the hoard is
incomplete, calculations based on this may be misleading. Debate anyway
goes on about the likely interval between the date of the youngest piece and
when the hoard was deposited, as over how long a coin took to reach
northern Europe. These questions segue into economic history and
anthropology: what was the ratio of silver found in the hoards to the amount
of silver circulating at any one time in the ninth and tenth centuries, the
period when most of the dirhams reached Gotland? And what was the point
of hoarding: does a single explanation fit all, or should one allow for a variety
of reasons, including symbolic and ritual ones? Finally, at the
straightforwardly historical end of the spectrum are the questions: what
brought so much silver to the island, who were the carriers, where were they
taking it and whence? Did the silver on Gotland serve as bullion, currency or

raw material for craftsmen to rework? And, if all three roles were in play, did any one of them predominate?

In the background lurks the question of whether all this silver necessarily registers commerce: might not some, at least, be the outcome of plundering, tribute demands or gift exchange? And if acquired through trading, what commodities were offered in exchange? Had they been grown or manufactured on Gotland? Were the Gotlanders processing items of foreign origin for re-export? Or was the island essentially a clearinghouse for transit trade? These questions raise the problem of 'exceptionalism': was Gotland's economy and society a case apart, functioning differently from those on other Baltic shores, including the Swedish mainland? Was the island significantly richer in silver? And, if so, why?

To begin to answer such questions one has to scan distant horizons: not only eastwards and south-east to Rus and the Eurasian steppes (across which most of the dirhams had travelled), but also to the North Sea and the Atlantic. Evidence of the trafficking there may provide points of comparison with Gotlandic goings-on, for all the variations in societies and economies within the British Isles themselves. Moreover, one must allow for the fact that trading networks stretched far to the west as well as eastwards, and the possibility that Gotland itself amounted to a kind of mega-emporium for high-value commodities shipped from afar.[3] Taking a turn to the west brings another advantage: the archaeological and literary materials from Ireland and Anglo-Saxon England do something to make up for a serious gap in the Gotlandic evidence. Our earliest writings from the island, a law code (*Guta Lag*) and a saga (*Guta Saga*), date from well after the Viking Age, while the handful of runestones bearing brief inscriptions do not fill the void.[4]

And here is the nub. The extraordinary wealth of Gotland – 'silver island' – has long been inferred, and gains corroboration from the studies below. But the dearth of indigenous written sources means that even less is known for sure about Gotland's socio-political structure and economic history than about, say, central Sweden, of which foreign churchmen offer a few descriptions.[5] A growing body of archaeological evidence, sometimes congruent with literary works, concerning Scandinavian arrivals and invaders in the British Isles, particularly their handling of silver and monetary competence, may shed light on the finds from Gotland, too. It may even help us begin answering the questions posed above. 'Begin' is the operative word, though, and few definitive answers are given. What is on offer is neither synthesis nor panorama, but a series of soundings and sightings carried out from and around the platform that Gotland constitutes. If much of Gotland's history remains enshrouded in uncertainty, this book may at least set out the 'known unknowns' and some legitimate grounds for contention, whilst making positive contributions to knowledge. The soundings sometimes go down unlikely – even sordid – channels, but they are suggestive about the dynamics of slave-trading, an activity bearing closely on dirhams and Gotland.

As in the Baltic, so in this book, Gotland sits in the middle of things, with our section on 'Gotland' taking up a third of the chapters. A recurring theme is the need for further excavations of the archaeological contexts of hoards. To fit the hoards into Gotlandic society, one needs to know the lie of the land – literally so, and in terms of their connection with settlements and individual buildings. The rolling countryside lends itself to easy cycle-riding in the twenty-first century, with few wholly inaccessible parts and nowhere more than 85m above sea level. The terrain is – and in the middle ages was – no less propitious for agriculture. However, the amount of cultivable land is finite and there are extensive tracts of ancient forest sometimes reaching down as far as the sea. Sandy beaches encircle long stretches of the island, although its rivers are not abundant and should more properly be termed brooks.[6]

Thorough reassessment of the settlements and of social structures is provided by Gustaf Svedjemo. Drawing on later seventeenth- and eighteenth-century maps, he argues in favour of the underlying stability of settlement patterns on Gotland, of both villages and solitary farmsteads. The former were often quite small, consisting of two or three farmsteads. These farms could, however, shift around within the bounds of a village. A certain trend towards sandy soils on higher ground from moraine soils is discernible in the Viking Age. Awareness of the agricultural potential of different soils was quite compatible with the amassing of silver through trade. Svedjemo envisages an elite engaging readily in commerce, whilst subject to and upholding legal constraints on the sale and reallocation of land, and he notes that although silver hoards mostly occur quite near settlement sites, only around half seem to have been deposited actually inside buildings.[7] Here he parts company with some of the other contributors to this volume, including the pioneering work of Majvor Östergren. The truly minute number of settlements to have undergone even small-scale excavation is emphasised by Per Widerström. His gazetteer of these settlements and their houses and other structures suggests not only a fair degree of prosperity, but also greater recourse to stone foundations than on the Swedish mainland; sometimes stone walls, too. That a great deal *can* be inferred emerges from Ny Björn Gustafsson's chapter. He emphasises the concern of Gotlanders for very high standards of silver. The artefacts they produced themselves seem to have been 'affirmation' of high quality, and the particular styles of Gotlandic jewellery may have been designed to stand out from other marks of silverware. In favour of this suggestion is the evidence from Fröjel of sophisticated non-ferrous metalworking: baser metals were removed from silver objects by means of cupellation. Many of the hoards may well have been assemblages for the purpose of such metalworking. Östergren highlights clear examples, including the famous Spillings hoard. In support of this, she argues for a close association between hoards and buildings, especially dwelling-houses. She points out the hazardousness of negative arguments from silence, given the very limited number of settlements excavated so far.

The opportunities for inhabitants of villages and individual farmsteads to trade overseas emerge from Dan Carlsson's study. Noting how many hoards consist wholly of hack-silver, clearly intended for manufacturing purposes, he points to the existence of some sixty places showing signs of Viking-Age activities along the coast. Here, too, generalisations have to be speculative, given the paucity of sites excavated. Carlsson is, however, able to give an authoritative survey of a variety of landing places. Many will have been small-scale, serving individual farmsteads or villages. But some are likely to have been ports, catering for a larger area and accommodating craftsmen and foreign traders. One such was Fröjel, where excavations under Carlsson's direction have borne fruit, although only a small fraction of its surface-area has undergone investigation. Several of Fröjel's crafts were reliant on imports, and manufacture was clearly for the market rather than the needs of the household or local neighbourhood. Besides cupellation – attested only rarely elsewhere in Scandinavia – there is plentiful evidence of the manufacture of combs from the antlers of red deer and elk, beasts not found on Gotland. Other products include glass-beads, produced en masse, and lenses made from rock crystal which was imported. Gotland seems to have been the earliest Scandinavian centre of manufacturing rock crystal lenses, and more are found there than in all other Scandinavian find-sites combined. Although exported across Scandinavia, the lenses have silver mountings reminiscent of jewellery found in Slav sites to the south and east. An original eastern derivation is suggested by their occurrence mainly in silver hoards. Women favoured them as ornaments or magnifying glasses, judging by their preponderance in female graves. A particular connection between women and silver hoards is drawn by Christoph Kilger. He discusses the elaborate provisions for bride price in *Guta Lag*, and its assumption that a bride's property was a 'pledge', reclaimable by her father's family in the event of her bloodline dying out. These possessions could have included silver given as bride price in addition to landed property and, Kilger suggests, the silver could have been kept in the ground for this reason. Conceding that to regard silver hoards as dowries is only one possible interpretation, he notes *Guta Lag*'s preoccupation with maintaining family farmsteads intact, especially its injunction that younger brothers should seek their fortune with scrip and scales, going in for trading.

The implications of this are followed through in Jacek Gruszczyński's survey of the social context of hoards. Highlighting the constraints imposed by the island's size and terrain, along with the desire of families to keep their landholdings intact, he proposes a connection with the deposition of hoards in marginal – generally sandier – soils: through burying silver on land newly acquired and newly cultivated, a man might symbolically bond with it and hope to retain it for himself and his heirs. Gruszczyński agrees with other investigators on the essentially 'egalitarian mentality' of Gotlanders. A substantial elite – an oligarchy of sorts – took pains to maintain its landholdings; but land, resources and power were not amassed by any one family, and (after the early Viking Age) weapons are notable largely by their absence from graves and settlements. And a broad cross-section of society seems to have had uniform access to silver.

How, though, was such silver acquired; how does Gotland's economy and society compare with other polities and peoples around the Baltic Rim; and what were its relations with them? Chapters in adjoining sections of this book go some way towards answering these questions. Ingmar Jansson sets Gotland within its Baltic context. The evidence of Gotland as a land under the king of the Svear does not go beyond some sort of deferential relationship involving tribute. What is clearer is the difference between 'the general richness of Gotlandic graves' and central Sweden, where a king reigned and the numerous boat- and chamber-graves are manifestations of wealthy and well-armed elite families. From his knowledge of burial grounds and designs of ornaments, Jansson argues for greater similarities between Gotland and east Baltic and Finnish societies. Cemeteries on, for example, the island of Saaremaa in modern Estonia show a fair degree of affluence, but without the obvious marks of social hierarchy or a warrior elite. And a sizeable assortment of Gotlandic artefacts have been unearthed on the south-east Baltic coast. However, the Gotlanders do not seem to have exported inanimate goods further east, to Rus, or to have left behind there ornaments and suchlike items of personal use. Yet they exported or re-exported vast amounts of dirhams to Scandinavia. The dynamics of Gotland's economy along with its distinctive culture set it apart from islands of the western Baltic such as Bornholm. Here, too, the settlement pattern was diffuse, and hoards were amassed and deposited for a variety of purposes. And yet, as Gitte Tarnow Ingvardson's pioneering study makes clear, Bornholm's silver hoards were smaller and they appear markedly later, registering the general upswing in commerce around 1000, when western coins were flowing into the Baltic Rim. Samanid silver from the east was not insignificant, though, some of it retaining the form of dirhams at the time of deposition, while a fair amount may have been melted down: there are strong hints of silversmithing on Bornholm.

The political and social setup to the south of the Baltic was also different from that of Gotland, whether at the emporia on the coast or further inland, as Dariusz Adamczyk shows. There, in the tenth century, large amounts of silver came into the hands of warlords, and huge hoards have been found in the heart of what became the Piast realm, in Wielkopolska.[8] Explaining what sort of activities could have generated such wealth is inevitably speculative, but Adamczyk points to slave-taking and slave-trading as powerful drivers. This accords with other contributions to this volume, notably that of Marek Jankowiak, who takes in not only the territories that make up the modern states of Sweden, Denmark and Estonia, but also the regions that came under the dominion of the Piasts and the rulers of Rus. The strong hints of disruption and depopulation, along with the distribution pattern of strongholds attested by archaeology, chime in with the findings of a recent study of early Slavonic place names in the fertile borderlands between the river San and the Middle Bug. Speculating about the reasons for large-scale depopulation of the region, the investigator notes what riches ruthless warlords could amass from the long-distance slave trade.[9] The fluctuations in the quantities of silver arriving from the east and marked variations in the routes it took over time are key themes to emerge from Jankowiak's wide-ranging survey of the chronology discernible from close study of more than 830 hoards. Supervision of the commercial exchanges responsible for the hoards could, he shows, give rise to durable political structures and reinforce existing powers, but all were vulnerable to shifts in the silver supply chain. Viacheslav S. Kuleshov traces the inflow back to the medley of mints and polities responsible for striking the dirhams. As all these chapters reaffirm, a critical change takes place in the composition of surviving hoards around the beginning of the tenth century, when dirhams struck in Central Asia by the Samanids began to stream westwards, only for the influx to slow down and then fall away rapidly from the 960s and 970s onwards. Kuleshov detects a fairly frantic attempt to find substitutes for their issues around the turn of the tenth and eleventh centuries, with a smattering of dirhams from minor dynasties reaching Rus and the Baltic Rim. But to no avail: by the second quarter of the eleventh century the stream had run dry.

Slaves were not the only commodity to be exchanged for dirhams, although individually they probably fetched higher prices than any other item on the market. Foremost among the other items were furs, although wax, honey and, from the far north, walrus tusks were in demand, too; one should also note that manufactured goods from the Latin West, 'Frankish swords', were already being brought by Rus traders to the markets of Baghdad in the mid-ninth century, and this particular commodity chain probably continued well into the tenth century. Furs also feature in the report of Ibn Khurradadhbih concerning their route, whereas he makes no mention of slaves for sale.[10] Being at once lightweight, durable and of proven value, furs came to provide a steady pulse of exchanges and, as James Howard-Johnston shows, it is no accident that the flaunting of furs became the winter style at the caliphal court around the time of the signs of the first Islamic silver arriving in the north; the fashion percolated down the Abbasid socio-political hierarchy. If, rather like modern drug traffickers, slave-dealers and their commodities have left few obvious material traces,[11] trafficking in furs has left a trail of archaeological 'footprints' and it drew in vast numbers of participants, without need of means of coercion. The fur trade's beginnings predated the period of intensive, long-haul slave-trading and it carried on long afterwards.[12] And yet for all this, one may doubt whether the sheer volume of the silver reaching eastern and northern Europe in the Viking Age can be explained by furs alone. Several chapters in this book signal a certain correlation between clusters of hoards and emergent centres of power, a pattern more suggestive of intensive slave-raiding and -trading than of dealings in furs. Moreover, if furs had been the commodity primarily responsible for the import of Islamic silver, one would not expect much of the silver to have made its way west to the British Isles, or to have done so rapidly. Yet there is intriguing evidence that this was happening: not just the finds and indications of silversmithing on Bornholm and at other Scandinavian settlements and workshops, but also the data coming to light from the Viking camp pitched at Torksey for the winter of 872/3.

As Andrew R. Woods' study indicates, dirhams are the second commonest type of coin to be found at Torksey. They are all in fragments, often very small and occurring as single finds, scattered across the campsite. They were probably intended for use as bullion in quite small-scale economic transactions alongside ingots and hack-silver, a pattern also seen at Kaupang in Norway and Uppåkra in southern Sweden. In 865 the Great Army brought stocks of dirhams (amongst much else) and someone, at least, saw fit to acquire pieces that had been struck in the Abbasid caliphate around the time of, or even after, the Army's arrival in England.[13] The latest of these took six or seven years at most to reach eastern England and, judging by all the weights and balances found at Torksey, the warriors envisaged dealings in both bullion and currency, equipping themselves with dies and other apparatus for metalworking, and probably issuing some imitative coinage. This is testimony to the newcomers' versatility, and their aptitude for catering for societies long familiar with monetary transactions. But it raises the question of what sort of commodity can have been desirable enough for the Vikings to bring silver to the British Isles for purposes of exchange. They can scarcely have come for the furs.[14] This is not to underrate either the stimulus given by the Vikings to a host of short- and medium-distance enterprises or the complexity of the interactions. Their multiplicity, together with the difficulties in evaluating them, are made clear by Elina Screen's survey of coins as indicators of communications between Scandinavia and the British Isles. Clearly, there were regional variations and fluctuations over time. Few Anglo-Saxon or Frankish coins are found in Scandinavia for the later ninth and early tenth century, while 'parcels' of coins of Æthelred II found in Scandinavia probably register his tribute-payments to Cnut. At the same time, Scandinavian settlement in eastern England seems to have done much to develop waterborne trading in wool, extending from the Lincolnshire Wolds to Northumbria and beyond, and also south to London and Flanders.[15]

That exchanges involving silver were underway in Ireland, too, not long after the Vikings' arrival there is suggested by John Sheehan's study of the hack-silver known from hoards and what appear to be single finds, set against the general background of the Islamic coins found in hoards. He also draws attention to recent investigations of the *longphort* at Woodstown, Co. Waterford, where finds of crucibles and of cupels for the assaying of silver attest intensive metalworking reminiscent of, respectively, Torksey and the workshop at Fröjel discussed by Gustafsson. This makes it all the more intriguing that the types and design of the arm-rings and similar items comprising the hack-silver have analogies in finds in the Baltic region, particularly on Gotland. The fragments of between two and four spiral rings found in Ireland are (as their nickname of 'Permian rings' suggests) pointers towards communications with the Baltic and lands still further to the east.[16] The pattern of finds of such hack-silver and dirhams includes Woodstown and other locations in eastern Ireland together with north-west England, southern Scandinavia and Gotland. There was a strong Scandinavian presence in Lancashire and Cheshire and yet, as Sheehan observes, 'four times as many coin-only hoards with an Islamic element [are known] in the Dublin region than in north-west England'. There may, he suggests, have been close, even direct, connections between that region and southern Scandinavia and the Baltic. Moreover, a sizeable proportion of the silver ended up within the purlieus of the foremost Irish clans and kings, and this points to their enrichment through active dealings in silver.

There are, then, several reasons for drawing north-west Europe within the same picture as the Baltic Rim and lands further east. Firstly, the evidence coming from Torksey, in particular, highlights Scandinavians' savoir faire in matters of currency and raises the question of whether they would not have been equally quick learners when it came to dealing with Islamic coins, far to the east of the Baltic. This fits well with the traces of cupellation and other hints of keen concern with the quality of silver apparent at Woodstown as well as Fröjel. This suggests a certain commonality in outlook and technical skills in markedly differing contexts, ranging from established emporia to the winter camps of large armies. This kind of get-rich-quick mentality went with awareness of what amassing of silver could do to enhance one's existing power, as witness some Irish rulers and those in charge at Torksey. Moreover, silver seems to have played an important role in the formation of new political nodes, among the Poles and the Rus as well as the Hiberno-Norse astride the Irish Sea and Western Isles. Direct or conclusive evidence may be lacking, but the dynamics and fortunes of modern drug trafficking provide points of comparison that are, at the very least, suggestive. The chapter by Andrew P. Roach and Alex Marshall highlights the drastic fluctuations in wealth, the role of ostentatiousness and violence, and the political dividends that might accrue to a suitably talented and ambitious operator.

Viewed against this background, there is nothing very surprising about the movement – sometimes very swift – of boats, persons and things between the Middle East or Central Asia and the Baltic and North Atlantic. The chronology of the Torksey dirhams – a fair proportion datable to around the mid-ninth century – exemplifies this circulation. So, too, do the similarities between the types of non-numismatic silver objects found in Ireland and on Gotland. An assortment of commodities might have given rise to such frenetic journeying and bartering across vast distances: furs, or the textiles, cattle and leather in which Ireland abounded.[17] Doubt, however, lingers as to whether these items can have had quite the allure or sheer marketability to account for the arrival of so much Islamic silver in the Baltic and numerous points further west. As noted above, one activity that leaves fewer archaeological 'footprints' than fur-trading is slave-trading. It may be no coincidence that raw materials for the latter trade were quite easy to come by, living as they often did in relatively dense clusters in the lowlands of Britain and also on the island of Ireland, and mostly within thirty miles or so of a navigable river or the sea. Conveyance by water was, after all, by far the most expedient and economical means of transporting goods: from this perspective, the British Isles were unusually well placed to provide readily conveyable commodities which showed promise of being, almost literally, worth their weight in silver. This would accord with Janel Fontaine's detection of a shift in the practices of the Vikings and others from around the mid-ninth century onwards: towards large-scale and multistage slave-raiding and -dealing around the British Isles, fuelled by networks of suppliers and sellers.[18] That men and women of high status could prosper from these activities is clear from the better-documented late Anglo-Saxon era. The wife of Earl Godwine of Wessex was accused by the twelfth-century writer William of Malmesbury of engaging in the purchase of many slaves in England, especially beautiful girls, for export to her native Denmark, 'so that by this hideous traffic she could accumulate vast wealth'.[19] The Godwine family, one may note, had estates strung across southern England, some of them (including ones belonging to Godwine's wife) looking towards the English Channel or that 'veritable "Viking lake"', the Irish Sea.[20]

These general considerations and bits of information fall short of answering all the questions raised at the outset. Given the shortcomings and imbalances of our data – the dirhams constituting a very particular type of evidence yet, through their sheer numbers, being difficult to catalogue and analyse – many problems defy neat resolution and, as will be clear from the lines taken in some of our chapters, different answers to key questions remain in play.[21] But what follows should set a number of points in sharper focus while opening up new channels for further exploration. And, it is hoped, the overall effect is to justify our treatment of silver, slaves and Gotland as being intertwined, important components in the workings of what has aptly been termed the Viking diaspora.[22]

Notes

1 Jonsson (2015); Jansson in this volume.
2 For a bibliographical discussion, see Gruszczyński in this volume. A minimum of five coins for the purposes of analysing hoard contents is the working method of, for example, Kilger (2008), p. 209.
3 On the likely interrelationship between a few far-flung emporia, see Sindbæk (2007), pp. 126–9; Sindbæk (2017).
4 On *GL* and *GS*, see Wyatt and Gruszczyński in this volume. One runestone does, however, mention the fur trade: see Svedjemo in this volume. See also Snædal (n.d.).
5 See Jansson in this volume.
6 On this, see Paal and Rajandu (2014).

7 See Svedjemo in this volume.
8 Regrettably, it did not prove possible to include in this volume a chapter on the dirham hoards from present-day Estonia and Finland. See Talvio (2017); Talvio (2002); Leimus (2007); Mägi (2018).
9 Zschieschang (2017), p. 183. See also Hardt (2008), pp. 746–8.
10 Ibn Khurradadhbih, *Kitab al-masalik*, ed. de Goeje, pp. 115–16; ed. Lewicki, pp. 76–7. Carolingian legislative measures to ban the export of swords and other weaponry are reviewed, along with a survey of blades with the name Ulfberht inscribed and other Frankish traits, by Stalsberg (2017), esp. pp. 262–8, 270.
11 They have not, however, escaped detection altogether: *IC*. See also Fontaine (2017b); Raffield (2019).
12 The longstanding nature of fur-trading nexuses spanning the Baltic and the Volga and Kama river basins is emphasised by Callmer (2017), pp. 137, 139, 153–5.
13 The latest examples are two fragments struck respectively at Merv in 864/5 and at an uncertain mint, perhaps Merv or al-Shash [Tashkent], between 866 and 868: Blackburn (2011), p. 230 and appendix 2, nos 92, 93, p. 258.
14 The principal investigators have remarked on the clear indications of 'intensive trade and exchange in goods and probably in slaves', as also on the predominantly Anglo-Saxon types of dress accessory and jewellery found there, presumably the belongings of their original wearers: Hadley *et al.* (2016), pp. 62, 57. The involuntary presence of large numbers of local persons could well have something to do with the remarkable size of the camps at Torksey and Aldwark, some 55ha and 31ha respectively, dwarfing such emporia as Birka and Kaupang (*ibid.*, p. 58). See now also Hadley and Richards (2018).
15 Faith (2012), pp. 683–9, 696–7. Unfortunately, the various relevant contributions in Kershaw *et al.* (eds) (2019) appeared too late to be taken full account of in this volume, and likewise with the contributions in Callmer *et al.* (eds) (2017). The same goes more generally for the works of Mägi (2018) and Korpela (2019).
16 See also Abrams (2012), pp. 31–4, 38.
17 Edwards (2008), pp. 264–6, 279, 281–3, 300; Ó Corráin (2008), pp. 568–75; Wallace (2008), pp. 833–4.
18 Fontaine (2017a), ch. 5. See also Holm (1986), esp. pp. 330–1, 333–40.
19 William of Malmesbury, *Gesta*, vol. 2, pp. 362–3. The slave dealer is identified with Godwine's first wife, Thyra, by Wyatt (n. 105) and Roach and Marshall (n. 15) in this volume.
20 Baxter (2007), appendix 4, pp. 316–17; plate 2, facing p. 143. For the characterisation of the Irish Sea, see Wallace (2008), p. 839.
21 See Wyatt, Brink and Skre in this volume.
22 Abrams (2012). What Abrams terms (*ibid.*, p. 32) 'the diversity of patterns of interaction between the overseas settlements and locations in the homelands' is consistent with the distribution-pattern and variegated uses of the dirhams, silver ornaments and other artefacts found between points on the Irish Sea and in the Baltic Rim and the lands still further east.

Bibliography

Primary sources

Ibn Khurradadhbih, *Kitab al-masalik*, ed. and French tr. M. J. de Goeje, *Kitab al-masalik wa-al-mamalik (Liber viarum et regnorum)*, BGA 6, Leiden (1889); ed. T. Lewicki, *Źródła arabskie do dziejów Słowiańszczyzny*, vol. 1, Wrocław (1956), pp. 63–81.

William of Malmesbury, *Gesta regum Anglorum*, ed. and tr. R. A. B. Mynors, 2 vols, Oxford (1998–9).

Secondary literature

Abrams, L. (2012), 'Diaspora and identity in the Viking Age', *Early Medieval Europe* 20: 17–38.

Baxter, S. D. (2007), *The Earls of Mercia: Lordship and Power in Late Anglo-Saxon England*, Oxford.

Blackburn, M. (2011), 'The Viking winter camp at Torksey, 872–3', in *VCC*, pp. 221–64.

Callmer, J. (2017), 'The rise of the dominion of the ar-Rus in the northern parts of eastern Europe, seventh to ninth centuries AD: a case of culture construction', in *IFD*, pp. 136–67.

Edwards, N. (2008), 'The archaeology of early medieval Ireland, *c.* 400–1169: settlement and economy', in D. Ó Cróinín (ed.), *A New History of Ireland*, vol. 1: *Prehistoric and Early Ireland*, Oxford, pp. 235–300.

Faith, R. (2012), 'The structure of the market for wool in early medieval Lincolnshire', *Economic History Review* 65: 674–700.

Fontaine, J. (2017a), 'Slave trading in the British Isles and the Czech lands, 7th–11th centuries', unpublished PhD dissertation, King's College London.

Fontaine, J. (2017b), 'Early medieval slave-trading in the archaeological record: comparative methodologies', *Early Medieval Europe* 25: 466–88.

Hadley, D. M. and J. D. Richards (2018), 'In search of the Viking Great Army: beyond the winter camps', *Medieval Settlement Research* 33: 1–17.

Hadley, D. M. *et al.* (2016), 'The winter camp of the Viking Great Army, AD 872–3, Torksey, Lincolnshire', *The Antiquaries Journal* 96: 23–67.

Hardt, M. (2008), 'Fernhandel und Subsistenzwirtschaft. Überlegungen zur Wirtschaftsgeschichte der frühen Westslawen', in U. Ludwig and T. Schilp (eds), *Nomen et Fraternitas. Festschrift für Dieter Geuenich zum 65. Geburtstag*, Berlin; New York, pp. 741–63.

Holm, P. (1986), 'The slave trade of Dublin, ninth to twelfth centuries', *Peritia* 5: 317–45.

Jonsson, K. (2015), 'Viking Age coins found in Sweden', in L. Larsson *et al.* (eds), *Small Things, Wide Horizons: Studies in Honour of Birgitta Hårdh*, Oxford, pp. 51–7.

Kershaw, J. *et al.* (eds) (2019), *Silver, Butter, Cloth: Monetary and Social Economies in the Viking Age*, Oxford.

Kilger, C. (2008), 'Kaupang from afar: aspects of the interpretation of dirham finds in northern and eastern Europe between the late 8th and early 10th centuries', in *ME*, pp. 199–252.

Korpela, J. (2019), *Slaves from the North: Finns and Karelians in the East European Slave Trade, 900–1600*, Leiden.

Leimus, I. (2007), *Sylloge of Islamic Coins: Estonian Public Collections*, Tallinn.

Mägi, M. (2018), *In Austrvegr: The Role of the Eastern Baltic in Viking Age Communication across the Baltic Sea*, Leiden.

Ó Corráin, D. (2008), 'Ireland *c.* 800: aspects of society', in D. Ó Cróinín (ed.), *A New History of Ireland*, vol. 1: *Prehistoric and Early Ireland*, Oxford, pp. 549–608.

Paal, J. and E. Rajandu (2014), 'Calcareous pine forests on Gotland, their typology and main soil properties', *Forestry Studies* 60: 5–23.

Raffield, B. (2019), 'The slave markets of the Viking world: comparative perspectives on an "invisible archaeology"', *Slavery & Abolition* 40: 682–705.

Sindbæk, S. M. (2007), 'Networks and nodal points: the emergence of towns in early Viking Age Scandinavia', *Antiquity* 81: 119–31.

Sindbæk, S. M. (2017), 'A site of intersection: Staraya Ladoga, eastern silver, and long-distance communication networks in early medieval Europe', in *IFD*, pp. 76–90.

Snædal, T. (n.d.), 'Rute socken G 319–G 326', *Gotlands runinskrifter* 3, RAÄ, raa.se/kul turarvet/arkeologi-fornlamningar-och-fynd/runstenar/digitala-sveriges-runinskrifter/ gotlands-runinskrifter-3 (accessed 16 December 2019).

Stalsberg, A. (2017), 'Swords from the Carolingian empire to the Baltic Sea and beyond', in *IFD*, pp. 259–80.

Talvio, T. (2002), *Coins and Coin Finds in Finland, AD 800–1200*, Helsinki.

Talvio, T. (2017), 'Dirham hoards from the Gulf of Finland region', in *IFD*, pp. 281–91.

Wallace, P. F. (2008), 'The archaeology of Ireland's Viking-age towns', in D. Ó Cróinín (ed.), *A New History of Ireland*, vol. 1: *Prehistoric and Early Ireland*, Oxford, pp. 814–41.

Zschieschang, C. (2017), 'Das Früh- und Hochmittelalterliche Siedlungsumfeld von Trepcza, Czermno und Gródek im Lichte der Toponomastik. Eine methodische und areale Standortbestimmung', in M. Wołoszyn (ed.), *From Cherven Towns to Curzon Line: The Lands on the Middle Bug during the Middle Ages and the Historiographic Perspective on the Formation of Poland's Eastern Border, 18th–21st Centuries*, Cracow; Leipzig; Rzeszów; Warsaw, pp. 161–83.

Part I
Cogs and drivers

Map I.1 Scandinavia and the British Isles.

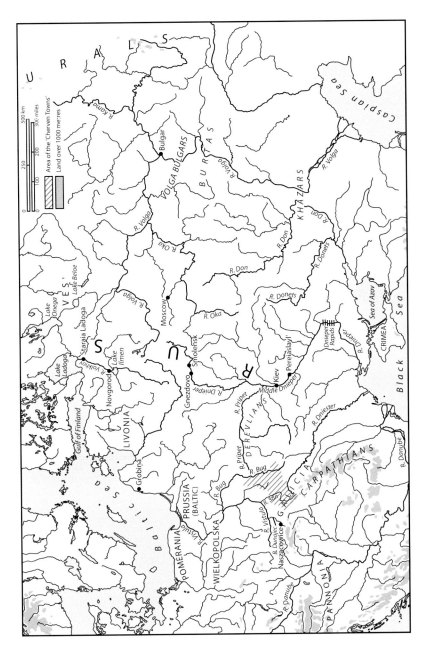

Map I.2 Rus and the Baltic.

2 Reading between the lines

Tracking slaves and slavery in the early middle ages

David Wyatt

Tracking slaveholding behaviours

Pre-history endured far longer in Scandinavia and the Baltic than in much of the rest of Europe. Although we have a few fragmented accounts of Viking raids in the region from the ninth century on, most of our textual evidence for slaves and slaving comes from twelfth- and thirteenth-century sources – ironically a period that many believe heralded the disappearance of slavery from northern Europe.[1] For much of the Viking Age, our only evidence for the enslavement and trading of people in the Baltic region is archaeological, yet the problems of detecting such evidence for slavery are manifold.[2] Numismatic, osteological, artefactual and archaeological site analysis can reveal information about slave-trading routes, transportation, diet, living conditions, possible occupations, levels of violence and even ritual sacrifice. Yet the complexities and contradictions in human behaviour inherent in slavery are far harder to unpick and the historical sources are equally fraught with interpretative problems and speculation.

In the west we tend to see slavery as historically distant, banished by the combined forces of economic progress, rational modernity and Christian morality.[3] Such perceptions colour our views of slaveholding in medieval British and Irish societies, and historiography in other regions shows similar impulses:[4] much of the discourse on medieval Scandinavian slavery, for example, tries to explain how and why it disappeared,[5] a key assumption being that by the mid-thirteenth century slavery was in significant decline and that in certain places, such as Iceland, it had vanished altogether.[6] Slavery is seen as predominantly a Viking-Age phenomenon, whose decline was inevitable in the face of various social, economic and religious factors that paved the way to a freer, less brutal era.[7]

Yet there are probably more slaves in the world today than ever before:[8] around 21 million individuals worldwide are estimated to be in some form of slavery,[9] with over 55% of them women and girls and one in four sexually exploited.[10] The prevalence of domestic servitude, sexual exploitation and a high proportion of enslaved women and children resonates with our evidence for medieval slaving.[11] In communities across northern Europe, the enslavement of both men and women was an important symbolic attribute of young male warriors, and slave-raiding one way to emphasise warrior prowess and virility.[12] Slaving was often synonymous with sexual violence and, more broadly, with patriarchal social structures: a range of medieval sources associate slaveholding and slave-taking with expressions of power, hierarchy and gender norms.[13] The slave trade certainly generated great wealth and nurtured exchange networks, yet far deeper human drives fuelled and sustained this trade.

While the nature of the sources and cultural contexts are very different, Steven Epstein's approach to Italian slaveholders can be applied to a range of medieval Nordic sources.[14] These sources were predominantly created by those who owned, raided and traded people, and it is their behaviours which have left a mark on the historical record.[15] But many others who did not own, raid or trade slaves were socialised into slaveholding communities; they participated in the formal legal systems and shared the less formal attitudes that reinforced and perpetuated slavery: their voices are also heard in our sources.[16]

The enslaved themselves, whether female or male, are most likely to be glimpsed in our sources during traumatic or liminal moments in their lives: when others sought to control them, justify their enslavement, stereotype or stigmatise them.[17] They are most visible when being enslaved, captured, transported, sold and accommodated, or when resisting, escaping or being manumitted, and at birth and death.[18] We therefore need to recognise and analyse our sources' evidence for the experiences of the enslaved in relation to violence, sexual and reproductive exploitation, social exclusion and attempts, however contradictory, to dehumanise them. We should also search for more circumstantial evidence of communal slaveholding behaviours, including strict codes of insult, honour and shame; placing great value on warrior raiding; practising sexual hospitality, concubinage and male guardianship of women; the stigmatisation and differentiation of outsiders; and geographical proximity to known slaving activities. Indeed, it was not only slaves – and by extension slaveholders – who risked being stigmatised and stereotyped, but also all those who saw themselves as belonging to the same social group; a sense of belonging cemented by networks of kinship and community.

We will begin by exploring *Guta Lag* (Figure 2.1), a legal text in which the stigma associated with slave status is particularly visible, before exploring contextual evidence from various sources – sagas, poetry, hagiographical texts, chronicles, annals and histories – to highlight the vibrancy and interconnectedness of slave-raiding and -trading networks and supply routes in northern Europe from the ninth to thirteenth centuries.

Tracking slaves and slavery in law codes

Gotland is our departure point for tracking slaves and slavery in northern Europe. Besides a short legendary history and a handful of runic inscriptions, *Guta Lag* is one of the island's earliest extant sources.[19] Composed in vernacular Gutnish, these law codes were later translated into Danish, Middle

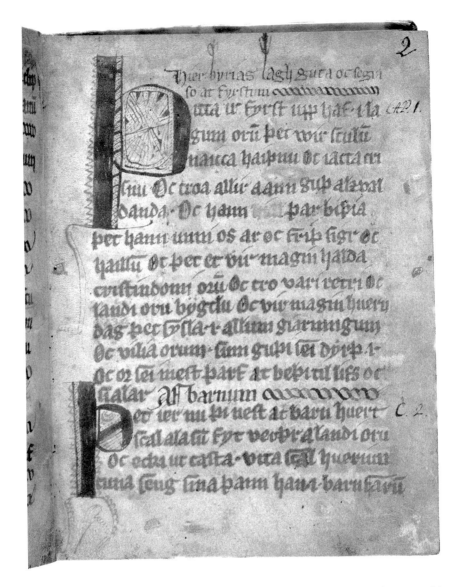

Figure 2.1 'Here begins the law of the Gotlanders and it says firstly this' – the first page of the earliest vellum manuscript (*Holm B 64*) of *Guta Lag* (mid-fourteenth-century).

Photo: Jens Östman; courtesy of the National Library of Sweden (Kungliga biblioteket).

High German and Middle Low German.[20] Eight manuscripts remain, although their dating and transmission is problematic. The earliest vellum manuscript (*Holm B 64*) is mid-fourteenth century and thought to be a copy of an original compiled in around 1300. A late sixteenth-century paper manuscript (*AM 54 4to*) contains a copy of the laws compiled in 1470, but is thought to derive from a version datable to *c*. 1260.[21] Interestingly, dating both manuscripts centres on their legal provisions for slavery.

Christine Peel argues that while *Holm B 64* is earlier, it actually contains a later version of the law codes and was probably compiled at a time of legal transition, since it omits the clauses dealing with the sale of, and punishments for theft by, slaves.[22] The later *AM 54 4to* contains these slave provisions, leading Peel to conclude that it must represent an earlier version of the laws.[23] She assumes that slavery had virtually disappeared from Gotlandic society by 1300,[24] and argues that because the slave provisions were no longer relevant to the redacting scribe of *Holm B 64*, he simply omitted them.[25] This conclusion is not without its problems: all the later *Guta Lag* manuscripts, including those in Danish and German, retain the slave provisions; and *Holm B 64* itself makes reference to them, albeit in an appended contents page of later, unknown date.[26] So how significant was the omission of the slave provisions from this single manuscript version of the laws? As Peel acknowledges, they also omit a number of other issues of relevance to Gotlandic society, including church law and, perhaps even more surprisingly given the island's trading traditions, commercial and maritime law.[27] Moreover, one slave provision *was* retained by the redactor of *Holm B 64* in the original manuscript: detailed rules for how fights between free men and slaves should be conducted and compensated, suggesting that this particular aspect of slaveholding behaviour continued to have relevance at least.[28]

Given that we have no way of knowing when slavery on Gotland ended, other than by speculating about the omission of the slave provisions in *Holm B 64*, Peel's argument is somewhat circular. As noted, it rests on the widespread assumption that slavery had all but disappeared from Gotland and Scandinavia in general by the end of the thirteenth century.[29] Yet while the date of *Guta Lag*'s compilation is relatively certain, when slavery ended is less so. The original thirteenth-century compiler clearly lived in a medieval slaveholding society and the laws were primarily a product of that society. Although Peel argues that *Guta Lag* may well contain pre-Christian elements,[30] its laws were mainly shaped by the concerns and conceptions of their thirteenth-century compiler.[31] It was a working guide to legal principle and process, rather than a repository of ancient custom and orally transmitted tradition,[32] yet the text neither simply transmits slaveholding traditions from a distant Viking Age, nor accurately represents thirteenth-century realities.[33] Rather, the laws represent a world of ideas. They provide us with a vision of how Gotlandic society was ordered and understood by its elite landowners,[34] and the fact that they were copied and translated suggests that they were still of relevance both on the island and further afield.[35] They also reveal some of the Gotlanders' underlying assumptions about enslaved people. By scrutinising the stigmas, stereotypes, punishments and conduct that masters attempted either to encourage or to prevent, we may be able to shed further light on the slaveholding behaviours of this island community.

Enslaved people are visible in *Guta Lag* at point of sale, procreation, resistance, escape, punishment and death. Its detailed provisions on slave purchase suggest an active slave-trading market, with buyers allowed to test out new slaves for up to six days before returning them, or paying for them, on the seventh. Anticipating possible tensions, with a vendor reluctant to accept 'returns', the buyer had to substantiate why they were unhappy with the slave's performance, although vendors remained liable to compensate the new owner for up to a year after purchase if one of three faults was later discovered: epilepsy, bed-wetting or leg impairment. The provisions also state that if a recently purchased slave were claimed by another slaveholder, the new owner had some redress and could 'call to the vendor and lead him [i.e. the slave] to him; he [i.e. the vendor] is then to defend your right to the man, or give you back as much as you previously paid for him'.[36] The legislation thus anticipates slaves being abducted and resold through some form of black market on the island, and this is an issue that we will return to later.

Guta Lag's depiction of enslavement has one unusual feature: it appears to have been fixed term. Ruth Karras suggests that this may refer to debt slavery,[37] and Christine Peel goes further, citing the earlier Danish translator Lis Jacobsen who argued that it indicated slavery 'was in the process of dissolving' on the island.[38] Yet *Guta Lag*'s many other slave provisions, including those regarding purchase, suggest otherwise. Indeed, the process of manumission has long been recognised as an integral, often essential, element of slaveholding systems, rather than a sign of their dissolution.[39] The promise of manumission, whether after a fixed period or not, encouraged obedience and accommodation, and there is often a striking correlation between manumission rates and a ready external supply of the recently enslaved to replace those freed.[40] Evidence from the *Legendary Saga of St Olaf*, probably compiled in the thirteenth century, may attest this elsewhere in Scandinavia. The saga offers a fictional account of the Norwegian noble Erling Skjalgsson (d. 1028), who is said to have granted his male slaves permission to work during their evening rest periods so that they might earn enough money to buy their freedom. Those who eventually attained manumission by these means continued to labour in Erling's service as freedmen, while he simply reinvested their redemption fees and 'bought other men'.[41] Close trading contacts with the slaving centre of Novgorod and the slave-raiding territories of the eastern Baltic during the thirteenth and fourteenth centuries suggest that Gotlandic merchants continued to have access to markets where they could buy slaves.[42] And slavery appears to have been hereditary on the island, supplementing external influxes.[43] It therefore seems likely that the fixed-term slavery seen in *Guta Lag* is indicative of slaveholding behaviour rather than of its dissolution. The law codes also clearly indicate that masters had the power to extend the period of enslavement to punish misdemeanours,[44] and such inherent uncertainty over honouring a fixed term would undoubtedly have facilitated exploitation of and control over the enslaved.[45]

Guta Lag suggests that violence pervaded the lives of the island's enslaved. A small fine was levied for punching, manhandling or grabbing another's slave by the hair, payable only if blood were drawn,[46] but no similar prohibitions seem to have applied for masters who beat their own slaves. An enslaved person accused of theft could be bound, led away and tortured by the injured party without the need to pay compensation to their master.[47] The potential for slave resistance and agency is evident from the brutal provisions for retributive violence on the masters' part. *Guta Lag* legislates against enslaved people running away, fighting back, stealing (both individually and in gangs), killing people, raping free women and committing infanticide on children fathered by a master or some other man.[48] Such provisions recognise that slaves had choices, albeit often desperate and limited ones. There is a common misconception that enslaved people in medieval Scandinavia were on a par with cattle.[49] I would argue that this assumption is based on a rather un-nuanced reading of aspects of the law codes. The compiler of *Guta Lag* clearly acknowledged the humanity of the enslaved, and this was fundamentally significant for facilitating not only their physical exploitation but also their broader cultural symbolic value as base 'others'. Like other medieval Scandinavian law codes, *Guta Lag* reflects a violent, hierarchical and intensely patriarchal society that revolved around notions of honour, shame, lineage and networks of kinship and affiliation. Identity and belonging were central to this vision of Gotlandic society: legal privileges and higher compensation payments for offences clearly favoured Gotlanders over the large number of free foreigners living there,[50] yet the marginality of those enslaved reinforced collective identity and morality for all legally free individuals, Gotlanders and non-Gotlanders alike.[51] The exclusion of slaves from the field of honour is clear from a provision on inflicting wounds, which states that 'no one pays fines for insults to a slave and similarly a slave does not pay fines for insult to anyone'.[52] Through such ingroup–outgroup constructions, the compiler of *Guta Lag* characterised slaves as liminal individuals who, through their exclusion from most legal processes, reinforced a sense of group identity, cohesion and belonging amongst slaveholders and non-slaveholders alike.

This is perhaps most apparent in the laws that relate both directly and indirectly to enslaved women. For example, a provision regarding physical assault states that a non-Gotlandic woman who suffered the dishonour of being manhandled, disrobed or groped by an assailant should receive only half the compensation due to a Gotlandic woman for a similar offence; but this was granted only if the foreigner were 'a free and freeborn woman'.[53] By implication, enslaved women were fair game with no honour to impugn –

provided they were not raped, since this would have clearly constituted an affront to their masters' honour.[54] *Guta Lag*'s compiler also noted that a priest who married a slave so debased his bloodline as to forfeit his own rights and those of his unborn children to hold the status of a Gotlander:[55] it was clearly important that the Gotlandic gene pool should not be polluted by servile blood.[56] The term for a slave woman's son (*þysun*) is used by the laws to denote any son born out of wedlock, and such individuals were strictly prohibited from inheriting property unless they were able to prove Gotlandic descent on both sides for three generations.[57] In Karras' view, the 'fact that the general term derives from the term for the son of a slave woman hints that originally the great majority of those born out of wedlock would have been the children of slaves'.[58] While this statement may be speculative, the compiler of *Guta Lag* very clearly and deliberately defined lineage and belonging in opposition to the exclusion and marginality of enslaved women.

Guta Lag depicts enslaved women as the weakest, most dishonourable and degraded of all individuals. Paradoxically, they appear to have mattered to the Gotlandic community precisely because they were so marginalised, embodying concepts of power, belonging, honour and superiority alongside deep-seated fears of deracination, dishonour, stigmatisation and exposure to arbitrary violation.[59] Such fears may have stemmed from genuine concerns that living in a slaving region engendered. Indeed, evidence for Baltic slave-raiding and -trading is relatively abundant between the twelfth and fourteenth centuries, particularly in the eastern coastal regions of Livonia and Estonia, where women and children were prime targets.[60] Gotlandic merchants regularly travelled through this region and maintained longstanding ties with the urban centre of Novgorod, with its lively slave trade and vibrant slave market.[61] Evidence for slaving in the Baltic occurs in a treaty struck between Magnus Eriksson, king of Sweden, and Prince Yuri Danilovich of Novgorod in 1327. This includes an agreement that any slaves who escaped from one ruler's territory to the other's should be captured and returned across the border.[62] Novgorodian warriors launched numerous raids on Finland and Estonia during the mid-fourteenth century, capturing men, women and children, some of them Swedes, and many appear to have ended up in the slave market at Novgorod.[63]

While we are not aware of any slave-raiding on Gotland in the thirteenth and fourteenth centuries, there is evidence to suggest that marauding fleets of raiders were active throughout the Baltic in this period,[64] and it seems plausible that legal preoccupations with belonging and exclusion should reflect insecurities about capture and abduction. Such insecurities are evident from *Guta Lag*'s provisions on land purchase:

> If someone is taken hostage and he ransoms himself with his land or property, then his nearest kinsman is to redeem it, if he wishes, and pay the money for it once the other comes home. If a farmer's son is captive,

or a minor, no one may ransom him for more than three marks in silver, unless authority exists from his father or kinsmen [. . .].[65]

Similarly, if a brother who owns shared property falls captive when travelling abroad, his sibling is to ransom him; but if he is travelling 'with divided goods then he is to ransom himself'.[66] While these provisions seem to relate to hostage taking and not enslavement, the implications are clear: the compiler of *Guta Lag* thought it possible, even probable, that individuals might be taken captive, either on Gotland or journeying abroad. As the laws were designed for relatively wealthy landowners, they probably reflect abductions where the hostages were ransomed and freed. But this may not always have been the case: significant areas of the Baltic were dangerous slave-raiding and -trading arenas at this time;[67] and poorer individuals or slaves taken captive were unlikely to have had wealthy relatives to ransom them. Their fates are not easily seen in *Guta Lag*, since they were of little or no consequence for the Gotlandic lawmakers, although the clauses on the purchases of slaves suggest they might be abducted and illicitly sold on to new owners, hinting that this may not have been an unusual occurrence.

There is no direct evidence in *Guta Lag* that free Gotlandic women might be abducted and sold, although it does depict a society in which some women were held as slaves, and several of its provisions suggest a real fear of female abduction. The crime is taken very seriously, with severe penalties for any man caught carrying off an honourable Gotlandic woman from her family by force: 'his neck[,] or wergild'.[68] More subtle indications of these insecurities can be seen in a provision regarding assaults on women, where anyone deliberately knocking the headdress off a woman had to pay a significant fine of one mark if her head was left partially exposed, and two marks if completely uncovered.[69] Hair coverings were important physical markers for women in Scandinavian societies, symbolic of both honourable status and sexual inaccessibility to all but her husband. Exposing a free woman's head and hair dishonoured both the woman and her male guardian, giving her the appearance of a slave.[70] If a female slave were assaulted in the same way, any fine related simply to the physical blow, since she could not be dishonoured.[71] This provision reinforces the legal constructions regarding identity and belonging discussed above. It also suggests that on Gotland appearances mattered, especially for women. How one looked and dressed could make the difference between being taken hostage for ransom or being trafficked and sold on the slave market.

Tracking slaves and slavery in literary sources and chronicles

We are able to glimpse such stark realities in a number of Old Norse sagas which, like *Guta Lag*, date from the thirteenth and fourteenth centuries. *Heimskringla* presents the Baltic as a politically fragmented yet closely interconnected maritime region characterised by endemic raiding, violence, slave-taking and struggles for power and honour between a bellicose elite.[72] The abduction of women features prominently, emphasising prestige and strength; an account in the *Saga of Harald Sigurtharson* of an expedition against the Danes of Funen in the mid-eleventh century shows this. A stanza by the praise-poet Valgard of Voll describes how Harald ravaged the local population:

> Down-cast, away drifted
> Danes who lived still, scattered
> in flight, while fair maidens
> fell into our power.
> With fetters fastened, women
> followed you down to your vessels;
> cut chafing chains the flesh of
> chattel maidens cruelly.[73]

Not just noteworthy but boast-worthy, such raiding for women was expected of a young warrior with pretensions to power.[74] This is not the saga's only account of female abduction: some years later, after becoming king, Harald raided Denmark once more, taking great booty in Jutland. His spoils included the daughters of the chieftain Thorkel Geysa, whom he 'led down to the ships bound'. Unlike the women from Funen's farming community, whose fate was clearly enslavement, these noblewomen were the offspring of a powerful guardian and thus bound rather than manacled with chains and later ransomed for an 'immense amount of money'.[75] The account suggests that Snorri and his audience clearly understood that the treatment and fate of captive women depended on their status, appearance, the wealth of their guardians – and a degree of luck.

The *Saga of Olaf Tryggvason* provides further insight into the nature of slave-raiding and -trading in the eastern Baltic through the eyes of our thirteenth-century author. Snorri relates events said to have taken place in the second half of the tenth century, when Olaf was only a child. Olaf and his mother Astrith sailed across the Baltic in the company of merchants to visit his uncle in Novgorod, but their ship was attacked by Viking pirates based in Estonia and they were enslaved and the group was then split up. Separated from his mother, Olaf was acquired by Klerkon, an Estonian warrior, who 'got him as his share' along with two other male captives, Thorolf and Thorgisl. Klerkon decided that Thorolf, Olaf's foster-father, was 'too old to be a thrall, nor able to do slave work', so killed him, but took the boys 'with him and sold them to a man called Klerk'. Olaf was soon sold on again, this time to a certain Reas, and worked on this master's farmstead for several years before being recognised at an Estonian market by the Norwegian noble Sigurth Eiriksson. Sigurth, who was on a diplomatic mission in the region, bought and freed the boy, taking him with him to Novgorod where Olaf was raised at the court of Prince Vladimir

[Valdamar].[76] Some years later, during a trading expedition in the Baltic, a rich Norwegian merchant called Lothin toured the markets of Estonia where 'many bondwomen' were for sale. At one of these markets Lothin spotted a woman he thought he recognised, 'who had been sold as a slave', and despite her changed appearance realised this was Astrith, Olaf's mother. Astrith begged Lothin to buy her and take her back to Norway; he agreed, on condition that she married him once there.[77] Astrith's position was so desperate that she was obliged to give in to Lothin's demands and later bore him several children.

The sagas of Olaf Tryggvason and Harald Sigurtharson depict the eastern and western Baltic as a slaving zone, where warrior groups forcibly abducted people – particularly women and children – to dishonour opponents, reward followers and gain wealth through their sale or ransom. In the account of Olaf's enslavement, the raiders executed his adult foster-father, while his mother and the two young boys were sold on, and according to Snorri, the Viking raiders would have been selective in their acquisitions, 'killing some and dividing others among them as thralls'.[78] Such targeting of women and children by slavers, and ridding themselves of adult males and the elderly, has analogies with raiding in many other slaveholding societies.[79] That slaving continued in the eastern Baltic is clear from the *Chronicle* of Henry of Livonia. Compiled in Livonia between 1225 and 1227, Henry's chronicle is considered to be a relatively first-hand – if clearly biased – account of events.[80] His text suggests that the capture and enslavement of women and children was a significant motive for warriors on either side of the crusading conflicts that raged across Baltic Prussia, Lithuania, Latvia, Estonia and Finland. The number of slave raids is staggering: between 1200 and 1227, Henry records 67 major raids, 25 by pagan warriors and 42 by Christian forces,[81] with most involving the enslavement of women and 'girls whom alone the army was accustomed to spare in these lands'.[82] It is perhaps unsurprising that Snorri's *Heimskringla* saw Estonia and Novgorod as areas where slave-raiding was endemic and where vibrant and expansive supply networks facilitated the sale and resale of captives on to new locations. Snorri's account of Lothin's trading mission to Estonia also illustrates the author's – probably accurate – assumptions about the prevalence and profitability of the tenth-century trade in enslaved women there, assumptions reinforced by the brutal realities of the Baltic conflicts in his own lifetime. While Snorri's depiction of Astrith's and Olaf's ransoming was a plot device, it also appears to reflect thirteenth-century insecurities about the abduction of women and minors in the region.[83] Such insecurities are also evident in *Guta Lag*. They show both the inherent dangers of living in a slaving zone and, for many captives, the stark uncertainty of whether they would be ransomed or trafficked.

At first glance, *Heimskringla* seems to offer unrivalled access to the history of the Baltic region in the early medieval period. The realism of the accounts, accessibility of the prose, convincing characterisation and close relationship to actual historical figures and locations make the text appear an objective and accurate reflection of events. In general, eighteenth- and early nineteenth-century historians regarded the sagas as reliable sources based on longstanding, orally transmitted traditions, although by the early twentieth century they increasingly came to be viewed as literary works, whose authors wrote with specific purposes, rather than a well-preserved snapshot of earlier oral traditions.[84] The author of *Heimskringla* certainly seems to have modified his sources for his own needs, and this collection of sagas is best regarded as a repository for historical tradition rather than historical fact.[85] In recent decades, scholars have interrogated these texts for concepts, behavioural codes and norms, focusing on what the sagas can reveal about the society in which they were composed.[86] They have thus tended to characterise references to enslaved people in *Heimskringla* and *Guta Lag* as anachronisms, looking back to a vanishing or vanished slaveholding past. Yet the authors of both texts clearly lived in a world where the enslavement and sexual trafficking of women prevailed, where the slave trade was far-reaching and economically significant, and where slaveholding continued to define cultural identity and patriarchal conceptions of power.

A similar world is evident in the anonymous *Laxdœla Saga*, one of the thirteenth-century Sagas of the Icelanders (*Íslendingasǫgur*) dealing with the island's settlement by Vikings over the tenth and eleventh centuries. It recounts in detail the purchase and sexual exploitation of Melkorka, an enslaved Irish princess, by the Icelandic noble Hǫskuldr.[87] This includes a particularly detailed depiction of the slave market on an island in the south of Norway, where Hǫskuldr selected Melkorka from a group of 12 women for sale in the highly decorated tent of a wealthy trader, Gilli the Rus (*Gilli in gerzki*). After some haggling, Hǫskuldr paid the substantial sum of three marks of silver for Melkorka, leading her away to his booth where he 'slept with the woman the same evening'.[88] Both author and audience of *Laxdœla Saga* clearly considered it plausible for a Rus slaver to trade his wares at a southern Norwegian market, and for these wares to include a teenage girl abducted in Ireland together with 11 other women of unknown origins. And this, in turn, implies awareness of the expansive and interconnected nature of raiding and trading routes in the Irish Sea region, the Baltic and the Scandinavian homelands, and familiarity with slave-trading mores and the likely nature of a slave market.

The British and Irish sources offer ample evidence to support the thirteenth-century Old Norse and Icelandic sagas' descriptions of Scandinavian slaving in the Irish Sea region.[89] Indeed, if the Old Irish texts provide any reflection of warrior raiding behaviour, then 'womenfolk and youths and boys' constituted typical plunder for Irish warriors.[90] Writing reasonably close to the events, the Irish annalists record extensive Scandinavian slave-raiding activity from the mid-ninth century onwards, with many raids taking large numbers of slaves, and the Hiberno-Norse town of Dublin seemingly a slave market from early on.[91] By the mid-tenth century, when Melkorka was supposedly abducted, slave raids by both the Irish, and the Irish in alliance with Hiberno-Norse raiders, appear to have been on the increase,[92] and over the next two centuries, Irish annalists record no fewer than 40 major slave raids, with many of the victims most likely women and children.[93] Occasionally the medieval annalists provide an explicit reference to this fact; for example, the *Annals of the Four Masters* records that, following an Irish raid on Dublin in 941, 'its women, boys and common folk were carried into bondage'.[94]

An account from the *Life* of St Findan adds further flesh to the bare bones of the annals' entries concerning slave raids. Findan was an Irishman from Leinster whose *Life*, written by a fellow monk shortly after his death in the late ninth century,[95] begins with the abduction of his sister and other local women by Viking raiders from Norway. Ordered by his father to secure his sister's release, Findan set out to ransom her with a small group that included an interpreter. Unfortunately, things did not go to plan. Findan himself was captured by the raiders, thrown into chains and transported to their ships, where 'all that day and the following night he suffered in his fetters without food or drink'. Findan's captors then 'held a council at which the more sensible of them – inspired in their humanity by God, we believe – argued that men who had come to ransom others ought not themselves to be held by force'.[96] Findan was freed through this divine intercession, although the fate of his unfortunate sister and the other women is unclear. This was not Findan's only deliverance from enslavement. Some years later he became involved in a blood feud with a rival Irish kin group. Although he accepted compensation for his father's slaying, Findan's enemies feared he might continue to desire revenge and so plotted with a band of Norse raiders. They invited Findan to a lavish banquet on the sea shore, when the Norsemen descended 'by prior agreement with his enemies, and seized him. They bound him tightly and immediately made off with him', selling Findan 'on to another, who sold him to a third, and the third to a fourth'.[97] His new master decided to return to Norway with the unfortunate saint and a number of other slaves in tow, but the party was ambushed en route by yet another war band: in the ensuing struggle, Findan fought on the side of his new master to repel the boarders, and was rewarded by the removal of his manacles. Once again he was favoured with divine intervention and managed to flee his captors on Orkney; after many hardships, Findan was eventually rescued by a group of fellow Christians and thereafter devoted himself to God.

Such hagiographical texts are problematic, much like the saga evidence, although they often include a great deal of incidental detail in order to make their miracle tales more believable to their audience. Thus although the *Life* of St Findan does not offer an accurate historical account, it does provide us with the author's assumptions about his social world, reflecting the ever-present possibility of enslavement, particularly of women, and where the process of ransoming captives was itself fraught with danger.[98] Indeed, it might even lead to the enslavement of those attempting to deliver the ransom. The author depicts a treacherous, volatile society in which inter-ethnic pacts were struck in order to acquire slaves. He suggests that successive resale through slaving networks took captives far from their point of origin, transporting them over great distances. He also reveals that masters might reward loyal slaves, while captives might strive to maintain their dignity and honour through accommodation, resistance or escape.

The reasons for slaving in the Irish Sea region are evident in ecclesiastical sources from further afield too. In the early years of the eleventh century, the Norman cleric Warner of Rouen composed a satirical poem on the enslavement by Viking pirates of another unfortunate Irishman and his wife, Moriuht and Glicerium. Spurred by the shame of his wife's abduction, Moriuht set out to reclaim her, as Findan had his sister. But he too was captured and enslaved, before being gang-raped by his captors. The poet employs graphic sexual imagery to emphasise conditions of power and powerlessness.[99] Warner reinforces Moriuht's dishonour through his portrayal of Glicerium's fate: bought by a poor widow, Baucis, she ended up a domestic drudge and prostitute in the Norman port of *Rudoil* near Rouen. Although stereotypical, Warner's graphic satire illuminates the processes of enslavement. His denigration of Moriuht was clearly informed by knowledge of how slave cargoes might be treated, a knowledge gained from the ports of Normandy which, he notes, were 'full to bursting with the merchandise of wealth supplied by the Vikings'.[100] For Warner, sexual slavery was an unpleasant fact of life in eleventh-century Norman society, where even lowly individuals like the widow Baucis might own and pimp their female slaves. Moreover, the author saw the Irish and North Sea regions as interconnected zones whose ports were bustling with trading activity and human merchandise.[101] Like Findan, Moriuht was apparently resold several times at various places, including an unspecified slave market in Saxony and at the river port of Corbridge in north-east England.[102] Slaving certainly appears to have been relatively common in England between the mid-tenth century and early twelfth centuries,[103] and Archbishop Wulfstan II of York complained in the early eleventh century about the sexual exploitation and trafficking of enslaved women around the North Sea:

> [...] it is shameful to speak of what has too commonly happened, and it is dreadful to know what many often do, who practise that wretchedness that they club together and buy one woman in common as a joint pur-chase, and with the one commit filth one after another and each after the other just like dogs who do not care about filth; and then sell for a price out of the land into the power of enemies the creature of God [...][104]

Like Warner of Rouen's account of the slave-owning Norman widow, Baucis, Wulfstan's condemnations suggest that the exploitation of sex-trafficked women was endemic at all levels of society. He, too, regarded such trafficking as prevalent, lucrative and international in scope.

Tracking slaving zones

Between the ninth and twelfth centuries the Irish and North Sea regions were slaving zones. The targeting and acquisition of enslaved women and young people was endemic. Scandinavian warriors were embroiled in such activities throughout this period. The huge wealth generated at centres like Dublin and York, evident in the archaeological record, is suggestive of the lucrative and expansive nature of the medieval slave trade. This trade linked both north to south and east to west through overlapping networks. Our written sources occasionally enable us to catch chance glimpses of these networks through the relationships between families who may have been players. For example, according to the early twelfth-century historian William of Malmesbury, the Anglo-Danish noblewoman, sister of King Cnut (d. 1035) and first wife of the powerful Anglo-Saxon earl Godwine, Thyra Sveinsdottir, was a successful slave dealer who would 'buy parties of slaves in England and ship them to Denmark'. William is explicit about the lucrative nature of this trade: Thyra dealt in 'young girls especially, whose beauty and youth would enhance their price, so that by this hideous traffic she could accumulate vast wealth'.[105] The Godwines' continuing connection with the slave trade is found in the *Anglo-Saxon Chronicle*, too. Reportedly, Earl Godwine himself sold the companions of Alfred the Ætheling into slavery after their capture in 1036;[106] and during his exile in 1052, Godwine's son, Harold, raided for slaves in the lands bordering the Severn estuary, not far from the well-established slave market at Bristol.[107] The Godwines may have had personal contacts and interests linking them both directly and indirectly with the slave trade. Following Harold's death at the Battle of Hastings, his daughter Gytha was exiled to the court of Svein Estrithson, king of Denmark, who granted licence for warriors to raid for slaves in the Baltic.[108] Shortly afterwards, Gytha was married to Vladimir Monomakh, then prince of Smolensk and later of Kiev. Smolensk lay at the point where portages and streams leading from the northern Rus river-systems (and thus Novgorod) brought travellers to the Upper Dnieper, whence boats could easily sail downstream to Kiev, the top princely seat of Rus and a flourishing commercial centre. Vladimir's father, Vsevolod, was at that time a senior prince established not far from Kiev in Pereiaslavl' and his mother was a close relative of the Byzantine emperor Constantine IX Monomachos. From her came the byname of 'Monomakh' which Vladimir sported on his earliest seals, suggesting a certain pride in ancestry.[109] Constantinople was even wealthier than Kiev, with slave-trading one source of its prosperity: it apparently had a market reserved for slaves brought in by the Rus.[110] Thus the wealth and connections generated by the slave trade had far-reaching and interconnected social, political and economic implications for dynasties across northern Europe and beyond.

Returning finally to Gotland, our textual exploration shows that the coastal regions and islands of the Baltic were a significant slaving zone for centuries.

They were not only connected with but were also similar to the Irish and North Sea littorals in a number of respects: political instability, ethnic differences and exposed coastlines facilitated endemic warfare and extensive slave-raiding there too. Writing in the 1070s – around the time Harold's daughter, Gytha, was married to Vladimir Monomakh – Adam of Bremen observed that the warriors of Zealand accumulated immense wealth through raiding the Slav populations for slaves, paying tribute to the Danish king to secure royal sanction 'for leave to plunder the barbarians who live about this sea in great numbers'.[111] Yet he also felt they cynically misused their royal licence, driven by ravenous hunger for captives, and he complained that they preyed upon their own people, trafficking them through wider networks: 'as soon as one of them catches another, he mercilessly sells him into slavery either to one of his fellows or to a barbarian'.[112] Besides highlighting the targeting of women and sexual exploitation of female captives, remarking that raiders would 'immediately sell women who have been violated',[113] Adam mentions an island that may well be Gotland and which he sees as the beating heart of maritime operations in the Baltic, noting its good harbours and expansive contacts that reach to the Mediterranean world.[114]

Other contributors address the evidence for long-distance contacts driven by slave acquisition and exchange.[115] But we do have written sources for such networks in a number of Arabic accounts describing the Viking Rus.[116] For example, Ibn Rusta provides a detailed description in his early tenth-century geographical treatise:[117] like Adam of Bremen, he remarks on the warriors' use of their ships to raid the Slavs, capturing people and selling them on to the Bulgars; he also notes that they deal in sable and squirrel pelts, live by raiding and trading and stash their profits in their belts.[118] The most famous and controversial Arabic account of the Rus, however, comes from an eyewitness, Ahmed ibn Fadlan.[119] He served as an envoy of the Abbasid caliph in Baghdad, who sent him on a mission in 921 to the ruler of the Volga Bulgars on the Middle Volga. He most probably wrote up his account soon afterwards, if not during the journey. While staying at the Bulgars' main town, 'a great market', he observed 'the Rus, who had come for trade and had camped by the river'.[120] Besides describing the funeral of one of their leading men, burnt in his boat along with an enslaved young woman, while ostensibly deploring their pagan ways, he offers a lurid account of the casual sex the Rus had with their enslaved women before selling them.[121] Ibn Fadlan's account might be discounted as a one-off, the product of the overactive imagination of an observer from a very different culture. Yet a significant body of source materials, tracking slaves and slavery across many cultures and over many centuries, suggests that there is more than a grain of truth to his observations about such slaveholding behaviours.[122]

Conclusion

The medieval societies of northern Europe were inherently violent; they expressed wealth and prestige through symbols of warriorhood. Naked power over people was equated with status. Identity was emphasised through reciprocal ties of dependence, kinship, lineage, gift-giving and codes of honour, and was defined in contrast to slavery. Thus the stigmas and stereotypes attributed to enslaved people had widespread social and cultural currency, extending far beyond the slavers and slaveholders themselves. Such behaviours have left their mark on the historical record, both directly and as circumstantial evidence in a wide range of sources. Despite their marginality, enslaved people – many of them women – are remarkably visible within these texts. In these societies, concepts of slavery were enmeshed with those of shame and wider expressions of honour and belonging. To be a slave was to exist in a state of shame, fear and marginality; to hold slaves was a mark of one's prestige and honour and to subsume, or indeed consume, the honour of those in one's power.[123] The capture, accumulation and sexual exploitation of enslaved people, especially women, was of significance for defining identities, power relationships and wider patriarchal systems. Moreover, the lucrative and opportunistic nature of the trade that was driven by such slaveholding behaviours linked individuals, dynasties and communities across northern Europe. The medieval authors who illuminate these links certainly regarded slaves as the weakest, most dishonourable and most degraded of all individuals. The paradox is that enslaved people were important to their communities precisely because they were so marginalised. Their lives are visible in the medieval texts, but only if we are prepared to read between the lines.

Notes

1 Wyatt (2009), pp. 10–23.
2 Parker Pearson (2005), p. 24; see also *IC*.
3 Wyatt (2009), pp. 54–60, 395–402.
4 Wyatt (2009), pp. 1–23.
5 See, for example, Lind (1978); Jón Hnefill Aðalsteinsson (1986–9); Iversen (2002).
6 Orrman (2003), pp. 308–11; Karras (1988), pp. 134–40.
7 Orrman (2003), pp. 308–11; see also Wyatt (2009), pp. 1–23, 54–60.
8 Taylor (2005), p. 225.
9 ILO (2017).
10 Kelly (2013).
11 Karras (1990); Stuard (1995); Wyatt (2009), pp. 123–47.
12 Wyatt (2009), pp. 61–172.
13 Karras (1994); Brink (2012), pp. 172–77.
14 Epstein argues that evidence of slave behaviour can be deduced from how slave-holders sought to justify their actions and to control their slaves and others. His methodology emphasises how trapped people accommodate and resist demands for work, obedience and sex: Epstein (2001), pp. 103–4.

15 Epstein (2001), pp. 106–7; see also Wyatt (forthcoming).
16 Epstein (2001), p. 107.
17 Wyatt (forthcoming).
18 Glancy (2002), p. 72.
19 Christine Peel has published excellent translated editions of both *Guta Lag* (*GL*) and *Guta Saga* (*GS*). Several picture stones dating to before 1100 contain memorials in runic script: Rainbird (2007), p. 132; see also Kilger, Svedjemo and Jansson in this volume.
20 *GL*, p. xiv.
21 *GL*, pp. xiv–xxii: Peel argues that the original version of the laws was first compiled *c.* 1220.
22 *GL*, p. xxi.
23 *GL*, p. xxi; see also Karras (1988), pp. 139–40, 244.
24 An assumption made by a number of other scholars: *GL*, pp. xxi, xxxviii–xxxix, 71.
25 *GL*, p. xv. Other provisions, including the omission of those relating to priests' children and the inclusion of inheritance rights for non-Gotlandic daughters, have been used to try and refine the dating of *GL*, although the slave provisions remain at the heart of this debate: *GL*, pp. xv–xxi, xxxvi–xl, 194.
26 *GL*, pp. xv–xxii, 194.
27 *GL*, p. xxv.
28 *GL*, pp. 26, 112–13, 194.
29 Karras (1988), pp. 134–63; Orrman (2003), pp. 308–11; see also nn. 5–6.
30 *GL*, p. xxxiv.
31 Karras (1988), pp. 176–8. See also Skyum-Nielsen (1978–9).
32 *GL*, pp. xxiv–xxxiv; Karras (1988), pp. 134–63.
33 Karras (1988), pp. 167–70.
34 Skyum-Nielsen (1978–9), pp. 145–6.
35 Karras (1988), p. 169; *GL*, pp. xiv, xl.
36 *GL*, pp. 60–1.
37 Karras (1988), p. 53. Similarly, Anti Selart notes the prevalence of urban and rural debt slavery in medieval Livonia and Russia: Selart (2014), pp. 360–1.
38 *GL*, p. 71.
39 Patterson (1982), pp. 209–39; Glancy (2002), p. 94, Kleijwegt (2006), pp. 18–38.
40 Kleijwegt (2006), p. 21.
41 Karras (1988), p. 146. However, there is no mention of Erling's female slaves ever purchasing their freedom. See also *Óláfs saga Helga*, ch. 23: *Hkr*[1], vol. 2, p. 30; tr. from *Hkr*[2], p. 261; *Hkr*[3], vol. 2, p. 18.
42 Ekdahl (1994); Hellie (2011), pp. 276–7; Selart (2014); Korpela (2014, 2015).
43 See nn. 55–8.
44 For examples, see *GL*, pp. 7, 11, 20, 71.
45 Kleijwegt (2006), pp. 18–38.
46 *GL*, p. 12.
47 *GL*, p. 61.
48 *GL*, pp. 7, 11, 20, 26, 33, 61–3.
49 '[...] as much his master's property as the calf from his master's cow or the colt from his mare': Jones (1968), p. 148.
50 *GL*, pp. xxvi–xxvii, 19–20, 29–30, 32–3, 57.
51 Patterson (1982), p. 47.
52 *GL*, p. 26.
53 *GL*, pp. 34–5.

54   The fine for raping a slave was only six *öre* in coin, presumably payable to her master: *GL*, p. 33. *Guta Lag* does provide a wergild for slaves. However, since it was less than the slave's worth, the wergild was probably a payment due to the master of a slain slave in addition to the slave's value. The laws make it clear that slaves did not have an honour price: Karras (1988), p. 103.

55   *GL*, pp. 57, 180.

56   Similarly, the twelfth-century Welsh law code *Llyfr Cyfnerth* reinforced notions of ethnic and cultural belonging by stating that a free and noble Welshman must be 'without slave and without alien (blood) and without one-sided pedigree in him': Wyatt (2009), p. 44.

57   *GL*, pp. 29–30.

58   Karras (1988), p. 74.

59   Wyatt (forthcoming).

60   See n. 42.

61   Jackson (2008); Hellie (2011), p. 277; Schaeken (2014), pp. 158–61.

62   Karras (1988), p. 48. For a similar agreement in thirteenth-century Livonia see Selart (2014), p. 359. Indeed, provisions for dealing with escaped slaves are the second most frequently recurring phrase in treaties from the whole of medieval Europe in the period between 700 and 1350: Benham (forthcoming).

63   Korpela (2015), pp. 177–8, 182.

64   See *GL*, pp. xii–xiii; Jensen (2002), pp. 180–6; Myrberg (2010), pp. 173–5.

65   *GL*, p. 42.

66   *GL*, p. 43.

67   Selart (2014), pp. 356–8; see also n. 42. Around 1130, a young Dane fell prey to Wendish raiders on no fewer than three separate occasions, and feared greatly that his kin would be unable to redeem him for a third time: *Magnússona saga*, ch. 31, *Hkr*[3], vol. 3, p. 167; see Jensen (2017), p. 291.

68   *GL*, pp. 32, 130–1.

69   *GL*, p. 34.

70   Wyatt (2009), pp. 237–41.

71   *GL*, p. 34.

72   There are 16 sagas of the kings of Norway extant in *Heimskringla*, attributed to the Icelandic scholar Snorri Sturluson (d. 1241). Snorri, who spent a number of years on the Scandinavian mainland, appears to have based his epic synthesis of Norwegian royal stories on a range of sources including oral traditions, skaldic verses and textual accounts that are no longer extant: Whaley (1993).

73   *Haralds saga Sigurðarsonar*, ch. 19: *Hkr*[1], vol. 3, p. 94; tr. from *Hkr*[2], p. 592; *Hkr*[3], vol. 3, p. 55.

74   Wyatt (2009), pp. 123–30.

75   *Haralds saga Sigurðarsonar*, ch. 32: *Hkr*[1], vol. 3, p. 110; tr. from *Hkr*[2], pp. 601–2; *Hkr*[3], vol. 3, p. 65. Similarly, the wearing of chains was a feature that defined the nature of slavery in medieval Livonia: Selart (2014), p. 364.

76   *Óláfs saga Tryggvasonar*, chs 6–8: *Hkr*[1], vol. 1, pp. 230–2; tr. from *Hkr*[2], pp. 147–9; *Hkr*[3], vol. 1, pp. 140–1.

77   *Óláfs saga Tryggvasonar*, ch. 52: *Hkr*[1], vol. 1, pp. 301–2; *Hkr*[2], pp. 194–5; *Hkr*[3], vol. 1, p. 187.

78   *Óláfs saga Tryggvasonar*, ch. 6: *Hkr*[1], vol. 1, p. 230; tr. from *Hkr*[2], p. 147; *Hkr*[3], vol. 1, p. 140.

79   Patterson (1982), pp. 120–1; see also Wyatt (2009), pp. 372–5; Selart (2014), pp. 355–9.

80   Brundage (2011).

81 For examples, see Henry of Livonia, *Chronicle* IX.3–4, XI.5, XII.6, XIII.4, XIII.5, XIV.6, XV.1–2, ed. Arndt, pp. 250, 259–60, 264, 265, 267–8, 271; tr. Brundage, pp. 48–9, 72–3, 84, 86, 91, 93, 100, 108–9.

82 Henry of Livonia, *Chronicle* XII.6, ed. Arndt, p. 265; tr. Brundage, p. 86; Jensen (2017), pp. 292–4.

83 *Óláfs saga Tryggvasonar*, ch. 52: *Hkr*[1], vol. 1, p. 301; *Hkr*[2], p. 194; *Hkr*[3], vol. 1, p. 187. That Lothin felt Astrith's appearance so altered he struggled to recognise her, years of servitude making her 'pale and peaked and poorly clad', highlights the relationship between appearance and status in Snorri's view.

84 Karras (1988), pp. 178–83.

85 Whaley (1993), p. 276.

86 This perspective is summed up by Karras (1992, p. 301), who argues that the sagas 'give us a past constructed, configured and organized by the author, so that they reveal to us neither tenth- and eleventh-century nor thirteenth-century practice, but rather thirteenth-century norms and thirteenth-century ideas about what tenth- and eleventh-century norms were'.

87 *Saga of the People of Laxardal*.

88 *Saga of the People of Laxardal*, p. 11. The next morning, noting her shabby rags, Hǫskuldr supplied Melkorka with some fine clothes which better suited her.

89 In his seminal article, Poul Holm places the Hiberno-Norse city of Dublin at the heart of an elaborate slave-raiding and -trading network that encompassed the Irish Sea region and stretched beyond it across north-western Europe: Holm (1986), p. 330.

90 Wyatt (2009), p. 125.

91 Holm (1986), p. 318.

92 Holm (1986), pp. 328–30.

93 Holm (1986).

94 Holm (1986), p. 328; see also Wyatt (2009), pp. 119–20.

95 *VF*, tr. Somerville, p. 195.

96 *VF*, ed. Holder-Egger, p. 503; tr. Somerville, p. 196.

97 *VF*, ed. Holder-Egger, p. 503; tr. Somerville, p. 197.

98 As is clear from *Guta Lag*'s provisions, as noted above.

99 Warner of Rouen, *Moriuht*, pp. 76–7; Wyatt (2009), pp. 229–37.

100 Warner of Rouen, *Moriuht*, pp. 90–3. See now also de Jong (2017).

101 Wyatt (2009), p. 232.

102 Warner of Rouen, *Moriuht*, pp. 82–3, 76–7.

103 Pelteret (1981, 1995, pp. 70–4); Wyatt (2009), pp. 123–30.

104 *Anglo-Saxon Prose*, ed. and tr. Swanton, p. 119.

105 William of Malmesbury, *Gesta*, vol. 2, pp. 362–3.

106 *ASC*[2] (C), p. 158.

107 *ASC*[2] (E), pp. 178–9. For the slave market at Bristol, see Pelteret (1995), pp. 76–8; Wyatt (2009), pp. 106, 219.

108 See n. 111.

109 Shepard (1973), p. 57; Nazarenko (2001), pp. 522–4; Mel'nikova and Petrukhin (2014), p. 183 (V. I. Matuzova), pp. 132–3 (A. V. Nazarenko).

110 Shepard (2015), pp. 284–5; Hardt (2017), pp. 88–93.

111 Ad*GH* IV.6, pp. 440–3; Adam, *History*, tr. Tschan, p. 190.

112 Ad*GH* IV.6, pp. 442–3; Adam, *History*, tr. Tschan, p. 190. Stefan Brink has identified a number of place names that incorporate Slavic ethnic designations alongside derogatory slave designations in the Älmeboda district of southern Sweden and suggests these indicate settlements of slaves or former slaves that date from the twelfth and thirteenth centuries: Brink (2002), pp. 119–24.

113 AdGH IV.6, pp. 442–3; Adam, *History*, tr. Tschan, p. 190. Adam also notes the prevalence of penal slavery among this slaveholding population.
114 AdGH IV.16, pp. 452–3; Adam, *History*, tr. Tschan, p. 197, describing it as 'the most celebrated port of Denmark and a safe anchorage for the ships'.
115 See, for example, Brink and Jankowiak in this volume; see also Shepard (2008), pp. 508, 509–10; and on the lack of firm archaeological evidence, see Fontaine (2017).
116 Hellie (2011), p. 278; Brink (2012), pp. 175–7; Karras (1988), pp. 46–7.
117 Perkins (1993); Montgomery (2008), pp. 552–3.
118 Ibn Rusta, 'On the Rus'; see also Jesch (2003), p. 118; Logan (2005), p. 179.
119 IbnF[1]; IbnF[2]; see also Karras (1988), pp. 46–7; Jesch (2003), pp. 119–23; Brink (2012), pp. 175–6.
120 IbnF[1], pp. 233, 241; IbnF[2], pp. 40, 45.
121 IbnF[1], pp. 243, 245–53; IbnF[2], pp. 46–7, 49–54; see also Taylor (2005), p. 230.
122 For assessments of Ibn Fadlan, his reasons for recounting his journey, his cultural context and the overall historicity of his report, see Shepard and Treadwell (eds) (2021 forthcoming).
123 Patterson (1982), p. 81; Philips (2003–4).

Bibliography

Primary sources

Adam of Bremen, *History of the Archbishops of Hamburg Bremen*, tr. F. J. Tschan, New York (1959).

Anglo-Saxon Prose, ed. and tr. M. Swanton, London (1975).

Henry of Livonia [Henricus Lettus], *Chronicle*, ed. W. Arndt, *Heinrici Chronicon Lyvoniae*, in *MGH Scriptores* 23, Hanover (1874), pp. 231–332; tr. J. A. Brundage, Madison, WI (1961).

Ibn Rusta, 'On the Rus 903–913', from *Kitab al-a'laq al-nafisah*, tr. P. Lunde and C. Stone in *Ibn Fadlan and the Land of Darkness: Arab Travellers in the Far North*, London (2012), pp. 126–7.

The Saga of the People of Laxardal, in *The Complete Sagas of the Icelanders, Including 49 Tales*, ed. and tr. Viðar Hreinsson *et al.*, 5 vols, Reykjavik (1997), vol. 5, pp. 1–119.

Warner of Rouen, *Moriuht*, ed. and tr. C. J. McDonough, *A Norman Latin Poem from the Early Eleventh Century*, Toronto (1995).

William of Malmesbury, *Gesta regum Anglorum*, ed. and tr. R. A. B. Mynors, 2 vols, Oxford (1998–9).

Secondary literature

Benham, J. (forthcoming), *Law, Treaties and International Relations, c.700–c.1200*, Manchester.

Brink, S. (2002), 'Slavery in Scandinavia, as reflected in names, runes and sagas', in T. Iversen and P. Hernæs (eds), *Slavery across Time and Space: Studies in Slavery in Medieval Europe and Africa*, Trondheim, pp. 107–58.

Brink, S. (2012), *Vikingarnas slavar: den nordiska träldomen under yngre järnålder och äldsta medeltid*, Stockholm.

Brundage, J. (2011), 'Introduction: Henry of Livonia, the writer and his chronicle', in M. Tamm *et al.* (eds), *Crusading and Chronicle Writing on the Medieval Baltic Frontier: A Companion to the Chronicle of Henry of Livonia*, Farnham, pp. 1–22.

de Jong, F. P. C. (2017), 'Rival schoolmasters in early eleventh-century Rouen with special reference to the poetry of Warner of Rouen (fl. 996–1027) (*The Marjorie Chibnall Memorial Essay*)', *Anglo-Norman Studies* 39: 45–63.

Ekdahl, E. S. (1994), 'The treatment of prisoners of war during the fighting between the Teutonic Order and Lithuania', in M. Barber (ed.), *The Military Orders: Fighting for the Faith and Caring for the Sick*, Aldershot, pp. 263–9.

Epstein, S. (2001), *Speaking of Slavery: Color, Ethnicity and Human Bondage in Italy*, Ithaca, NY; London.

Fontaine, J. M. (2017), 'Early medieval slave-trading in the archaeological record: comparative methodologies', *Early Medieval Europe* 25: 466–88.

Glancy, J. (2002), *Slavery in Early Christianity*, Oxford.

Hardt, M. (2017), 'The importance of the slave trade for the Slavic princes of the early and high middle ages', in V. Loré *et al.* (eds), *Acquérir, prélever, contrôler: les ressources en compétition (400–1100)*, Turnhout, pp. 81–94.

Hellie, R. (2011), 'Russian slavery and serfdom, 1450–1804', in D. Eltis *et al.* (eds), *The Cambridge World History of Slavery*, vol. 3: AD 1420–AD 1804, Cambridge, pp. 275–95.

Holm, P. (1986), 'The slave trade of Dublin, ninth to twelfth centuries', *Peritia* 5: 317–45.

ILO (2017), 'Global estimates of modern slavery: forced labour and forced marriage', *International Labour Organization, Walk Free Foundation and International Organization for Migration Report*, Geneva (19 September 2017), ilo.org/global/publications/books/WCMS_575479/lang--en/index.htm (accessed 16 December 2019).

Iversen, T. (2002), 'The dissolution of medieval slavery in Norway in a western European context', in T. Iversen and P. Hernæs (eds), *Slavery across Time and Space: Studies in Slavery in Medieval Europe and Africa*, Trondheim, pp. 129–45.

Jackson, T. N. (2008), 'Novgorod the Great in Baltic trade before 1300', *Acta Borealia* 25: 83–92.

Jensen, K. V. (2002), 'The blue Baltic border of Denmark in the high middle ages: Danes, Wends and Saxo Grammaticus', in D. Abulafia and N. Berend (eds), *Medieval Frontiers: Concepts and Practices*, Aldershot, pp. 173–93.

Jensen, K. V. (2017), 'Prisoners of war in the Baltic in the XII–XIII centuries', *e-Stratégica* 1: 285–95.

Jesch, J. (2003), *Women in the Viking Age*, Woodbridge.

Jones, G. A. (1968), *A History of the Vikings*, London.

Jón Hnefill Aðalsteinsson (1986–9), 'The position of freed slaves in Medieval Iceland', *Saga-Book* 22: 33–49.

Karras, R. M. (1988), *Slavery and Society in Medieval Scandinavia*, New Haven, CT.

Karras, R. M. (1990), 'Concubinage and slavery in the Viking Age', *Scandinavian Studies* 62: 141–62.

Karras, R. M. (1992), 'Servitude and sexuality', in Gísli Pálsson (ed.), *From Sagas to Society: Comparative Approaches to Early Iceland*, Enfield Lock, pp. 289–304.

Karras, R. M. (1994), 'Desire, descendants, and dominance: slavery, the exchange of women, and masculine power', in A. J. Frantzen and D. Moffat (eds), *The Work of Work: Servitude, Slavery, and Labor in Medieval England*, Glasgow, pp. 16–29.

Kelly, A. (2013), 'Modern-day slavery: an explainer', *The Guardian* (3 April 2013), the guardian.com/global-development/2013/apr/03/modern-day-slavery-explainer (accessed 16 December 2019).

Kleijwegt, M. (2006), *The Faces of Freedom: The Manumission and Emancipation of Slaves in Old World and New World Slavery*, Leiden.

Korpela, J. (2014), 'The Baltic Finnic people in the medieval and pre-modern eastern European slave trade', *Russian History* 41: 85–117.

Korpela, J. (2015), '"... and they took countless captives": Finnic captives and the east European slave trade during the middle ages', in C. Witzenrath (ed.), *Eurasian Slavery, Ransom and Abolition in World History, 1200–1860*, Farnham, pp. 171–90.

Lind, J. D. (1978), 'The ending of slavery in Sweden: social structure and decision making', *Scandinavian Studies* 50: 57–71.

Logan, F. D. (2005), *The Vikings in History*, 3rd edn, London.

Mel'nikova, E. A. and V. I. Petrukhin (eds) (2014), *Drevniaia Rus' v srednevekovom mire: entsiklopediia*, Moscow.

Montgomery, J. E. (2008), 'Arabic sources on the Vikings', in *VW*, pp. 550–61.

Myrberg, N. (2010), 'A worth of their own: on Gotland in the Baltic Sea, and its 12th-century coinage', *Medieval Archaeology* 54: 157–81.

Nazarenko, A. V. (2001), *Drevniaia Rus' na mezhdunarodnykh putiakh*, Moscow.

Orrman, E. (2003), 'Rural conditions', in K. Helle (ed.), *The Cambridge History of Scandinavia*, vol. 1: *Prehistory to 1520*, Cambridge, pp. 250–311.

Parker Pearson, M. (2005), 'Warfare, violence and slavery in later prehistory: an introduction', in M. Parker Pearson and I. J. N. Thorpe (eds), *Warfare, Violence and Slavery in Prehistory*, Oxford, pp. 19–33.

Patterson, O. (1982), *Slavery and Social Death: A Comparative Study*, Cambridge, MA.

Pelteret, D. A. E. (1981), 'Slave raiding and slave trading in early England', *Anglo-Saxon England* 9: 99–114.

Pelteret, D. A. E. (1995), *Slavery in Early Mediaeval England: From the Reign of Alfred until the Twelfth Century*, Woodbridge.

Perkins, R. (1993), 'Arabic sources for Scandinavia(ns)', in P. Pulsiano *et al.* (eds), *Medieval Scandinavia: An Encyclopedia*, New York, pp. 17–18.

Philips, J. E. (2003–4), 'Slavery as a human institution', *Afrika Zamani* 11/12: 27–48.

Rainbird, P. (2007), *The Archaeology of Islands*, Cambridge.

Schaeken, J. (2014), 'Don't shoot the messenger (part two): pragmaphilological notes on birchbark letters nos. 497 and 771 from Novgorod and no. 2 from Zvenyhorod', in E. Fortuin *et al.* (eds), *Dutch Contributions to the Fifteenth International Congress of Slavists*, Amsterdam, pp. 155–66.

Selart, A. (2014), 'Slavery in the eastern Baltic in the 12th–15th centuries', in S. Cavaciocchi (ed.), *Serfdom and Slavery in the European Economy, 11th–18th Centuries*, Florence, vol. 1, pp. 351–65.

Shepard, J. (1973), 'The English and Byzantium: a study of their role in the Byzantine army in the later eleventh century', *Traditio* 29: 53–92.

Shepard, J. (2008), 'The Viking Rus and Byzantium', in *VW*, pp. 496–516.

Shepard, J. (2015), 'Things, persons and practices in circulation between Byzantium and the British Isles in the Viking Age: a role for Rus?', in P. G. Gaidukov (ed.), *Goroda i vesi srednevekovoi Rusi: arheologiia, istoriia, kul'tura: k 60-letiiu Nikolaia Andreevicha Makarova*, Moscow, pp. 274–85.

Shepard, J. and L. Treadwell (eds) (2021 forthcoming), *Muslims on the Volga in the Viking Age: Diplomacy and Islam in the World of Ibn Fadlan*, London.

Skyum-Nielsen, N. (1978–9), 'Nordic slavery in an international setting', *Mediaeval Scandinavia* 11: 126–48.

Stuard, S. M. (1995), 'Ancillary evidence for the decline of medieval slavery', *Past & Present* 149: 3–28.

Taylor, T. (2005), 'Ambushed by a grotesque: archaeology, slavery and the third paradigm', in M. Parker Pearson and I. J. N. Thorpe (eds), *Warfare, Violence and Slavery in Prehistory*, Oxford, pp. 225–33.

Whaley, D. E. (1993), 'Heimskringla', in P. Pulsiano *et al.* (eds), *Medieval Scandinavia: An Encyclopedia*, New York, pp. 276–7.

Wyatt, D. (2009), *Slaves and Warriors in Medieval Britain and Ireland, 800–1200*, Leiden.

Wyatt, D. (forthcoming), 'Slavery in northern Europe (Scandinavia and Iceland) and the British Isles 500–1420', in S. Engerman *et al.* (eds), *The Cambridge World History of Slavery*, vol. 2: *The Medieval Period, 500–1420*, Cambridge.

3   Slavery in medieval Scandinavia

Some points of departure

Stefan Brink

Slavery in the Scandinavian laws

> [...] then they all should provide him with twelve cows and two horses and three thralls.[1]

This paragraph from the *Older Frostathing Law*, in force throughout Trøndelag and the surrounding provinces in central Norway during the middle ages, regulates the compensation due to a man who has been blinded and is thus unable to work.[2] Many scholars have taken this single paragraph to represent a 'normal' farm for Trøndelag – and for Norway as a whole – in the late middle ages, and have used it to estimate the slave population: if the unfree numbered between 50,000 and 75,000,[3] depending on the total Norwegian population at the time, slaves may have represented some 20–30% of the total.[4] Other scholars have argued that this estimate of the slave population is far too high,[5] although the scarcity of our historical sources makes it difficult to know one way or another.

If we extrapolate from these Norwegian estimates, a quarter to a third of the Scandinavian population in the late twelfth and thirteenth centuries would have been legally unfree people – slaves. And this was in a period when slavery was starting to diminish and to be abandoned in parts of Scandinavia, meaning that in earlier periods – such as the Viking Age and the early twelfth century – there must have been an even higher percentage of slaves in Scandinavian society, perhaps 40% or even 50%. If this estimate of the unfree population in Scandinavia is correct, in Viking-Age society every other individual might have been a slave, although admittedly 'individual' is an infelicitous choice of word for beings considered little better than objects in that society. Is this really likely?

Unfortunately, there are several problems with our paragraph from the *Frostathing Law*. We cannot take for granted that it is describing a 'normal' farm. Even if it were and it took three farmhands to run such a farm – in this case, the three thralls mentioned – a sighted farmer may have needed fewer farmhands than a blind one,[6] since the law assumes that slaves normally worked the fields and forest and took care of the animals *with* their master.[7] A further problem is that the word used in the *Law* often denotes a slave, but it could equally well mean a farmhand, a free servant.[8] However, analysis of other paragraphs in the *Law* shows that slaves (thralls) were found on average, 'normal' farms in Norway, and not only on the larger ones or on manorial estates.[9] Based on the evidence available to us, it is therefore difficult to discuss slave numbers – quantity – and I will return to this problem.

We are a little better equipped when it comes to analysing the 'quality' of medieval slavery in Scandinavia, thanks firstly to our medieval laws, and secondly to the terminology for slaves. The earliest laws in Scandinavia are provincial ones: almost every province had its own specific law, although the legal districts in Norway were somewhat larger. We know of some 15 provincial laws, and slaves and slavery are mentioned in all bar one, the *Hälsinge Law* from northern Sweden and Finland. Slavery either never found its way into these northerly provinces, where farming was based on animal husbandry rather than extensive arable cultivation; or the law was written down after slavery was prohibited in Sweden by royal statue, probably around 1335.[10]

If we start with the medieval Danish laws, we can see that slaves were treated more or less on a par with animals: if either were injured or killed, the wrongdoer was liable to pay damages; if either were killed, no levelling oath was sworn;[11] and owners were responsible for their animals' or slaves' violent behaviour. The *Law of Scania* has many paragraphs concerning slaves. One deals with granting freedom to a slave and how he should be treated thereafter:

> If a man grants freedom to an unfree servant, or if they redeem their freedom themselves, he who granted freedom or he who lets them redeem their freedom or the closest heir goes to the assembly and declares him to be free from him, and another man shall take him into his kin and answer for his actions, pay half a man's compensation for him if he kills a man, and likewise take payment for him with his other heirs if he is killed. For everything he does or for what another man does to him, there shall always be a lesser compensation than if he had been born free. If no man will take him into his kin and he later commits a crime, he shall pay belt-fine for himself in the first, second and third year, or he shall flee and take responsibility for himself.[12]

Clearly a slave could either be granted freedom by his owner, or could get himself out of slavery, either by buying himself out or working for a stipulated period. But – crucially – the slave had to be accepted back into his former kin group, or into any kin group who would receive him. If none would, he had to 'take responsibility for himself', placing him outside the kin community and hence outside society. It was absolutely fundamental in medieval Scandinavia for an individual to have this kind of kin affiliation, otherwise that person faced 'social death', in principle having no legal rights whatsoever.[13]

In the same *Law of Scania*, we have an interesting paragraph which shows that it was possible for a free man who had broken the law of the land to lose his freedom, becoming a slave on one of the royal estates:

> If a man steals and is handed over to the king's official, he shall become a slave in the king's manor until he is redeemed from this or until he is given freedom.[14]

The law for Gotland, *Guta Lag*, has several cases that indicate that slavery could sometimes be for a fixed period:

> If such a case [of killing a child] is brought against someone's female slave, no one is to lay any higher fine against her than six öre in coin. If she is found guilty, then her master is fined six öre in coin on her behalf, and six years are added after her time of slavery is complete.[15]

> If a male or female slave is caught working on a holy day, their master is fined three öre for them, and they are to have their time of slavery extended by three years.[16]

> But a slave who has worked through his time of slavery is to embrace his freedom at the church door with the witness of the parishioners and then the slave is himself responsible for his actions.[17]

There were two obvious ways in which you could enter into slavery: either to compensate for a criminal act, or to work your way out of debt. Yet punishments were extremely harsh. A slave on Gotland could have their term of bondage extended by three years for working on a holy day, despite the likelihood of them having been forced to do so by their master.

The laws show how slaves were looked upon as not human in medieval Scandinavian society – and treated accordingly – although such treatment of slaves was not confined to Scandinavia, but was widespread in the middle ages. For example, in the *Östgöta Law* if a master whose slave (*þræll*) had committed an offence failed to pay the fine within a given period, the slave was to be hanged on his farm-gate.[18] The same law stipulated that should the master refuse to pay for the slave's offence, an oak withe should be wound around the slave's neck before hanging him on the farm gatepost, with no one allowed to cut him down 'until the withe rots'.[19]

The Scandinavian provincial laws and their full provision for slaves and slavery in the period *c.* 1100 and 1300 mirror a society where slaves were probably to be found even on normal farms, but more frequently on estates and magnates' lands. In this period we should not assume that slaves had primarily been taken during raiding expeditions or even bought at slave markets abroad. When reading the laws, one gets the impression that these slaves[20] were mainly born and raised in Scandinavia and if there was a slave trade, it must have been an internal one. There are a few – admittedly inconclusive – linguistic indications that slaves may have been taken from neighbouring countries, in this case across the Baltics, and settled in Sweden.[21] For example, four place-names in southern Småland – *Estamåla, Kuramåla, Summemåla* and *Iremåla* – are linked to small farms established in the thirteenth (or even the twelfth) century which may have been farmed by freed slaves.[22]

However, the categories of slaves mentioned in the laws do seem to refer to slaves born and bred in Scandinavia. This is no doubt the case for the *fostre* (m.) and *fostra* (f.).[23] The *Older Västgöta Law* states that a widow who wanted to remarry could only leave her farm and children if a *fostre* and *fostra* were living there and able to manage it (and apparently also take care of the children).[24] That the *fostre* and *fostra* were more trustworthy and held a more prominent social and legal position than other thralls is supported by a clause in the *Younger Västgöta Law*,[25] which says that an 'unfree *fostra*' was to be entrusted with the master's keys. Finally, according to the *Västmanna Law*,[26] in certain circumstances a *fostre*'s position was so independent that he could perform military duty, which seems very strange, since this was the prerogative of free men. Even so, a *fostre* was clearly unfree in law, as the *Östgöta Law* shows: he could be sold, and children born to a *fostre* outside marriage belonged to his master.[27]

Yet there were slave raids in the Baltic region even in the thirteenth century. According to the *Chronicle* of Henry of Livonia, there were 67 slave raids between 1200 and 1227, 25 by 'pagan warriors' and 42 by Christians, with most of the enslaved said to be women and girls.[28] Henry leaves it unclear whether Scandinavians participated in these raids, but they may have done; and this, in turn, could support the idea that places such as *Estamåla* and *Kuramåla* mark the presence of eastern Baltic captives who were brought to Sweden as slaves, even as late as in the thirteenth century, but were quickly freed to become tenant farmers. There is also information in various chronicles and Icelandic sagas about slaves being taken in Danish, Norwegian and Polabian regions in the twelfth and thirteenth centuries. Snorri Sturluson's *Saga of Magnus the Blind and of Harald Gille* in *Heimskringla* offers a vivid description of Duke Ratibor of Pomerania's sacking, in 1135, of Kungahälla in Norway (today western Sweden):

[They] took all the people, men and women and children, slew many, all those that were wounded or young and they felt would be a nuisance to take with them [...] King Rettibur and his troops, what remained of them, went away and back to Vindland, and many of the people that had been captured in Konungahella were for long after in Vindland in bondage, while those that were ransomed and returned to Norway to their native places prospered very little. The market town at Konungahella has never recovered the success it had before.[29]

In 1168, according to the *Chronicle* of Helmold of Bosau, 700 captured Danes were to be sold in Mecklenburg castle,[30] and trade in humans was very much part of the twelfth-century economy in the Baltic region.[31]

The slave population mentioned in the provincial laws shows not only a social hierarchy (as we have seen with the *fostre* and *fostra*), but also geographical diversity and change over time. Slaves were not a homogeneous group. Many were purely farm workers, little better than livestock, but others performed specific, sometimes highly skilled tasks. One such was the *deigja*, a maid in the household equivalent to the Anglo-Saxon *lady* < *hlaf-díghe* 'the one who bakes the bread'. Such individuals came close to being trusted servants and officials. The *bryti* is a good example.[32] Originally assumed to be foremost among thralls, a particularly trusted slave whose job it was to watch over others and to distribute food (bread) among them, the *bryti* must have been a sort of farm manager or bailiff. We have evidence from runestones that during the Viking Age *bryti*s could be stewards or managers of royal estates,[33] which implies that – although legally unfree – they held quite a high social position. The term *bryti* appears to have undergone a shift in meaning in the medieval written sources, rising from a possibly unfree farm steward to ombudsman, before declining in social value and coming to refer simply to a farmer, especially a tenant farmer. This change in the *bryti*'s status is most apparent in Denmark: originally an unfree, later a free, farm manager, the *bryti* developed into a sort of ombudsman (*villicus*), especially in the king's service, where he administered taxes and justice. But from the 1200s on, the *bryti* or *villicus* became practically synonymous with a tenant farmer, and the term *bryti* is often used in contrast to a tax-paying farmer.[34] Much as *deigja* is related to the Anglo-Saxon for lady (< *hlaf-dighe*, 'bread baker'), so *bryti* must be to *hlaf-brytta*, the 'bread breaker and [possibly] distributor' (i.e. steward).[35]

The picture of slavery that emerges from analysing the medieval Nordic laws is closer to Anglo-Saxon 'serfdom'[36] – with semi-free tenants working estates and tenanted farms – than to classical Roman chattel slavery. Thralls were still the lowest class in society. But within that class there was a hierarchy, which ranged from chattel slaves living in barns alongside the cattle,[37] or possibly in small separate farm buildings,[38] via house-maids and farmhands such as the *fostre* and *fostra*, to the steward on a king's manor, a *bryti*.[39]

In the late middle ages, Nordic slavery started to disappear: in England this seems to have happened in the early twelfth century,[40] while Scandinavia followed perhaps a century or so later. In Norway, only 'former slaves' (*frialsan mann*, 'freed man', *passim*) are mentioned in the new *Law of the Realm* of 1274,[41] which implies that slavery had been abolished there sometime before 1274. A qualified guess suggests that Denmark followed suit,[42] while for Sweden we have a royal decree (*Skarastadgan*) for Västergötland from 1335 prohibiting the keeping of thralls,[43] which may have extended to Sweden as a whole.

Of course we find this process of 'feudalisation' throughout Europe in the late middle ages, when slavery was transformed into a system of semi-free, dependent farmers of different shades,[44] and the Scandinavian peasantry was no exception.[45] The process seems to have been two-way: while freed slaves became dependent tenant farmers, many formerly free farmers were also forced into semi-free, tenant serfdom. A new class of peasants emerged. But what was the situation before this late medieval transformation? Do we know anything about Viking-Age slavery in Scandinavia?

Slavery in Viking-Age Scandinavia

The big problem we face when trying to understand Viking-Age slavery is, of course, the lack of written sources. The few we have offer us glimpses – Arabic travelogues, Anglo-Saxon, Frankish and Irish annals and chronicles, and some hagiographies of 'missionaries' who were in contact with Scandinavians – yet they all describe meeting Scandinavians *outside* Scandinavia. In 2012 I tried to build up a picture of earlier medieval slavery in Scandinavia using all the evidence we have from these sources, which is meagre, often implicit, difficult to interpret and sometimes contradictory.[46] Clearly I could not establish an absolutely 'true' picture, but rather a model, which is open to interpretation.

Important as archaeology is as a source, it is more or less impossible to excavate slavery.[47] For example, were slaves buried in graves and, if so, how can we identify whether a particular individual was legally unfree? According to the Arabic emissary Ibn Fadlan: 'They [the Rus, i.e. Scandinavians] do not bury dead slaves but leave them as food for the dogs and the birds'.[48] One of the strongest archaeological indications of slavery may be 'double burials', where one of the dead had been beheaded, tied up or placed in a lesser position in the grave.[49] DNA analysis is likely to help us in the future. For example, Viking graves with more than one occupant have been analysed in northern Norway and DNA analysis shows that the dead cannot have been related – an indication that slaves may have been thrown into the graves.[50] The results are interesting, but are of course still guesswork when it comes to these individuals' status as free or unfree. But we may soon be able to complement such findings with DNA and other types of analysis to identify individuals in Scandinavian burials who came from afar and may thus have been brought to Scandinavia as slaves.

Mats Roslund has introduced potential new evidence for tracing slaves in Scandinavian Viking society from his studies of pottery in southern and central Sweden.[51] His analysis shows a radical stylistic change in eastern Denmark and southern Sweden around 1000 when, he argues, Slavic pottery techniques and patterns were adopted, reflecting a corresponding change within society. Roslund discerns a process of hybridisation between unfree Slavs and Scandinavians, with regional production and consumption patterns emerging, hinting at political and economic differences between various

Swedish regions. This change is apparent at major markets and trading places such as Birka, Lund and Skänninge – likely centres of pottery production – but Roslund argues that such hybrid forms are also detectable in everyday ceramics at the household level for perhaps two centuries before pottery production began to professionalise at the start of the thirteenth century. If Roslund is correct, and I have no reason to doubt his expertise here, we have another source that could be used to trace slaves in the late Viking Age and middle ages, in this case female slaves originating from western Slavic areas.

When summing up my 2012 book, I suggested that thralls were quite rare in the farming society of Viking-Age Scandinavia.[52] The average farmer may have owned one or more work thralls, but this was probably quite unusual. Slaves were more often 'prestige property', kept by large landowners, noblemen and chieftains partly as chattels to work their great farms, but also as servants of various rank in their entourage.[53] There were probably considerable regional differences in slaveholding, with a higher proportion of slaves found in southern Scandinavia and fewer – if any – in the north, although this is largely guesswork. The vast numbers of slaves that the Scandinavians bought or captured were probably sold off as quickly as possible at slave markets and converted into more easily handled goods – such as jewellery and, above all, precious metals, gold and especially silver.[54] However, some slaves were brought back to Scandinavia – especially women to be concubines – as our written sources from both east and west show.

Perhaps the most important evidence for Scandinavians keeping slave women as concubines is found in Ibn Fadlan's account of his travels.[55] Sent to the Volga Bulgars by Caliph al-Muqtadir of Baghdad in 921, Ibn Fadlan's mission was both diplomatic and religious, and selected parts of his account are included in works from the 1100s and later. During his visit, Ibn Fadlan encountered a people called 'Rus', generally taken by scholars to be Swedes who were trading on the Middle Volga. His description of them is detailed and tallies with early tenth-century archaeological finds from Gotland and Sweden. Ibn Fadlan's account of the sacrifices made by the Rus to their gods and idols to ensure trading success is well known, as is his extensive and apparently reliable description of the funeral and cremation of one of their chieftains. The chieftain's slave women play a significant role in the latter. Asked who among them wishes to die with her master, the chosen slave is tended by two others who wash her feet and stay with her for the several days of preparations, during which she is said to be 'happy and high-spirited', drinking and singing. A ship is brought onto dry land and rigged out for the funeral pyre, ready for the chieftain and his slave, and at this point an older woman, the 'angel of death', enters the proceedings. The chosen slave woman passes from tent to tent having sex with the Rus, after which the men say to her: 'Tell your master that I have done this purely out of love for you'. Towards evening she is taken to the ritual place, the 'gate', apparently a metaphor for the realm of the dead.[56] Given copious amounts of beer to intoxicate her and dull her senses, once groggy she is dragged into a tent where six men copulate with her. Finally, she is placed next to her dead master: two of the men hold her hands and two her feet. The 'angel of death' winds a rope around the woman's neck and gives the ends to the remaining two men, who tighten them while she repeatedly plunges a broad knife between the woman's ribs. The slave woman and her master were then placed on the ship, which was set alight.

A Rus chieftain clearly had several slave women. Elsewhere Ibn Fadlan describes how, in his 'castle', the king of the Rus had 400 men who are said to die for and with him – presumably his guard. Each had a slave woman to serve him – washing him and preparing his food and drink – and another to sleep with; and sex with these slave women in the presence of their comrades-in-arms was commonplace. Such wanton behaviour among the Rus clearly shocked Ibn Fadlan: he returns to the theme on several occasions. For example, he describes the Rus as filthy, akin to stray donkeys, living jam-packed some 10 to 20 per cabin on the banks of the Volga, adding indignantly:

> They are accompanied by beautiful female slaves for trade with the merchants. They have intercourse with their female slaves in full view of their companions. Sometimes they gather in a group and do this in front each other. A merchant may come in to buy a female slave and stumble upon the owner having intercourse. The Rus does not leave her alone until he has satisfied his urge.[57]

We learn two things from this eyewitness account. Firstly, the Viking-Age Rus appear to have had a fairly shameless attitude to sexuality: copulation was clearly no private matter. And secondly, many Rus seem to have brought slave women home to Scandinavia as concubines.

There are at least two other Arabic sources that mention the Rus in relation to capturing, keeping and selling slaves. Ibn Rusta was a Persianised Arab from Isfahan, whose *Kitab al-a'laq al-nafisah* (*The Book of Precious Things*) was written *c.* 903–13.[58] In his description of the Rus he explains:

> Among them is a king who is called *Khaqan Rus*.[59] They wage war against the Saqaliba, travelling in ships until they reach them. They take the Saqaliba captive, transport them to *Khazran* and *Bulkar* and sell them there. [...] Among them are shamans, who have great authority over all things. They tell the people which women, men, and animals are to be offered to their god. [...] When the shaman orders a human or animal [to be sacrificed], he throws a rope around the neck and hangs the sacrifice from a piece of wood until it falls down. They call this the sacrifice to the god. They possess manliness and courage when they attack other tribes on an open field, and persist in combat until they kill them, seizing their women and making the men their slaves. [...] When an important

man among them dies, they dig him a grave like a spacious house and they lay him inside, including with him clothing for his body, an armband of gold, in which he used to dress, as well as a quantity of food and drink and coins. And they place his woman whom he loved in the grave with him while she is alive. They close the lid of the grave on her and she perishes inside.[60]

Ibn Rusta's account is similar to Ibn Fadlan's, but we learn more from him about the Rus' slave-trading. They raid and fight other tribes in order to capture slaves for sale in the Khazar and Bulgar slave markets. We are also told that they make human sacrifices, hanging their victims by the neck using a rope attached to a piece of wood and leaving them there until the wood collapses. This is highly reminiscent of the clause in the much later Swedish *Östgöta Law*, where a slave was to be hanged by the neck on the farm gatepost and left there 'until the withe rots' (above, p. 42). But the most important and oft-discussed part of Ibn Rusta's description is the burial of a Rus chieftain. The ritual differs from the ship burial seen by Ibn Fadlan. Ibn Rusta describes a burial in what must be a chamber grave of the kind found in, for example, Birka, often furnished with weaponry, jewellery, food, animals, horses and perhaps also a slave.

The third Arabic source to mention the Rus and slaving, Ibn al-Athir's *al-Kamil fi 'l-ta'rikh* (*The Complete History*), dates from around 1231. Primarily a reworking of earlier material into one of the first Arabic 'annalistic histories',[61] the Rus appear frequently, but not always as victors: we are told about several battles where they were defeated, killed or themselves taken captive. However, under the year 943–4, Ibn al-Athir describes how the Rus seized the town of Barda near the Caspian:

[T]he Rus then killed many people, and they took some ten thousand souls captive. They gathered those who remained in the Friday Mosque, and they said to the remaining townsmen: 'You can either ransom yourselves or we will kill you.' A Christian came forth and settled on twenty dirhams for each man. But the Rus did not keep to their bargain, except for the sensible ones, after they realized that they would not receive anything for some townsmen. They massacred all of those [for whom they could receive no ransom], and only a few fled from the massacre. The Rus then took the valuables of the people and enslaved the remaining prisoners, and took the women and enjoyed them.[62]

We get a vivid impression from these Arabic sources of the raiding and seizing of slaves – not only by the Scandinavian Rus – and of the trade in captives at major slave markets in the east such as Itil and Bulgar. But not one source suggests that the Rus acquired slaves to take home: most were sold at market in exchange for silver. However, these authors do talk frequently of the Rus keeping slave women as concubines, and even of burying them with their dead master, so we must assume that at least some of their female captives were taken home to Scandinavia.

If we turn to the chronicles and annals from western Europe, for example Ireland, we also find plenty of evidence of a thriving slave trade. For example, in 821 the *Annals of Ulster* record that 'Étar [Howth, Co. Dublin] was plundered by the heathens, and they carried off a great number of women into captivity';[63] in 831 'the heathens defeated the community of Ard Macha in a battle at Aignig, and great numbers of them were taken captive';[64] and in 836 'the first prey was taken by the heathens from southern Brega, i.e. from Telcha Dromáin and Dairmag of the Britons; and they carried off many prisoners, and killed many and led away very many captive'.[65]

These written sources are confirmed by large-population DNA analysis, which has shown that a major part of Iceland's female population is of Celtic ancestry.[66] If proved correct, this new evidence is staggering: female slaves were clearly brought from Ireland and the Celtic world to Iceland, and the magnitude of Celtic ancestry on the female side may be as high as 50%.

This hypothesis that slaves were akin to 'prestige goods' and their ownership a form of ostentation finds support in the archaeological material, sparse as it is. From the Stengade excavations in Denmark, which have been interpreted as the grave field of an ordinary Viking-Age village, one grave stands out from the rest. This is a large chamber grave containing a tall youth equipped with weapons. In the grave lies a second, decapitated male, whose hands and feet had been tied together, probably the youth's slave. Nothing similar is found anywhere else in this grave field; no indications of slave burials are found in the more ordinary graves. I believe this suggests that slaves were owned predominantly by the upper social classes and that they were considered 'prestige goods'. But in my opinion, Viking-Age Scandinavian society scarcely merits being called a 'slave society'. Slaves were not as common as one might think, and owned mainly by the affluent.

Such a hypothesis would also, I believe, find support from anthropological analogies. Analyses of various kinds of slave societies show that extensive slaveholding requires a certain level of social complexity, an agrarian-economic system that necessitates a large slave population.[67] The Roman empire and the American plantation economy are good examples. A huge number of slaves worked the Roman *latifundia* and mines, as well as in people's homes, while the need for manual labour in the American cotton plantations was vast and, in both cases, slaves had a significant economic function within society. In societies of lesser economic complexity, such as the New Zealand Maori or native Americans, slaves had a different socio-economic function: 'prestige goods' owned predominantly by leading social groups. One could say that in the former cases, slavery was financially conditioned, and in the latter socially conditioned.

I would argue that the agrarian-economic system of Viking-Age Scandinavia did not require a high degree of slaveholding for the reasons outlined above.

However, when society gradually feudalised in the early medieval period, a potential economic need for slaves developed within the emerging estate system, with work thralls becoming more common on farms and possibly also as a sort of tenant on dependent farms. Seen in Sweden during the late middle ages, this system changed relatively quickly, once more for economic reasons, with slaveholding being abolished and replaced by the more lucrative and easily maintained tenant system, with 'semi-free' farmers on tenant farms. The preconditions for extensive slaveholding – high numbers of purely work slaves – are thus unlikely to have existed in earlier medieval Scandinavia.

Yet thralls were important in Scandinavian society during the Viking and early middle ages, for different, social reasons. The thrall constituted a social and moral contrast to the free man. A thrall had no honour or worth, or the possibility of obtaining such; nor did he have family or kin – all key concepts within Viking-Age society. This polarity was important in order to validate the social order, not only in Scandinavian society but also more widely.[68]

Finally, I would suggest that in the medieval period, the concept of the *thrall* held a more nuanced semantic content than simply that of an 'unfree slave'. As we have seen, it may have referred to a dependency relationship between a powerful individual and his servant or subject, a type of 'patron–client' relationship. The 'client' may have ended up by force or voluntarily in a dependent position – whether in short-term service or longer-lasting servitude. This could take various forms: the running of a farm as bondsman-cum-tenant; assistance on trading expeditions; employment as a craftsman, such as a blacksmith; serving as a warrior for a nobleman or king, presumably with an oath of allegiance being sworn; or possibly eventually becoming legally recognised as an individual. According to Mats Roslund, some women were also producing pottery, most probably at trading sites and emporia. Yet at the lowest rung on the social ladder we also have chattel slaves, sleeping in barns with the cattle, working the fields, herding livestock and doing all the dirty work on an estate or farm. The lack of written sources and the complexity of slaveholding in early Scandinavia make its study extremely difficult. But both western and Arabic written sources support the idea that the Vikings abroad were heavily involved in the slave trade, capturing or buying slaves, and selling them off at slave markets. I would suggest that slaving was the major income stream of Viking traders, but that they were not particularly seeking slaves for their own use at home in Scandinavia. We have too much evidence that what they wanted was not humans, but silver – silver that obviously formed part of the many, huge silver hoards found in Scandinavia, especially on Gotland.

Notes

1 [...] *þá sculo þeir aller gera honum .xij. kúa bú. oc .ij. rossa oc .iij. mansmanna*: Frosta-tingslagen IV.44, ed. Keyser and Munch, p. 171; tr. Hagland and Sandnes, p. 72.
2 In this chapter, I will use the terms slave and thrall interchangeably. The word *thrall* (ON *þræll*) was one of the more common, generic terms for a (male) slave

in medieval Scandinavia, and was absorbed into English. See also the discussion below.

3 Sandnes (1979, 1983).
4 Benedictow (1996).
5 Krag (1982).
6 Iversen (1997), p. 115; Sandnes (1983), pp. 81–2.
7 Karras (1988), pp. 78–9.
8 The term *mansmannr* (pl. *mansmenn*) literally means 'a man's man': Brink (2012), p. 260.
9 Iversen (1997), p. 116.
10 Henning (1930), pp. 93–5; Brink (2012), pp. 288–9 n. 460.
11 The levelling oath was sworn by the perpetrator's kin after compensation had been paid for a killing or wounding, acknowledging that the perpetrator would have accepted the same compensation from the injured or dead man's kin had the roles been reversed.
12 *DML* § 126, p. 77; belt-fine: 'he should pay all he owned until only the belt was left' (*ibid.*, p. 77, n. 206).
13 Patterson (1982).
14 *DML* § 130, p. 78.
15 *GL*, p. 7.
16 *GL*, p. 11.
17 *GL*, p. 20.
18 *Edsöresbalken* ('On the King's oath of peace') 16, ÖgL, p. 37: [. . .] *þa skal þrælin up hængia uiþ garþzs liþ þæs sum han a.*
19 *Dråpsbalken* ('On manslaughter') 13 § 2, ÖgL, p. 59: [. . .] *taka eki uiþiu ok binda um hals þrælinum ok up hængia uiþ liþstolpa bondans. huggær för niþær æn uiþian rutnar.*
20 The generic terms in Scandinavia were *thrall* or *ambátt* (female): Brink (2012), p. 121.
21 Brink (2012), p. 211.
22 The first element in *Estamåla*, the word *est* (pl. *ester*), can mean 'slave, unfree' in medieval Swedish as well as 'Estonian': 'ester' in Söderwall, *Ordbok*, vol. 1, p. 228; Brink (2012), p. 134. Similarly, *Kur-* in *Kuramåla* could denote 'Courland' in Latvia (*Kurzeme*; Swedish *Kurland*), and rather more speculatively, *Sum-* in *Summemåla* someone from *Suomi* or Finland. *Iremåla* is different and, to my knowledge, unique: the first element here could indicate someone from Ireland.
23 Brink (2012), p. 149.
24 *Ärvdabalken* ('On inheritance') 4 § 2, VgL, p. 25: *Kona giftiss bort fræ barnum sinum. eghu barn ambut ællær þræll. þa ma þem firi bo sætiæ. þa mughu fæþærnis frænþer skiptæ or barnæ lot. faþur broþir barnæ mæli mælæ. ok fostræ skal firi bo sitiæ.*
25 *Giftermålsbalken* ('On matrimony') 11, VgL, pp. 146–7.
26 *Manhelgdsbalken* ('On personal protection') 25 § 9, VmL, p. 159.
27 *Edsöresbalken* 23 and *Giftermålsbalken* 29, ÖgL, pp. 39–40, 111.
28 For examples, see Henry of Livonia, *Chronicle* IX.3–4, XI.5, XII.6, XIII.4, XIII.5, XIV.6, XV.1–2, ed. Arndt, pp. 250, 259–60, 264, 265, 267–8, 271; tr. Brundage, pp. 48–9, 72–3, 84, 86, 91, 93, 100, 108–9.
29 *Hkr*[3], vol. 3, pp. 180, 181.
30 Helmold of Bosau, *Chronicle*, ed. Lappenberg, p. 98; tr. Tschan, p. 278; see also Roslund (2020 forthcoming).
31 Lübke (2001), p. 120. See also Biermann (2021 forthcoming).
32 The term may derive from the proto-Nordic verb *★brutjan* 'to break' and is then a *nomen agentis* constructed on the stem of the weak verb Old Swedish *brytia*, ON

brytja 'break into pieces, break asunder'. For a long time this has been assumed originally to have designated 'one who breaks (bread and distributes food)'. The word appears in Old Swedish with meanings such as a 'manager (of someone else's property), farm bailiff, particularly one who in return for a share in the yields runs and farms someone else's farm': 'bryti' in Söderwall, *Ordbok*, vol. 1, p. 156. The word *bryti* has also been borrowed by Finnish as *ruttio, ruttia* 'steward, slave': de Vries (1962), p. 62.

33 Brink (2012), p. 140.

34 That the *bryti* was originally a sort of farm manager seems to be generally accepted in the literature. See Velschow (1840); Erslev (1898), pp. 90, 101, 226, 252; Hjärne (1947), p. 36; Skrubbeltrang (1957); Riis (1970); Gissel (1981).

35 The kind of household defined on the basis of bread (*hlaf*) that we find in Anglo-Saxon, where the lord was 'bread keeper' (< *hlaf-weard*) and those he was responsible for feeding the *hlaf-gang*, was probably also found in early Scandinavia, although we lack the qualifier *hlaf* in Old Nordic: Brink (2008), pp. 8–9.

36 Vinogradoff (1911); Kahan (1973); Bailey (2014).

37 Nordström and Herschend (2003).

38 Hansson (2014).

39 Brink (2008, 2012, pp. 139–54, 2014).

40 Dyer (2005), p. 422.

41 *Magnus Lagabøtes landslov.*

42 Gelting (2005), p. 343.

43 Hasselberg (1944).

44 See e.g. Bloch (1961, 1975); Duby (1980); Dockès (1982); Fourquin (1988); Bonnassie (1991).

45 See e.g. Lindkvist (1979, 2014); Bøgh (1994); Iversen (1995, 1996); Gelting (2005).

46 These included runology, archaeology, toponymy, anthroponymy, linguistics and contemporary terms for slaves. I also considered what late medieval documents, laws and the Old Norse sagas could tell us about the earlier period, as well as drawing a comparison with other northern European societies where more is known about medieval slavery.

47 See e.g. Randsborg (1986); Hodges (1989); Theuws (2012 unpublished). See now, though, *IC*.

48 IbnF[1], pp. 244–5.

49 Brink (2012), pp. 224–36.

50 Neumann *et al.* (2014).

51 Roslund (2005, 2007, forthcoming); and especially Roslund (2020 forthcoming).

52 For similar arguments, see Bull (1931), pp. 15–16; Krag (1982); Sawyer and Sawyer (1993), p. 132. More recently Thomas Lindkvist (2003, p. 19) has suggested: 'Om det en gång existerat ett slavsamhälle [...] har träldomens betydelse inte legat i dess kvantitet' ('If a slave society once existed [...] the significance of slavery lay not in its quantity'). Others reckon that Scandinavia had a sizeable slave population and that slavery was of great economic importance: Lunden (1976), pp. 268–73 [Norway]; Moberg (1970–1), vol. 1, pp. 38–40 [Sweden].

53 More generally, Phillips (1985), p. 8, notes: 'As servants, guards, and sexual partners, their [the slaves'] primary function in many cases was to demonstrate the wealth and luxury enjoyed by their owners'.

54 Krag (1982), p. 214, even suggests that they demanded ransom for those they took captive, rather than aiming to make slaves of them; and if ransoms were not paid, the Vikings often killed their prisoners.

55 IbnF[1].

56 Schjødt (2007).

57 IbnF[1], pp. 242–3.

58 Watson (2004), p. 290.
59 Franklin and Shepard (1996), pp. 29–32; see also Garipzanov (2006).
60 Watson (2004), pp. 291–2.
61 Watson (2001), p. 425.
62 Watson (2001), p. 434.
63 *Annals of Ulster*, p. 277; Holm (1986), p. 319; Downham (2009).
64 *Annals of Ulster*, p. 289.
65 *Annals of Ulster*, p. 295.
66 Agnar Helgason *et al.* (2000a); Agnar Helgason *et al.* (2000b); Agnar Helgason *et al.* (2001).
67 Gronenborn (2001), p. 21.
68 Patterson (1982), p. 47; Wyatt (2001), p. 341; see also Wyatt in this volume.

Bibliography

Primary sources

Annals of Ulster (to AD 1131), ed. S. Mac Airt and G. Mac Niocaill, Dublin (1983).

DML = *The Danish Medieval Laws: The Laws of Scania, Zealand and Jutland*, tr. D. Tamm and H. Vogt, Abingdon; New York (2016).

Helmold of Bosau, *Chronicle*, ed. J. M. Lappenberg, *Chronica Slavorum*, in *MGH Scriptores* 21, Hanover (1868), pp. 1–99; tr. F. J. Tschan, *The Chronicle of the Slavs*, New York (1935).

Henry of Livonia [Henricus Lettus], *Chronicle*, ed. W. Arndt, *Heinrici Chronicon Lyvoniae*, in *MGH Scriptores* 23, Hanover (1874), pp. 231–332; tr. J. A. Brundage, rev. ed., New York (2003).

Frostatingslagen, ed. R. Keyser and P. A. Munch, in *NGL* 1, pp. 119–258; Norwegian tr. J. R. Hagland and J. Sandnes, *Frostatingslova*, Oslo (1994).

Magnus Lagabøtes landslov, ed. R. Keyser and P. A. Munch, in *NGL* 2, pp. 1–178.

NGL = *Norges gamle Love indtil 1387*, ed. R. Keyser, P. A. Munch *et al.*, 5 vols, Christiania (1846–95).

ÖgL = *Östgöta-lagen* [The Östgöta Laws], ed. H. S. Collin and C. J. Schlyter, *CIS* 2, Stockholm (1830).

Söderwall, K. F., *Ordbok öfver svenska medeltids-språket*, 2 vols, Lund (1884–1918).

VgL = *Westgöta-lagen* [The Västgöta Laws], ed. H. S. Collin and C. J. Schlyter, *CIS* 1, Stockholm (1827).

VmL = *Westmanna-lagen* [The Västmanna Laws], ed. C. J. Schlyter, *CIS* 5, Lund (1841).

Secondary literature

Agnar Helgason, E. Hickey *et al.* (2001), 'mtDNA and the islands of the North Atlantic: estimating the proportions of Norse and Gaelic ancestry', *American Journal of Human Genetics* 68: 723–37.

Agnar Helgason, Sigrún Sigurðardóttir, J. R. Gulcher *et al.* (2000a), 'mtDNA and the origin of the Icelanders: deciphering signals of recent population history', *American Journal of Human Genetics* 66: 999–1016.

Agnar Helgason, Sigrún Sigurðardóttir, J. Nicholson *et al.* (2000b), 'Estimating Scandinavian and Gaelic ancestry in the male settlers of Iceland', *American Journal of Human Genetics* 67: 697–717.

Bailey, M. (2014), *The Decline of Serfdom in Late Medieval England: From Bondage to Freedom*, Woodbridge.

Benedictow, O. J. (1996), 'The demography of the Viking age and the high middle ages in the Nordic countries', *Scandinavian Journal of History* 21: 151–82.

Biermann, F. (2021 forthcoming), 'Archaeological evidence for slavery among the early medieval northwestern Slavs', in *IC*.

Bloch, M. (1961), *Feudal Society*, tr. L. A. Manyon, 2 vols, London.

Bloch, M. (1975), *Slavery and Serfdom in the Middle Ages: Selected Essays*, tr. W. R. Beer, Berkeley, CA.

Bøgh, A. (1994), 'Feudalisering og bondekommunalisme: noget om samfundet i senmiddelalderen', in P. Ingesman and J. V. Jensen (eds), *Danmark i Senmiddelalderen*, Aarhus, pp. 88–105.

Bonnassie, P. (1991), *From Slavery to Feudalism in South-Western Europe*, tr. J. Birrell, Cambridge.

Brink, S. (2008), *Lord and Lady – Bryti and Deigja: Some Historical and Etymological Aspects of Family, Patronage and Slavery in Early Scandinavia and Anglo-Saxon England*, London.

Brink, S. (2012), *Vikingarnas slavar: den nordiska trädomen under yngre järnålder och äldsta medeltid*, Stockholm.

Brink, S. (2014), 'Bryten', in O. Karsvall and K. Jupiter (eds), *Medeltida storgårdar: 15 uppsatser om ett tvärvetenskapligt forskningsproblem*, Uppsala, pp. 59–82.

Bull, E. (1931), *Det norske folks liv og historie gjennem tidene*, vol. 2: *Fra omkring 1000 til 1280*, Oslo.

de Vries, J. (1962), *Altnordisches etymologisches Wörterbuch*, 2nd edn, Leiden.

Dockès, P. (1982), *Medieval Slavery and Liberation*, tr. A. Goldhammer, London.

Downham, C. (2009), 'The Viking slave trade', *History Ireland* 17: 15–17.

Duby, G. (1980), *The Three Orders. Feudal Society Imagined*, tr. A. Goldhammer, Chicago, IL.

Dyer, C. (2005), 'Villeins, bondmen, neifs, and serfs: new serfdom in England, *c.* 1200–1600', in P. Freedman and M. Bourin (eds), *Forms of Servitude in Northern and Central Europe: Decline, Resistance, and Expansion*, Turnhout, pp. 419–35.

Erslev, K. (1898), *Valdemarernes storhedstid*, Copenhagen.

Fourquin, G. (1988), 'Serfs and serfdom: western European', in J. R. Strayer *et al.* (eds), *Dictionary of the Middle Ages*, New York, vol. 11, pp. 199–208.

Franklin, S. and J. Shepard (1996), *The Emergence of Rus, 750–1200*, London.

Garipzanov, I. (2006), 'The Annals of St Bertin (839) and *Chacanus* of the *Rhos*', *Ruthenica* 5: 7–11.

Gelting, M. (2005), 'Legal reform and the development of peasant dependence in thirteenth century Denmark', in P. Freedman and M. Bourin (eds), *Forms of Servitude in Northern and Central Europe: Decline, Resistance, and Expansion*, Turnhout, pp. 343–67.

Gissel, S. (1981), 'Bryte', *RGA* 4: 26–7.

Gronenborn, D. (2001), 'Zum (möglichen) Nachweis von Sklaven/Unfreien in prähistorischen Gesellschaften Mitteleuropas', *Ethnographisch-Archäologische Zeitschrift* 42: 1–42.

Hansson, M. (2014), 'Att hysa forlk på gården: ett försök till byggnadsarkeologi', in O. Karsvall and K. Jupiter (eds), *Medeltida storgårdar: 15 uppsatser om ett tvärvetenskapligt forskningsproblem*, Uppsala, pp. 165–87.

Hasselberg, G. (1944), 'Den s.k. Skarastadgan och träldomens upphörande i Sverige', *Västergötlands fornminnesförenings tidskrift* 5(3): 51–90.

Henning, S. (1930), 'Träldomens försvinnande och de svenska landskapslagarna', *Historisk tidskrift* (Stockholm) 50: 86–95.

Hjärne, E. (1947), 'Roden. Upphovet och namnet. Området och jarlen', *NoB* 35: 1–96.

Hodges, R. (1989), 'Archaeology and the class struggle in the first millennium AD', in K. Randsborg (ed.), *The Birth of Europe: Archaeology and Social Development in the First Millennium AD*, Rome, pp. 178–87.

Holm, P. (1986), 'The slave trade of Dublin, ninth to twelfth centuries', *Peritia* 5: 317–45.

Iversen, T. (1995), 'Fremveksten av det norske leilendingsvesenet i middelalderen ± en forklaringsskisse', *Heimen* 32: 169–80.

Iversen, T. (1996), 'Jordleie, patroner og klienter før høymiddelalderens leilendingsvesen i Norge', *Heimen* 33: 147–56.

Iversen, T. (1997), *Trelldommen: norsk slaveri i middelalderen*, Bergen.

Kahan, A. (1973), 'Notes on serfdom in western and eastern Europe', *The Journal of Economic History* 33: 86–99.

Karras, R. M. (1988), *Slavery and Society in Medieval Scandinavia*, New Haven, CT.

Krag, C. (1982), 'Treller og trellehold', *Historisk tidskrift* (Oslo) 61: 209–27.

Lindkvist, T. (1979), *Landborna i Norden under äldre medeltid*, Uppsala.

Lindkvist, T. (2003), 'Från träl till landbo: uppkomsten av det medeltida godssystemet i Europa och Norden', in T. Lindkvist and J. Myrdal (eds), *Trälar: ofria i agrarsamhället från vikingatid till medeltid*, Stockholm, pp. 9–21.

Lindkvist, T. (2014), 'En feodal revolution i Sverige och frågan om stora och små gårdar', in O. Karsvall and K. Jupiter (eds), *Medeltida storgårdar: 15 uppsatser om ett tvärvetenskapligt forskningsproblem*, Uppsala, pp. 9–21.

Lübke, C. (2001), *Fremde im östlichen Europa: von Gesellschaften ohne Staat zu verstaatlichten Gesellschaften (9.–11. Jahrhundert)*, Cologne.

Lunden, K. (1976), *Norge under Sverreætten, 1177–1319*, Norges historie 3, Oslo.

Moberg, V. (1970–1), *Min svenska historia: berättad för folket*, 2 vols, Stockholm.

Neumann, E. *et al.* (2014), 'Slaves as burial gifts in Viking Age Norway? Evidence from stable isotope and ancient DNA analyses', *Journal of Archaeological Science* 41: 533–40.

Nordström, K. and F. Herschend (2003), 'Det ideologiska inslaget i väven', in T. Lindkvist and J. Myrdal (eds), *Trälar: ofria i agrarsamhället från vikingatid till medeltid*, Stockholm, pp. 50–76.

Patterson, O. (1982), *Slavery and Social Death: A Comparative Study*, Cambridge, MA.

Phillips, W. D. (1985), *Slavery from Roman Times to the Early Transatlantic Trade*, Manchester.

Randsborg, K. (1986), 'The study of slavery in northern Europe: an archaeological approach', *Acta Archaeologica* 55: 155–60.

Riis, T. (1970), 'Villici og coloni indtil 1340. Et forsøg på en begrebsanalyse', in S. Gissel (ed.), *Landbohistoriske studier tilegnede Fridlev Skrubbeltrang*, Copenhagen, pp. 1–20.

Roslund, M. (2005), 'Transcending borders: social identity in the middle ages and in medieval archaeology', *Arheo: Glasilo arheološkega društva Slovenije* 23: 63–78.

Roslund, M. (2007), *Guests in the House: Cultural Transmission between Slavs and Scandinavians 900 to 1300 AD*, Leiden.

Roslund, M. (2021 forthcoming), 'Legacy of the disowned: finding *ambátt*s in high medieval Scania and Östergötland through ceramic production', in *IC*.

Roslund, M. (forthcoming), 'Tacit knowing of thralls: style negotiation among the unfree in 11th and 12th century Sweden', in T. Clack (ed.), *Archaeology, Syncretism, Creolisation*, Oxford.

Sandnes, J. (1979), 'Bondesamfunnet', in I. Semmingsen *et al.* (eds), *Norges kulturhistorie*, vol. 1: *Vår fjerne fortid*, Oslo, pp. 33–68.

Sandnes, J. (1983), '"Tolv kyr, to hester og tre træler": litt om omfanget av træleholdet i Norge i vikingtid og tidlig kristen tid', *Historisk tidsskrift* (Oslo) 62: 79–83.

Sawyer, B. and P. Sawyer (1993), *Medieval Scandinavia: From Conversion to Reformation circa 800–1500*, Minneapolis, MN.

Schjødt, J. P. (2007), 'Ibn Fadlan's account of a Rus funeral: to what degree does it reflect Nordic myths?', in P. Hermann *et al.* (eds), *Reflections on Old Norse Myths*, Turnhout, pp. 133–48.

Skrubbeltrang, F. (1957), 'Bryde', *KLNM* 2: 269–72.

Theuws, F. (2012 unpublished), 'The free and unfree of the historians and the rural population of the archaeologists'.

Velschow, H. M. (1840), 'Om Bryderne, en egen Classe af den danske Bondestand i Middelalderen', *Historisk Tidsskrift* (Copenhagen) 1: 112–47.

Vinogradoff, P. (1911), 'Serfdom', in *The Encyclopædia Britannica*, vol. 24, 11th edn, Cambridge, pp. 664–7.

Watson, W. E. (2001), 'Ibn al-Athir's account of the Rus: a commentary and translation', *Canadian-American Slavic Studies* 35: 423–38.

Watson, W. E. (2004), 'Ibn Rustah's *Book of Precious Things*: a reexamination and translation of an early source on the Rus', *Canadian-American Slavic Studies* 38: 289–99.

Wyatt, D. (2001), 'The significance of slavery: alternative approaches to Anglo-Saxon slavery', *Anglo-Norman Studies* 23: 328–47.

4   The fur trade in the early middle ages

James Howard-Johnston

There are many, many different sorts of trade. The goods may be necessities, commodities or luxuries. Producer and consumer may be separated by shorter or longer distances, with lesser or greater hazards en route. There may or may not be limitations on supply. Demand will vary according to size of population and wealth. The value of goods may be artificially enhanced or depressed by cultural, particularly religious, considerations. At one extreme should be placed the virtually autarkic peasant or crofter family; at the other a globalised world in which everyone trades with everyone else in all manner of goods, the chief intermediaries being great, transnational corporations. For much of human history, the market has operated somewhere in between these extremes.

At the western end of Eurasia in antiquity, the Mediterranean, united under Roman rule, formed a distinct economic space. Natural produce (grain, wine, olive oil and garum), manufactured goods (textiles, glass, jewellery and tableware) and imports from the outside world (silks, spices, ivory and precious and semi-precious stones) were traded from one end to the other of that inland sea, and penetrated deep into the surrounding lands. A selection of the more notable items in demand across the Roman world, with their place or region of origin, is given in the fourth-century *Expositio totius mundi*, a general guide to the Mediterranean-centred world evidently written with a mercantile readership in mind.[1] Another, even larger single market took shape several centuries later in the early Abbasid caliphate. It was a highly urbanised world where there was a remarkable degree of specialisation (above all in textile production) and the range of goods on offer was extended to embrace sweetmeats and, on a far larger scale than before, medicines and cotton textiles. Given the proliferation of well-heeled merchants who formed a key element in the governing elites of the cities, it should come as no surprise that there a demand for geographies detailing the particularities of regions and cities, including the produce and goods for which they were known, and that a specifically Arab genre of geographical writing developed to satisfy it.[2]

There were two basic patterns of trade in the caliphate. Production of staples, foodstuffs and many raw materials (such as mulberry leaves for silk worms, wool, linen and cotton) was dispersed over the countryside and demand was concentrated in cities. For manufactured goods, on the other hand, production was concentrated in urban workshops, large and small, and demand was dispersed over a greater or lesser extent of the surrounding world (over the whole of the Islamic world and beyond in the case of prestigious items).[3] The same two patterns are easily discerned in the caliphate's small, north-western neighbour, Byzantium. Constantinople, the only city on a par with those of Islam, drew on the plain of Thrace and the coastlands of the Sea of Marmara and the Aegean for its grain, while exporting the products of many crafts, notably high-quality tableware, to the provinces and beyond.[4]

If we raise our eyes and look out beyond the horizon of the first of these great single markets, the Roman, we will see a case of trade in raw materials, where extraordinary concentration of supply was combined with extraordinary dispersal of demand. Production of aromatic resins (frankincense and myrrh) was limited to a small area in south-east Arabia and the Horn of Africa, while consumers were to be found all over the Mediterranean world and its European hinterland. Incense was a religious staple (or indispensable luxury) of everyday life in the Roman empire. The high level of demand could be met because small quantities could fill large enclosed spaces with sweet-smelling smoke.[5] The medieval fur trade lies at the other end of the spectrum, with extreme concentration of demand and maximum extension of supply. For the demand generated by wealthy elites in the south could only be met by the most primitive form of economic activity – hunting and trapping – over huge areas of the north.[6]

Demand for furs

Millions of pelts from the small fur-clad creatures of the northern forests were bought every year by the populations of Europe and the Islamic world in the late middle ages. Five to ten thousand could be packed into a single barrel for transport to market.[7] Some idea of the scale of demand may be obtained from an important consumer, England. Fur lining provided vital insulation for cloaks and outer garments. Furs could also be used in hats, gloves, slippers, boots and for bed covering. The nobility, clergy and many of those who served them wore fur-lined clothes as a matter of course, sumptuous furs being appreciated for their elegance and as marks of status. After the failure of an attempt in 1337 to limit fur-wearing to those of gentle birth, a statute was issued in 1363 that calibrated furs for different social grades. A single outfit or *robe* might require thousands of individual furs. One of the most splendid belonging to Henry IV consisted of nine garments (two mantles, one tabard, two supertunics [open and closed], a short and long kirtle [i.e. tunic], and large and small hats), and used up nearly 12,000 squirrel pelts and 80 ermine. Almost 80,000 pelts of trimmed minever (squirrel) were sewn into furs for the royal household in 1344–5, when 42.2% of expenditure by Edward III's Wardrobe went on furs. Of those 79,220 pelts, 32,762 were for the trousseau of Princess Philippa (which included eleven furred gowns) and the liveries of her escort.[8]

Imagine, then, the aggregate demand that could be generated by the court, nobility, clergy and merchants of a single kingdom in Latin Christendom. Then extrapolate to the rest of Latin Christendom and to the whole of the larger and more developed Islamic world. No wonder that Scandinavians, Finns, Rus and Tatars were, through intermediaries, scouring the forests of the north for fur-rich creatures, principally martens, squirrels, foxes and beavers. No wonder that the mercantile antennae of the more developed components of the northern world, in the Baltic and in Rus, penetrated deep into their hinterlands, and that Muscovite fur traders eventually, after 1600, began pushing deeper and deeper into the forests of Siberia beyond the Urals.[9]

This had not always been so. There is no evidence of trading in fur on any scale in classical antiquity, or of fur-wearing in the Greco-Roman world, save in a few cases (for example, rebellious youth and federate Germanic troops in the eastern empire in late antiquity). Neither Greek nor Latin made the distinction between skins (relatively hairless) and pelts (with a dense covering of hair), as we would expect of any culture that appreciated and made use of the insulating qualities of fur. Fur-wearing was viewed as a quintessentially barbarian habit by classical writers such as Aeschylus (writing about Thracian maenads), Caesar, Ovid in exile on the Black Sea coast of Thrace, Virgil and Tacitus. It was only to be expected of uncivilised northerners, whose minds were prey to greed and anger. The Persian-dominated world to the east, from which a rival model of the barbarian as effete, wallowing in luxury, had been conjured up by Athenian propagandists in the fifth century BC, was no more given to fur-wearing, to judge by the reports of Herodotus and Ammianus Marcellinus. So, while it is easy to imagine (as many archaeologists have done) that southerners, who had to live through cold winters or cold spells, were importing furs along with honey, wax, amber and other products from their northern neighbours throughout antiquity, this thoroughly natural trade was suppressed – a striking example of cultural depreciation. Little surprise should be occasioned. For the same was true in China, where there is very little evidence of trading in furs and fur-wearing was likewise viewed as characteristic of the northern nomad.[10]

A new culture, that of Islam, habituated to the hot desert in which it had been incubated, was responsible, after the end of antiquity, for the casting aside of the compunctions of the old world, in the course of the advance from its initial conquests in the Middle East north-eastwards over Iran and into Central Asia. Early Arab settlers in Khorasan may be envisaged as seizing on the example of the nomads they encountered and taking to furs, for clothing and bedding. Certainly it took less than a century for the habit to reach Baghdad, the new governing centre of the caliphate. The great historian al-Tabari noted the occasion in AH 166 when a man clad in furs was received in audience by the caliph al-Mahdi (775–85).[11] Whether or not this was the first such occasion, it made an impression on al-Mahdi who is reported by Mas'udi, possibly apocryphally (although Mas'udi was a well-informed and generally reliable historian and geographer), to have conducted experiments to find out which was the warmest fur, during a stay in Rayy (near modern Tehran) in a period of intense cold, with deep snow on the ground. An inventory of the treasury carried out after Caliph Harun al-Rashid's death in 809 is said to have listed a large number (grossly exaggerated to 8,000) of long outer garments, half of which were made of pure silk and lined with fur.[12]

It was presumably by a process of diffusion from capital to provincial cities, from the court and higher echelons of government to the elites of greater and lesser cities and the general administrative apparatus, that the habit of fur-wearing spread through the caliphate over the following few generations. As it did so, it undoubtedly generated a rapidly escalating demand which probably peaked in the tenth century when the economy was at its apogee after two centuries of sustained growth. Its scale cannot be overestimated, if we remember the demand a single prosperous individual could generate and the very large number of city notables (merchants, religious scholars and officials), of courtiers at the centre and in the entourage of governors, and of those staffing the bureaucracy who could afford the cost and were anxious to keep up appearances (and fur-wearing may well have reached further down the social order). It follows that a new set of trading relationships were established between south and north in the second half of the eighth century and that the flow of goods in both directions, furs (and to a lesser extent slaves and the traditional products of the forest) from the north and all manner of manufactured goods from the south, increased exponentially through the ninth and tenth centuries.

There is abundant direct testimony to the new relationships and to the predominance of furs in the exports of the north in the geographical texts written in the tenth century for the information and delectation of urban notables throughout Islam. The Bulgars who had established themselves on the Middle Volga after losing the struggle for hegemony in the western steppes to the Khazars in the seventh century were the first fur entrepreneurs. Their commercial activities are mentioned by Ibn Fadlan who visited the city of Bulgar on the Volga in 922 as a member of a caliphal diplomatic mission. Supplementary information is given by Arab geographical writers later in the century. Besides the furs gathered in their own territory, the Bulgars obtained them from their southern neighbours, the Burtas, from the Finno-Ugrian Ves' further north, and via the Viking Rus who sailed down the Volga, bringing furs from the distant north-west as well as slaves and swords. Bulgar developed into a great fur emporium, dispatching the precious merchandise south by two routes: either down the Volga and across the Caspian to the

Transcaucasus and the central lands of the devouring Arab market; or in large defended caravans across the steppes south-east to Khwarazm.[13]

Khwarazm was a highly urbanised region which straddled the lower courses of the Oxus and Jaxartes rivers where they flow into the Aral Sea. It acted as the clearing house for furs and slaves. From there furs were distributed all over the caliphate, along with locally manufactured cotton and woollen textiles. The region's wealth, lauded by tenth-century geographers, was based mainly on its role as an entrepot for livestock (bought from the neighbouring Turks), for slaves (Slavs, bought from the Volga Bulgars, and Turks, obtained in the borderlands) and for furs. Furs – sable, grey squirrel, ermine, mink, fox and beaver – head the comprehensive list of merchandise from Bulgar that passed through Khwarazm. The list includes many other items – including familiar exports of the north (wax, amber and honey), fish glue and arms – and ends with Slav slaves, sheep and cattle.[14]

The geographers were less interested in the caliphate's exports to the north. But it may be conjectured that some of the goods, natural produce and manufactures, which were brought into Khwarazm by merchants from within Islam, were forwarded to the north. Silks and brocade were probably intended for the local market, along with wine and much of their other merchandise. But some of their itemised merchandise – spices, scent, weapons, armour and jewellery – may well have made its way north to the Bulgars and Rus, as well as locally procured goods. Not unnaturally it was the silver taken north, presumably representing the difference in value between northern exports and what was bought in the south, that attracted attention. Humdrum objects like knives, glass beads, glass bracelets, cotton and woollen textiles, as well perhaps as spices (ubiquitous in the south and surely highly prized in the north), are scarcely noted, if at all, in the texts and, with the exception of beads and coins, have not survived to be disinterred by archaeologists.

The distribution of dirhams that flowed north, first mainly from the central lands of the caliphate and later, in the first half of the tenth century, from the eastern lands of the Samanid emirate, has been well documented, above all from the records of hoards found throughout the north. Their numbers leave no doubt about the importance of the new axes of trade running north across the Caspian and north-west from Khwarazm to Bulgar and thence through the Rus lands to the Baltic and Poland. So do the glass beads that were obtained by Slavs and Finno-Ugrians living on or close to the trade routes and which ended up in their graves. It is a great pity, though, that study of the diffusion of Islamic glass (bracelets as well as beads) in the north lags well behind that of dirhams, above all because the chemical analysis that can determine their provenance is in its infancy and also because systematic archaeological exploration has not extended much beyond the lake region of northern Russia (around Lakes Ladoga, Onega and Beloe).[15]

What triggered the inflow of silver?

The volume of coined silver that made its way north was astonishingly large. Some 2,000 Viking-Age hoards have been recovered in European Russia, Poland, the south coast of the Baltic, Scandinavia and the British Isles, with the principal clusters on Gotland and in central Sweden, Estonia and Wielkopolska. Of the million coins they contain, 400,000 are dirhams.[16] These 400,000 represent the known (reported) fraction of the recovered fraction of the unretrieved fraction of the originally concealed fraction of the capital and bullion stocks of the original owners. We should probably envisage a cumulative inflow of hundreds of millions of dirhams over some two centuries (from the later eighth to the later tenth century).

This northern leakage probably amounted to no more than a very small percentage of the output of Islamic mints over those two centuries. For dirhams were issued primarily for circulation within the caliphate. Used for commercial (as well as governmental) purposes across the length and breadth of a huge single market, the issues of regional mints were mixed together and formed a variegated circulating medium, until they were, in due course, recalled for reminting. But there is no denying that the volume of silver flowing north indicated that a new axis of long-distance commerce was opened up in the eighth and ninth centuries, far to the east of the traditional routes from the Baltic to the Mediterranean, which debouched either at Marseilles or Venice. If, as seems probable, the dirhams taken north simply represented a balance of trade surplus, they point to a very high level of activity, both in terms of the volume and the value of goods exchanged.

The outflow to the north began as a trickle in the eighth century. Single finds of dirhams suggest that a route south had been opened and that goods from the south were beginning to reach the Baltic, probably passing through intermediaries on the way.[17] Corroboration comes from the arrival of oriental beads in the Kama basin in the eighth century, from which they percolated north to the Ilmen basin, Staraia Ladoga, Finland, the Åland islands, central Sweden and round the Baltic.[18] The earliest dirham hoard in the north (with thirty-one coins) was concealed at Staraia Ladoga sometime after the minting of the latest coin (786–7).[19] It should probably be associated with the first phase of Viking Rus trading ventures to the south. The northward flow of dirhams gradually increased through the ninth century, before a sharp drop in the 870s and 880s. Then, at the beginning of the tenth century, there was a surge, when Samanid mints, at Samarqand and al-Shash, feeding off silver from the newly opened mines of the Panjshir valley, started pumping out massive amounts of new coin. The flow tailed off after 950 when the purity of the dirhams fell below 80% and an alternative source of coined silver (in Germany) became available.[20]

What triggered the start of north–south exchanges in the eighth century across uncharted territory far to the east of the established trade routes from the Baltic to the Mediterranean? How on earth is one to explain the phenomenal growth in exchange, represented by the northward flow of dirhams through the ninth and the first half of the tenth century? It seems clear to me that new commodities must have come on to the market and must have roused interest in the south where, from the first, Islam fostered growth in a huge economic space. That being so, the commodities must have come from the north. But what were they? Why did they suddenly stimulate demand in the caliphate and, above all, why did the market for them grow so rapidly, climaxing in the early tenth century in something akin to an explosion of demand?

They cannot have been those commodities of the north – amber, honey and wax – that had percolated south in antiquity. They were familiar, so unlikely to trigger a devouring appetite in southerners, let alone the numismatically documented explosion in demand. Were they then slaves hunted and captured by predatory powers in the north? Slaves were certainly transported and sold in the south. Tenth-century Arab geographers mention them as part of the northern merchandise on offer. They were also taken down the Dnieper and sold in Constantinople.[21] But the main flow of slaves from eastern Europe was not south, but west through France to Muslim Spain and beyond, while the main inflow of slaves into Khwarazm and Transoxiana came from the steppes – in the shape of the Turkish mamluks who were sought by rulers all over the Islamic lands.[22] There is nothing in the geographical texts, our main source of information, to suggest that there was a large enough influx of slaves from the north to explain the scale of the dirham outflow. The rate of growth attested by the rate of dirham outflow is even less explicable, if the key commodities were slaves. The only scenario that might account for it would be one in which the great and the good throughout Islam were investing in plantations and, because of a shortage of labour, were in need of ever-increasing numbers of slaves. Such an important development in the economic and social history of Islam would not have gone unrecorded.

We are left, then, with the commodities that are highlighted in contemporary sources – the various sorts of furs listed by geographers. The removal of an age-old cultural barrier explains the sudden development of demand in the developed southern world. The eastward movement of the economic centre of gravity of the southern world, from the east Mediterranean to Iraq and Iran, explains the eastward shift in the main axis of trade between north and south from the Rhine–Rhone axis to one running diagonally south-east from the Baltic to the Volga and thence either south to the Caspian and the Transcaucasus or south-east to Khwarazm. Finally – and this is the crucial argument – the exponential growth in demand for furs in the south over two centuries provides the only satisfactory explanation for the rapid growth in the outflow of dirhams over the same period.

There is, however, little correlation between the find spots of dirham hoards and the principal routes by which furs reached the south, with two important exceptions: the portages around Lakes Ladoga, Onega and Beloe, in what was an important intermediary zone between the deep forest and the main trunk route down the Volga; and Estonia, at the Baltic end of the northern section of the main trunk route.[23] Apart from Estonia, the main trunk route is virtually denuded of dirhams. Few have been found on or near the portages over the watersheds between the rivers flowing north-west into the Baltic and those flowing south, or along the whole course of the river Volga, except for the core territory of the Volga Bulgars in the tenth century. Large numbers of hoards have also been found where we would not expect them, first and foremost on Gotland but also in the western and south-west Baltic (central Sweden and Denmark), i.e. well away from the direct routes between the northern forests and the Volga. It is equally surprising to find dirhams deposited on or near the Middle and Upper Dnieper and east towards the Don (those were the two main waterways leading to the Black Sea) since there was little, if any, demand for furs in Byzantium where the classical antipathy for fur-wearing remained strong in the early middle ages.[24] The hoards there should be viewed as tracers of economic and political relations among the Viking Rus, and between them and the Khazars to the east, and, just possibly, as representing the medium of exchange used by the Rus in their dealings with Byzantium which banned the export of precious metals.[25] Finally, the cluster of tenth-century hoards between the Vistula and Elbe had little to do with the fur trade but rather documented surpluses generated from the sale of slaves, denominated in eastern dirhams that formed the main circulating medium of the north at the time.[26]

There is, then, a very significant discrepancy between what we know of the geographical patterning of the fur trade from texts and the material evidence of economic activity in the north furnished by dirham hoards. There is no obvious explanation for the presence of large numbers of hoards on Gotland and in southern Sweden and Denmark. But their dearth on the main trade route, on the portages leading south from the catchment areas of rivers flowing into the Baltic and along the Volga may be understood if we bear in mind the factors affecting the original deposition and subsequent non-retrieval of hoards. Hoards would only be concealed if the sums were large or the danger of loss was high or both. The most likely scenarios were these: a trader on the move would be likely to hide his travelling purse during a stop, especially perhaps if he were part of a group; a trader established at a larger or smaller emporium on or close to an important trade route would take care to keep safe his reserves of cash. Such hoards would only be left concealed if something happened to prevent their owners from retrieving them – say they died suddenly, without telling their companions or relatives, or they were killed or taken prisoner on a foreign venture, or they suffered a failure of memory – or if no-one else was able to find them. Non-retrieval was the crucial factor, likely to be very rare on a frequented trade route and in larger emporia, where there were plenty of prying eyes.

Finally, we cannot expect to use dirhams, or indeed oriental beads, to trace the capillary system in the northern forests, along which pelts of martens, squirrels, foxes and beavers were conveyed, from those who trapped them or shot them (with blunt-headed arrows) via small peripatetic traders operating deep in the forest zone to the outermost trading posts used by fur-dealers. The goods, such as textiles, knives and tools, that were sought by Finno-Ugrians and Saami in the far north have perished long ago. Hunters, trappers and traders would have had no use for coined silver in the recesses of the forest, save perhaps as the raw material for jewellery. It is more surprising that beads did not penetrate deeper than dirhams into the forest zone, notwithstanding their arrival in much greater numbers in the region of outer emporia in the lake region of Russia.[27] However, this may be an optical illusion, resulting from the paucity of serious study of beads in the far north.

What changed in the Baltic?

What the puzzling dirham hoards of the north-west document is the economic articulation of the Baltic in the ninth and tenth centuries. The coined silver that arrived from the south provided a plentiful and convenient medium of exchange which was promptly put to use in the commercial centres of what had become in the course of the eighth century a well-developed northern market. There was active exchange across the sea, both along the traditional diagonal trade route between Denmark, central Sweden, the Åland Islands and south-west Finland, and along an increasingly trafficked lateral route between the west and east Baltic, which met the trunk route to the south in Estonia.[28]

This Baltic trade zone had been centuries in gestation. It was not the creation of the fur trade, although it was naturally affected by it. Its origins go back to the first millennium BC, but it went through an important developmental phase in the Roman Iron Age and did not regress much during the Migration and Vendel Periods (from the mid-sixth to the late eighth centuries).[29] The nearby presence of a huge, Mediterranean market and a great imperial power had a profound effect on southern Scandinavia in antiquity, just as it did on other peripheral regions populated by Germanic peoples. The general trend was for a coagulation of power and wealth, most marked in the formation of new political and military federations in the inner zone just beyond the frontier. Further out, in what may be defined as an intermediate zone, it took the form of social stratification and concentration of wealth and power at the level of chiefdoms (evident in richly furnished burials, up to the late fifth century, and a clear hierarchy of settlement).[30] This has been well documented in the two main southern components of Scandinavia, Denmark and central Sweden. A good example is the site of Gudme on the island of Funen, between Jutland and Zealand, where there was a cluster of at least fifty fenced farmsteads, a great hall, evidence of craft production and real concentration of wealth, to judge by finds of concealed gold and silver, dating from the fifth and sixth centuries. Similar juxtapositions of craft production and centres of aristocratic/princely power have been found on Jutland (Dankirke) and Bornholm (Sorte Muld), and in Zealand (Boeslunde) and Scania (Uppåkra).[31]

This social and political order, with its centres of power and production, withstood the various shocks of late antiquity, not least the northward lapping of Hun power.[32] Except for south and central Norrland in central Sweden where the elites lost control of the hinterland after the middle of the sixth century, it seems to have survived through the Migration and Vendel Periods. The basic settlement pattern, a substructure of small villages beneath aristocratic/princely sites, can be seen to have endured.[33] There were some forty-five of the high-level sites at the centre of identifiable chiefdoms around the year 800.[34] Some were new, having supplanted the old, as in Denmark where Gudme on Funen was succeeded by three sites combining elite residence and craft production on Zealand (Toftegård, Lejre and Tissø).[35] Equally old centres might retain their position and continue to develop, as happened at two notable sites in central Sweden: Helgö, where manufacturing and trading grew up around a cult centre; and Gamla Uppsala, which consolidated its position as a central place between the fourth and seventh centuries, with clear evidence of aristocratic/princely power (a grand residence and large burial mounds) and craft production.[36]

There was no slackening in commercial exchange in the sixth and seventh centuries, but rather an intensification stimulated by developments to the west. Under the benign influence of a single hegemonic power, Merovingian Francia, a new economic zone of active exchange developed in the North Sea, embracing the south and east coasts of England, the low country where the Rhine debouches into the sea (the base for Frisian traders) and Jutland. In due course it expanded to the east to include Denmark and the western Baltic.[37] It was within this enlarged North Sea–west Baltic arena that demand was generated and satisfied for garnet-inlaid metalwork and a mythically charged animal style of decoration. As well as such luxury goods, humdrum durable artefacts were exchanged, such as Rhineland ceramics, Eifel quernstones and glass beads.[38] Of the continuing growth of this northern maritime market through the seventh century there can be no doubt, given the reaction of kings who controlled key sectors of the North Sea and Baltic coasts. From the late seventh century they sponsored the establishment of secure gateway ports, where tolls were collected in exchange for protection: first Quentovic in northern Francia, Dorestad in Frisia, Hamwic (Southampton), Lundenwic (London) and Ipswich in England; then, in the course of the eighth century, Ribe and Hedeby on the west and east coasts of Jutland, Kaupang commanding Oslo fjord, and Birka (the successor to Helgö) in central Sweden.[39]

The clearest evidence of all that this northern market – a distant precursor of the principal driving force of the European economy in the middle ages and early modern period – had acquired a momentum of its own is provided by the currency used to facilitate exchange. The coin was a small, silver coin, the sceat (1.3g), without any indication of an issuing authority. There were several types, some of which (probably the earliest) were issued for use within individual kingdoms in England in the middle of the seventh century. Before the end of the century, the sceat's potential as a convenient medium of exchange in longer-distance trade was appreciated in Frisia, where types D ('Frisian runic') and E ('porcupine') were minted, the latter in large numbers if, as has been calculated, over 5,000 dies were used between 695 and *c.* 750. The mints have been tentatively placed at Quentovic (or possibly Domburg) for type D, and Dorestad for type E. It may well be that the issuing authorities were the leading Frisian merchants. Use of the sceat spread along the North Sea coast to Jutland and beyond into the west Baltic. It was probably under royal authority and on Jutland that a third commercial type, X ('Wodan' or 'monster'), was minted in large numbers. There is no die duplication among the 173 specimens in the Hallum hoard (Netherlands). It was the type in most common use in the west Baltic.[40]

A thick scatter of sceat finds documents the impact of the northern market on the Rhineland corridor leading south in the eighth century. Sceats also circulated in west Francia, as is shown by a number of hoards, including one found not far from Marseilles.[41] They were superseded on the continent by the new, heavier Carolingian silver pennies (1.7g) issued from the 750s, and, in the north, by dirhams after the first exploratory Rus expeditions opened the new eastern trade route in the late eighth and early ninth centuries.

It was only to be expected that the flow of silver from the south in exchange for furs from the north would have an effect on the Baltic component of the developing northern market, pulling it eastward and drawing out a line of trading places (smaller than emporia and unaffected by royal authority) along the south coast of the Baltic – Menzlin, Ralswiek, Wolin and Grobiṇa.[42] The mid-eighth century foundation of a trading place and settlement at Staraia Ladoga, on the Lower Volkhov river, commanding a key section of the northern trunk route, marked an early appreciation by the Rus of the commercial potential of the fur trade.[43] The principal longer-term consequence of the entry of furs onto the northern market and their dispatch to the south, however, was the emergence of Gotland as a new, increasingly dominant commercial centre in the eastern Baltic. Almost 350 dirham hoards have been found on the island, containing some 32,000 whole coins (94kg) and a similar number of fragments (almost 38kg). Like the contemporary hoards on the much smaller island of Bornholm well to the west, they may be categorised either as savings the owners intended to retrieve (so normally placed in containers); as stocks of bullion kept in or near a workshop (like the huge Spillings hoard, concealed in Bogeviken in the north-east, which contained almost 500 bracelets, scrap silver and 14,300 coins); or as coins permanently buried for ritual reasons (say, to secure property or as votive offerings).[44]

The concentration of dirham hoards on Gotland makes it plain that the island was the directing centre of the eastern trade, from the middle of the ninth century at the latest. It is puzzling, though, that the hoards are to be found dispersed over most of the island, as if trade were carried on at or near a multitude of beach landings, and that there is no tell-tale cluster to indicate the location of a financial centre. Part of the explanation is to be found in local law (codified in *Guta Lag* of *c.* 1220) which laid down that farms should be transmitted undivided from generation to generation within the family and that sons who left the family farm should receive a purse and scales (i.e. should go into trade).[45] Consequently there was a remarkably even distribution of landed property across the island. There were gradations among the 1,500–2,000 farms that existed in the Viking Age, but no great estates.[46] Most of the savings hoards that have been found and were intended to be retrieved should probably be interpreted as future endowments of younger sons who grew up on these small or medium-sized farms.

But how on earth is one to explain the apparent absence of a mercantile centre on Gotland in the Viking Age? Surely it must have existed, on the analogy of the older central places of Scandinavia, whether aristocratic/princely centres or emporia? It is also hard to conceive of such an apparently egalitarian society acting as the prime driving force of so massive a commercial enterprise as that which engaged the Rus and took them deep into and across the Rus lands in the ninth and tenth centuries.

We should perhaps beware of becoming too positivist; of relying on what evidence there is (even if it is as plentiful as dirham hoards on Gotland) to recapture the shape of things in the past, in this case the settlement pattern of the island of Gotland. We should be ready to extrapolate boldly and to home in on what we do not know about Gotland in the early middle ages, on the great void in the distribution of hoards in and around its capital Visby (except for a few found in its extensive cemeteries). The inference to be drawn is surely that almost all capital kept safe in the town, some of the sums probably very large, was retrieved by the owners and that the few hoards left in concealment were discovered over the following centuries in what was from the ninth century a thriving town and became, alongside Lübeck, one of the two main commercial centres in the Baltic in the late middle ages.[47] Visby was, I submit, for the small world of Gotland, analogous to Alexandria in late antique Egypt. We may conjecture the existence at Visby of a body of urban notables, consisting in the main of plutocratic merchants, who became masters of the northern world because of their financial power and ramified commercial and political connections. No trace remains of their fine town houses, any more than of those of the great merchants of late antique Alexandria, because, like Alexandria, Visby has remained continuously inhabited and any vestiges of ancient or medieval structures were recycled and destroyed long ago. The only physical trace of their once dominant presence is to be found in the stone houses which they began to build in the twelfth century on their larger-than-average farms. As one might expect, the largest concentration (40 out of a total of 200) is to be found in an arc around Visby.[48]

Conclusions

The rise of an Islamic single market, with a common currency, a shared law based on the Qur'an and a universal commercial language, was the most important economic phenomenon of the early middle ages. The Mediterranean was sidelined in favour of the Persian Gulf and the Indian Ocean, and transcontinental trade routes. The growth of commerce, which fed and fed off increasing urbanisation, specialisation in manufacturing and demand for non-essentials on the part of urban elites, was one of the preconditions for the beginnings of large-scale trading in fur. The other was a shift in mentality on the part of southern elites: the dissolution of the culturally constructed barrier to fur-wearing, which can be dated to the second half of the eighth century. From then on, the caliphate generated an ever-increasing demand for fur, which led to the exponential growth in north–south trade documented by the export of dirhams to the north. The key point is this *exponential growth* – inexplicable, it seems to me, if any other commodity had been the prime one involved.

It is the pre-existence of a thriving zone of commercial exchange in the North Sea and west Baltic that explains the angling to the north-west of the stream of dirhams once it crossed the watershed between the great rivers draining the lands to the west of the Urals into the Caspian and Black Seas, on the one hand, and the rivers flowing into the Gulf of Finland and the Baltic, on the other. Had there been no extraneous force, we would have expected the stream to have flowed due north and to have dissipated itself among small trading places in the region of lakes on the edge of the deep forest zone of north-east Russia. Instead the Baltic and its emporia exerted a strong gravitational pull, bending the trunk route between south and north, to the west, into the eastern Baltic, where dirhams congregated in Visby and trickled out (in surprisingly large numbers) throughout the island. From Gotland, dirhams were drawn westward by natural commercial processes in a developed market for which they were acting as the main medium of exchange. Hence the large number of hoards found in the western Baltic, in particular in the most active zones of exchange, in central Sweden and Denmark, and the percolation westward of small numbers of dirhams into the North Sea and the British Isles.

The scenario that has been conjured up of Visby's presiding over the northern end of the new eastern axis of trade between north and south should not cause surprise, given what is known of Khwarazm, where much of the northern commerce debouched in the south. Khwarazm's wealth and ramified trading connections were, I suggest, mirrored in the north. Visby in the ninth to twelfth centuries should be viewed as a northern Venice, run by a mercantile oligarchy, dominating two great arenas of trade: one (maritime) to the west where a voracious appetite for furs developed in the eleventh century,[49] and the other (transcontinental) to the east from where that new European appetite could be satisfied. It is to Visby that we should envisage the landless sons of Gotland's farmers as walking with purses containing the working capital needed to start off in business. Sustained by a steady flow of young talent and of substantial profits from trade, it is no wonder that Visby maintained its hegemony in the Baltic until the rise of Lübeck in the second half of the twelfth century.[50]

The maritime world of the Baltic and North Sea would be dominated in the late middle ages by Lübeck and the Hanseatic League, while the much larger expanse of forest and wooded steppe to the east would be brought under the rule of rival Rus regional powers competing for control of the fur trade, among which Moscow would emerge as the most powerful in the fifteenth century.[51] The foundations of Russia, however, had been laid down in the ninth and tenth centuries, when small Rus colonies, established at great distances from each other, managed to extend a light authority over huge tracts of land. It is the hunt for furs that largely explains the dispatch of small bands of Rus on circuits among their Slav neighbours and the conciliatory approach adopted. They sought only a modest tribute and were ready otherwise to pay for goods.[52] The good relations generated made it possible for Slavs to congregate in the nascent towns of Rus and, in a very few generations, for Slavs and Scandinavian Rus to merge their ethnic identities. Thereafter it was the search for furs that drove Rus colonisation of the north, first on the west side of the Urals, then to the east, and thus contributed to the development of a great continental empire.

Notes

1 *Expositio totius mundi*, ed. Rougé.
2 Miquel (1967).
3 Lombard (1971).
4 Cheynet (1999); François (2016).
5 Groom (1981), pp. 96–213.
6 Lombard (1969); Martin (1986); Franklin and Shepard (1996), pp. 20–1, 61–5, 76–8.
7 Martin (1986), p. 65.
8 Veale (1966), pp. 1–21.
9 Parker (1968), pp. 22–4, 87–9, 110–11, 123–4, 156–8.
10 Howard-Johnston (1998); Honey (1992).
11 al-Tabari, *Ta'rikh*, ed. de Goeje, vol. 3.1, p. 508, ll. 5–6; tr. Kennedy, p. 225.
12 Mas'udi, *Tanbih*, ed. de Goeje, p. 63, ll. 14–18; tr. Carra de Vaux, p. 94; *Book of Gifts* § 302, tr. al-Hijjawi al-Qaddumi, pp. 207–8.
13 IbnF^1, pp. 232–3, 238–9, 242–3; IbnF^2, pp. 39, 44, 48; Ibn Rusta, *al-A'laq*, ed. de Goeje, pp. 141–2, 145–7; tr. Göckenjan and Zimonyi, pp. 57–64, 81–6. See also Martin (1986), pp. 5–14.
14 Mas'udi, *Muruj al-dhahab*, ed. Pellat, vol. 1, p. 215, ll. 14–19; rev. tr. Pellat, vol. 1, p. 164; al-Muqaddasi, *Ahsan al-taqasim*, ed. de Goeje, pp. 324, l. 21–325, l. 7, tr. Collins, p. 264; Ibn Hawqal, *Surat*, ed. Kramers, vol. 2, pp. 481–2; tr. Kramers and Wiet, vol. 2, pp. 462–3.
15 Makarov (1996).
16 Kovalev and Kaelin (2007).

17 Linder Welin (1974).
18 Callmer (1995), pp. 50–3; Makarov (1996), pp. 37–9.
19 Noonan (1981), p. 82.
20 See Jankowiak in this volume.
21 *DAI* ch. 9, pp. 58–63.
22 Gordon (2001), pp. 15–46; McCormick (2001), pp. 733–77; Jankowiak (2013).
23 See Jankowiak in this volume.
24 Byzantine resistance seems to have collapsed in the thirteenth and fourteenth centuries: Parani (2003), pp. 57–63 with appendix 2, no. 50 (pl. 7) and appendix 3, nos 60 (pl. 71), 61–2, 69, 70 (pl. 73).
25 Franklin and Shepard (1996), pp. 75–9.
26 Jankowiak (2013).
27 Zakharov (2012), pp. 135–8. See also Makarov (2012), pp. 386–8.
28 Myhre (2003), pp. 77–9, 90.
29 Myhre (2003), pp. 61–8, 69–77, 83–6.
30 Randsborg (1991), pp. 138–47, 171–3; Heather (2009), pp. 37–93.
31 Myhre (2003), pp. 76–7; Hedeager (2011), pp. 152–7.
32 Hedeager (2011), pp. 177–228.
33 Myhre (2003), pp. 81–90.
34 Christiansen (2002), pp. 160–3.
35 Jorgensen (2003).
36 Gyllensvärd *et al.* (2004); Arrhenius (2011); Ljungkvist and Frölund (2015).
37 Wood (1983); Lebecq (1983).
38 Lebecq (1983), vol. 1, pp. 77–83; Callmer (1977); Hedeager (2011), pp. 61–80; Hamerow (2017).
39 Lebecq (1983), vol. 1, pp. 83–8, 90–1, 149–63; Andersson (2003), pp. 317–20; Christiansen (2002), pp. 70–4.
40 Callmer (1984); Hill and Metcalf (eds) (1984), esp. Op den Velde *et al.* (1984), Bendixen (1984) and Metcalf (1984); Abramson (ed.) (2008–14), esp. Feveile (2008); Op den Velde (2008); Op den Velde and Metcalf (2011) and Op den Velde and Metcalf (2014).
41 Callmer (1984), pp. 14–17, 38–44, 53–6.
42 Andersson (2003), p. 320; Christiansen (2002), pp. 83–4.
43 Franklin and Shepard (1996), pp. 12–21.
44 Gruszczyński (2019), pp. 67–82; see also Ingvardson in this volume.
45 *GL*, p. 27; *LD*, pp. 198–202.
46 *LD*, pp. 108–9, 121–5, 130–1, 191–6.
47 See Widerström in this volume for what is known and what is contested about Visby.
48 *LD*, pp. 124–5, 134–7, 196–8.
49 Ad*GH* IV.18, pp. 454–7; Adam, *History*, tr. Tschan, p. 199.
50 Martin (1986), pp. 49–52; Gläser (2015).
51 Martin (1986), pp. 110–50.
52 Franklin and Shepard (1996), pp. 46–50.

Bibliography

Primary sources

Adam of Bremen, *History of the Archbishops of Hamburg Bremen*, tr. F. J. Tschan, New York (1959).

Book of Gifts and Rarities (Kitab al-hadaya wa al-tuhaf), tr. G. al-Hijjawi al-Qaddumi, Cambridge, MA (1996).

Expositio totius mundi et gentium, ed. J. Rougé, Paris (1966).

Ibn Hawqal, *Surat*, ed. J. H. Kramers, *Kitab surat al-'ard: opus geographicum auctore Ibn Haukal*, 2 vols, BGA 1, 2nd edn, Leiden (1938–9); French tr. J. H. Kramers and G. Wiet, *Configuration de la terre*, 2 vols, Paris (1964).

Ibn Rusta, *al-A'laq*, ed. M. J. de Goeje, *Kitab al-a'laq al-nafisah*, BGA 7, pp. 3–229; partial German tr. H. Göckenjan and I. Zimonyi, in *Orientalische Berichte über die Völker Osteuropas und Zentralasiens im Mittelalter: Die Ğayhani-Tradition*, Wiesbaden (2001), pp. 51–94.

Mas'udi, *Tanbih*, ed. M. J. de Goeje, *Kitab al-tanbih wa al-ishraf*, BGA 8, Leiden (1894); French tr. B. Carra de Vaux, *Le livre de l'avertissement et de la revision*, Paris (1896).

Mas'udi, *Muruj al-dhahab wa-ma'adin al-jawhar*, ed. C. Pellat, 7 vols, Beirut (1966–79); French tr. C. Barbier de Maynard and A. Pavel de Courteille, rev. C. Pellat, *Les prairies d'or*, 5 vols, Paris (1962–97).

al-Muqaddasi, *Ahsan al-taqasim fi ma'rifat al-aqalim*, ed. M. J. de Goeje, BGA 3, Leiden (1877); tr. B. Collins, *The Best Divisions for Knowledge of the Regions*, Reading (2011).

al-Tabari, *Ta'rikh*, ed. M. J. de Goeje *et al.*, *Annales quos scripsit Abu Djafar Mohammed ibn Djarir at-Tabari, Ta'rikh al-rusul wa-al-muluk*, 15 vols, Leiden (1879–1901); tr. H. Kennedy, *The History of al-Tabari*, vol. 19: *Al-Mansur and al-Mahdi*, Albany, NY (1990).

Secondary literature

Abramson, T. (ed.) (2008–14), *Studies in Early Medieval Coinage*, 3 vols, Woodbridge; London.

Andersson, H. (2003) 'Urbanisation', in K. Helle (ed.), *The Cambridge History of Scandinavia*, vol. 1: *Prehistory to 1520*, Cambridge, pp. 312–42.

Arrhenius, B. (2011), 'Helgö: pagan sanctuary complex', in B. Arrhenius and U. O'Meadhra (eds), *Excavations at Helgö*, vol. 18: *Conclusions and New Aspects*, Stockholm, pp. 11–43.

Bendixen, J. (1984), 'Finds of sceattas from Scandinavia', in D. H. Hill and D. M. Metcalf (eds), *Sceattas in England and on the Continent*, BAR BS 128, Oxford, pp. 151–7.

Callmer, J. (1977), *Trade Beads and Bead Trade in Scandinavia ca.800–1000 AD*, Lund.

Callmer, J. (1984), *Sceatta Problems in the Light of the Finds from Åhus*, Lund.

Callmer, J. (1995), 'The influx of oriental beads into Europe during the 8th century AD', in M. Rasmussen *et al.* (eds), *Glass Beads: Cultural History, Technology, Experiment and Analogy*, Lejre, pp. 49–54.

Cheynet, J.-C. (1999), 'Un aspect du ravitaillement de Constantinople aux Xe/XIe siècles d'après quelques sceaux d'hôrreiarioi', in N. Oikonomides (ed.), *Studies in Byzantine Sigillography 6*, Washington, DC, pp. 1–26.

Christiansen, E. (2002), *The Norsemen in the Viking Age*, Oxford.

Feveile, C. (2008), 'Series X and coin circulation in Ribe', in T. Abramson (ed.), *Studies in Early Medieval Coinage*, Woodbridge; London, vol. 1, pp. 53–67.

François, V. (2016), 'A distribution atlas of Byzantine ceramics: a new approach to the pottery trade in Byzantium', in P. Magdalino and N. Necipoğlu (eds), *Trade in Byzantium*, Istanbul, pp. 143–55.

Franklin, S. and J. Shepard (1996), *The Emergence of Rus, 750–1200*, London.

Gläser, M. (2015), 'The development of Lübeck into a medieval metropolis', in M. S. Kristiansen *et al.* (eds), *Medieval Archaeology in Scandinavia and Beyond: History, Trends and Tomorrow*, Aarhus, pp. 335–54.

Gordon, M. (2001), *The Breaking of a Thousand Swords: A History of the Turkish Military of Samarra, AH 200–275/815–889 CE*, Albany, NY.

Groom, N. (1981), *Frankincense and Myrrh: A Study of the Arabian Incense Trade*, London.

Gruszczyński, J. (2019), *Silver, Hoards and Containers: The Archaeological and Historical Context of Silver Coin Deposits in the Baltic c. 800–1050*, Abingdon.

Gyllensvärd, B. *et al.* (eds) (2004), *Excavations at Helgö*, vol. 16: *Exotic and Sacral Finds from Helgö*, Stockholm.

Hamerow, H. (2017), 'The circulation of garnets in the North Sea Zone, ca 400–700', in A. Hilgner *et al.* (eds), *Gemstones in the First Millennium AD: Mines, Trade, Workshops and Symbolism*, Mainz, pp. 71–86.

Heather, P. (2009), *Empires and Barbarians: Migration, Development and the Birth of Europe*, London.

Hedeager, L. (2011), *Iron Age Myth and Materiality: An Archaeology of Scandinavia AD 400–1000*, London.

Hill, D. H. and D. M. Metcalf (eds) (1984), *Sceattas in England and on the Continent, BAR BS* 128, Oxford.

Honey, D. B. (1992), *Stripping of Fur and Felt: An Essay on Nomad Sinification*, Bloomington, IN.

Howard-Johnston, J. (1998), 'Trading in fur, from classical antiquity to the early middle ages', in E. Cameron (ed.), *Leather and Fur: Aspects of Early Medieval Trade and Technology*, London, pp. 65–79.

Jankowiak, M. (2013), 'Two systems of trade in the western Slavic lands in the 10th century', in M. Bogucki and M. Rębkowski (eds), *Economies, Monetisation and Society in West Slavic Lands 800–1200 AD*, Szczecin, pp. 137–48.

Jorgensen, L. (2003), 'Manor and market at Lake Tissø in the sixth to eleventh centuries: the Danish "productive" sites', in T. Pestell and K. Ulmschneider (eds), *Markets in Early Medieval Europe: Trading and 'Productive' Sites, 650–850*, Macclesfield, pp. 175–207.

Kovalev, R. K. and A. C. Kaelin (2007), 'Circulation of Arab silver in medieval Afro-Eurasia: preliminary observations', *History Compass* 5: 560–80.

Lebecq, S. (1983), *Marchands et navigateurs frisons du haut moyen âge*, 2 vols, Lille.

Linder Welin, U. S. (1974), 'The first arrival of oriental coins in Scandinavia and the inception of the Viking Age in Sweden', *Fv* 69: 22–9.

Ljungkvist, J. and P. Frölund (2015), 'Gamla Uppsala: the emergence of a centre and magnate complex', *Journal of Archaeology and Ancient History* 16: 1–29.

Lombard, M. (1969), 'La chasse et les produits de la chasse dans le monde mususlman (VIIIe–XIe siècles)', *Annales* 24: 572–93; repr. in his *Éspaces et réseaux du haut moyen âge*, Paris (1972), pp. 177–204.

Lombard, M. (1971), *L'Islam dans sa première grandeur (VIIIe–XIe siècles)*, Paris.

Makarov, N. A. (1996), *Kolonizatsiia severnykh okrain Drevnei Rusi v XI–XIII vekakh*, Moscow.

Makarov, N. A. (2012), 'The fur trade in the economy of the northern borderlands of medieval Russia', in M. A. Brisbane *et al.* (eds), *The Archaeology of Medieval Novgorod in Context: Studies in Centre/Periphery Relations*, tr. K. Judelson, Oxford, pp. 381–90.

Martin, J. (1986), *Treasure of the Land of Darkness: The Fur Trade and its Significance for Medieval Russia*, Cambridge.

McCormick, M. (2001), *Origins of the European Economy: Communications and Commerce AD 300–900*, Cambridge.

Metcalf, D. M. (1984), 'A note on sceattas as a measure of international trade, and on the earliest Danish coinage', in D. H. Hill and D. M. Metcalf (eds), *Sceattas in England and on the Continent*, *BAR BS* 128, Oxford, pp. 159–64.

Miquel, A. (1967), *La géographie humaine du monde musulman jusqu'au milieu du 11e siècle: géographie et géographie humaine dans la littérature arabe, des origines à 1050*, Paris.

Myhre, B. (2003), 'The iron age', in K. Helle (ed.), *The Cambridge History of Scandinavia*, vol. 1: *Prehistory to 1520*, Cambridge, pp. 60–93.

Noonan, T. S. (1981), 'Ninth-century dirham hoards from European Russia: a preliminary analysis', in *VACNL*, vol. 1, Oxford, pp. 47–117.

Op den Velde, W. (2008), 'The sceattas of Series D', in T. Abramson (ed.), *Studies in Early Medieval Coinage*, Woodbridge; London, vol. 1, pp. 77–90.

Op den Velde, W. and M. Metcalf (2011), 'Series E reconsidered', in T. Abramson (ed.), *Studies in Early Medieval Coinage*, Woodbridge; London, vol. 2, pp. 104–10.

Op den Velde, W. and M. Metcalf (2014), 'The hexagram ("Herstal") type sceattas', in T. Abramson (ed.), *Studies in Early Medieval Coinage*, Woodbridge; London, vol. 3, pp. 122–40.

Op den Velde, W. *et al.* (1984), 'A survey of sceatta finds from the Low Countries', in D. H. Hill and D. M. Metcalf (eds), *Sceattas in England and on the Continent*, *BAR BS* 128, Oxford, pp. 117–45.

Parani, M. (2003), *Reconstructing the Reality of Images*, Leiden.

Parker, W. H. (1968), *An Historical Geography of Russia*, London.

Randsborg, K. (1991), *The First Millennium AD in Europe and the Mediterranean: An Archaeological Essay*, Cambridge.

Veale, E. M. (1966), *The English Fur Trade in the Later Middle Ages*, Oxford.

Wood, I. N. (1983), *The Merovingian North Sea*, Alingsås.

Zakharov, S. D. (2012), 'Glass beads from the Minino archaeological complex', in M. A. Brisbane *et al.* (eds), *The Archaeology of Medieval Novgorod in Context: Studies in Centre/Periphery Relations*, tr. K. Judelson, Oxford, pp. 122–38.

5   The dynamics of the drugs trade

A model for the study of the medieval trade in slaves?

Andrew P. Roach and Alex Marshall

Our problem with both the medieval slave trade and the modern drug business is the difficulty of obtaining reliable evidence. This may be inevitable in any enterprise where rewards are high, competition fierce and people tend not to leave records while busy making money. Exact figures or maps of trading patterns are elusive where enterprises are not bound to a location and are highly market sensitive. And the 'balloon effect', where repression of supply in one area leads to it springing up elsewhere, is likely to hold true then as now.[1] The situation is further complicated by the narcotics trade being illegal almost everywhere. So when it comes to identifying winners and losers, estimating profit scales, and pinpointing the sites and agencies where capital most accumulates and where profits are re-invested, the medieval historian and the scholar of the modern drugs trade may find they have much in common.

The modern drugs trade has, for example, built up a substantial network of increasingly sophisticated money-laundering techniques. Land and property portfolios can be accumulated. Profits can be re-invested in corner shops or car washes, where cash turnover is high and tax scrutiny correspondingly low. Money can be hidden in off-shore tax havens, in shell networks that use correspondent accounts to abuse the banking system and in digital currencies such as Bitcoin – or simply by bribing high-ranking bank officials to look the other way. Ironically, even with this abundance of techniques, concealing large quantities of cash – literally tons of dollars in some cases – remains a problem for the most successful modern drug traders, leading some Latin American cartels to warehouse dollars in a manner not dissimilar to the medieval practice of hoarding silver.[2] Some business techniques that can further obstruct the study of modern narcotics and terrorist financing would also be recognisable to medieval merchants, such as the Islamic *hawala* system of informally transferring cash through agents on no more than verbal contracts.

Some of the methods that social scientists have used in attempting to model the drugs economy may provide insights into the medieval slave trade in three particular aspects: the drugs trade as a global commodity chain; how it is structured at the retail end and how it functions on the ground; and its role in the development (or otherwise) of governance.

The drugs trade as a global commodity chain

Arguments around prohibition, regulation, decriminalisation or legalisation have dominated the literature on the drugs trade for over forty years, often to the detriment of analysing the system as it actually exists or the power relationships within it. To bring fresh insight, a recent project has used the global commodity chain as a prism through which to analyse the trade. This highlights the moment when a product or material was commodified and asks why, when and how such commodification occurred. Global commodity chains date back to the first regular trans-oceanic voyages of the early modern era. The discovery overseas of highly desirable, sometimes addictive, substances played a significant role in early forms of globalisation. The trade in precious metals and minerals (gold, silver and diamonds), as well as in human slaves and luxury goods (silks, perfumes and ceramics), and the early 'drug plagues' (including coffee, alcohol, tobacco and spices, as well as opium) contributed to the birth of modern global capitalism and the shift towards a more globally organised consumer society.[3] Consumer fetishisation – giving many of these products a price far above their actual worth – made long-distance dealing profitable almost overnight. It has been suggested that by the late twentieth century, the sheer length of these commodity chains and their geographical sweep enabled those who controlled them to work outside customary authority, making them economically independent of any single market.[4]

Plant-based narcotics have been used throughout human history, particularly for spiritual, ritual and medicinal reasons. However, their global commodification did not occur on a large scale until the seventeenth century.[5] Once underway, this process had significant – and often apparently perverse or irrational – consequences for how they were legally framed by modernising western societies. Yet industrial synthetic drug production for many decades escaped both the moral demonisation and correspondingly tight legal regulation that plant-based narcotics such as opium, coca leaves and marijuana faced from the 1910s on. This was partly thanks to the greater political and economic lobbying power of the major industrial drug companies, which also had a perceived strategic importance and inviolability within industrial economies increasingly 'mobilisation-ready' for war.[6] Thus some industrially manufactured narcotics were not subject to the same comprehensive prohibitions by the United Nations (UN) as cocaine or heroin until 1971, and it took almost twenty more years for the manufacturers to be regulated.[7]

Responses to different aspects of the trade vary, depending on the economic or political influence of those involved. Large quantities of acetic anhydride manufactured in Germany (among other countries) continue to be smuggled into Afghanistan for use in heroin laboratories there, yet no-one suggests that bombing German chemical manufacturers would solve the global heroin problem. But Afghan opium farmers face prosecution, physical harassment, a complete absence of property or labour rights, and the frequent physical destruction of their crops by a 'supply-based' drug prohibition regime which continues to demonise the crop itself as the core of the problem. Ironically, the globalisation of manufacturing means that regulatory panic has now swung towards industrial-style synthetic drug production rather than focusing on the older, plant-based narcotics, given that a new amphetamine-type substance appears for sale on the internet as a 'legal high' nearly every month.[8]

The global commodity chain approach raises a question fundamental both to trafficking in drugs and in slaves: where does power sit across the overall chain? Is it with those able to establish a monopoly of supply (the producer), or those able to fashion and shape demand (the buyer)? This affects all commodity chains, regardless of their formal legality or illegality. An example of a consumer- or buyer-driven commodity chain is the modern textile trade. The raw materials and human labour needed for manufacture are abundantly available, with the main barriers to market entry for new entrepreneurs being the fashion diktats and taste of consumers, as well as existing retailers who have access to market research and large advertising and marketing budgets. In contrast, within a producer-driven commodity chain such as car manufacturing, the barriers to market entry are the enormous start-up costs of research and development, materials, infrastructure investment and technological expertise. Such resources are husbanded and almost monopolised by existing producers such as Volkswagen or General Motors. Industrial manufacture in the twentieth century in general became vertically integrated, with American firms leading the way in seeking to establish a fully sealed chain of commodity ownership and production, from raw material development to marketing and retail sale. Both drug production and human trafficking remain decentralised outliers to this general trend, making it possible to draw interesting parallels between the medieval and modern global economy in these particular commodities. While the medieval slave trade has some of the characteristics of a producer-driven chain – investment was needed in boats, geographical expertise and ready cash – the stronger parallel is the buyer-driven chain, since the most important determinants were the wealth and fashion of the consumer market in the east. Global value chain theory offers a possible bridge between the medieval and modern when considering the trafficking of goods that continue to be part of the 'shadow economy', and where clan-based or family-style social networks continue to matter.

Comparing routes: from origin to point of sale

Tenth-century Scandinavian traders took their Slav human merchandise from the fairly vulnerable or loose-knit societies of Poland, Belarus and Ukraine, moving them eastwards along land routes and river systems to the sophisticated urban markets of Constantinople or Itil. In the twenty-first century, poppies are harvested in the relatively undeveloped agricultural regions of Afghanistan and the raw material makes its way westwards by lorry across Iran, Uzbekistan, Turkey and Russia to Europe. Then as now, routes change in response to political and economic circumstances, while making use of local connections and contacts along the way. And then as now, supply regions may be chosen precisely because they have always been relatively 'off the radar' of political authority.

Both slaves and drugs have a high bulk-to-value ratio, making transport over long distances economically viable and helping the rapid development and institutionalisation of both industries. During the nineteenth and early twentieth centuries, the production of many drugs was banned, except for medical purposes. Yet they had already emerged as lightly regulated global commodity chains, much like any other. After 1780, Warren Hastings and the British East India Company centralised and took over the market for poppy cultivation in north-eastern India. They created a cartel that was effectively able to compel farmers to grow poppies, to restrict and control cultivation and production levels, and to implement quality control measures. By 1797 this opium monopoly was under the direct management of a government agency, even though the drug remained prohibited in the Company's main target market: China. After land, opium was the second largest source of the British East India Company's revenue in India by the 1820s, and carried the additional benefit of delivering large and immediate cash payments into British government coffers – effectively financing its empire.[9] Again there are similarities with the later drug, or indeed the medieval slave, trade: those involved were concerned to keep arrangements covert and unknown to rival operations, partly through fears for security, and partly through concerns about the moral opprobrium that might result; and those not involved had little incentive to publicise matters. Violence and distorted ecological systems were not results the trade wanted advertised.

Opium was the largest single export item in world trade for the first two-thirds of the nineteenth century, and Chinese efforts at prohibition led to the Anglo-Chinese Opium Wars. By the end of the nineteenth century, the Dutch administered 1,065 opium retail outlets in Indonesia, which paid for around 15% of their colonial administrative costs, and opium sales covered 53% of overall administrative costs in the British colony of Malaya (Malaysia). Another high-value, far-travelled drug to emerge at this time was cocaine. British and Dutch pharmaceutical companies and commercial interests transplanted coca bush cultivation to Jamaica, Sri Lanka, Malaysia, India, Indonesia and Guyana in order to reduce shipping times and to meet rising demand. The Dutch were more successful, and by 1900 they were the world's leading cocaine producer.[10]

The shapes of medieval trade and modern capitalism are obviously different, but three things are worth noting from this early modern global commodity chain. Firstly, the astonishing amounts of profit to be made once supplies have been secured and demand established. Secondly, within a single generation, the trade moved from being speculative venture to staple cash cow. And thirdly, the products were essentially hedonistic: although cocaine and heroin have medicinal properties, their prime use has always been recreational; and although Slav slaves were used as domestic servants and fighters, their trade was primarily oriented around sex. This is suggested by Ibn Rusta's description written between 913 and 920, but using information dating perhaps from the 860s:

> The Rus raid the *Saqaliba* (Slavs), sailing in their ships until they come upon them. They take them captive and sell them in Khazaran (Itil) and Bulkar (Bulghar). They have no cultivated fields and they live by pillaging the land of the *Saqaliba* [...] They sell them for silver coins which they set in belts and wear round their waists [...] They treat their slaves well and dress them suitably, because for them they are an article of trade.[11]

The sexual aspect was highlighted – for moralising purposes, but not necessarily fictitiously – by Ibn Fadlan in reporting his mission of around 922:

> They [the Rus] arrive, moor their boats by the Itil (Volga) and build large, wooden houses on its banks. [...] They are accompanied by beautiful female slaves for trade with the merchants. They have intercourse with their female slaves in full view of their companions.[12]

Boys also fetched a high price and were likely to be used for pleasure. The admittedly late Ziyarid text *Qabus-nama* ('mirror for princes') from 1082 outlines seven uses for slaves, the most important being for the ruler's 'private service and conviviality'. Great importance is placed on physiognomy and checking for disease, while the author advises the prince not to 'have a slave-girl brought before you when your appetites are strong upon you', and to let his desires incline towards women in winter and youths in summer.[13] It is ironic that the India Office manuscript of this work once belonged to Warren Hastings.[14] The value of this type of 'private service' would have been equally familiar to western traders such as the sister of Cnut (d. 1035) and wife of Earl Godwine, Thyra Sveinsdottir. William of Malmesbury, writing in the twelfth century, accused her of trading in 'young girls especially, whose beauty and youth would enhance their price'.[15]

Commodity chain theory can offer insights into the relative distribution of power and resources in the medieval slave trade which, as noted above, shares some features with both the producer-driven and buyer-driven model. In the former category, the cash, boats, weapons and shackles needed to supply Slavic slaves from the north and west to the Islamic east made it a capital-intensive industry that required an institutional context to set the 'rules of the game' (the attitudes of the Muslim courts, Christian and pagan rulers and, increasingly, the papacy). In the latter category was the importance of market information: certain slave types could fall in or out of fashion in a given market, and being able to provide the correct 'brand' could mean the difference between profit and disaster. However, the most useful way of analysing the medieval slave trade is as a global value chain.[16] The advantage with this model is that it offers a rationale for whether to conduct the whole trade yourself (vertical integration) or whether to pass the product on through a series of middlemen. This decision depends on three important factors: level of information, complexity of transactions and the capabilities of the supply base.

Given that Viking or Rus traders knew that they had ready sources of northern Slavs and that the transactions involved were relatively simple, their key driver was probably the level of information they had about the market (market intelligence). This is crucial in today's drugs trade, where the percentage difference between the selling and buying price (the 'mark-up') is huge, and where the higher the mark-up, the greater the costs – or risks – to the dealer.

As with the medieval slave trade, there is a shortage of data. However, a 2008 case study on the import of heroin to the UK showed that the price per kilo rose from £450 at the 'farm gate' in Afghanistan to £75,750 on the

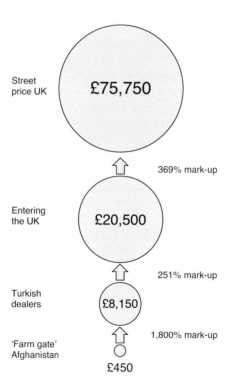

Figure 5.1 Heroin from Afghan farm to UK street: price per kg and mark-up in transit.

streets of the UK – a mark-up of over 16,800% (see Figure 5.1). The mark-up within the country of consumption (the UK) is roughly the same as for licit goods; far more striking are the mark-ups in transit.[17] Dealers in slaves faced considerable problems in realising a profit: the vicissitudes of the journey were compounded by their cargo's fragility and propensity to escape. The 'produce' had to arrive looking highly attractive and desirable. There were probably considerable profits to be made by taking the slaves all the way to the retail market in distant Baghdad or Itil; but there were also advantages in handing the goods over at a certain point along the road to those with local knowledge, who could take charge and bear the risk. So intermediary markets such as Bulgar on the Volga, as described by Ibn Fadlan, probably made economic as well as logistical sense, and slaves may well have changed hands several times before they reached their final destination.

There is also the problem of pricing. Ibn Fadlan describes a fairly schematic system, with the Northmen literally displaying the profits from their trading on their women:

> The [Rus] women wear neck rings [torques] of gold and silver. When a man has amassed ten thousand dirhams, he has a neck ring made for his wife. When he has amassed twenty thousand dirhams, he has two neck rings made. For every subsequent ten thousand, he gives a neck ring to his wife.[18]

These traders did not just want to turn a profit: they wanted to guarantee a fairly substantial profit margin, and it made commercial sense to flaunt their capacity to do this. The same goes for drug dealing: the trade is so profitable that there is always the risk of oversupply, but at the same time the substantial risks in production or of seizure in transit mean that a degree of overproduction is a wise insurance policy. Such overproduction must clearly be kept well away from the point of consumption: for the Afghan heroin trade, stockpiles have been posited to exist in Russia or Iran.[19] While drug dealers have the fallback of altering purity to try and maintain a reasonably constant profit margin, slave traders do not, making them even more reliant on market intelligence to maintain profit margins, ensuring shipments go to the most appropriate – and profitable – centres. In the twenty-first century, market intelligence comes by computer or mobile phone; in the ninth and tenth, it came by word of mouth or letter. Marek Jankowiak's analysis of archaeological findings may fit the overall model: one factor behind mid-tenth-century depopulation in the area around the river Obra may have been 'overproduction' in the slave trade. The hillforts built around then in central and south-western Poland, notably the vast ones in present-day Poland, the Czech Republic, Slovakia and western Ukraine, could be holding-camps for slaves, given the lack of archaeological finds of the sort that permanent settlement entails. It is credible that at least one of these forts, Naszacowice on the Dunajec, was such a camp: slaves could have been held there ready for despatch to the Prague market, but just as likely to be diverted overland east to the Dnieper for the route south to Constantinople, depending on market intelligence on where prices were highest.[20]

Who's in charge?

How drug dealing operations are structured is also of interest, since they both mimic and differ from conventional capitalist enterprises. A 2007 report showed that most drugs trafficked from Turkey were organised by a small number of family groups. Without effective law enforcement, the drugs trade shows the same general tendency at the highest levels in most countries: vertical integration of patronage and concentration of the means of intimidation and violence.[21] Network analysis of Turkish drug trafficking cases in the early 2000s reveals interesting patterns: traffickers either belonged to family-based groups; were part of no structured organisation; or they worked for, or paid taxes to, a terrorist organisation.[22] In Afghanistan, drug crop cultivation remains highly decentralised. However, the management of drug trafficking within Afghanistan, and the handover of trafficked narcotics to counterparts in Iran and Central Asia, is thought to be predominantly in the hands of just eight main drug trafficking organisations.[23] While Ibn Fadlan reported on enterprises that were still fairly fluid and individualistic, there are hints that kin structures were important: for example, he assumed that any Rus merchant who died while trading would be looked after by his household.[24]

Who's selling?

This structural pattern can be augmented by glancing at the retail drugs trade in Chicago.[25] Street gangs had been a feature of new immigrant life for young men and adolescent boys there since the nineteenth century. However, in the 1980s their nature changed quite radically, and these gangs became the main retailers of crack cocaine in poorer areas. In one sense this is very different from the slave-trading described obliquely by Ibn Fadlan: the customers were poor and the gangs were retailers, not wholesalers like the Rus. However, a common factor was the take-over of an existing trade by a new group looking for substantial economic benefits. Street gangs had prospered in the 1960s and 1970s under relatively liberal policing and sentencing regimes. Turf wars and petty crime were their stock-in-trade, although the income streams were never enough to support members fully. At a certain point in their teens and twenties, members tended to leave and get a legitimate job in Chicago's manufacturing industry or in an office, in order to support a family. But in the 1980s, more illiberal attempts were made to clamp down on violence and crime, while manufacturing jobs disappeared and, as the decade wore on, computerisation reduced the number of menial office jobs available. The advent of crack cocaine – cocaine produced in South America adapted into smokable form – made a desirable, high-class drug affordable for even the poorest. The only problem was distribution, and this gap was filled by the gangs whose close links with local neighbourhoods were ideal for this purpose. The new role, in turn, changed the nature of the gangs.

It became possible to make a living from selling crack, sometimes a spectacularly good one, and the average age of gang members, especially the leaders, rose accordingly. They developed into economic enterprises – 'outlaw capitalism'. Dealing in other drugs was licensed to individuals for a fee, as was most other economic activity in the area controlled by a gang, while the gang itself focused on what brought in 80% of their revenue: dealing crack. Greater rewards led to increasing tension between the gang's collectivist ethos – 'a new family, a brotherhood that will always be with you', as new recruits were told – and individual aggrandisement.[26]

Similar tensions can be seen among the Rus traders as they sought their rich rewards from selling Slavs, despite ethnic and familial solidarity. In describing them, Ibn Rusta initially emphasises their collectivist ethos: '[i]f an enemy makes war against them, they all attack together, and never break ranks. They form a single fist against the enemy, until they overcome them'. But he later describes their mutual mistrust, worried about even relieving themselves unless accompanied by armed guards.[27] The Chicago gangs' sheer wealth is also evocative: one gang leader was taking home at least $100,000 a year, much of which went on conspicuous consumption not dissimilar to the neck-rings of the slave traders' wives.

The Chicago gangs' structure was pyramidal, with a very broad base. The local gang leader reported to the 'board of directors', a citywide grouping of around twenty, paying almost 20% of his revenue for the right to sell crack in a designated twelve-block square.[28] Three officers answered directly to the leader on, respectively, security, liquid assets and transporting drugs from the supplier, earning just $8,400 a year. Below them were some fifty 'foot soldiers' who actually sold the drugs: facing a one-in-four chance of being killed for less than the minimum wage, they often had to combine gang membership with other low-paid jobs. Finally came the 'rank and file', about two hundred unpaid volunteers who paid dues to the gang, ran errands and hoped someday to be taken on the payroll. Families were also important: both literally, because only the gang leader could afford to live independently, so most members still lived with their parents; and metaphorically, because there were large incentives to distribute a little of the wealth to the wider community. Anyone who died in service, even if murdered by the gang, had their funeral expenses paid and their families received a stipend for up to three years. As a gang leader put it: 'their families is our families. [. . .] You got to respect the family'.[29]

However, gang leaders feared a backlash from the wider community because the enterprise was so obviously destructive in a number of ways.

Foot soldiers did not last long. Quite apart from the risks, most became frustrated by the low wages and within three or four years had dropped back into the rank and file, or had taken legitimate, less dangerous, if low-paid employment. This made gang politics very unstable. To make money through drug dealing, you had to rise quite quickly up the hierarchy, and the best way of doing so was to establish a reputation for toughness through violence. Yet one of the most important managerial tasks for gang leaders was to restrain their own foot soldiers:

> We try to tell these shorties [foot soldiers] that they belong to a serious organization. It ain't all about killing [...] You gotta learn how to be part of an organization, you can't be fighting all the time. It's bad for business.[30]

Bad for business in two ways: the risks of being caught up in crossfire put customers off; and the risks of dealing led foot soldiers to demand higher wages. Similar dynamics and tensions may have been found among Rus slave traders: Ibn Fadlan's emphasis on kin is contrasted by the deep insecurity described by Ibn Rusta: 'for they have little trust in one another. Treachery is endemic, and even a poor man can be envied by a comrade, who will not hesitate to kill or rob him'.[31]

The drugs trade and governance

Finally, we turn to the problem of state formation. Managing illicit flows can, to put it mildly, be a profitable enterprise for states that straddle production sites or form gateways along major transit routes. In March 2016, in an agreement with the European Union (EU), Turkey effectively monetised (in its own interest) managing the flow of refugees who were inundating Europe from Afghanistan, Iraq, Eritrea and Syria, arriving via human trafficking routes through Turkey and the Mediterranean. They did so by offering to take back Syrian refugees and accommodate them, in exchange for extra EU funding, visa-free travel for Turkish nationals in Europe and fast-tracking progress on Turkey's integration into the EU. However, this instrumental use by Turkey of human trafficking as a means of diplomatic and monetary leverage followed decades of a less well-known or scrutinised story: the state's ambiguous management of the international drugs trade.[32]

Turkey itself was a significant opium producer until well into the twentieth century, and overspill from licit production there fed the infamous 'French Connection' that supplied most of North America's heroin addicts between 1945 and 1971. The Nixon-led international crackdown on the trade, culminating in the incarceration of its main players, and diplomatic pressure on Turkey to restrict domestic opium production to medical use, led the Turkish state to adopt a different form of international leverage after 1973: it became the gatekeeper and international policeman charged with interdicting the majority of Afghan and South East Asian heroin before it reached Europe. Turkey continues to use its expertise in this field, combined with North American and EU readiness to offer substantial funding and equipment towards the same goal, to expand its regional sphere of influence dramatically through training other countries' law enforcement officers in counter-narcotics investigation techniques.[33] Yet there is a parallel relationship between the Turkish state and internal organised crime: this complex, informal, managed coexistence of forces is known in Turkey itself as the 'deep state'. Its potency has led to many conspiracy theories, from the disappearance of inconvenient political figures and occasional bombing campaigns laid at the door of Kurdish separatists, to slum clearance during anti-crime drives, where the cleared land ends up in lucrative investment portfolios of prominent politicians. Overall, it is hard not to conclude that the management of illicit flows – whether of goods or people – has been central to the shaping of Turkey itself as a nation state since 1922. And for production states such as Afghanistan, the dilemma or opportunity is even more obvious: at the very least, the cultivation of drug plants can operate as a sort of informal development strategy, attracting capital and creating jobs, even if most capital stays abroad, and most of the jobs are low quality.

Parallels can also be found in the Middle East. The attempt at building a theocratic state in the 'caliphate' proclaimed by Islamic State (IS) in 2014 is reminiscent of medieval European Christian state structures. Founding a state is an expensive business and led IS to some thought-provoking expedients and accommodations. One little-documented, but clearly lucrative, economic activity is kidnapping – much as medieval slavers looked to raise a local ransom from prominent captives before shipping them off. IS also looted capital from captured Iraqi banks, and sold oil on the Turkish black market, before United States air strikes deterred them.[34] As their 'state' developed, IS made money selling services to their 'citizens', including electricity (mainly from hydro-electric dams on the Euphrates), access to internet cafes and a number of other methods certainly recognisable to the Chicago gangs. They also taxed economic activity and imposed more theologically driven taxes on non-Muslim communities.[35] Lucrative sources of income were the licensing (and possible manufacture) of an amphetamine popular in the Middle East,[36] and of pornography, as well as smuggling DVDs and allowing websites to serve the rest of the region.[37] More mundane and better documented is IS's licensing of the cigarette smuggling business, despite imposing fines for smoking. There are reports from existing smugglers that they were taxed at sustainable levels, and even recruited into the religious police as informers.[38] Many of these activities had the potential to evolve into more stable sources of revenue collection, along the lines of those used by the early institutions of the British empire noted above.

It would be inaccurate to characterise the local accommodations and political management of the modern drugs trade as 'corrupt', since the trade itself often involves job creation otherwise lacking. Glimpses of such arrangements can perhaps be seen in the medieval slave trade. It certainly played its part in the late medieval and early modern period: the agreements of 1262 and 1281 between Mamluk Egypt and Michael VIII Palaiologos, newly restored to Constantinople and desperately short of resources, allowed Crimean slavers free passage through Byzantine lands to Egypt.[39] From 1468, Crimean Tatars regularly raided Galicia, Poland and even up to Moscow for captives to sell as slaves; their main market was the Ottoman empire, with over two-thirds ending up there. The khan of Crimea was a semi-independent Ottoman vassal, who financed himself by now familiar methods: appropriating one in ten of all slaves taken, levying an annual tax on his fellow slave-owners in the peninsula and receiving sweeteners from the sultan when 'invited' to participate in Ottoman campaigns. The sheer scale is striking: thousands – even hundreds of thousands – were recorded as being taken captive during individual raids, with the men used in the Ottoman navy and the women in domestic service or the harem. And that is without counting the many dying en route or slain by their captors if thought unsalable. Even if Alan Fisher's numbers are incorrect by a factor of ten, this would still be a major outflow of people from west to east.[40]

We have far less evidence for the early middle ages, but some speculation on the role of slave-trading in the politics and economics of early medieval state formation may be possible by comparing what meagre evidence we do have with our relatively plentiful, if anecdotal, intelligence about the role of the drug trade in the modern world. Take the 'blinging' drug dealer: someone whose taste in personal decoration might be ostentatious and vulgar but is rarely cheap, combining this with advanced technology. But a flashy new car and a high-end mobile phone are not just useful business tools or a commitment to mobility and communication: they signal wealth and status, as much to be seen as to be used. One much-discussed account of the trappings of tenth-century power is Ibrahim ibn Ya'qub's report on the Slav nations. King Mashaqqah of the north, seemingly the wealthiest of the four, has generally been identified with Mieszko I of Poland (d. 992). His three thousand warriors wear coats of mail, and are supplied with clothes, horses and 'everything they need': Mieszko's largesse extends to their families, with maintenance paid to the warriors' sons and daughters, and capped with a dowry on their marriage. The parallels with our gang leader 'respecting the family' are noteworthy. Mieszko had some impressive trappings himself (admittedly in common with other Slav leaders), travelling in a large, four-wheeled van with a primitive, yet reportedly effective, suspension system covered in gold brocade 'so that [...] [he] does not shake when the van shakes'. The source of this colossal wealth is left rather vague. Ibrahim ibn Ya'qub makes reference to taxes collected in 'market weights': 'those are the salary of his men in every month, and each of them has a certain amount of them to get'.[41] Again, the quite elaborate 'licences', 'taxes' and indication of pay being linked to transactions are reminiscent of the Chicago gangs or IS, as are the remarkable sums raised.

All this may have had an impact on the opening stages of the Polish state. If we accept that Ibrahim ibn Ya'qub's account comes from the mid-960s, 'Mashaqqah' would then have been a young, brash warrior leader, doubtless respected for the strength of his arm, who had acquired a fortune through looting and trading – not least in the merchandise so favoured in eastern slave markets. Mieszko had links with both east and west – he presented the German emperor Otto III with a camel.[42] He kept seven concubines, whom the first Polish chronicler Gallus Anonymus, writing in the early twelfth century, is polite enough to term wives, according to the pagan custom,[43] and his 'blinging' court culture was remembered into the fifteenth century. Długosz (Longinus) reports that Mieszko dismissed his seven concubines in 965, ordering the nation's 'most eminent matrons and maidens, in all their finery, wearing their gold, silver and other ornaments' to greet his new Christian bride, Dąbrawa, daughter of the duke of Bohemia.[44] The image is reminiscent of Ibn Fadlan's description of the Rus traders' women; virtual human balance sheets weighed down by gold and silver rings. The Bohemian connection was Mieszko's route to respectability. It brought him conversion to Christianity, a family tie to the dukes of Bohemia and relations with the Christian west in general. There is some controversy about Dąbrawa's age at marriage; but her reported reluctance to wed a Polish warrior-entrepreneur whose career might yet be a short one, without the insurance of at least his conversion to Christianity, would seem a shrewd, mature judgement.[45]

Mieszko would doubtless have had all the worries and insecurities of our gang leaders, but there was one pressing problem he could do nothing about. His most lucrative market, the Samanid state based around distant Samarqand and Bukhara, was beginning to disintegrate and the ready supplies of eastern dirhams with which he had bought himself both loyalty and protection were drying up.[46] By the 980s the flow was in steep decline and ceased entirely shortly after Mieszko's death in 992.[47] However, there was still the southern route to the Spanish markets and the Mediterranean through Prague, so vividly described by Ibrahim ibn Ya'qub, and this seems to have been the focus of Mieszko's later years and the reign of his son, Bolesław Chrobry (992–1025). Mieszko survived long enough to seize Prague's important trading partner, Cracow, from his in-laws and Bolesław briefly snatched Prague itself.[48] The Czech chronicler Cosmas may have confused father and son when he attributed the blinding of Boleslav III of Bohemia and the seizure of Prague to Mieszko, but his assessment that there was 'no other [...] more deceitful than him' was probably not wide of the mark, as was his report of Polish attempts to expand along the route leading south and south-west.[49]

Furs were undoubtedly being traded, but it is difficult to avoid the conclusion that Mieszko's astounding wealth came from trafficking slaves and that later chroniclers were unwilling to associate it with Poland's first Christian ruler.[50] The evidence is circumstantial, but compelling.

Neighbouring contemporaries were involved: after Olga of Kiev's final attack on the Derevlians in 946, she killed some captives and gave others to her followers as slaves.[51] And according to Thietmar, in 1009 Henry II received numerous complaints about Gunzelin, margrave of Meissen: not only was he selling dependants to the Jews, but significantly he also enjoyed more favour than appropriate with his brother-in-law, Bolesław.[52] Długosz records a similar late tenth-century episode, alleging that Adalbert (Wojciech) resigned his bishopric in Prague in 989 because, among other reasons, the locals were selling Christian children to the Jews.[53] On his return to Prague four years later, one of the first moves Adalbert made was to prevent some Christians being sold to Jews in the market by buying them himself.[54]

Chroniclers may have been reluctant openly to accuse Polish rulers, but they were masters of suggestion. Gallus Anonymus' famous depiction of the hospitality lavished on Otto III at Gniezno in 1000 – when 'gold [...] was held by all to be as common as silver, and silver deemed as little worth as straw' – is swiftly followed by Bolesław's raid on Rus, implying that this was to restore the newly crowned king's wealth (and ignoring the fact that it actually happened some seventeen years later).[55] In 1006, a few months after a peace agreement ended Henry II's campaign against Bolesław, Thietmar records Henry's ban on selling Christians to heathens.[56] And the Poles' neighbours, the pagan Prus (Baltic Prussians) whom Thietmar describes and whom Adalbert sought to convert, seem to have used and probably to have dealt in slaves, too:

> The Prussians buy their wives and make them work like slaves. They burn the bodies of the dead together with their horses, arms, clothing and other things dear to their hearts [...] Prussians can have an unlimited number of wives, just as many as each can afford to buy; consequently they do not respect them, but force them to perform the servile duties of slaves.[57]

There are strong hints of slaving in the reign of Bolesław II Szczodry 'the Bountiful' (1058–79). Once again there are the tales of fabulous wealth and the ruler's generosity, enhanced by an expedition to Kiev in 1069 and a further one against Rus in 1077.[58] This might also explain the lack of concern in Poland about the pagan reaction among their neighbours in Pomerania.[59]

The thirteenth-century chronicle of Vincent Kadłubek also hints at the problems of a ruling elite dependent on their household slaves early in his account of Bolesław's reign, when a 'plague of slaves [...] bubbled up'.[60] This could have been a literal plague, but is more likely refer to the crisis that led to the martyrdom of Stanislaus, bishop of Cracow, in 1079 and Bolesław's exile soon after. Bolesław's restless foreign policy seems to have brought matters to a head: with their husbands away with Bolesław on expedition to Kiev, 'free-born women were given to slaves for debauchery, that the sanctity of marriage was so shamefully tainted'.[61] It is not clear exactly what went on, but *servi* were prominent and the domestic context suggests these were household slaves. Kadłubek describes Bolesław as a man 'so devoted to waging war that he was deficient, rarely in a house, always in camp; rarely in his homeland, always among enemies'.[62] However, the womenfolk were not the only ones to be deserted: Bolesław himself was furious when his nobles returned home without him and responded by 'transferring the war from his enemies to his own'. Protesting against these punishments seems to have led to Stanislaus' downfall.[63] Conjugal deprivation or worries about bringing in the harvest are plausible reasons for the army's unauthorised return. But since one of the expedition's aims may have been slave gathering, alongside its ostensible objective of restoring Prince Iziaslav to the Kievan throne, perhaps the real reason was an eagerness to return to Cracow with booty from their successful mission.

Where does the money go?

Chicago's 'outlaw capitalists' claimed that selling drugs locally and the gang's regular philanthropic work kept money within their community. It did not: people were left less economically productive, and the big money went out of the area, to where the gang elite lived. A global commodity chain approach suggests a similar trend in money's final destination. Without western military intervention, Afghanistan might have gained a measure of prosperity from producing and manufacturing heroin; but the real profits go to the traffickers, who recycle them back to the west. Revenues from drugs and organised crime have increased in the era of globalisation, and in 2009 the head of the UN Office for Drugs and Organised Crime acknowledged that some major banks had only been kept liquid during the previous year's financial crisis by the proceeds of laundering illicit drug money.[64] Such criminality considerably affects the developing world. For example, between 2000 and 2010, international development assistance rose from $58 billion to a projected $125 billion. Yet in 2005, Raymond Baker estimated that more than $540 billion a year flowed *out* of developing countries through a combination of tax evasion, fraud in international trade, drug trafficking and corruption.[65] The clear implication is that western development assistance will never keep pace with the amount of capital flowing *out* of developing countries, most of it by formally 'illicit' routes.

Poland's position in the early middle ages may have had certain parallels. The vast inflows of eastern silver were short-lived and may represent a brief period when local rulers exercised tight control over trade. The slave trade continued (along with furs), and vast quantities of German silver *denarii* circulated in place of dirhams in the Baltic Rim and northern Rus. But much of this silver seems to have been in the hands of others. Adalbert's money at the Prague slave market probably travelled south with the city's famous Jewish traders.[66] Some also found its way to Scandinavia: as noted above,

William of Malmesbury accused the Danish-born wife of Earl Godwine, Thyra Sveinsdottir, of being a successful trader of slaves from England to Denmark. Her mother, Sygryda Świętosława, was Bolesław I's sister.[67]

Yet the Pomeranian coastline and its buoyant markets eluded the permanent grasp of the Piasts and their adherents. As for their eastern approaches, the *Russian Primary Chronicle* records Prince Iaroslav's seizure in 1031 of the highly prosperous 'Cherven Towns'.[68] Mieszko II was in no position to retaliate, as he had to reckon with the Czech duke Břetislav on his southern borders, while Lusatia and Milzen came under the German emperor's rule to the west. To some extent, Mieszko's plight may be ascribed to dynastic problems, the rivalry of his brothers – who could look to the Rus and German rulers for support – compounded by his own apparent lack of political or military flair. To try and pin down Piast decline to a single cause would probably be misguided and, in any case, Casimir the Restorer regained a fair level of political stability with the aid of Emperor Henry III. But such reliance on powerful neighbours reflects the inability of Mieszko II and his successors to dominate markets, trade-routes and outlets, or to redistribute proceeds to the same degree as their predecessors. And they may also have faced a problem not unlike that of their twentieth- and twentieth-first-century counterparts – sudden inability to gather produce close at hand, the 'crops' in their case being slaves.

Conclusion

Rather than adducing fresh evidence, this chapter has tried to show a range of scenarios, working with what little we do have.[69] For some of the time at least, medieval slaves and modern illicit drugs are most instructively viewed as just another commodity, with all the possibilities and limitations that implies. Those trading in them saw massive opportunities for self-enrichment and were, unsurprisingly, able to harness the most basic social structures, such as family and local community, to their enterprises. The reward was a degree of social mobility for all concerned, despite the risks. Much as yesterday's dubious businessman is today's philanthropist and entrepreneur, the most successful slave traders of medieval Europe now pass muster as pious state founders.

Notes

1 This has been the scourge of drug crop eradication programmes: Friesendorf (2007); Chouvy (2012).
2 Platt (2015), chs 2 and 4.
3 Trocki (1999), pp. 28–32.
4 Marshall (2012), pp. 5–7.
5 Narcotics became competing marketable, manufactured products, able to be copyrighted and patent protected, with their own chains of labour and delineated patterns of ownership.

6 In 1945, the United States' pharmaceutical lobby became almost overnight the most powerful such lobby in the world: Reiss (2014).

7 Including synthetic amphetamine-type stimulants such as LSD and speed; only in 1988 was UN-level regulation applied to the predominantly western industries producing chemicals such as acetic anhydride – essential for heroin production, but also used in perfume, aspirin and cigarette filter manufacture.

8 On this alarm, see Hallam *et al.* (2014). On the transformative role of the internet, see Martin (2014).

9 Trocki (1999).

10 Buxton (2006), pp. 10, 16.

11 Ibn Rusta, 'On the Rus', p. 126.

12 IbnF[1], p. 243.

13 Kay Kawus, *Qabus-nama*, pp. 99–108, 78.

14 Kay Kawus, *Qabus-nama*, p. xii.

15 William of Malmesbury, *Gesta*, vol. 2, pp. 362–3; see also Wyatt in this volume.

16 Bair (2009).

17 Figure 5.1 adapted from Wilson and Stevens (2008), p. 2.

18 IbnF[1], p. 241.

19 Easton (2008).

20 Jankowiak (2021 forthcoming).

21 Pierre Kopp has termed this a 'non-cartelised oligopoly': Kopp (2004), pp. 27–31.

22 Ünal (2009), p. 31.

23 Buddenberg and Byrd (2006), p. 200; Gatton (2011), p. 19.

24 IbnF[1], p. 247.

25 Based on Sudhir Venkatesh's studies of the Chicago housing projects in the 1990s, including a co-authored article with Steven Levitt which formed the basis of a chapter on the economics of drug selling in the latter's *Freakonomics*.

26 Venkatesh and Levitt (2000), pp. 439, 441; with thanks to Paul Ormerod for the initial reference.

27 Ibn Rusta, 'On the Rus', p. 127; Franklin and Shepard (1996), p. 40.

28 Levitt and Dubner (2006), p. 89.

29 Levitt and Dubner (2006), p. 101.

30 Levitt and Venkatesh (2000), p. 781.

31 Ibn Rusta, 'On the Rus', p. 127.

32 On this, see Massicard (2010); Gingeras (2014).

33 In 2010 alone, the Turkish International Academy against Drugs and Organised Crime (TADOC) ran such training for Uzbekistan, Kazakhstan, Afghanistan, Kosovo, Saudi Arabia, Palestine, Mongolia, Belize, El Salvador, Costa Rica, Mexico, Panama, Honduras and Guatemala. In addition, eighty-three law enforcement officers from Afghanistan, Pakistan, Tajikistan and Turkmenistan attended TADOC training activities organised with the cooperation of UN Office for Drugs and Organised Crime (UNODC) Regional Offices: KOM (2011), pp. 96–100.

34 For oil sales and kidnapping, see *Economist* (2015); on broader finance, see Shatz (2014); Robinson (2016).

35 Mohammed (2015).

36 This caused production of Captagon (phenethylline) in Lebanon to collapse after 2011: Henley (2014).

37 Shelley (2015); Milter and Slade (2005), p. 174.

38 Solomon (2015).

39 Irwin (1986), pp. 52, 69.

40 Fisher (1972), pp. 580–2.

41 Ibrahim ibn Ya'qub, 'Account of the Slavs', pp. 187–8, 191.

42 Thietmar, *Chronicon* IV.9, ed. and tr. Holtzmann and Trillmich, pp. 124–5; tr. Warner, p. 156.

43 [. . .] *quod sua consuetudine VII uxoribus abutebatur:* Gallus Anonymus, *Gesta* I.5, pp. 28–9. A century or so later, they are bluntly called 'mistress-whores': [. . .] *quod septem pelicum scortis, quas coniuges nuncupabat, nocturnas uariare uices consueuerat:* Vincent Kadłubek, *Chronik* II.8.2, p. 140.

44 Jan Długosz, *Annals*, ed. Dąbrowski *et al.*, vol. 1, p. 176; tr. Michael, p. 1.

45 Gallus Anonymus, *Gesta* I.5, p. 28; Cosmas of Prague reports her as 'already advanced in age' (*iam mulier provecte etatis*): *Chronicle* I.27, ed. Bretholz, p. 49; tr. Wolverton, p. 77. See also Urbańczyk and Rosik (2007), pp. 275–6.

46 Frye (1975), pp. 152–6.

47 See Adamczyk and Jankowiak in this volume.

48 Carter (1994), p. 47.

49 Cosmas of Prague, *Chronicle* I.34, ed. Bretholz, pp. 60–1; tr. Wolverton, pp. 87–8.

50 Berend *et al.* (2013), pp. 307–8.

51 *PVL*, pp. 28–9; *RPC*, pp. 80–1; see also Adamczyk in this volume.

52 [*Rex*] *adiecit autem, quod familias multorum sepe id sibi querentium Iudeis vendidit* [. . .] *Insuper questus est maiorem apud Bolizlauum fratrem gratiam hactenus habuisse, quam* [*ei*] *deceret aut sibi placere deberet:* Thietmar, *Chronicon* VI.54, ed. and tr. Holtzmann and Trillmich, pp. 302–3; tr. Warner, p. 275.

53 Jan Długosz, *Annals*, ed. Dąbrowski *et al.*, vol. 1, p. 202; tr. Michael, p. 5. On Adalbert's buying of Christian slaves and his disquiet at the flourishing of the slave trade in Prague, see Fontaine (2017), pp. 168–71.

54 Jan Długosz, *Annals*, ed. Dąbrowski *et al.*, vol. 1, p. 210; tr. Michael, p. 8 (which is mistranslated).

55 Gallus Anonymus, *Gesta* I.6, pp. 36–7.

56 Thietmar, *Chronicon* VI.28, ed. and tr. Holtzmann and Trillmich, pp. 272–3; tr. Warner, p. 256.

57 Jan Długosz, *Annals*, ed. Dąbrowski *et al.*, vol. 1, pp. 216, 218; tr. Michael, p. 9.

58 Długosz is the only chronicler to give a full account of a second expedition to Kiev by Bolesław, dating it to 1076: Jan Długosz, *Annals*, ed. Dąbrowski *et al.*, vol. 3, pp. 119–23; tr. Michael, pp. 53–4. However, the *Russian Primary Chronicle* tersely notes under 1077 that 'Iziaslav advanced with Polish support', before describing his entry into Kiev on 15 July of that year: *PVL*, p. 85; *RPC*, p. 165. Gregory VII wrote to both Iziaslav, the exiled ruler of Kiev, and Bolesław within three days of each other in April 1075, sending legates to both: Gregory VII, *Register*, pp. 168–70. Christian Raffensperger's suggestion that the same legates could have approved Bolesław's coronation at Christmas 1076, having extracted a promise from him to put Iziaslav back on the throne at Kiev, seems reasonable: Raffensperger (2012), pp. 166–8. Even if Bolesław did not go to Kiev in person, a prolonged absence on his campaign in Hungary and the division of forces through some nobles choosing to accompany Iziaslav to Kiev would have created the crisis described by Kadłubek.

59 Manteuffel (1982), pp. 94, 97.

60 *Nec uero minus inaudita post obitum Kazimiri seruorum pestis ebuliit:* Vincent Kadłubek, *Chronik* II.16.1, p. 162.

61 *Nam quod mulieres ingenue seruili prostitute sunt incestui, quod genialis tam spurce inquinata est religio, quod factio seruorum in dominos conspirata:* Vincent Kadłubek, *Chronik* II.20.12, p. 178; tr. from Skibiński (2017a), p. 96.

62 *Fuit* [. . .] *hic belli gerendi tam studiosus, ut rarus in aula continuus in castris, rarus in patria, semper aput hostes defuerit* [Mühle reads *deguerit*]: Vincent Kadłubek, *Chronik* II.18.12, p. 170.

63 *Boleslaus bellum in suos ab hostibus transtulit*: Vincent Kadłubek, *Chronik* II.20.1, p. 174; see also Skibiński (2017b), p. 111.
64 Syal (2009).
65 Reuter (2012), pp. 1–2.
66 Ibrahim ibn Ya'qub, 'Account of the Slavs', p. 186; see also Fontaine (2017).
67 Thietmar, *Chronicon* VII.39, ed. and tr. Holtzmann and Trillmich, pp. 396–7; tr. Warner, pp. 334–5 and see above n. 15.
68 *PVL*, p. 65; *RPC*, p. 136. See now, on archaeological evidence for the economic significance of the 'Cherven Towns', Wołoszyn (ed.) (2017).
69 Although Michał Kara (2010, esp. pp. 48, 51) does not mention the slave trade, highlighting rapid expansion by conquest, violent subjugation of neighbouring areas and the 'significant role of an outstanding family' as underlying the origins of the Polish state, our conclusions are not incompatible.

Bibliography

Primary sources

Cosmas of Prague, *Chronicle*, ed. B. Bretholz, *Chronica Boemorum, MGH Scriptores rerum Germanicarum* n.s. 2, Berlin (1923); tr. L. Wolverton, *Chronicle of the Czechs*, Washington, DC (2009).
Gallus Anonymus, *Gesta*, tr. P. W. Knoll and F. Schaer, *Gesta principum Polonorum/The Deeds of the Princes of the Poles*, Budapest (2003).
Gregory VII, *Register*, tr. H. E. J. Cowdrey, *The Register of Pope Gregory VII, 1073–85*, Oxford (2002).
Ibn Rusta, 'On the Rus 903–913', from *Kitab al-a'laq al-nafisah*, tr. P. Lunde and C. Stone in *Ibn Fadlan and the Land of Darkness: Arab Travellers in the Far North*, London (2012), pp. 126–7.
Ibrahim ibn Ya'qub, 'Account of the Slavs', tr. D. Mishin, 'Ibrahim ibn-Ya'qub at-Turtushi's account of the Slavs from the middle of the tenth century', *Annual of Medieval Studies at the CEU* 1994–5: 184–99.
Jan Długosz, *Annals*, ed. I. Dąbrowski *et al.*, *Annales seu Cronicae incliti regni Poloniae*, 7 vols to date, Warsaw (1964–); abridged tr. M. Michael, *The Annals of Jan Długosz*, Chichester (1997).
Kay Kawus, *Qabus-nama*, tr. R. Levy, *A Mirror for Princes: The Qabus Nama*, London (1951).
Thietmar of Merseburg, *Chronicon*, ed. R. Holtzmann, rev. and German tr. W. Trillmich, Darmstadt (2002); tr. D. A. Warner, *Ottonian Germany: The Chronicon of Thietmar of Merseburg*, Manchester (2001).
Vincent Kadłubek, *Die Chronik der Polen des Magisters Vincentius*, ed. and German tr. E. Mühle, Darmstadt (2014).
William of Malmesbury, *Gesta regum Anglorum*, ed. and tr. R. A. B. Mynors, 2 vols, Oxford (1998–9).

Secondary literature

Bair, J. (2009), *Frontiers of Commodity Chain Research*, Stanford, CA.
Berend, N. *et al.* (2013), *Central Europe in the High Middle Ages: Bohemia, Hungary and Poland c. 900–c. 1300*, Cambridge.

Buddenberg, D. and W. Byrd (eds) (2006), 'Afghanistan's drug industry: structure, functioning, dynamics, and implications for counter-narcotic policy', *World Bank Report* 38931, Washington, DC, unodc.org/pdf/Afgh_drugindustry_Nov06.pdf (accessed 15 December 2019).

Buxton, J. (2006), *The Political Economy of Narcotics: Production, Consumption and Global Markets*, London.

Carter, F. W. (1994), *Trade and Urban Development in Poland: An Economic Geography of Cracow, from Its Origins to 1795*, Cambridge.

Chouvy, P.-A. (2012), 'A typology of the unintended consequences of drug crop reduction', *Journal of Drug Issues* 43: 216–30.

Easton, M. (2008), 'Map of the week: the mystery of the missing opium', *BBC News Website, Mark Easton's Blog* (8 October 2008), bbc.co.uk/blogs/thereporters/markeaston/2008/10/map_of_the_week_the_mystery_of.html (accessed 15 December 2019).

Economist, The (2015), 'Where Islamic State gets its money', *The Economist explains* (4 January 2015), economist.com/blogs/economist-explains/2015/01/economist-explains (accessed 15 December 2019).

Fisher, A. (1972), 'Muscovy and the Black Sea slave trade', *Canadian-American Slavic Studies* 6: 572–94.

Fontaine, J. (2017), 'Slave trading in the British Isles and the Czech Lands, 7th–11th centuries', unpublished PhD dissertation, King's College London.

Franklin, S. and J. Shepard (1996), *The Emergence of Rus, 750–1200*, Harlow.

Friesendorf, C. (2007), *US Foreign Policy and the War on Drugs: Displacing the Cocaine and Heroin Industry*, Abingdon.

Frye, R. (1975), 'The Samanids', in R. Frye (ed.), *The Cambridge History of Iran*, vol. 4: *The Period from the Arab Invasion to the Saljuqs*, Cambridge, pp. 136–61.

Gatton, A. (2011), 'The opium cables: how *Druglink* used Wikileaks to reveal the secret story of heroin's journey from Afghanistan to the UK', *Druglink* 26(6) (November/December 2011), pp. 18–21, drugwise.org.uk/wp-content/uploads/Opium-cables.pdf (accessed 15 December 2019).

Gingeras, A. (2014), *Heroin, Organized Crime, and the Making of Modern Turkey*, Oxford.

Hallam, C. *et al.* (2014), 'Scheduling in the international drug control system', *TNI-IDPC Series on Legislative Reform of Drug Policies* 25, undrugcontrol.info/images/stories/documents/dlr25.pdf (accessed 15 December 2019).

Henley, J. (2014), 'Captagon: the amphetamine fuelling Syria's civil war', *The Guardian* (13 January 2014), theguardian.com/world/shortcuts/2014/jan/13/captagon-amphetamine-syria-war-middle-east (accessed 15 December 2019).

Irwin, R. (1986), *The Middle East in the Middle Ages: The Early Mamluk Sultanate, 1250–1382*, Carbondale, IL.

Jankowiak, M. (2021 forthcoming), 'Tracing the Saqaliba: slave trade and the archaeology of tenth-century northern Europe', in *IC*.

Kara, M. (2010) 'Medieval historical studies and medieval archaeology about the origin of the Piast state: an overview', *Archaeologia Polona* 48: 37–58.

KOM (2011), *Department of Anti-Smuggling and Organized Crime: Annual Report 2010*, Ankara, egm.gov.tr/kom/raporlarimiz (accessed 15 December 2019).

Kopp, P. (2004), *The Political Economy of Illegal Drugs*, London.

Levitt, S. D. and S. J. Dubner (2006), *Freakonomics: A Rogue Economist Explores the Hidden Side of Everything*, London.

Levitt, S. D. and S. A. Venkatesh (2000), 'An economic analysis of a drug-selling gang's finances', *Quarterly Journal of Economics* 115: 755–89.

Manteuffel, T. (1982), *The Formation of the Polish State: The Period of Ducal Rule, 963–1194*, Detroit, MI.

Marshall, A. (2012), 'Global commodity chains and LINKSCH', University of Glasgow Working Paper (on behalf of the LINKSCH Consortium), eprints.gla.ac.uk/110110 (accessed 15 December 2019).

Martin, J. (2014), *Drugs on the Dark Net: How Cryptomarkets Are Transforming the Global Trade in Illicit Drugs*, London.

Massicard, E. (2010), '"Gangs in uniform" in Turkey: politics at the articulation between security institutions and the criminal world', in J.-L. Briquet and G. Favarel-Garrigues (eds), *Organized Crime and States: The Hidden Face of Politics*, Basingstoke, pp. 41–71.

Milter, K. S. and J. W. Slade (2005), 'Global traffic in pornography: the Hungarian example', in L. Z. Sigel (ed.), *International Exposure: Perspectives on Modern European Pornography, 1800–2000*, New York, pp. 173–204.

Mohammed, A. (2015), 'How ISIS dodges western attempts in controlling its financial resources', *Raqqa is Being Slaughtered Silently* website (20 February 2015), raqqa-sl.com/en/?p=624 (accessed 15 December 2019).

Platt, S. (2015), *Criminal Capital: How the Finance Industry Facilitates Crime*, Basingstoke.

Raffensperger, C. (2012), *Reimagining Europe: Kievan Rus' in the Christian World*, Cambridge, MA.

Reiss, S. (2014), *We Sell Drugs: The Alchemy of US Empire*, Berkeley, CA.

Reuter, P. (ed.) (2012), *Draining Development? Controlling Flows of Illicit Funds from Developing Countries*, Washington, DC.

Robinson, E. (2016), 'Cutting the Islamic State's money supply', *The National Interest* (20 July 2016), nationalinterest.org/blog/the-buzz/cutting-the-islamic-states-money-supply-17046 (accessed 15 December 2019).

Shatz, H. J. (2014) 'To defeat the Islamic State, follow the money', *Politico Magazine* (10 September 2014), politico.com/magazine/story/2014/09/to-defeat-isil-follow-the-money-110825 (accessed 15 December 2019).

Shelley, L. (2015) 'Islamic State is a diversified criminal operation', *Spiegel Online* (6 January 2015), spiegel.de/international/business/terror-expert-shelley-speaks-of-islamic-state-business-model-a-1011492.html (accessed 15 December 2019).

Skibiński, E. (2017a), 'The language of Vincentius's *Chronicle*', in D. Von Güttner-Sporzyński (ed.), *Writing History in Medieval Poland: Bishop Vincentius of Cracow and the 'Chronica Polonorum'*, Turnhout, pp. 79–98.

Skibiński, E. (2017b), 'The narrative in Vincentius's *Chronicle*', in D. Von Güttner-Sporzyński (ed.), *Writing History in Medieval Poland: Bishop Vincentius of Cracow and the 'Chronica Polonorum'*, Turnhout, pp. 99–118.

Solomon, E. (2015), 'Syrian smugglers ignore harsh penalties and turn to cigarettes', *Financial Times* (16 May 2015), ft.com/content/081071ee-f975-11e4-ae65-00144feab7de (accessed 15 December 2019).

Syal, R. (2009), 'Drug money saved banks in global crisis, claims UN advisor', *The Observer* (13 December 2009), theguardian.com/global/2009/dec/13/drug-money-banks-saved-un-cfief-claims (accessed 15 December 2019).

Trocki, C. A. (1999), *Opium: Empire and the Global Political Economy*, London.

Ünal, M. (2009), 'Application of situational crime prevention to cross-border heroin trafficking in Turkey', unpublished PhD dissertation, University of Cincinnati.

Urbańczyk, P. and S. Rosik (2007), 'The kingdom of Poland, with an Appendix on Polabia and Pomerania between paganism and Christianity', in N. Berend (ed.), *Christianization and the Rise of Christian Monarchy*, Cambridge, pp. 263–318.

Venkatesh, S. A. and S. D. Levitt (2000), '"Are we a family or a business?" History and disjuncture in the urban American street gang', *Theory and Society* 29: 427–62.

Wilson, L. and A. Stevens (2008), 'Understanding drug markets and how to influence them', *The Beckley Foundation Drug Policy Programme Report* 14, Oxford, beckleyfoun dation.org/resource/understanding-drug-markets-and-how-to-influence-them (accessed 15 December 2019).

Wołoszyn, M. (ed.) (2017), *From Cherven' Towns to Curzon Line: The Lands on the Middle Bug during the Middle Ages and the Historiographic Perspective on the Formation of Poland's Eastern Border, 18th–21st Centuries*, Cracow; Leipzig; Rzeszów; Warsaw.

Part II

Flows from Islam

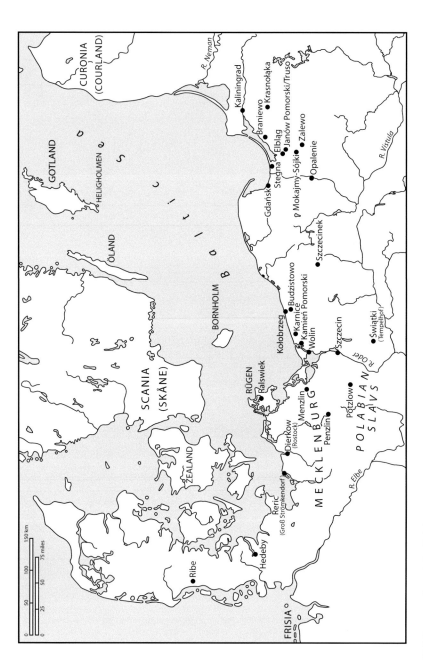

Map II.1 Pomerania and the Baltic.

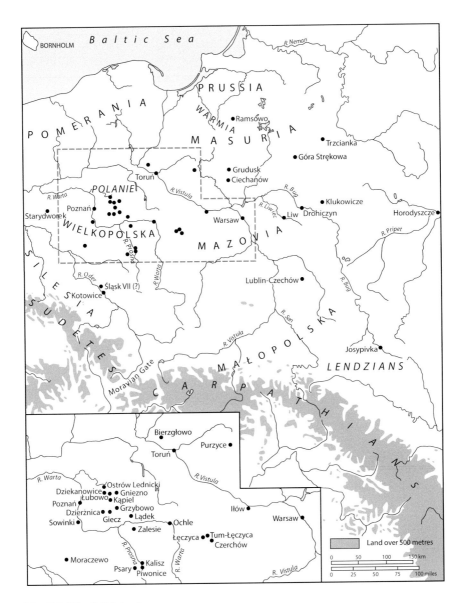

Map II.2 The Polish lands.

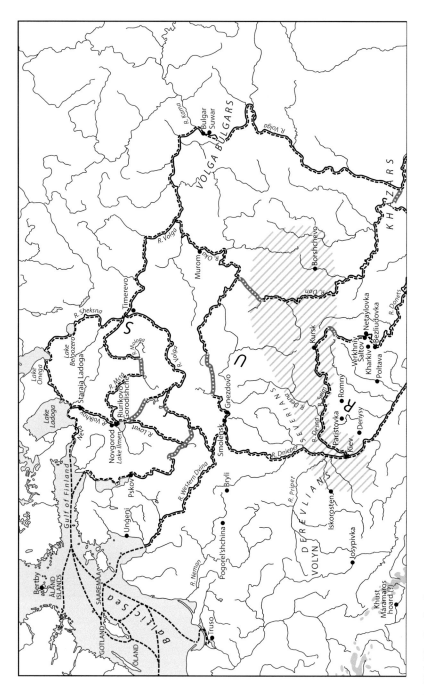

Map II.3 The Rus lands.

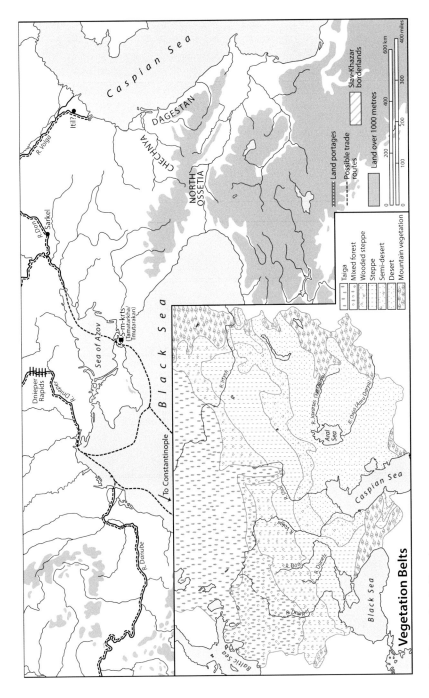

Map II.3 The Rus lands (Cont.).

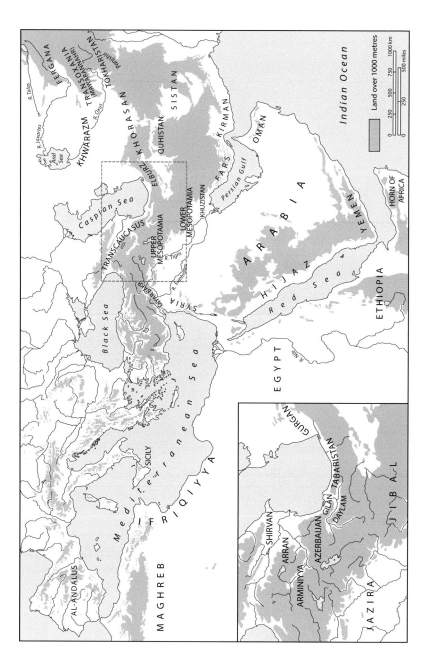

Map II.4a The Muslim world (geography and regions).

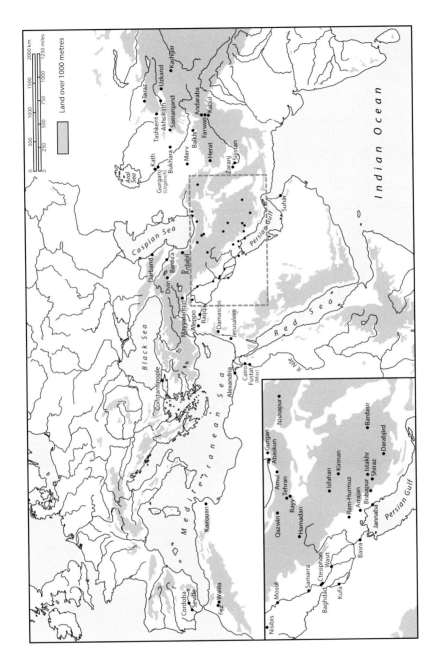

Map II.4b The Muslim world (mints and key places).

6 Dirham flows into northern and eastern Europe and the rhythms of the slave trade with the Islamic world

Marek Jankowiak[1]

To the memory of Richard Vasmer (1888–1938)

In 1933 Richard Vasmer planned a new catalogue of dirham hoards found in 'eastern Europe' to replace Aleksei Markov's 1910 *Topography*.[2] In addition to a full listing of coins and hoards, he proposed periodising the latter and explaining how they were accumulated, as well as taking note of imitation coins and secondary treatments such as fragmentation and perforation. He also planned to map all known hoards from the four major inflow periods that he defined (see Table 6.1). But Vasmer died in a Soviet gulag in 1938 and almost a century later, Markov's is still the most recent catalogue covering the whole of northern and eastern Europe. Vasmer's vision remains a wish list, and the quality of available information varies widely: while catalogues exist for Poland and Estonia, we have no published data for most hoards, including those from countries such as Ukraine and Sweden.

This helps explain why the dirham hoards from northern and eastern Europe[3] have not been integrated into the historical narrative of early medieval western Eurasia.[4] The sheer quantity and complexity of the material adds to the difficulty. The hoards are possibly the largest body of quantifiable data we have for the region. As of 2007, the catalogue compiled by Thomas Noonan and Roman Kovalev contained 1,246 hoards with dirhams.[5] Using published catalogues and the Numismatic Institute in Stockholm's archive, I have gathered data on 833 hoards where dirhams make up more than 50% of the coins and whose find spot is known.[6] We have insufficient information to date 124 of them, leaving 709 datable hoards.[7] Both Noonan and Kovalev's catalogue and my data estimate the number of dirhams found in northern and eastern Europe at between 350,000 and 400,000. Of course, this represents only a fraction of the original inflow of coins, which must have been in the millions, if not tens of millions.

This importing of Islamic coins in such vast quantities over thousands of kilometres was one of the largest flows of precious metal in pre-modern times. Muslim geographers, diplomats and travellers such as Ibn Rusta and Ibn Fadlan were aware of its remarkable scale.[8] They describe a trading system in which northern slaves and furs were exported to the Islamic world by Rus merchants in exchange for dirhams and glass beads. We find Slavic slaves (*Saqaliba*) frequently mentioned in the ninth- and tenth-century Islamic world, as we do the slave trade in Byzantine, Latin, Slavic and Scandinavian sources, corroborating a picture of widespread slave-trading in the Viking Age. I will use this as the main framework explaining the inflow of dirhams to northern and eastern Europe.[9]

This chapter aims to reconstruct these dirham flows on the basis of hoarding patterns in northern and eastern Europe, using written and archaeological sources to contextualise the trade between the Islamic world and the north. I will use the shifting concentrations of Islamic silver to shed light on the political and social history of Scandinavia and the Slavic lands at the time of state formation in the ninth and tenth centuries.[10] Such an exercise is fraught with risks: the complexity of the material inevitably leads to overemphasising some patterns at the expense of others, and dirham flows do not translate directly into hoarding patterns, which in turn do not have a simple connection to political history. But a comprehensive and detailed chronology of dirham hoards and flows of Islamic silver, however tentative, seems worthwhile, as does taking a global view of the system that transported dirhams from Iraq, Iran and Central Asia to the furthest corners of Scandinavia and the Slavic lands.

Geographical distribution of dirham hoards

The 833 hoards analysed here mostly come from Sweden (294), Russia (198), Poland (126), Ukraine and Belarus (40 each). The most prominent hoard clusters are found on the Baltic islands, principally Gotland (199), but also Öland (19), the Åland islands (8) and Bornholm (7) (see Map 6.1). Others come from various contexts around the Baltic: from the core, densely populated Scandinavian areas (Uppland and Denmark); from major river-mouths (the Oder, Vistula and Western Dvina) where emporia were often located (Wolin and Truso); or from the coasts (of Estonia and Scania). Moving further inland, hoards line major riverways (the Oka, Dnieper and Bug); mark portages connecting their basins (the regions around Gnezdovo and Kursk); and are concentrated in areas of emerging political structures (such as Wielkopolska and Kiev). The cluster where the Kama meets the Volga owes its existence to the market town of Bulgar, the main tenth-century gateway for Islamic silver heading north-westwards. That dirham hoards are found in such diverse contexts no doubt reflects the equally diverse reasons for their deposition: some may have been lost in transit or buried in an emergency, whereas others were stored in temporary settlements such as winter quarters, or accumulated over generations as family savings in farmsteads and villages.

But proximity to an emporium, newly forming polity or communication artery does not guarantee the presence of hoards. Relatively few are known from emporia such as Birka or Hedeby, or from Uppland, the core area of the emerging Swedish state. Even the trunk road of tenth-century trade – the 900km stretch of

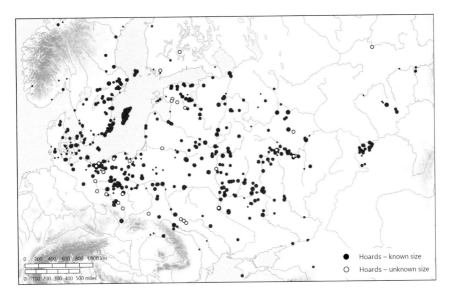

Map 6.1 Northern and eastern European dirham hoards with known find spots.

the Volga between Bulgar and Timerevo – is entirely devoid of finds and, in contrast to Bulgar, the slave markets of Khazaria have left little imprint in the hoard material.

Two possible reasons for such irregularities in hoarding patterns should be noted. Firstly, use depended on the cultural values attached to silver: in Scandinavian and some Slavic societies, silver coins served as status markers and the main repository of wealth, while other Slavs and nomads treated it as raw material from which to craft prestige items. Secondly, just as they reflect involvement in the silver trade, our hoarding distribution maps illustrate patterns of non-recovery. The high number of hoards in Wielkopolska, for instance, is due not only to the existence of the powerful Piast state, capable of acquiring vast quantities of silver, but also to its collapse in the 1030s and the consequent dispersal of its elites and population. No such cataclysm occurred in Uppland or Kievan Rus, where the emerging central powers gradually brought local stocks of precious metals under their control. Non-recovery may help explain the puzzling case of Gotland. Hoarding by the island's farmers was probably of a comparable scale to their counterparts elsewhere in Scandinavia. But the century or so between Christianisation – which modified behaviours related to silver and hoarding – and the extension of a central (Swedish) authority capable of reintroducing hoarded wealth into circulation was sufficiently long for silver to fall out of use as the main marker of status and for hoards to lie forgotten in the ground.[11]

Hoarding was thus the result of a number of factors: although most often ascribed to insecurity and ritual, these may have played a secondary role. And a contemporary map of dirham hoards would have looked very different from Map 6.1. But even allowing for such reservations, the evidence from our hundreds of preserved hoards still allows a detailed analysis of the rhythms of dirham inflows and of its mirror reflection, the slave trade.

Interpreting *termini post quem*

Dirhams bear the date and place of their minting, allowing us to date the most recent coin in a hoard and thus the hoard's earliest possible deposition date (*tpq*).[12] The time lag between the *tpq* and the actual deposition of a hoard is more difficult to estimate. However, we have little evidence for dirham circulation – and more broadly for a monetary economy, i.e. the use of coins as means of payment in everyday transactions – in the ninth- and tenth-century Baltic and Slavic lands outside the emporia and main marketplaces. When used as payment for goods exported to the Islamic world, coins moved quickly along the chain of intermediaries; but once they reached their final destination, most were simply hoarded. *Tpqs* are therefore likely to correspond quite closely to deposition dates; and although they cannot be treated as absolute, they can be used to establish the chronology of dirham inflows to northern and eastern Europe.

They are not, however, a simple reflection of the rhythms of dirham inflows. If the *tpq* indicates when a hoard was sealed and coins ceased to be added, it does not say much about its accumulation pattern. Indeed, hoard deposition was not necessarily a single act. Interpreting the *tpq* depends on the hoard type. Some 'merchant's hoards', such as the earliest Samanid ones discussed below, may represent banked takings from the slave market, and thus shed direct light on dirham flows. Others were probably accumulated over extended periods of time: the *tpq* tells us only when their owners lost access to new coins, not when most were acquired. Although it is rarely possible to categorise a hoard unambiguously or to reconstruct precisely when it was accumulated,[13] the degree of fragmentation and chronological span of its coins, its proximity to slave markets or communication routes, the presence or absence of earlier hoards in the vicinity, and the archaeological context can all help. Most Gotlandic hoards, for instance, have a long chronological span and were found in the context of farmsteads,[14] making it likely they were accumulated over several generations.

Figure 6.1[15] shows the hoards' *tpqs*, and illustrates the need to take into account diverse accumulation patterns in any attempt to reconstruct the rhythms of dirham inflows. It suggests that dirhams came to northern and eastern Europe in several waves peaking around 810, 840, in the 860s and again in the 950s. The ninth-century inflow, however, should really be seen as a single period, since no major discontinuities in trade between Scandinavia and the Islamic world can be detected before *c.* 875. A hiatus of a quarter-century separates this first wave from the second, which encompassed most of the tenth century and petered out after 980. The two waves differed both in scale (75% of hoards have *tpqs* after 900) and in composition: Abbasid dirhams from Iraq and western Iran dominate the first wave, Samanid coins from Central Asia the second.

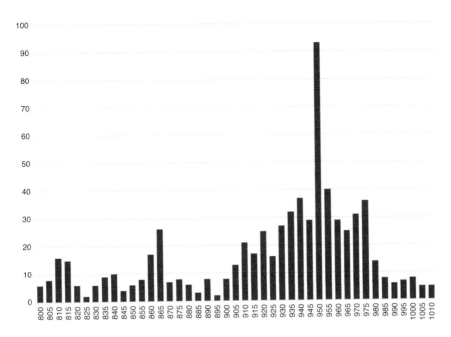

Figure 6.1 Tpqs of the northern and eastern European dirham hoards.

But these peaks could either indicate periods of particularly intensive inflow, or of accumulation being discontinued. The remarkable number of hoards with *tpq*s between 950 and 955, for instance, is more likely to correspond to the latter. Since most appear to be accumulation hoards, their simultaneous sealing suggests an interruption – or at least limitation – of dirham inflow to Rus and the Baltic soon after 950.

This impression is supported by a comparison of the Gotlandic hoards' *tpq*s and the chronology of the dirhams that they contain (Figure 6.2).[16] The two peak together in the 860s, but are separated by several decades in the tenth century. That the rapid increase and subsequent collapse in the number of imported dirhams around 867/8 (AH 253) was accompanied by intensive hoarding suggests something of a 'bubble': a swift expansion of trade followed by an equally swift disintegration of the trading networks. However, the relationship between inflow and hoarding of dirhams in the first half of the tenth century seems different. Despite a very high inflow, few hoards were sealed in the early decades and dirhams continued to accumulate as long as fresh coins were available. But in 954/5 (AH 343) the import of Central Asian dirhams to Gotland all but stopped. They continued to trickle into Gotland in the following decades – helping to explain the significant number of hoards with later *tpq*s which were mostly composed of much older coins – but for many hoarders, the caesura of the 950s spelled the end of half a century of accumulating dirhams.

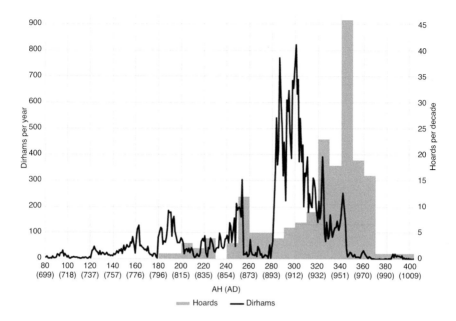

Figure 6.2 *Tpq*s and minting dates of the Gotlandic dirham hoards.

These interpretations are based on two assumptions: that dirhams, as a rule, left the Islamic world soon after they had been minted; and that the fluctuations in their quantities reflect the rhythms of their inflow, and not variations in their production. These rules of thumb are supported by the Middle Eastern hoards. Their relatively short chronologies show that the monetary stocks circulating in the Islamic world contained a high proportion of recent coins. They also show that the coin dates in Figure 6.2 do not fully reflect the rhythms of dirham production: this did not stop between 867/8 (AH 253) and 893/4 (AH 280),[17] nor after 954/5 (AH 343), despite our deep troughs. The peak in the early ninth century, however, probably does reflect the particularly abundant issues of the first Abbasid caliphs, rather than prompt importing of dirhams to Gotland.

Chronological overview

Despite minor modifications, Vasmer's tentative periodisation of dirham hoards remains commonly accepted, categorising them on the basis of the most common coin types that they contain (Table 6.1). However, his periodisation did not take into account the hoards' topography, nor did Vasmer attempt to establish the rhythms of their importation, and thus his four periods should not be interpreted as 'waves' of dirham inflows.

Table 6.1 Vasmer's periodisation of dirham hoards[1]

Period	Chronology	Dominant coins
1	800–25	Abbasid (high proportion of North African coins)
2	825–905	Abbasid (absence of North African coins)
3	905–60	Samanid
4	960–1012	Samanid, Buyid, Ziyarid

Note
1 Adapted from Vasmer (1933), p. 478.

I propose to extend Vasmer's approach to include variations in hoard topography and the conjectured fluctuations in dirham inflows. Although I will use the general framework of two waves separated by a hiatus in the last quarter of the ninth century, I will avoid an overly systematic approach: periodisations based on one region are rarely satisfactory for others. Instead, I will proceed by decade, using the hoards' distribution maps and structures, while taking into account what we know about the slave trade and the political history of the areas concerned.

The 800s: the earliest hoards

The earliest relatively securely dated dirham hoard comes from Staraia Ladoga (*tpq* 786/7), and is currently the only one likely to have been imported in the late eighth century.[18] A steadier flow of dirhams northwards began after 800: we have a number of hoards with *tpq*s in the 800s spread from the Caucasus to the Baltic. The finds concentrate in two clusters: in the steppe between the Black Sea and the Caspian, an area associated with the Khazar khaganate; and along the Volkhov and Neva rivers in northern Rus, the main riverway from the Baltic into the interior. Although relatively small – generally no more than several dozen dirhams – their number and geographical distribution indicate regular early contacts between Scandinavians and Khazars.

These early contacts were driven by the Scandinavians' exploration of the eastern Baltic coast and Rus riverways in the course of the eighth century.[19] But the sudden inflow of Islamic dirhams to the north around the year 800 was, above all, due to favourable conditions in the northern marches of the caliphate, especially in the Caucasus. A period of internal instability, repressive policies and conflict with the Khazars had followed the establishment of the Abbasid caliphate in 750, but Caliph al-Mahdi (775–85) 'opened the marches of Armenia' to merchants and promoted trade. At the same time, the mines of North Africa and Armenia enabled the production of vast quantities of dirhams.[20] The unprecedented availability of silver coinage, as seen in the many hoards from the Caucasus dating to the 780s, quickly attracted the Scandinavians.

At first, the Khazars and Scandinavians probably supplied highly prized furs to the first Abbasid caliphs.[21] But before long they realised that the slave trade was more lucrative and slaves soon became an important, if not the dominant, article of trade. The first *Saqaliba* appear in our Islamic sources at the very beginning of the ninth century and are frequently mentioned in the following decades.[22]

The 810s and 820s: Russia and Prussia

Hoards grew in size during the first two decades of the ninth century, and the main hoarding zone shifted: from Khazaria and northern Rus to an intermediate area roughly corresponding to the southern fringes of the forest zone and probably also to the southern limits of Slav settlement. This, together with the frequent mentions of *Saqaliba* in the sources, suggests these hoards may have been related to Scandinavian slave-taking. Quantities of dirhams also start to appear in the Baltic: not, however, on Gotland or in mainland Sweden, but in Baltic Prussia on its southern shore. There can be little doubt that they were channelled there through the emporium of Truso, where hundreds of stray coins dating from precisely this period have been discovered.[23] Archaeological material from Truso, and Wulfstan's late ninth-century account of his journey there from Hedeby, suggest strong connections between the emporium and Denmark. That the earliest dirhams found in the Baltic flowed towards Denmark rather than Sweden or Gotland is reinforced by the string of finds along the southern Baltic coast and by the near absence of early ninth-century hoards in Sweden and Gotland.

Despite similar *tpqs*, our hoards from Rus and Baltic Prussia differ sharply in composition. Like many early ninth-century finds from Iraq and the Caucasus, the Rus hoards contain a high proportion (20–60%) of North African dirhams struck between 776/7 and 795/6 (AH 160 and 179),[24] which are almost entirely absent from the Baltic finds. This has puzzled numismatists, who have suggested alternative routes for dirhams to reach the Baltic, bypassing Rus, possibly via the Carolingian empire.[25] But North African dirhams gradually disappeared from circulation within the caliphate in the first decades of the ninth century, no doubt because they were of lower weight and quality than their Middle Eastern counterparts.[26] Thus dirhams probably reached Baltic Prussia later than those circulating in Rus, and by a direct route.[27] Overall, the existence of two contemporary clusters of hoards in Russia and Prussia suggests a growing demand and increasing competition for Islamic silver (Map 6.2).

The 830s: helping the Khazars

The 830s saw major changes in hoard topography, both in the Baltic and in Rus. Dirhams ceased to flow into Baltic Prussia: very few coins struck after 833 made their way to Truso and no later hoards are known from the area. Instead, they start to appear in Gotland and the northern Baltic, areas so far absent from our hoard map. This shift from the southern to the central and northern Baltic seems to have been mirrored in Rus, where hoards with

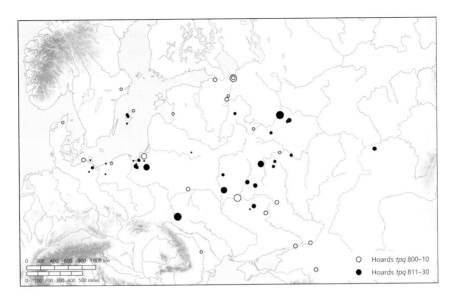

Map 6.2 Northern and eastern European dirham hoards with *tpq*s between 800 and 830.

*tpq*s between the 830s and 850s are found slightly further north compared to previous decades, roughly along the Oka and Dvina rivers.

A group of some 20 hoards, all with *tpq*s of 837 or slightly later, suggests that this geographical reconfiguration was accompanied by fluctuations in dirham inflows. Although they are scattered across much of northern and eastern Europe, the presence of early Khazar imitation dirhams clearly connects these hoards. Most Khazar imitations simply replicated Abbasid dirhams, but two dies inscribed 'Ard al-Khazar' ('the land of the Khazars') and dated to 837/8 (AH 223) firmly place their minting in Khazaria. The die links established by Gert Rispling show that these imitations were produced on a remarkably large scale: at least 200 dies are currently known, more than the number used for the yearly production of any big Samanid mint in the tenth century.[28]

The shift in hoarding zones, the appearance of a group of contemporaneous hoards, and the production of Khazar imitations took place in a context of unrest in the steppes, apparently triggered by Magyar migration from the Volga-Kama region to the Pontic steppe, where they are first mentioned in 836.[29] The Magyars were undoubtedly the 'very fierce and savage barbarous tribes' who prevented a group of Rus from returning home from Constantinople: when Emperor Theophilos (829–42) sent these Rus to the court of Louis the Pious (814–40) in 838, requesting their safe passage through Frankish lands, they were famously identified as belonging 'to the people of the Swedes'.[30] Around the same time, the Khazars sought Byzantine assistance to build a fortress at Sarkel on the Don, presumably to protect their western flank from the invaders.[31]

In this fraught context, the minting of the earliest dirham imitations in the Khazar khaganate has been interpreted as a proclamation of its political and religious independence. This interpretation relies on coins bearing the inscription 'Moses is the prophet of God', our earliest evidence for the Judaism in Khazaria.[32] But the significance of these coins should not be overestimated: the seven specimens known to me were all struck with a single die, the only one of some 200 early Khazar imitative dies to carry this type of message. Propaganda is therefore unlikely to have been the main reason for producing this coinage; nor is trade, if the Magyar migration was as disruptive as our sources suggest. This leaves military considerations as the likeliest explanation for the short-lived outburst of the Khazar monetary production around 837 and the inflow of silver to the northern Baltic shortly thereafter: the need to enlist troops, some of whom may have been of Scandinavian stock.

The 840s and 850s: low-key stability

Finds from the 840s and 850s are rarer and smaller than in preceding decades. But low numbers do not necessarily mean the inflow of dirhams decreased: rather, the abundance of hoards sealed in the turbulent 860s and 870s suggests that trade had continued, even if at a relatively low level, in the preceding decades. Hoards from the 840s and 850s contain a higher proportion of Central Asian coins (10–15%, compared to below 10% before *c.* 837). This may indicate more direct contacts with Central Asia, although still probably via the Khazars; or perhaps simply changes in the monetary stock of the Abbasids' central lands (Map 6.3).

The 860s and 870s: climax and collapse

The exceptionally high number of hoards sealed in the 860s and 870s, their larger size – at least nine contained more than 1,000 dirhams, compared to five in the whole of the preceding period – and a high proportion of recent coins all indicate an intensification in the inflow of dirhams in this period. But climax was quickly followed by collapse, as shown by the sealing of over 50 hoards within a short period (*tpqs* between 862 and 877) and by the scarcity of hoards and coins in the next two decades.

Written sources attest a sudden increase of Scandinavian activity in the Black Sea and the Caspian in this period. A Rus fleet reportedly numbering 200 ships unprecedentedly threatened Constantinople in June 860.[33] This was followed by diplomatic exchanges and a Byzantine attempt to convert the Rus to Christianity, although these ended in the early 870s for reasons left unexplained by our Byzantine sources.[34] Few Islamic sources are available for this period, but a later text mentions a Rus raid against Abaskun on the south-eastern shore of the Caspian during the time of Hasan ibn Zayd, governor of Tabaristan in 864/5–883/4 (AH 250–70), without giving a precise date.[35]

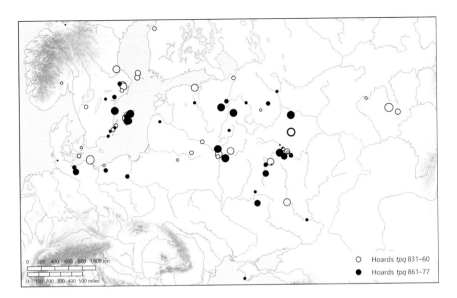

Map 6.3 Northern and eastern European dirham hoards with *tpqs* between 831 and 877.

The reasons for this surge of Rus activity are not known. The crisis of the Abbasid caliphate, engulfed in the 860s by a succession of coups known as the 'Samarra anarchy', may have attracted Rus raiders, but Byzantium showed no similar signs of weakness under the energetic rule of Emperor Michael III (842–67) and his accomplished administrator Caesar Bardas (d. 866). Nor are there many signs of instability in the steppe, although the reaffirmation of Judaism by the Khazar elites around 861 may hint at some threat to the khaganate.[36] This leaves us with the internal dynamics of Scandinavia and Rus as the most likely cause for their increased interest in the east in the 860s. It coincided with an escalation of Viking invasions into the Carolingian and Anglo-Saxon realms, raising possibilities of inter-connectedness: the success of western Scandinavian raids up the Seine and Loire in 856–8[37] may have whetted the appetites of Swedes, Gotlanders and Rus for silver and sent them east. However, the Byzantine and Islamic empires weathered the Viking storm better than the western kingdoms, managing to persuade the Rus that trading, not raiding, was a more secure means of acquiring silver.

While the earliest Islamic account of the Rus, dating perhaps from the 840s, reports that they sometimes sold their goods directly in Baghdad,[38] the Gotlandic hoards suggest that merchants from the northern borders of the caliphate had become involved by the 860s. Dirhams from the mints of Armenia and Transoxiana, notably issues from Arminiyya in 866/7 (ᴀʜ 252) and from Samarqand and al-Shash [Tashkent] in the following year, are among the most frequently found on Gotland. Even the rare, later coins that made their way onto the island came mostly from the Caucasus and Central Asia,[39] although dirhams of caliphs al-Muʿtazz (866–9) and al-Muʿtamid (870–92) minted in Iraq and Iran are common in the few known hoards from the Middle East.[40] Production of dirhams in the central caliphate seems to have been less affected by the 'Samarra anarchy' than was demand for slaves and furs, since the latter was mostly generated by the caliphal court.

Until *c.* 870, the Armenian connection appears to have been the more active;[41] thereafter, the silver flowing northwards mostly came from Central Asia. But merchants from both regions were at pains to meet the Rus' demand for silver coins. Shortages are indicated by irregular, poorly struck dirhams, often single-faced or struck using dies with blundered legends, hastily struck in official mints or produced in unofficial workshops.[42]

These issues sustained the trade until the flow of the dirhams to the north stopped around 877. It is tempting to link this disruption to the collapse of the earliest Rus polity in the early to mid-870s. Traces of destruction from this time have been uncovered in a number of major sites in northern Rus, including Staraia Ladoga, Riurikovo Gorodishche and Pskov, and the Rus khaganate disappears from our written sources.[43] We also find echoes in the *Russian Primary Chronicle*'s description of the northern tribes' revolt against the heavy tribute imposed by the Varangians and the latter's expulsion 'beyond the sea'.[44] Thus ended what appears to have been a decade or two of overly enthusiastic slave-taking, which eventually provoked the local tribes to rise up against the Rus. Trade between Scandinavia and the Islamic world was disrupted for a quarter-century.

The 880s and 890s: a hiatus?

Trade did not, however, stop altogether. Some 20 hoards are known from the last quarter of the ninth century, although their geographical distribution differs sharply from previous decades (Map 6.4). Only four come from beyond Gotland and the Baltic.[45] Found far to the west of the earlier hoarding areas, they perhaps attest a search for alternative river routes, bypassing the core territories of the Rus now closed to business.[46] The impression that Baltic Scandinavians traded directly with Khazaria is confirmed by the Bertby hoard from the Åland islands (*tpq* 890/1), which contains large numbers of imitation dirhams struck from identical dies.[47]

Most of our late ninth-century hoards contain imitation dirhams, sometimes totalling 20–25% of the coins. The irregular issues of the earlier period continue, but a new group of 'ugly' imitations also appears. Characterised by distorted, illiterate legends, only distantly resembling Arabic script, they were nevertheless carefully executed and had a high silver content; and unlike earlier imitations, we can trace long die-chains, implying stable, centralised production. They were minted on a relatively large scale at a workshop which we can tentatively place in Khazaria and date to *c.* 880–910.[48] It seems that the Khazars, faced with a limited availability of Islamic silver and an unrelenting Scandinavian demand for dirhams, tapped

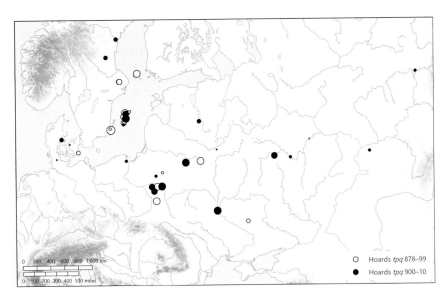

Map 6.4 Northern and eastern European dirham hoards with *tpq*s between 878 and 910.

into their accumulated silver reserves and converted them into dirham-like objects, the only form of silver accepted by the northerners.

The movement of steppe peoples around 890 further affected the already moribund trade of this period. Forced out of the north-eastern Caspian steppes by the Khazars and Oghuz, the Pechenegs moved into the Pontic steppes, duly ejecting the Magyars who migrated to Pannonia. But a new route opened up further east, after the Samanid governor of Transoxiana, Isma'il ibn Ahmad, defeated the Qarluq Turks on the Talas river in 892/3 (AH 279).

The 900s: the Samanid wave

In the same year, Isma'il started to mint vast quantities of high-quality silver coins. Reviving trade between northern Europe and the Islamic world after quarter of a century in the doldrums was not Isma'il's intention: he was involved in a complex, costly, but ultimately victorious struggle for control of Central Asia and eastern Iran. But it was a side-effect and the trade picked up as soon as silver coins once again became available.

Hoards of Samanid dirhams first appear in an unlikely place: on the Middle Bug in eastern Poland, an area virtually devoid of earlier numismatic and archaeological finds. Typically for 'merchant's hoards', they are almost exclusively made up of very recent, unfragmented coins. The best-known hoard from Klukowicze (*tpq* 901/2) also contains a high number of illiterate 'ugly' Khazar imitations (146 or 15%). Their production continued until around 910 and shows not only that the Khazars remained the main intermediaries between Scandinavia and the Islamic world in the early tenth century, but also that access to the new Samanid silver was still irregular.[49]

The hoarding area on the Middle Bug is best interpreted as a landing point (or winter quarters) on the route from Khazaria to the Baltic. It may also have been an area where slaves were captured, a hypothesis supported by the construction of large fortifications tentatively dated to the early tenth century.[50] Another early Samanid hoard from Kiev (*tpq* 905/6)[51] suggests the city's early tenth-century rise to prominence was related to its ability to control the stream of Isma'il's dirhams; indeed, the earliest traces of activity in Kiev date from the 880s, just after the collapse of the ninth-century system of trade. In contrast, and judging from the scarce numismatic record, northern Rus remained isolated until the 930s, despite the revival of Scandinavian settlements such as Staraia Ladoga and Riurikovo Gorodishche at the end of the ninth century. However, the Baltic appears to have been the main recipient of Islamic silver and our Gotlandic hoards – where the earliest Samanid dirhams are mixed with older Abbasid coins – suggest that the islanders had continued access to oriental silver throughout the last quarter of the ninth century.

The 910s and 920s: from Khazaria to Volga Bulgaria

Enthusiasm for the newly available oriental silver perhaps accounts for the surge of Rus activity in the southern seas around 910. In September 911, Karl and 14 other envoys of 'Oleg, great prince of Rus' signed a trade treaty with Byzantium regulating, among other things, the slave trade.[52] Ibn Isfandiyar reports Rus raids against the southern shores of the Caspian in two consecutive years, possibly 909/10–910/11 (AH 297–8), and their destruction by the king of the Khazars.[53] Mas'udi's description of the massacre of a Rus fleet of '500 ships, each carrying 100 people' on its return from a plundering expedition in the Caspian by Muslim mercenaries of the Khazars probably refers to the same event.[54] Although Mas'udi places it after 912/13 (AH 300), Ibn Isfandiyar's chronology seems more reliable and the Rus' defeat probably occurred around 910, suggesting that the Russo-Byzantine trade treaty of 911 represents an attempt to compensate for the breakdown in their relations with the Khazars.

If we take our Arabic sources at face value, the Rus defeat at Itil would have had a significant impact on the Scandinavians' trade with the Islamic world. It is possible to detect traces in the numismatic material. Production of the illiterate 'ugly' imitations attributable to the Khazars ceased around 910 and they were quickly replaced by a new group of imitation dirhams minted in Bulgar on the Volga.[55] The early tenth-century hoard map (Map 6.5) also shows that the stream of Islamic silver now flowed from Bulgar up the Volga and the Oka, crossing Rus towards the Baltic. Hoards with *tpqs* in the 910s and 920s are particularly abundant all around the Baltic: on the islands of Gotland, Öland and Bornholm and in southern Sweden, Pomerania, Denmark and even Norway. The shift of the routes northwards appears to have marginalised Kiev, which perhaps accounts for its absence from the written sources in the next two decades.

When the main market moved from Khazaria to Bulgar, a caravan route across the steppe from Khwarazm to Bulgar soon followed. In his famous account of 921–2, Ibn Fadlan describes such a convoy: numbering over 5,000,[56] the Khwarazmian merchants made their way northwards towards Bulgar to buy female slaves and furs from the Rus. There are hints that the geography of trade had changed recently, but also that there were already regular exchanges along this new route. Even if trade with Bulgar was underway before the Rus were massacred in Khazaria, and even if trade with the Khazars may have continued beyond *c.* 910, Bulgar's emergence as the main slave market of western Eurasia was a momentous event that structured the tenth-century slave trade.

The 930s and 940s: bonanza!

The map of hoards with *tpq*s in the 930s and 940s (Map 6.5) is marked above all by the extension of the hoarding area into modern-day Poland and Ukraine, with new clusters in western Ukraine, Wielkopolska and around the emporium of Wolin. Hoards also appear in the region around Kursk, a convenient portage connecting the Oka and Seim rivers and, through them, the basins of the Volga and the Dnieper. The earliest hoards from here date to *c.* 920, but become more frequent only after *c.* 940. They are characterised by a high number of clipped coins that follow a consistent

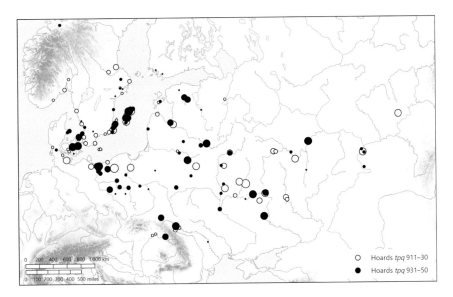

Map 6.5 Northern and eastern European dirham hoards with *tpq*s between 911 and 950.

weight standard decreasing from around 1.35g in *c.* 940 to less than 0.5g in *c.* 990.[57] Their absence from hoards found on the Oka implies that dirhams were systematically clipped in the Kursk region, which in turn suggests the existence of a political structure capable of controlling the flow of silver.

The high proportion of clipped coins connects the Kursk cluster with the lesser-known dirham hoards from western Ukraine.[58] The only published find from this group, the Máramaros hoard (*tpq* 935/6), contains 34% imitations, mostly attributable to Volga Bulgaria. Remarkably, they are die-linked with coins from the important Bezliudovka hoard found near Kharkiv (*tpq* also 935/6),[59] which is composed almost exclusively of clipped imitations (89%) and which provides a geographical link between the clusters in the Kursk region and in western Ukraine.

Given that the names of the East Slav 'tribes' appear for the first time in sources written in the 940s and 950s, it is tempting to map these hoard clusters onto the emerging political geography of eastern Europe. Whereas the cluster from the Kursk region is usually attributed to the Severians,[60] labelling the peoples of western Ukraine is more controversial. There is, however, reason to identify this hoard cluster with the Lendzians, whose trade links reached as far as 'al-Andalus, Rome, Constantinople, and Khazaria'.[61] The archaeological remains of enormous yet ephemeral fortifications in western Ukraine[62] are most plausibly explained as enclosures for resettled populations, some of whom were no doubt sold on for dirhams. These, too, suggest that an impressive but short-lived political structure may have flourished there in the 930s and 940s, but had disappeared by *c.* 955.

Despite the shift of the main commercial route to Bulgar on the Volga, the Khazars continued to play a significant role in the Pontic steppe. However, hostile remarks about the Rus in our Khazar sources make it unlikely that they were still willing to act as their middlemen.[63] Indeed, none of our hoards or imitations can be associated with the Khazars in this period. The so-called *Schechter Letter* sheds some light on the complicated politics of the steppe in the 930s. This tells the story of an attack by Helgu, the Rus prince of Kiev, on the Khazar city of 'S-m-k-r-ts' (Tmutarakan), his defeat and forced alliance with the Khazars, which led to the Rus raid against Constantinople in 941. We know from other sources that the Byzantines defeated the Rus fleet. Helgu was killed in a bid to establish a base in Barda in the eastern Caucasus, and in 944 his successor Igor signed another trade treaty with the Byzantines which normalised their relations for the decades to come.[64]

Limited access to Samanid silver may have driven the Kievan Rus to turn their attention so forcefully on Byzantium. Even if the dearth of hoards around Kiev does not, in itself, indicate a low dirham inflow, our clipped coin hoards support this theory. Although yet to be studied in detail, their geography in this period suggests that the clipped dirham route connecting the Kursk region with western Ukraine, via Bezliudovka, bypassed Kiev; and that the rarely clipped dirhams flowing to Sweden and Wielkopolska took a more northerly route, perhaps along the upper reaches of the Oka, Dnieper and Western Dvina. The emergence of such settlements as Gnezdovo and Novgorod in the

930s confirms that northern Rus was increasingly involved in long-distance trade. And around 940, dirham hoards appear in Estonia and on the Finnish coast, suggesting that by then the Gulf of Finland had been opened to traffic.

Another area that appears on the map of dirham hoards in the 930s is Wielkopolska. The earliest finds are quite small, but within a decade they had grown in size and began to concentrate around the core area of the future Polish state. Their topography and the high incidence of Samanid coins suggest that they came from the east, but the Piast elites had soon also gained access to dirhams circulating in the Baltic area.[65] Around this time we also see the construction of large fortresses, most notably at Gniezno, several of which have been dendrochronologically dated to winter 940–1. Taken together with the evidence we have for depopulation in neighbouring areas, this suggests that, by supplying captives, the Piasts were able to gain access to the dirham circuits of northern and eastern Europe. Their position as the last link in the chain of suppliers and intermediaries conveying slaves to the market at Bulgar is confirmed by the extreme fragmentation of the dirhams in the hoards from Wielkopolska.[66]

Finally, in the Baltic itself, the hoard topography suggests widespread access to dirhams, with major concentrations found on Gotland and Öland as well as in Denmark and around the Scandinavian emporium of Wolin at the mouth of the Oder. The overall impression is one of intensive trading, ready availability of dirhams and large-scale slave-taking to the south of the Baltic. This is consistent with the widespread violence and population transfers shown in the archaeology of the Slavic lands.[67] Scandinavian and Slav enthusiasm for trading slaves for silver put the dirham supply under huge strain: in order to fill the gap that a decrease in Samanid coin exports caused (Figure 6.2), the Volga Bulgars had to use their own silver reserves to produce imitations, notably in the decade between 935 and 945 when, it seems, particularly large numbers were minted.[68]

The 950s: farewell Scandinavia

Exchanges between Scandinavia and the Islamic world ground to a halt around 954/5 (AH 343). Very few coins struck after that date are found in our Swedish hoards (Figure 6.2), and even if the drop was less pronounced in Rus and Poland, it is clear that the export of Samanid dirhams from Central Asia decreased in the 950s.[69] Signs that supplies were dwindling could be seen even in the roaring '30s and '40s. Apart from the introduction of Volga Bulgar imitations, Samanid dirhams were supplemented with other Middle Eastern coins, especially those of the Abbasid, Buyid and Hamdanid rulers (although the latter could have been acquired as plunder by Scandinavians serving as Byzantine mercenaries). Their quantities are, however, too small to imply any other trade connection than the caravan route between Central Asia and Bulgar described by Ibn Fadlan.

We do not know whether the drop in the quantities of dirhams exported northwards in the early 950s corresponded to a decrease in Samanid monetary production. Ibn Hawqal's glowing description of the Samanid state, penned in the late 960s, suggests otherwise.[70] But signs of a deepening monetary crisis can be detected from the metal content of their dirhams: silver began to slide below 90% in the late 930s, dropping to 70–80% in the 960s. It improved slightly in the 970s, only to collapse in the 980s.[71] The Scandinavians were preoccupied by silver quality, as can be seen by the abundance of testing marks on dirhams found in the north, and this debasement is likely to have affected trade. Mounting external and internal pressures on the Samanid state doubtless lay behind it, but a more immediate reason is suggested by the sudden disappearance of bismuth in dirhams minted between 946/7 and 951/2 (AH 335 and 340) from silver mined in the Panjshir valley. This suggests that one of the two richest sources of Samanid silver was then shut,[72] adding to the financial strain and compelling the Samanid authorities to restrict the export of silver.

The repercussions in the north were immediate. The 950s saw a spike in the number of hoards being sealed after several decades of accumulation (at least 133: Figure 6.1) and this occurs throughout northern and eastern Europe, showing that all parts of the system were affected. The Baltic was worst hit, being situated furthest from the sources of Islamic silver. Rough estimates suggest that the share of Samanid dirhams reaching Sweden dropped from an average of 60% in 893/4–954/5 (AH 280–343) to 15% in 955/6–78/9 (AH 344–68).[73] It is tempting to link this with the *Russian Primary Chronicle*'s claim that, around the middle of the decade, Kiev established control over the main riverways of northern Rus,[74] which would probably have resulted in the re-routing of the northern flow of silver towards Kiev.

The slave trade still flourished. Around 950, Constantine Porphyrogenitus mentions the winter *poliudia* of the Kievan Rus, probably tribute rounds that involved the taking of captives.[75] The significant number of hoards with *tpq*s in the 950s from Wielkopolska, Silesia and the region around Wolin suggests that many captives at the slave market in Bulgar came from further west.[76] And the Lendzians' disappearance from our written sources around 955 points to the fierce competition between warrior groupings for captives and Islamic silver. The contours of the winners were emerging ever more clearly, and the advent of Christianity in the coming decades would transform them into permanent boundaries.

The 960s and 970s: looking for non–Islamic silver

The densely populated map for this period (Map 6.6) is misleading, since the inflow of dirhams to northern Europe diminished in the 960s and 970s. Hoard density in Scandinavia is particularly deceptive: very few of these hoards contain more than a handful of coins struck after 954/5 (AH 343), and such dirhams as the Gotlanders and Swedes were still able to obtain were all struck before 978/9 (AH 368) when inflow stopped entirely.

The situation was different in Rus, where dirhams of the Samanid emirs 'Abd al-Malik I (954–61) and Mansur I (961–76), and of their contemporaries from other dynasties, were still relatively common, and inflow continued until around 980/1 (AH 370). Dirhams flowed further west to Wielkopolska, where they are found in hack-silver hoards together with cut silver ornaments characteristic of Rus. This suggests that Islamic silver was imported to the Piast state *via* Kievan Rus and, therefore, that the captives exchanged for dirhams in Bulgar continued to come from the western Slavic lands. This impression tallies with the image of a powerful military organisation that emerges from the first texts to mention the Piasts in the 960s.[77] The combined evidence from our written sources, archaeology and numismatics suggests that they were engaged in cut-throat competition for captives and silver with neighbours such as Wolin or Mazovia – where the disappearance around 975 of a short-lived cluster of hoards and a discontinuity in settlement patterns probably mark the Piasts' elimination of a rival for Islamic silver.

Much of the activity in northern and eastern Europe in the 960s and 970s can be explained by the growing tension between the shortage of Islamic silver and a need to pay increasing numbers of warriors recruited by the forming polities. The Rus first vented their frustration against the Khazars and the Volga Bulgars, whose capitals at Itil and Bulgar they sacked in the late 960s,[78] but increasingly their attention turned to Byzantium. After ultimately unsuccessful campaigning against the Bulgarians and then the Byzantines between 968 and 972, they were taken on as mercenaries and provided vital support to Emperor Basil II (976–1025) against both internal and external foes. Judging by the dearth of Byzantine coins in the north, Rus mercenaries were not often paid in silver, but may have brought other luxury goods back home with them.[79]

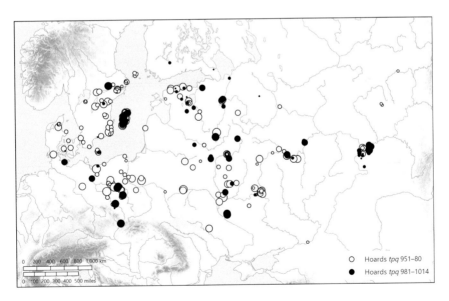

O Hoards *tpq* 951–80
● Hoards *tpq* 981–1014

Map 6.6 Northern and eastern European dirham hoards with *tpq*s after 950.

Meanwhile, the Scandinavians and western Slavs turned west. It may be no coincidence that silver ore was discovered in Saxony a decade and a half after the closure of the Panjshir mines. Even though the earliest coins minted from this silver are hard to identify, increasing numbers of German and Anglo-Saxon coins begin to appear on Gotland and in Sweden and Wielkopolska from the 950s on.[80] The decreasing supply of dirhams may also have helped push the Piast duke Mieszko towards an alliance with the ruler of Prague, sealed by Mieszko's adoption of Christianity in 966. Even though the market at Prague did not initially rely on silver, it does appear to have supplied Umayyad Spain with Slavic slaves throughout the tenth century, and to have offered access to the luxury goods necessary to maintain the loyalty of armed warriors.

From the 980s to the 1010s: the end

Very few Islamic coins made their way to Rus, Poland and the Baltic after *c.* 980: we have only a handful of dirham hoards from this period,[81] with virtually no Samanid coins minted after 985/6 (AH 375).[82] A gap of a decade and a half separates these late Samanid coins from the equally scarce issues of their successors in Central Asia, the Qarakhanids, which date to 998/9–1013/14 (AH 389–404). This points to a break in Rus contacts with Central Asia between around 985 and 1000, and to a small-scale, short-lived revival early in the eleventh century.

However, a remarkable cluster of late tenth-century hoards from Volga Bulgaria is puzzling.[83] We currently know of over a dozen hoards with *tpq*s in the 980s and 990s, mostly with short chronologies and mostly composed of very late Samanid dirhams and the otherwise very rare coins of the Khwarazmshahs. This cluster suggests that the caravan route across the steppe from Khwarazm to Bulgar survived the political instability in Central Asia, and that the region's rulers strove to keep it alive. It is intriguing that this period of hoarding in Volga Bulgaria coincided with our conjectured gap in the inflow of Islamic coins to Rus. Why did these coins not get through to Rus? The answer may partly lie in the low quality of late tenth-century Central Asian coins, but the reasons why the Bulgars and the Rus were not then engaged in trading with each other have yet to be fully explained.

Another very late group of Islamic coins to flow into northern Europe was struck between 994/5 and 1013/14 (AH 384 and 404) by two Middle Eastern dynasties, the Marwanids (who ruled over south-eastern Anatolia) and the Uqaylids (established in Mosul and the Jazira). These coins are more likely to have been brought back by Rus mercenaries fighting for the Byzantines on the empire's eastern border than to have arrived through trade.

These late coins were mostly hoarded in Rus and Estonia, with only single specimens reaching Scandinavia. However, the very latest hoard to be made up entirely of dirhams comes from a small island off the southern tip of Gotland, Heligholmen (*tpq* 1012/13). Its unique composition – all the coins come from al-Andalus – suggests an attempt to establish a direct link between

Spain and the Baltic, perhaps motivated by the attempts of the *Saqaliba* party at the Umayyad court to boost its numbers.[84] It is a remarkable coincidence that all the three sources of Islamic silver – Central Asia, the Middle East and Muslim Spain – dried up simultaneously around 1013.

Conclusion

Our interpretation of the hoard maps is certainly not the only possible one. But even this preliminary narrative of dirham inflows to Scandinavia and the Slavic lands in the ninth and tenth centuries highlights two main characteristics of the region's trade with the Islamic world: its remarkable survival, for more than two centuries from *c.* 800 to 1015; and its complexity and extreme volatility, as reflected in the ever-changing kaleidoscope of hoards. Its survival can, to a large extent, be attributed to the Scandinavians' appetite for silver and their capacity to extort it by every means possible, including the slave trade. Its complexity and volatility is a not unexpected outcome of the slave trade, which drove warrior groupings to organise, compete for captives and secure access to prestige goods. This competition for slaves and silver encouraged the emergence of political structures in northern and eastern Europe, a process on which our hoard maps can, if interpreted with due caution, shed much light.

Notes

1 Research for this chapter was carried out thanks to a British Academy Newton Fellowship and DfS.
2 Vasmer (1933); Markov (1910). For Markov, imperial European Russia encompassed Poland, Finland and the Baltic states, as well as what are now Belarus and Ukraine.
3 Defined here as European Russia, Belarus, Ukraine, Lithuania, Latvia, Estonia, Finland, Sweden, Norway, Denmark, Poland, the Czech Republic, Slovakia, Hungary, Moldova and Romania. The number of dirhams found in western Europe is negligible.
4 However, for narratives concentrating on one area or hoarding period, see Noonan (1992); Kilger (2008); Adamczyk (2014).
5 Kovalev and Kaelin (2007), table 2 on p. 564 (including the Netherlands, which is excluded here). The authors define dirham hoards as 'deposits of five or more coins with dirhams' (p. 562).
6 We only have an approximate provenance for some hoards, and only assemblages of at least five dirhams are included. This excludes 'productive sites' such as Truso, Roma and Kaupang, which in some cases have yielded hundreds of stray dirhams. The list of hoards discussed here will be published in Jankowiak (in preparation).
7 That is, hoards for which a *tpq* can be determined on the basis of five or more coins. The 124 undatable hoards appear on Map 6.1, but not on the maps that follow.
8 These sources are conveniently collected in Lunde and Stone, *Ibn Fadlan*.
9 On the importance of the slave trade for the early medieval European economy, see McCormick (2001); McCormick (2002); Rio (2017); the chapter by Wyatt in this volume; Jankowiak (in preparation).
10 The standard accounts are Franklin and Shepard (1996) [Rus]; Berend *et al.* (2013) [central Europe]; Helle (ed.) (2003) [Scandinavia].
11 See Part III of this volume.

12 *Tpq*s are given for Arabic coins only. Further study is needed of hoards with out-lying coin(s) whose dates are significantly later than the rest of the hoard. Here they are mostly considered under the date of the outlying coin.

13 For attempts to classify Gotlandic hoards, see e.g. Odebäck (2009); Gruszczyński (2016), pp. 28–32, 249–53.

14 See Svedjemo in this volume.

15 Seven hundred and eight hoards are included; I omit the insecurely dated hoard from Kaliningrad (*tpq* 745/6); see below, n. 18.

16 With thanks to Gert Rispling from the Coin Cabinet in Stockholm for making his database of dirhams from Swedish collections available to me.

17 See, for instance, the Amuda I (*tpq* 874/5) and Jazira (*tpq* 885/6) hoards: Ilisch (1990); Susa (*tpq* 878/9): Miles (1960); and Iran (*tpq* 889/90), summarised in *Coin Hoards* 6 (1981), pp. 75–6, no. 272.

18 The *tpq*s of Kaliningrad (*tpq* 745/6), Paristovka (*tpq* 787/8), Unġeni (*tpq* 792/3) and Penzlin (*tpq* 798/9, excluded from the sample because fewer than five coins have been identified) are not sufficiently secure. On the beginnings of the inflow of dirhams to Rus, see Kropotkin (1978); Noonan (1980); Noonan (1981).

19 Callmer (2000); Price *et al.* (2016).

20 Ghewond, *History* XLIII(37), pp. 188–9. Noonan (1980) demonstrates that the earliest dirhams came to Rus via the Caucasus.

21 See Howard-Johnston in this volume.

22 Mishin (2002), pp. 288–90.

23 Bogucki (2007).

24 Noonan (1980), pp. 421, 423, 442–3.

25 See discussion in Kilger (2008), pp. 218–20.

26 Vasmer (1933), p. 477.

27 The large hoard from Josypivka near Lviv (*c.* 5,000 coins, *tpq* 813/14) may indicate such a route, although this find is isolated and imperfectly known. As I write, how-ever, news is spreading of a find near Lviv with a provisional *tpq* 833/4.

28 Rispling *et al.* (in preparation); Treadwell (2011), pp. 101–16.

29 Symeon the Logothete, *Chronicon*, ed. Wahlgren, pp. 235–7. For the date, see Treadgold (1988), p. 439 n. 397.

30 *Annales Bertiniani* s.a. 839, ed. Grat, p. 31; tr. Nelson, p. 44. See also Shepard (1995).

31 Theophanes Continuatus, *Chronographia* III.28, ed. Featherstone and Signes Codoñer, pp. 176–7; *DAI* ch. 42, pp. 182–5; Zuckerman (1997), pp. 52–9.

32 Kovalev (2005).

33 Shepard (2017).

34 Zuckerman (2000), pp. 104–6.

35 Ibn Isfandiyar, *History of Tabaristan*, tr. Browne, p. 199.

36 See Zuckerman (1995), pp. 241–50.

37 See e.g. Nelson (1992), pp. 181–8.

38 Ibn Khurradadhbih (tr. in Lunde and Stone, *Ibn Fadlan*, p. 112) only notes the Rus selling pelts and swords, but slightly later he mentions eunuchs who speak the lan-guage of the *Saqaliba*. They were, presumably, recruited from *Saqaliba* slaves.

39 The prominent issues are Panjhir 260, Samarqand 260, Arminiyya 267 and 277, and Bardha'a 277.

40 See above, n. 17.

41 For instance, the Spillings hoard (*tpq* 870/1) contains over a hundred Arminiyya 252 dirhams, many of them die-identical (data from Gert Rispling's database; see above, n. 16).

42 See Rispling *et al.* (in preparation).

43 Zuckerman (2000), pp. 106–14.

44 *PVL*, p. 13; *RPC*, p. 59. The *Chronicle* places these events in 859–62, but its early chronology is not at all accurate.
45 Poltava (*tpq* 882/3), Lublin-Czechów (*tpq* 883/4), Bryli (*tpq* 890/1) and Drohic-zyn (*tpq* 893/4?). The find from Trzcianka (*tpq* 879/80) is too small (eight coins) to allow for any conclusions. On this period, see Noonan (1985).
46 Judging from the total absence of hoards with *tpq*s between 878/9 and 899/900 (AH 265 and 286).
47 This is the only northern hoard known to me that contains several large groups of die-identical coins. Among its 882 coins are 42 imitations S46, 49 imitations S87, 15 imitations S383 and 54 'Samarqand 253' coins (possibly not all die-identical): Gran-berg (1966), pp. 50–112; Rispling *et al.* (in preparation).
48 Rispling *et al.* (in preparation).
49 Rispling *et al.* (in preparation).
50 Wróblewski (2001).
51 Noonan (1987), pp. 411–13, hoard A.4. Another hoard from Kiev (A.16), mostly composed of Abbasid dirhams, has the same *tpq*.
52 *PVL*, pp. 18–20; *RPC*, pp. 65–8. The earlier deed of 907 seems to be a fabrication: Zuckerman (2007), p. 346.
53 Ibn Isfandiyar, *History of Tabaristan*, tr. Browne, p. 199.
54 Mas'udi, *Muruj al-dhahab* §§ 458–62, ed. Pellat, vol. 1, pp. 218–21; rev. tr. Pellat, vol. 1, pp. 165–7.
55 Rispling *et al.* (in preparation). The earliest imitation of the main Volga Bulgar die-chain K101 comes from the Viken hoard (*tpq* 907/8).
56 IbnF[1], pp. 206–7; IbnF[2], p. 17.
57 Koloda *et al.* (2014), fig. 14, p. 47. Clipping coins, or shaving metal from their circumference, was a form of coin debasement.
58 Fomin and Kovács (1987), fig. 2, p. 78.
59 Petrov (ed.) (2014).
60 Mentioned by Constantine Porphyrogenitus (*DAI* ch. 9, pp. 62–3) and perhaps in the 'Letter of King Joseph' (long version) (in *Evreisko-khazarskaia perepiska*, ed. Kokovtsov, p. 98 and n. 4, where note is taken of the case for identifying the S-v-r with the Severians).
61 Mas'udi, *Muruj al-dhahab* § 458, ed. Pellat, vol. 1, p. 218; rev. tr. Pellat, vol. 1, p. 165. He speaks of the 'Rus tribe' of al-Ludh'ana whom I will propose to iden-tify with the Lendzians in a future article. They are also mentioned by Constan-tine (*DAI* chs 9, 37, pp. 56–7, 168–9) and probably in the *Schechter Letter* (*Khazarian Hebrew Documents*, pp. 120–1).
62 Fylypchuk (2012).
63 See e.g. the 'Letter of King Joseph' (long version) in *Evreisko-khazarskaia perepiska*, ed. Kokovtsov, p. 102: 'I guard the mouth of the [Itil] river and do not permit the Rus who come in ships to enter into the sea so as to get at the Ismaelites. [...] I wage war with them, for if I would leave them [in peace] for an hour they would lay waste the whole land of the Ismaelites as far as Baghdad' (a possible allusion to the raid of *c.* 910).
64 *Khazarian Hebrew Documents*, pp. 106–21; *PVL*, pp. 23–6; *RPC*, pp. 73–7; Zuck-erman (1995), pp. 256–9.
65 Bogucki and Miłek (2010), pp. 53–4. See also Adamczyk in this volume.
66 On patterns of dirham fragmentation, see Jankowiak (2019).
67 *IC*.

68 Jankowiak (2021 forthcoming).
69 See the figures in Kovalev (2001); Kovalev (2002); Kovalev (2002–3); and Noonan and Kovalev (2002). Gert Rispling's database contains 618 dirhams found in Sweden that can be dated to between AH 344 and 403, compared to 702 for the three years between AH 341 and 343.
70 Ibn Hawqal, *Surat*, ed. Kramers, vol. 2, pp. 464–72; tr. Wiet and Kramers, vol. 2, pp. 446–54.
71 Based on Ilisch *et al.* (2003).
72 The other being the Ilaq mines in the region of al-Shash. On bismuth, see Jankowiak (forthcoming).
73 Data for the mints of Balkh, Bukhara, Samarqand and al-Shash; see above, n. 69.
74 *PVL*, p. 29; *RPC*, p. 81: 'Olga went to Novgorod, and along the Msta she established trading-posts (*pogosty*) and tributes, and along the Luga annual payments (*obroki*) and tributes' (author's translation). The *Chronicle* places this in 946/7 (AM 6455), an approximate date: see Zuckerman (2007) on its early chronology.
75 *DAI* ch. 9, lines 105–9, pp. 62–3. He also mentions (ch. 9, line 52, pp. 60–1) the transport of slaves (*psycharia*) by the Rus to Constantinople.
76 See also Adamczyk in this volume.
77 Ibrahim ibn Ya'qub, tr. in Lunde and Stone, *Ibn Fadlan*, pp. 165–6; Widukind of Corvey, *Res gestae Saxonicae*, III.66 and 69, tr. Bachrach and Bachrach, pp. 140 and 143–5.
78 In 968/9 (AH 358), according to Ibn Hawqal, *Surat*, ed. Kramers, vol. 2, p. 392; tr. Wiet and Kramers, vol. 2, p. 382.
79 Jankowiak (2016).
80 Jonsson (1990).
81 Once again, Map 6.6 is misleading: it shows mostly accumulation hoards with few late coins and only includes hoards where dirhams account for more than 50% of coins.
82 The hoard from Denysy (*tpq* 1008/9) is a rare exception: Noonan (1987), no. A.28 on pp. 416–19. Remarkably late hoards are also known from Estonia.
83 Kovalev (2015).
84 Jonsson and Östergren (1983).

Bibliography

Primary sources

Annales Bertiniani, ed. F. Grat *et al.*, *Annales de Saint-Bertin*, Paris (1964); tr. J. Nelson, *The Annals of St-Bertin*, Manchester (1991).

Evreisko-khazarskaia perepiska v X veke, ed. and tr. P. Kokovtsov, Leningrad (1932).

Ghewond, *History*, ed. A. Hakobian, French tr. B. Martin-Hisard, in *Łewond Vardapet: Discours historique*, Paris (2015), pp. 1–342.

Ibn Hawqal, *Surat*, ed. J. H. Kramers, *Kitab surat al-'ard: opus geographicum auctore Ibn Haukal*, 2 vols, BGA 1, 2nd edn, Leiden (1938–9); French tr. J. H. Kramers and G. Wiet, *Configuration de la terre*, 2 vols, Paris (1964).

Ibn Isfandiyar, *History of Tabaristan*, tr. E. G. Browne, *An Abridged Translation of the History of Tabaristan by Ibn Isfandiyar*, Leiden (1905).

Khazarian Hebrew Documents of the Tenth Century, ed. and tr. N. Golb and O. Pritsak, Ithaca, NY (1982).

Lunde, P. and C. Stone (tr.), *Ibn Fadlan and the Land of Darkness: Arab Travellers in the Far North*, London (2012).

Mas'udi, *Muruj al-dhahab*, ed. C. Pellat, *Muruj al-dhahab wa-ma'adin al-jawhar*, 7 vols, Beirut (1966–79); French tr. C. Barbier de Maynard and A. Pavel de Courteille, rev. C. Pellat, *Les prairies d'or*, 5 vols, Paris (1962–97).

Symeon the Logothete, *Chronicon*, ed. S. Wahlgren, *Symeonis magistri et logothetae Chronicon*, Berlin (2006).

Theophanes Continuatus, *Chronographia*, ed. and tr. M. Featherstone and J. Signes Codoñer, *Chronographiae quae Theophanis Continuati nomine fertur libri I–IV*, CHFB 53, Berlin (2015).

Widukind of Corvey, *Res gestae Saxonicae*, tr. B. S. Bachrach and D. S. Bachrach, *Deeds of the Saxons*, Washington, DC (2014).

Secondary literature

Adamczyk, D. (2014), *Silber und Macht. Fernhandel, Tribute und die piastische Herrschaftsbildung in nordosteuropäischer Perspektive (800–1100)*, Wiesbaden.

Berend, N. *et al.* (2013), *Central Europe in the High Middle Ages: Bohemia, Hungary and Poland c. 900–c. 1300*, Cambridge.

Bogucki, M. (2007), 'Coin finds in the Viking-Age emporium at Janów Pomorski (*Truso*) and the "Prussian phenomenon"', in S. Suchodolski and M. Bogucki (eds), *Money Circulation in Antiquity, the Middle Ages and Modern Times: Time, Range, Intensity*, Warsaw, pp. 79–108.

Bogucki, M. and S. Miłek (2010), 'Monety, ich pochodzenie oraz obieg w Kaliszu i jego najbliższych okolicach w X i pierwszej połowie XI wieku', in S. Suchodolski and M. Zawadzki (eds), *Od Kalisii do Kalisza. Skarby doliny Prosny*, Warsaw, pp. 49–59.

Callmer, J. (2000), 'From west to east: the penetration of Scandinavians into eastern Europe ca. 500–900', in M. Kazanski *et al.* (eds), *Les centres proto-urbains russes entre Scandinavie, Byzance et Orient*, Paris, pp. 45–94.

Fomin, A. V. and L. Kovács (1987), *The Tenth Century Máramaros County ('Huszt') Dirham Hoard*, Budapest.

Franklin, S. and J. Shepard (1996), *The Emergence of Rus, 750–1200*, London.

Fylypchuk, M. (2012), *Slov'ians'ki poselennia VIII–X st. v ukraïns'komu Prykarpatti*, Lviv.

Granberg, B. (1966), *Förteckning över kufiska myntfynd i Finland*, Helsinki.

Gruszczyński, J. (2016), 'Comparative study of archaeological contexts of silver hoards c. 800–1050 in northern and central Europe', unpublished DPhil dissertation, Oxford.

Helle, K. (ed.) (2003), *The Cambridge History of Scandinavia*, vol. 1: *Prehistory to 1520*, Cambridge.

Ilisch, L. (1990), 'Whole and fragmented dirhams in Near Eastern hoards', in *SP*, pp. 121–8.

Ilisch, L. *et al.* (2003), *Dirham und Rappenpfennig: Mittelalterliche Münzprägung in Bergbauregionen*, Bonn.

Jankowiak, M. (2016), 'Byzantine coins in Viking-Age northern lands', in *BVW*, pp. 117–39.

Jankowiak, M. (2019), 'Silver fragmentation: reinterpreting the evidence of the hoards', in J. Kershaw *et al.* (eds), *Silver, Butter, Cloth: Monetary and Social Economies in the Viking Age*, Oxford, pp. 15–31.

Jankowiak, M. (2021 forthcoming), 'The Volga Bulgar imitative coinage', in J. Shepard and L. Treadwell (eds), *Muslims on the Volga in the Viking Age: Diplomacy and Islam in the World of Ibn Fadlan*, London.

Jankowiak, M. (forthcoming), 'Metallography and history: interpreting the trace elements in Islamic coins', in *Medieval Money in Eastern Eurasia, Proceedings of the Western Eurasian Currency History Study Group Meeting, 3–4 November 2017, Shimonoseki City University*.

Jankowiak, M. (in preparation), *Dirhams for Slaves: Slave Trade between the Islamic World and Northern Europe in the Ninth and Tenth Centuries*.

Jonsson, K. (1990), 'The import of German coins to Denmark and Sweden *c.* 920–990', in *SP*, pp. 139–43.

Jonsson, K. and M. Östergren (1983), 'Spansk-arabiska köpmän på Gotland i början på 1000-talet?', *GA* 55: 122–5.

Kilger, C. (2008), 'Kaupang from afar: aspects of the interpretation of dirham finds in northern and eastern Europe between the late 8th and early 10th centuries', in *ME*, pp. 199–252.

Koloda, V. V. *et al.* (2014), 'Bezliudovskii klad i ego mesto v denezhnoi sisteme Severskoi zemli', in P. N. Petrov (ed.), *Bezliudovskii klad X v.: materialy i issledovaniia*, Kazan, pp. 6–76.

Kovalev, R. K. (2001), 'Mint output in tenth-century Bukhara: a case study of dirham production and monetary circulation in northern Europe', *Russian History* 28: 245–72.

Kovalev, R. K. (2002), 'Dirham mint output of Samanid Samarqand and its connection to the beginnings of trade with northern Europe (10th century)', *Histoire & Mesure* 17: 197–216.

Kovalev, R. K. (2002–3), 'The mint of al-Shash: the vehicle for the origins and continuation of trade relations between Viking-Age northern Europe and Samanid Central Asia', *Archivum Eurasiae Medii Aevi* 12: 47–79.

Kovalev, R. K. (2005), 'Creating Khazar identity through coins: the special issue dirhams of 837/8', in F. Curta (ed.), *East Central and Eastern Europe in the Early Middle Ages*, Ann Arbor, MI, pp. 220–53.

Kovalev, R. K. (2015), 'O roli Rusov i Volzhskikh Bulgar v importe severoiranskikh dirkhemov v Evropu vo vtoroi polovine X – nachale XI v.', *DG* 2015, pp. 95–143.

Kovalev, R. K. and A. C. Kaelin (2007), 'Circulation of Arab silver in medieval Afro-Eurasia: preliminary observations', *History Compass* 5: 560–80.

Kropotkin, V. V. (1978), 'O topografii kladov kuficheskikh monet IX v. v vostochnoi Evrope', in T. V. Nikolaeva (ed.), *Drevniaia Rus' i Slaviane*, Moscow, pp. 111–17.

Markov, A. K. (1910), *Topografiia kladov vostochnykh monet, sasanidskikh i kuficheskikh*, St Petersburg.

McCormick, M. (2001), *Origins of the European Economy: Communications and Commerce, AD 300–900*, Cambridge.

McCormick, M. (2002), 'New light on the "Dark Ages": how the slave trade fuelled the Carolingian economy', *Past & Present* 177: 17–54.

Miles, G. C. (1960), 'A ninth-century hoard of dirhams found at Susa', *Mémoires de la Mission archéologique en Iran* 37: 67–145.

Mishin, D. E. (2002), *Sakaliba (slaviane) v islamskom mire v rannee srednevekov'e*, Moscow.

Nelson, J. (1992), *Charles the Bald*, London.

Noonan, T. S. (1980), 'When and how dirhams first reached Russia', *Cahiers du monde russe et soviétique* 21: 401–69.

Noonan, T. S. (1981), 'Ninth-century dirham hoards from European Russia: a preliminary analysis', in *VACNL*, vol. 1, pp. 47–117.

Noonan, T. S. (1985), 'The first major silver crisis in Russia and the Baltic, *c.* 875–*c.* 900', *Hikuin* 11: 41–50.

Noonan, T. S. (1987), 'The monetary history of Kiev in the pre-Mongol period', *Harvard Ukrainian Studies* 11: 384–443.

Noonan, T. S. (1992), 'Fluctuations in Islamic trade with eastern Europe during the Viking Age', *Harvard Ukrainian Studies* 16: 237–59.

Noonan, T. S. and R. K. Kovalev (2002), 'The dirham output and monetary circulation of a secondary Samanid mint: a case study of Balkh', in B. Paszkiewicz (ed.), *Moneta Mediævalis*, Warsaw, pp. 163–74.

Odebäck, K. (2009), 'Familje- och släktskatter under äldre vikingatid', *Myntstudier* 2009 (2): 9–25.

Petrov, P. N. (ed.) (2014), *Bezliudovskii klad X v.: materialy i issledovaniia*, Kazan.

Price, T. D. *et al.* (2016), 'Isotopic provenancing of the Salme ship burials in pre-Viking Age Estonia', *Antiquity* 90: 1022–37.

Rio, A. (2017), *Slavery after Rome, 500–1100*, Oxford.

Rispling, G., M. Jankowiak and L. Treadwell (in preparation), *Catalogue of Dirham Imitations from Northern European Viking-Age Finds*, CNS n.s., Stockholm.

Shepard, J. (1995), 'The Rhos guests of Louis the Pious: whence and wherefore?', *Early Medieval Europe* 4: 41–60.

Shepard, J. (2017), 'Photios' sermons on the Rus attack of 860: the questions of his origins, and of the route of the Rus', in A. Beihammer *et al.* (eds), *Prosopon Rhomaikon*, Berlin, pp. 111–28.

Treadgold, W. (1988), *The Byzantine Revival, 780–842*, Stanford, CA.

Treadwell, W. L. (2011), *Craftsmen and Coins: Signed Dies in the Iranian World (Third to the Fifth Centuries AH)*, Vienna.

Vasmer (Fasmer), R. R. (1933), 'Ob izdanii novoi topografii nakhodok kuficheskich monet v Vostochnoi Evrope', *Izvestiia Akademii Nauk SSSR. Otdelenie obshchestvennykh nauk* 1933(6–7): 473–84.

Wróblewski, W. (2001), 'U źródeł kasztelanii liwskiej. Wczesnośredniowieczne struktury osadnicze w dorzeczu Liwca', in B. Bryńczak and P. Urbańczyk (eds), *Najstarsze dzieje Podlasia w świetle źródeł archeologicznych*, Siedlce, pp. 205–28.

Zuckerman, C. (1995), 'On the date of the Khazars' conversion to Judaism and the chronology of the kings of the Rus, Oleg and Igor: a study of the anonymous Khazar Letter from the Genizah of Cairo', *Revue des études byzantines* 53: 237–70.

Zuckerman, C. (1997), 'Les Hongrois au pays de Lebedia: une nouvelle puissance aux confins de Byzance et de la Khazarie *ca* 836–889', in K. Tsiknakis (ed.), *To empolemo Vyzantio: 9.–12. ai.*, Athens, pp. 51–74.

Zuckerman, C. (2000), 'Deux étapes de la formation de l'ancien état russe', in M. Kazanski *et al.* (eds), *Les centres proto-urbains russes entre Scandinavie, Byzance et Orient*, Paris, pp. 95–120.

Zuckerman, C. (2007), 'Perestroika drevneishei russkoi istorii', in E. N. Nosov and A. E. Musin (eds), *U istokov russkoi gosudarstvennosti. Istoriko-arkheologicheskii sbornik*, St Petersburg, pp. 343–51.

7 Trading networks, warlords and hoarders

Islamic coin flows into Poland in the Viking Age

Dariusz Adamczyk

Nearly 40,000 Islamic coins in more than 160 hoards have been found on Polish lands to date,[1] mostly tenth-century dirhams struck by the Samanids of Central Asia. Numerous pieces of jewellery and ingots made of melted dirhams have also been discovered in Pomerania, Wielkopolska, Mazovia and Silesia, and we can safely assume that the actual number of Arabic coins was far higher and they may have circulated in their millions.

This raises several questions. Why did such large quantities of dirhams make their way to the southern Baltic and Polish interior? How did the different waves of silver inflow affect economic and political developments in Viking-Age Poland and how did these developments, in turn, change the channels by which dirhams were distributed (the redistribution networks)? And last but not least, who circulated the silver? Were these people with commercial interests – traders or those who put precious metal hoards to creative use (for example, jewellers) – or people whose interests were predatory or tributary (for example, slavers, chieftains and warlords)? Or were both interests in play?

In the ninth and for much of the tenth centuries, there was no 'Poland' to speak of: it was rather a mosaic of kinships, clans, tribes and chiefdoms scattered throughout the regions that now constitute Poland, often with connections to communities settled in areas beyond. Thus in order to examine the chronology and geography of the Polish hoards, a conceptual framework for reconstructing the dirham redistribution networks is needed. This involves three steps: firstly, locating the hoards and determining where and when their coins were struck; secondly, establishing the hoards' archaeological contexts; and thirdly, contextualising them using the written sources available. A full description of this analysis can be found elsewhere and the results are only summarised here.[2]

The various networks had their own logistics and structures. These ranged from caravans of merchants, reliant on the infrastructure of an existing polity or empire and levying tribute besides trading – as the transfer of dirhams within the sphere of influence of the Khazar khaganate shows – to local or regional exchange in central Europe and the Baltic, based on luxury goods and often involving the use of violence. These networks were not driven purely by supply and demand: they were founded on personal connections between merchants, ruling elites, clans, tribes and peripatetic craftsmen and could equally well involve bartering and gift-giving, as well as the payment of tributes and rents, and even extortion. Some lapsed within a couple of decades; others stretched over several generations, mutating to meet changing circumstances. Finally, silver and other precious metals could fulfil different roles within a network: a means of payment for market transactions, rents, tributes or taxes; remuneration for a retinue or a client potentate; or, more generally, as a way of establishing relationships within a society. They could also be used to produce jewellery, bars, ingots and coins, or to serve as prestige objects, for cult or magic.

Early Norse trading networks centred on Truso

The first dirhams began to flow into Warmia, Masuria and the eastern parts of Pomerania in the early ninth century; these were mostly struck by the Abbasids in Iraq and Iran, but had some older coins mixed in. Several small hoards dated to the 810s and 820s have been found in the vicinity of the emporium at Janów Pomorski, a few kilometres from Elbląg (Table 7.1). This trading port has been identified as Truso, well known from Wulfstan's late ninth-century account: it was then inhabited by a Scandinavian community of possible Danish origin. These Norsemen created a trading network which linked up the main centre for dirham redistribution in north-western Rus, Staraia Ladoga, with the Baltic and Slavic societies who populated the interior of Warmia, Masuria and eastern Pomerania. The hoard find spots are all roughly within a 100km radius of Truso.[3]

Table 7.1 Early Pomeranian hoards from Janów Pomorski and its hinterland[1]

Find spot	Hoard tpq	Number of dirhams or dirham fragments
Zalewo	811/12	40
Stegna	811/12	17
Krasnołąka	813/14	10
Janów Pomorski I	815/16	16
Braniewo	816/17	47
Mokajmy-Sójki	817/18	124
Ramsowo	828/9	336

Note
1 *PSW* 2, nos 103, 159; *PSW* 4, nos 3, 7, 13, 19; Czapkiewicz *et al.* (1988).

The Norsemen's role in redistributing these early dirhams along the southern shores of the Baltic can be seen from the finds of single coins or coin fragments at Truso. In addition to almost a thousand dirhams, thirteen deniers, sceattas or pennies from Hedeby, Ribe, Frisia, the Frankish and Anglo-Saxon realms have been found, all struck before 860.[4] And finds of some 1,110 weights and balances, possibly used to weigh silver fragments, emphasise the importance of trade at the emporium,[5] although a couple of coins were worn as necklaces or had been melted down and refashioned as jewellery.

The location of these early dirham hoards and the context of the archaeological finds from Janów Pomorski (Truso) lead us to believe that the emporium's main role was the exchange of dirhams and dirham fragments for raw materials from the Slavic and Baltic Prussian hinterland. These, in turn, could either be used by the inhabitants of Truso, or re-exported to the Arab world via the networks of Rus and other Norse groupings living in the lands of northern Rus. The raw materials included amber and beaver furs – possibly also slaves – and later on swords manufactured at Truso.[6] These are the sorts of goods that the Persian geographer Ibn Khurradadhbih (d. *c.* 912) notes in his description of the Rus' trading expeditions to the markets in Khazaria, the Caspian Sea and even Baghdad as early as the 840s (and probably based upon earlier sources).[7] Thus, demand for furs, slaves, swords or amber in the Abbasid caliphate and Staraia Ladoga was the main reason for dirhams flowing into the southern Baltic.

But why did the various ethnic groupings in the hinterland of Truso collect Arabic silver? Wulfstan gives us a hint, in his description of the funeral rites of an Old Prussian chieftain:

> Then the same day that they wish to carry him to the funeral pyre, they then divide up his property (*or* money), what there is left over after the drinking and the entertainment, into five or six parts, sometimes into more, according to the amount of property there is.[8]

Dirhams and dirham fragments may have held prestige and ritual functions and the description is reminiscent of the potlach. During this gift-giving ceremony, common to many indigenous peoples, members of the elite would redistribute or destroy their property in order to maintain or strengthen their own social status. By redistributing goods, social ties could be reinforced particularly within a kinship group. The collapse of demand for silver in Truso's hinterland around 830 could be interpreted as a saturation of 'the prestige market' after only a generation.

The Scandinavians of Truso used silver not only to pay for raw materials from the hinterland, but also as money in the transit trade between Staraia Ladoga and the various settlements to the west of Janów Pomorski. Clearly Scandinavian and Slavic merchants from the western Baltic visited Truso: Wulfstan himself is thought to have been a seafarer of Anglo-Saxon origin, who had sailed to Truso via Hedeby by *c.* 880/90; and pottery characteristic of Pomerania and Mecklenburg has been found in Janów Pomorski.[9] The concentration of early dirham hoards in the area, together with the number of single coin finds in and around Janów Pomorski, suggest that in the first phase of silver inflow this emporium was a key nodal point for the surrounding communities.[10] The numbers speak for themselves: finds of coins and weights in Janów Pomorski number around 1,100 each, in contrast, for example, with Menzlin where just sixty coins and roughly the same number of weights have been excavated to date.[11] Many of the dirhams found in Pomerania and Mecklenburg could have been purchased in Truso (Map 7.1).

The Norsemen of Truso may also have used routes along the rivers Vistula and Bug, which would have connected them directly with the East Slav tribes on the left bank of the Middle Dnieper – bypassing Staraia Ladoga altogether – and which would have involved paying tribute to the Khazars. This could explain the finds of Romny-Borshchevo pottery at Janów Pomorski,[12] as well as two early dirham hoards discovered on the Upper Pripet and Upper Bug,[13] although this evidence remains inconclusive. What is less open to debate, however, is the lack of dirham hoards in the southern Baltic from around 830, and of single coin finds from 860, implying a significant shift in the circulation of silver within the Baltic region. What could explain this shift?

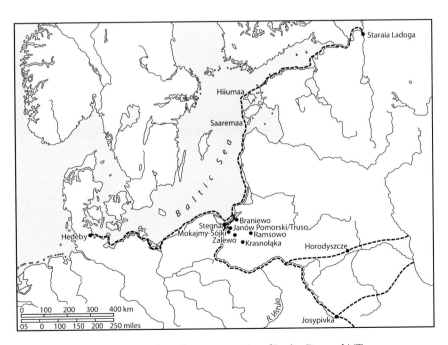

Map 7.1 Dirham networks of the Viking community of Janów Pomorski/Truso.

Pomerania in the late ninth century

A striking reorientation in western Eurasian dirham flows took place around 840: away from the Khazar khaganate and the southern Baltic, to northern Rus and Scandinavia. Some 50% of hoards dating from the second half of the ninth century have been found in Sweden, primarily Gotland, in contrast to the first four decades of the century, when the figure was a bare 20%. Inflows of silver to Truso and other trading places in Pomerania or Mecklenburg decreased significantly. The only find we have in Pomerania between 840 and 900 has a *tpq* of the later 860s and was buried in Karnice – some 50km south-west of the Slav settlement near Kołobrzeg (Kolberg) and 300km west of Janów Pomorski; and only a few hoards from this period have been excavated in Mecklenburg and on the island of Rügen.[14]

In order to explain this shift, we need to look at external as well as internal factors,[15] and Wulfstan may have light to shed on the latter:

> The above-mentioned *Estland* is very large, and there is very many a town (*or* stronghold), and in each town there is a king [...] There is very much (*or* great) conflict between them.[16]

He seems to be describing internecine warfare between local warlords. Unfortunately, we do not know the cause of these conflicts: they could have been triggered by dealings with the Norsemen of Truso and their demand for slaves; or by a range of internal pressures, whether political, economic, demographic, environmental or social. This seems to have been the case in Middle Pomerania, where a transformation from larger settlements to smaller hillforts dominated by local warlords had taken place by the later ninth century.[17] It is, however, no coincidence that finds of late ninth- and tenth-century Frankish swords have been made in Prussia:[18] silver would seem to have been replaced by 'high-tech' Viking-Age weaponry. One final factor affecting inflows of Islamic silver could have been a change in the attitude of Slav chieftains themselves, on seeing the effect of precious metals on their clans.[19] But whatever the reasons, hoarders who had earlier collected coins no longer seem to have needed dirhams.

Turning to external factors, we have some evidence of Viking raids on the southern Baltic in the mid-ninth century from *Vita Anskarii*. Rimbert reports that bands of Danes, dissatisfied with the tribute they had just collected at the emporium of Birka, attacked a Slav stronghold in 845 or 849 and seized 'loot and many treasures' (*captis in ea spoliis ac thesauris multis*).[20] And in 852 Danes tried to plunder the Curonians (in what is today Latvia and Lithuania), but were vanquished. Shortly after, the Swedish king Olof raided the same Curonians, but unlike the Danes, he was able to defeat them. According to *Vita Anskarii*, Olof forced them to pay tribute in the form of 7,500 pounds of silver, equivalent to about 500,000 dirhams.[21] Although we cannot take the amounts mentioned at face value, these stories nevertheless illustrate Scandinavian pillaging of the Slavic and Baltic communities and extortion from them of, among other things, silver.

This could explain why only a very few hoards from the second half of the ninth century have been found in Pomerania and Prussia.

We also have possible archaeological evidence for the use of violence. Around 65km inland from the Baltic, at Potzlow, a large Slav stronghold measuring 360m by 230m has been excavated. According to Felix Biermann, clues such as burn marks on the walls, the large number of human bones and weapons found in the fort's layers, as well as a dozen dirhams struck between the late eighth and tenth centuries suggest ongoing hostilities between various Slav warlords and their neighbouring communities and the capture of people for sale to Scandinavian traders on the coast.[22] However, it may not have been the Slav warlords who organised such raids, but the Scandinavian slave-traders themselves.

New silver flows, new networks

Let us now move inland to Mazovia, some 400km south-east of Truso, and to an important cluster of early tenth-century dirham finds on the Middle Bug, a right tributary of the Vistula. What brought this silver to eastern Poland?

By around the year 900, long-distance trade in western Eurasia had undergone a fundamental change. The Samanids controlled all the important silver mines in Central Asia and the Middle East and, driven primarily by the demand for slaves and furs, they struck millions of dirhams for export to Bulgar and Khazaria. Dirhams flooded out – either through Bulgar or through the Khazar networks – with many ending up in Kiev where a mixed population of locals and incomers, including Scandinavian arms-bearing traders, had settled and started to impose tribute on the surrounding East Slav tribes. Some years ago Johan Callmer showed that at the turn of the ninth and tenth centuries, Kiev evolved from being a couple of dispersed agrarian settlements into a significant political and economic centre.[23] And according to the *Russian Primary Chronicle*, a Rus warlord from the north, Oleg, had conquered Kiev and imposed tribute on the various East Slav tribes inhabiting both the left and right banks of the Dnieper by 882–5. The Derevlians, who lived along the river Pripet, were forced to pay 'a black marten-skin apiece'.[24] Thus, the *Chronicle* seems to confirm the increasing amount of archaeological and numismatic evidence showing that the Rus had penetrated the Middle Dnieper basin by the late ninth century.

The *Chronicle* also gives us an idea of how Rus raids might have played out in its report on a Rus attack on Iskorosten, the 'capital' of the Derevlians, in 945: goaded by his retinue's complaint at their lack of 'weapons and fine raiment',

> Igor' heeded their words, and he attacked Dereva [the Derevlians] in search of tribute. He sought to increase the previous tribute and collected it by violence from the people with the assistance of his followers.[25]

Such tribute-collecting expeditions probably brought with them the chance to barter with subject peoples for furs, wax, honey and slaves, and it is with this in mind that we should look for an explanation as to why dirhams flowed into eastern Poland in the early tenth century.

Our cluster of early tenth-century dirham finds along the Middle Bug lies more than 700km west of Kiev. The largest (Klukowicze, *tpq* 901/2) was made up of 1,508 dirhams, although 565 had been dispersed before they could be identified, and only 943 were fully recorded. Within roughly a 100km radius, hoards were unearthed to the west and north-west of Klukowicze, near Liw (502 dirhams, *tpq* 900/1) and in Góra Strękowa (thirty-three dirhams and silver jewellery, *c.* 900). Further finds in this region include a slightly older hoard (at Drohiczyn, *c.* 893) and several finds which are either below our hoard threshold of ten coins, or which contain coins of unknown date,[26] as well as a few single dirhams excavated at the hillfort of Trzcianka, around 90km north-east of Góra Strękowa.[27] The hoards from Klukowicze and Liw are strikingly similar: both contain a very high percentage of new, unfragmented dirhams, mostly struck at Samanid mints shortly after 890.[28] Some 15% of the Klukowicze hoard is made up of imitation dirhams issued in Volga Bulgaria or Khazaria, and a couple of its coins bear Scandinavian runes.[29] The structure and chronology of these early dirham hoards suggest that they can be traced back to a single expedition by the Kievan Rus: after collecting tribute from the people living along the Pripet, they moved on to the region of the Western Bug in search of new furs and slaves (Map 7.2).

We do not know the extent to which these Rus traders, warlords or slave-hunters cooperated with local groupings. Interestingly, all three hoards were found in the vicinity of either settlements or hillforts, and it has been suggested that the settlement enclave established by around 900 on the river Liwiec, a left tributary of the Bug, was connected with Slav migration to the east of the Western Bug:[30] tribes who settled there from the region of the Pripet, possibly seeking refuge from Rus tribute-collecting expeditions. And in western Mazovia at this time, heavily fortified hillforts emerged and disappeared within a generation,[31] a development that has been attributed to raiding by Scandinavian slavers.[32] Yet the Rus seem to have been attracted to the area around the Western Bug by the prospects of cooperation with local chieftains who were able to supply them with furs or help them to hunt slaves – wherever the slaves came from. The widely scattered cluster along the Middle Bug implies the Rus came to trade at various places in this area.

The next wave of silver that flowed into Mazovia shows a different geographical and structural pattern from that of our early tenth-century hoards. From the 930s and 940s onwards, dirhams reached the Middle Vistula and the region to its west that was inhabited by various Slav tribes, among them the Polanie in what is now Wielkopolska (Table 7.2). A couple of finds show this, including those at Iłów (*tpq* 937/8), at Ochle on the Middle Warta (*tpq* 936/7) and at Piwonice near Kalisz on the Prosna (*tpq* 934/5).

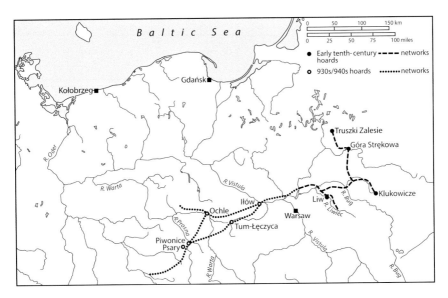

Map 7.2 Dirham networks in Mazovia.

Two silver chains have also been unearthed from this period, both inside strongholds close to Łęczyca some 150km west of Warsaw. The first was found in a hoard dated 936/7 at Tum–Łęczyca, and the second at Czerchów, 10km to the south–east, which seems to have burned down in the mid–tenth century. They show clear parallels to jewellery known from the Kievan Rus, and Czerchów's fortifications also contained arrowheads of north or east European nomadic origin. Interestingly, a couple of other artefacts from there suggest Moravian provenance, while those unearthed at Tum–Łęczyca hint at contacts with Scandinavia, western Europe or Rus.[33] And last but not least, the hoard from Psary included an earring similar in style to those of the Volga Bulgars.[34] All of this suggests that Rus – and possibly also Bohemian or Moravian – traders, slave–hunters or warlords may have penetrated to the west of the Middle Vistula; and that the various Polan chiefdoms by now established in the region supplied the foreigners with slaves and furs – or helped them capture slaves. So the networks of the Kievan Rus seem to have extended into

Table 7.2 Hoards from the Middle Vistula (900s–40s)

Number of securely dated hoards found	East of the Vistula	West of the Vistula
from the 900s–20s	3	–
from the 930s–40s	1	5

Wielkopolska by the 930s and 940s and this, in turn, could have stimulated some of the chieftains there to penetrate further into Mazovia, in particular the grouping that would later become the Piast dynasty.

The emergence and expansion of the Piast realm

According to Ibrahim ibn Ya'qub, a Jewish merchant from al-Andalus, Mieszko's realm in around 965 was the largest Slav polity, bordered to the east by the Rus and to the north by Prussian tribes.[35] This would imply that Mieszko (*c.* 960–92) already controlled the area east of the Vistula. An analysis of several hoards from Wielkopolska shows that early dirhams flowed into the region, at least in part from the east.[36]

The emergence of power centres in Wielkopolska is reflected by several strongholds built between around the 920s to the 940s; these are significantly different from the older hillforts in the area. We know of six central strongholds, all situated within a square of around 50 square kilometres: Poznań, Gniezno, Ostrów Lednicki, Giecz, Grzybowo and Moraczewo.[37] Most of our mid- to late tenth-century hoards have been discovered in the vicinity of these strongholds; some actually inside them (including Grzybowo-Rabieżyce, *c.* 952/3 and Ostrów Lednicki, *c.* 985).[38] Weights and balances have been found close to Giecz; and at the burial ground of Sowinki (near Poznań) archaeologists discovered a set of scales and balances, with further scales excavated in Dziekanowice near Łubowo, where a couple of graves indicate the presence of Scandinavian or Rus warriors.[39] These dirham hoards may well have belonged to the followers of the Piasts, but perhaps also to the jewellers who fashioned the silver coins into arm-rings, necklaces or earrings (Map 7.3).

Several hoards from the core area of Piast power are really huge and contain mostly fragmented silver, including Poznań (*c.* 961/76), Zalesie (*c.* 976), Dzierżnica II (*c.* 983) and Kąpiel (*c.* 985).[40] Dzierżnica II includes at least 18,200 highly fragmented dirhams and its silver weighs 15kg – the equivalent to purchasing fifty female slaves. The Kąpiel hoard contains almost 2,500 fragmented coins and many pieces of jewellery of Scandinavian origin.[41] A similar pattern can be seen in some Mazovian finds, including a very impressive hoard found almost 100km north of Warsaw. Ciechanów III (*tpq c.* 975) weighs 1,554g and contains fifty-six whole and 3,824 fragmented dirhams, ninety-two German deniers (of which seven were cross-deniers), and

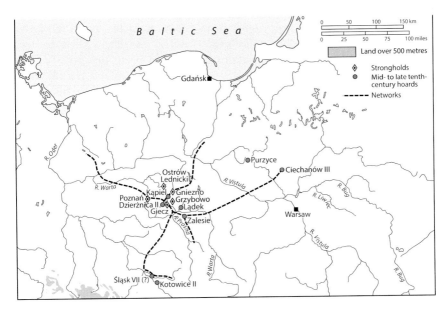

Map 7.3 Dirham networks of the Piasts.

three fragmented Danish coins, as well as jewellery of Rus provenance – for example, Borshchivka- or Volyn-type earrings.[42] There can be little doubt that the owner of this silver belonged to the local elite.

The importance of Arabic silver is clearly reflected in Ibrahim ibn Ya'qub's account:

> [Mieszko's] taxes are levied in *mathaqil al-marqatiyya*, and they are used to pay the monthly salaries of his men, each of whom receives a fixed number. He has 3,000 shield-bearers. One hundred of his soldiers are the equal of 1,000.[43]

The term *mathaqil* was used to indicate a monetary unit equal to a dinar,[44] and Mieszko clearly levied tribute from some tribes – and paid his retinue –

by weight in hack-silver. As we have seen, many of the hoards in Wielkopolska, as well as Ciechanów III in Mazovia, contained fragmented dirhams and weights and scales have been found close by. If some of the tribute collected by Mieszko or his predecessors came from Mazovia, this would suggest the inhabitants of eastern Poland had been incorporated into the Piast dirham circulation networks. But finds of German and Danish coins at Ciechanów III suggest that the redistribution mechanisms were becoming more complicated and that silver was flowing not only from east to west, but from west to east, too.

The Piasts' expansion into Mazovia to raise tribute does not necessarily exclude cooperation with local elites and groupings there: some of the hacked coins and rings may have been gifts to express friendship and ensure political alliances – particularly as many dirhams flowed into eastern Europe as bullion. Hence strongholds along the Warta in Mazovia and eastern Wielkopolska may have served both as centres for tribute collection by the Piasts and as places for various forms of exchange. This could explain why jewellery and dirhams were fragmented – for use by weight in the form of bullion or hack-silver, rather than holding a monetary value – and also why western coins reached Mazovia. German and Danish deniers may not have arrived in the region with traders, but rather with members of the Piast elite as gifts for them to exchange, and the very small fragments of silver do not necessarily reflect trading activities. On the contrary, they could reflect the circulation of luxury goods as facilitators of interaction between and within elites.

The chronology of several silver hoards from Lower Silesia indicates that dirhams also flowed into this region through the Piast redistribution networks.[45] Two hoards have been found at Kotowice II (*c.* 985) and Śląsk VII (942/54–1019/20),[46] containing respectively 570 and 1,797 mostly fragmented dirhams alongside German, Danish and Bohemian deniers and jewellery – and even a coin minted at Ribe around 850.[47] The Piasts could have been bribing the local elites with silver to gain their cooperation – especially in the 980s, when Mieszko was about to take over Silesia. Precious metals may have been a universal medium with which to influence, and a significant mechanism for regulating, relationships between the elites of Mieszko's polity and various local clans or groupings. Table 7.3 shows the geography of dirham hoards.

Several hoards can be used to illustrate the various levels of redistribution and communication between elites. Our first level – that of silver arriving

Table 7.3 Hoards from the core Polish lands (950s–80s)

	Number	Percentage of total
Mazovia	4	13%
Wielkopolska	19	61%
Silesia	8	26%

into Mazovia – is exemplified by earrings from the hoard at Ciechanów III (*c.* 975), which are likely of Rus provenance and show a marked similarity to those found in the Borshchivka hoard of the same date, some 340km west of Kiev.[48] The distance of 600km between these two find spots would imply some sort of long-distance exchange between the Rus – whether from Kiev or Gnezdovo – and the Mazovian elite; and the region of Ciechanów could have been a kind of contact zone, for exchanges between Rus and Mazovians.

The second level of circulation – the flow of precious metals between the Piast elites and their tributary peoples in Mazovia – is demonstrated by the analogous structures of the Ciechanów III hoard and that found at Zalesie (*c.* 976), nearly 300km west in Wielkopolska on the Middle Warta. The Zalesie hoard contained more than 1,200 coins and coin fragments, mostly dirhams but also German pennies and Saxon cross-deniers, as well as numerous jewellery pieces. A second hoard has been found close by, in the vicinity of a mid-tenth-century Piast stronghold: the Lądek hoard (*tpq* 952/3), which comprised 163 dirhams along with silver and gold jewellery. Thus the geography, archaeological context and particularly the composition of the 970s hoards hint at flows between the Piast elites and Mazovian tributaries.[49]

And last but not least, redistribution within Mazovian groupings themselves can be seen from parallels between Ciechanów III and the hoard at Purzyce (*c.* 975/6), some 18km to its north in the vicinity of the early medieval stronghold at Grudusk.[50] The deposit from Purzyce was composed of 153 coins, mostly fragmented dirhams, but also containing some German deniers and jewellery. Structural similarities between the two hoards – notably in the jewellery and coins of western origin – and the short distance between the find spots suggest some sort of exchange system of prestige or luxury goods was at work among local elites.

Silver exchange at elite level can also be seen in several hoards from Silesia. Among the whole and fragmented jewellery found at Kotowice II were pieces of Świątki (Tempelhofer) type, also found at Ciechanów III, and Śląsk VII contained a fragmented piece of Scandinavian jewellery bearing a striking similarity to some finds from Wielkopolska, in particular the Kąpiel hoard. And besides seven dirhams and a coin struck in York under Athelstan (924–39), the Śląsk XIII hoard contained more than 500 fragments of jewellery and raw silver.[51] All these finds seem to reflect contacts between members of the Piast power circle and various local chieftains, warlords and other hoarders of silver, such as jewellers.

The Piast elite may have obtained dirhams not only through tribute, but also through exchange: by selling slaves and furs to Rus traders. Archaeological excavations in the south-western periphery of Wielkopolska show that, in the mid-tenth century, several local hillforts were burned down – probably during a slaving raid by the neighbouring Piasts.[52] We do not have any sources that describe such raids by the Piasts, but the *Russian Primary Chronicle* gives us a flavour of how the Rus collected tribute from the Derevlians:

> Thus she [Princess Olga] took the city [Iskorosten] and burned it, and captured the elders of the city. Some of the other captives she killed, while she gave others as slaves to her followers. The remnant she left to pay tribute. She imposed upon them a heavy tribute [...].[53]

Thus in terms of political economy, the early Piast realm was no more than a hierarchical redistribution network of silver and luxury goods obtained by force – or threat of force – and by long-distance trade. Taking of tribute could sometimes evolve into predation for its own sake, but often coincided with exchange mechanisms.

To the north again

Dirhams were transported to Wielkopolska not only from the east, but also from the north, and after a break of around fifty to sixty years, Arabic coins began to flow into Pomerania once more. No Pomeranian hoards can be securely dated to the first three decades of the tenth century. The latest coin in the Bierkowo hoard is from the reign of Emperor Constantine VII (between 913 and 959),[54] and in the Opalenie hoard from 917 to 941.[55] A huge hoard has quite recently been unearthed at Szczecinek, 110km southeast of Kołobrzeg; this includes more than 1,000, mostly fragmented, dirhams and an initial dating is to the 900s.[56] Unfortunately we cannot say with certainty whether the coins giving these finds their *tpq* were minted before 930, but it would seem that the inflow of new Samanid dirhams into Pomerania only began in the 930s and 940s. In contrast to the first two – ninth-century – phases of dirham imports, we see a shift from eastern to western Pomerania, and in particular to the region around Wolin and its hinterland, stretching from Szczecin to Kamień Pomorski (see Table 7.4).

But why and how did dirhams flow to Wolin? According to our archaeological data, a settlement on the island of Wolin emerged and grew in strength from the early tenth century onwards, in tandem with the inflow of Arabic silver. In contrast to older trade emporia like Truso, Wolin's merchant elite were not just traders of amber and slaves: their rise was also an important political factor in the region. Widukind of Corvey reports that Wolinians fought against Mieszko and Adam of Bremen calls it 'the largest European town',[57] while Ibrahim ibn Ya'qub describes Wolin in the 960s thus:

Table 7.4 Pomeranian hoards (900–80)

	Number	Percentage of total
Western Pomerania	16	55%
Central Pomerania	6	21%
Eastern Pomerania	7	24%

They have a great city on the Surrounding Ocean. It has twelve gates and a harbour [...] They make war on Mieszko and are very courageous. They have no king [...] their judges are their old men.[58]

It was primarily the long-distance trade boom of the tenth century that stimulated the rise of this emporium.[59] Several hoards have been found in the region between Kamień Pomorski and Szczecin, about 20km north and 80km south of Wolin respectively.[60] In Wolin itself, workshops for glass, amber, metal and antlers have been excavated. Intensive contacts with the Arabic world are attested not only by the numerous hoards containing Islamic coins and jewellery found around Wolin, but also by the dirham finds in the settlement complex itself, as well as cowrie shells from the Indian Ocean, glass beads from Syria and Egypt, and silk fragments from Central Asia.[61] One of the emporium's most important exports was amber – more than 270,000 pieces were found there.[62]

Besides huge numbers of fragmented dirhams, finds of more than forty weights and balances show the importance of weighing silver for use in both long-distance and regional trade. Wolinian chieftains may have paid in precious metal for the slaves, furs and possibly also the timber supplied by inland groupings, and it is no coincidence that in the first half of the tenth century, high-quality pottery from western Pomerania also starts to appear in Wielkopolska.[63] Yet as in central and eastern Poland, jewellery finds suggest the existence of a prestige economy, too, and the emporium's wealth lured the Piasts to move into Pomerania and attempt to impose tribute on the Wolinians.

The town saw serious development in the first quarter of the tenth century, when the core settlement and southern suburb were fortified, and a rampart built to protect 'silver hill' to the north (Srebrne Wzgórze/ Silberberg). At the same time, a new suburb to the west of the emporium was fortified and a harbour settlement emerged on the southern slopes of 'gallows hill' (Wzgórze Wisielców/Galgenberg) to the south. The scale of these fortifications is in contrast to other emporia in the mouth of the Oder, such as Menzlin, and hints at strong power structures forming in Wolin,[64] while the archaeological material points to Slav merchants and chieftains controlling trade there for much of the tenth century,[65] with Norsemen only becoming more actively involved from around 970 on (Map 7.4).[66]

In order to establish how Islamic coins reached the Polish shores of the Baltic, we need to examine the chronological composition of the dirhams in the Pomeranian hoards.[67] Two patterns emerge: the first is of early ninth-century Abbasid coins which had flowed into Pomerania from northern Rus a century or so earlier. These were collected by local communities in eastern and central Pomerania from the 810s onward and apparently came back into circulation during the 930s and 940s, although mixed with newer coins, suggesting a regional circulation of dirhams. Because we know of no ninth-century dirham hoards from Wolin, we can assume that the old Abbasid silver coins probably reached this area in the first half of the tenth century via

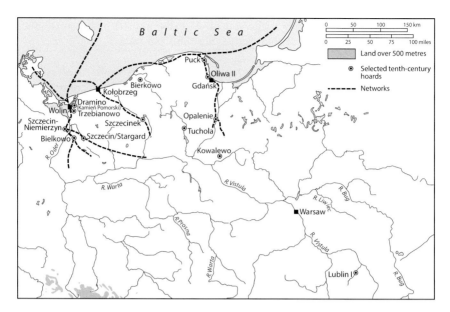

Map 7.4 Dirham networks of Wolinians and Pomeranians.

central Pomerania (Kołobrzeg) or eastern Pomerania (Truso and Gdańsk), or via neighbouring harbours on the German coast of the Baltic, such as Menzlin. The second pattern is of newer Samanid coins, struck from the 890s and 900s on, which seem to have reached Wolin from around 930 and become preponderant in Pomerania after 950. The Samanid dirhams may have been transported by the Wolinian network, either directly from Staraia Ladoga, or by way of Gotland and Birka.

But why did the rise of Wolin occur in the first half of the tenth century? Błażej M. Stanisławski has suggested an 'ideological revolution' occurred among the Wolinians, reflected in the development of the settlement complex, the emergence of new elites and the appearance of dirham hoards[68] – all phenomena seen in Wielkopolska, too. We should take into account a fundamental transformation that was taking place to the west of Wolin in this period. Between 928 and 934 the formidable king of East Francia, Henry the Fowler (919–36), imposed tribute on all the Polabian Slavs and Bohemians. A huge area was brought under Saxon control – from the Baltic rim in the north to Prague in the south, and from the Elbe in the west and the Oder to the east – and in 934 Henry also captured the important emporium of Hedeby.[69] The pressure Henry put on the Polabian tribes and Danes between 928 and 934 created opportunities for Wolinian expansion into the Polish interior as well as in the Baltic region.[70] It is probably no coincidence that Wichmann, a member of the Saxon House of Billung, fled to the Wolinians after banishment by Henry's son Otto I and led them against Mieszko in the 960s. And according to Adam of Bremen, the trading centre of Birka was plundered by pirates,[71] and there is no reason why some of the Slavic ships arriving at Birka should not have hailed from Wolin.[72] There is a striking difference between Wolin and the settlements at Kołobrzeg-Budzistowo in central Pomerania and Gdańsk in eastern Pomerania, however: the latter do not seem to have organised predatory raids into the Polish interior. On the contrary, they were themselves subdued by the Piasts, who by the later tenth century concretised their control over these areas by building strongholds.[73]

The great reorientation of the late tenth century

Demand for silver, mainly elite driven, was the prime mover of dirham circulation in the Polish lands. In the 970s and 980s, Mieszko consolidated his power in Wielkopolska, Mazovia and eastern Pomerania; by the later 980s, he controlled Silesia and Małopolska and was also probably collecting tribute from the Wolinians in the form of precious metals. Dirhams helped Mieszko to pay his warriors and to 'induce' local chieftains to join him. Islamic coins thus made a significant contribution to the formation of a Polish realm and, ironically, to establishing it within Christian Europe.[74]

However, an examination of the structure of hoard finds clearly shows that dirhams struck during and after the 980s hardly appear in the Polish lands. In some regions, such as Pomerania, a collapse in the inflow of Islamic silver occurred slightly earlier, possibly in the 970s, as in Sweden. We know of only a few deposits that include later dirhams. In the hoard from Bierzgłowo (*c.* 1024), found 19km from Toruń on the Middle Vistula, dirhams from the 1000s formed only around 18% of the coin stock. Dirhams of the 990s, in turn, constituted 17% in the deposit from Starydworek in the western part of Wielkopolska (*c.* 1025). So we can safely say that the last Islamic coins flowed into central Europe by the 1000s or the early 1010s.[75] This is more or less in step with the situation in Kievan Rus and Volga Bulgaria where, basically, several newer dirhams appeared no later than the 1010s.[76]

But how did the cessation of the inflow of dirhams influence the state building of the Piast dynasty? I have already mentioned that western coins first began to reach Poland during the 970s, notably Bavarian deniers as well as silver pennies of Otto III and Adelheid. The Harz silver mines started operations around 970, and by the 980s/90s they made it possible to mint millions of cross-deniers destined for long-distance trading with the Slavs. However, some coins struck by Danes, Bohemians and, from around the year 1000, Anglo-Saxons also started to appear. The old connections to the Arab world came to an end, but new ones were established instead. The Piasts now used their political contacts with neighbouring dynasties, above all the Ottonians, to reorient the silver inflow from east to west.[77] But this is another story.

Notes

1 Kovalev and Kaelin (2007), p. 564, alongside recently discovered hoards listed in Andrałojć *et al.* (2011); *FMP* 4; *FMP* 3. In this chapter, a hoard is taken to mean ten or more dirhams.

2 Adamczyk (2014a); Adamczyk (2015a), pp. 97–8. See now Adamczyk (2020).

3 Stegna lies around 40km north-west of Elbląg, Mokajmy-Sójki and Zalewo 20–40km to the south, Braniewo some 50km to the east, and the most remote deposit from Ramsowo is around 110km south-east of Truso. We might also add the Pomerania V hoard, a find whose exact location is unknown and which contained fifty-three dirhams with a *tpq* of 839/40.

4 Auch *et al.* (2012), p. 120; Bogucki (2012).

5 Auch *et al.* (2012), p. 121.

6 Biborski *et al.* (2010).

7 Ibn Khurradadhbih, *Kitab al-masalik*, ed. Lewicki, pp. 76–7.

8 Bately, 'Wulfstan', pp. 16 (text), 24–5 (comm.).

9 Auch *et al.* (2012), p. 96.

10 These included settlements such as Kołobrzeg (Kolberg), Menzlin, Ralswiek, Dierkow (Rostock) and Reric (Groß Strömkendorf). See Sindbæk (2007).

11 Kleingärtner (2014), pp. 365–7.

12 The distinctive material culture of East Slav settlements on the left bank of the Dnieper from the eighth to tenth centuries, named after two of the settlements.

13 Found at Horodyszcze and Josipyvka respectively: Auch *et al.* (2012), p. 151; Suchodolski and Malarczyk (2007).

14 Adamczyk (2014a), p. 104.

15 One external factor might have been the interruption of trade with the Islamic world, although this did not take place until the 880s/890s – a generation after the sudden increase in the number of hoards in Scandinavia and Rus from the 860s on, and considerably after the decline in Pomeranian hoards around 840.

16 Bately, 'Wulfstan', p. 16. See also the chapter by Jansson in this volume.

17 On the nature of these hillforts, see Łosiński (1990), esp. p. 299; Biermann (2016).

18 Steuer (1987), pp. 154, 157.

19 Adam of Bremen (Ad*GH*, IV.18, pp. 456–7) reports that the Prussians condemned gold and silver.

20 Rimb*VA*, ch. 19, pp. 62–3.

21 Rimb*VA*, ch. 30, pp. 94–9.

22 Biermann (2013), pp. 227–8.

23 Callmer (1987); Mühle (1987).

24 *PVL*, p. 14; *RPC*, pp. 60–1.

25 *PVL*, p. 26; *RPC*, p. 78.

26 Czapkiewicz and Kmietowicz (1960); Czapkiewicz *et al.* (1964); *PSW* 3, nos 16, 33; Bartczak (1999); *FMP* 3, no. 67.

27 Andrzejewska and Stankiewicz (2009); Ścibior (2008).

28 The Klukowicze hoard is made up of roughly 80% of these complete, freshly minted Samanid dirhams; Liw and Góra Strękowa around 90% and 75% respectively.

29 Dobrovol'skii *et al.* (1991), pp. 108–9.

30 Wróblewski (2001).

31 Dulinicz (2000), pp. 209–10; Buko (2008), pp. 199–206.

32 Jankowiak (2015), p. 50.

33 Kara (2009), p. 313 and n. 1681.

34 Near the stronghold of Kalisz, almost 100km south-west of Łęczyca: Kara (2009), p. 312.

35 Ibrahim ibn Ya'qub, *Account of the Slavs*, ed. Kowalski, p. 50; tr. Lunde and Stone, pp. 165, 166.

36 Adamczyk (2014b), pp. 42–6.

37 Kara (2009).

38 Adamczyk (2014a), Annex 2, Großpolen, no. 3, p. 304; Annex 1, Großpolen, no. 19, p. 295.

39 Wrzesińska and Wrzesiński (2006).

40 Adamczyk (2014a), Annex 1, Großpolen, nos 12, 14, 16, 18, p. 294.

41 Kmietowicz (1994); Andrałojć *et al.* (2005).

42 Bartczak (1996); Nowakiewicz (2003).

43 Ibrahim ibn Ya'qub, *Account of the Slavs*, ed. Kowalski, p. 50; tr. Lunde and Stone, p. 165.

44 Kubiak (1956); Gumowski (1958–9), p. 24; Zaborski (2008), pp. 41, 43–51.

45 Adamczyk (2013).

46 The Śląsk VII hoard has two parts: the first contains dirhams of *tpq* 942/54 and the second, smaller part contains only European coins struck between *c.* 990 and 1019/20.

47 *FMP* 4, nos 31, 102.

48 Liwoch (2013), p. 7.

49 Adamczyk (2014a), Annex 1, Großpolen, nos 14, 6, pp. 294, 293.

50 *FMP* 3, no. 129.

51 *FMP* 4, nos 31, 102, 108.

52 Brzostowicz (1993); Brzostowicz and Stempin (eds) (2009), p. 60.

53 *PVL*, pp. 28–9; *RPC*, p. 81.

54 Near Słupsk in central Pomerania: *PSW* 2, no. 10.

55 Near Gdańsk in eastern Pomerania: *PSW* 2, no. 117.

56 Lewczuk (2015); 'Niezwykłe znalezisko' (n.d.).

57 Widukind, *Res gestae Saxonicae*, III.69, pp. 172–3; *Est sane maxima omnium, quas Europa claudit, civitatum, quam incolunt Sclavi cum aliis gentibus, Grecis et Barbaris*: AdGH, II.22(19), pp. 252–3.

58 Ibrahim ibn Ya'qub, *Account of the Slavs*, ed. Kowalski, p. 50; tr. Lunde and Stone, p. 166.

59 Stanisławski and Filipowiak (eds) (2013–14).

60 Adamczyk (2014a), Annex 1, Pommern und Kujawien, nos 2, 4, 8, 12, 16–18, p. 295.

61 Filipowiak (1988), p. 699; Bogucki and Malarczyk (2014); Horoszko (2014).

62 Filipowiak (2000), p. 153.

63 Kara (2009), pp. 255, 257.

64 Wehner (2010), p. 348; Cnotliwy (2014).

65 Łosiński (1991), p. 253.

66 Stanisławski (2013), esp. pp. 244–5.

67 Adamczyk (2014b), pp. 45–6.

68 Stanisławski (2013), pp. 231–40.
69 *Regesten*, ed. Lübke, p. 62.
70 Gorjunova (2001), p. 345.
71 Ad*GH*, I.60(62), pp. 230–1.
72 *Regesten*, ed. Lübke, no. 16, p. 30.
73 Dulinicz (2008), p. 150; Rębkowski (2010).
74 Adamczyk (2002); Adamczyk (2012); Adamczyk (2015b).
75 Adamczyk (2014a), p. 50.
76 Noonan (1988), p. 415; Noonan (1992), p. 404.
77 Adamczyk (2007).

Bibliography

Primary sources

Bately, J., 'Wulfstan's voyage and his description of *Estland*: the text and the language of the text', in A. Englert and A. Trakadas (eds), *Wulfstan's Voyage: The Baltic Sea Region in the Early Viking Age as Seen from Shipboard*, Roskilde (2009), pp. 14–28.

Ibn Khurradadhbih, *Kitab al-masalik*, ed. T. Lewicki, *Źródła arabskie do dziejów Słowiańszczyzny*, vol. 1, Wrocław (1956), pp. 63–81.

Ibrahim ibn Ya'qub, *Account of the Slavs*, ed. T. Kowalski, *Relacja Ibrahima Ibn Ja'kuba z podróży do krajów słowiańskich w przekazie Al-Bekriego*, Cracow (1946); partial tr. P. Lunde and C. Stone, 'Ibrahim ibn-Ya'qub on northern Europe 965', in *Ibn Fadlan and the Land of Darkness: Arab Travellers in the Far North*, London (2012), pp. 162–8.

Regesten zur Geschichte der Slaven an Elbe und Oder (vom Jahr 900 an), vol. 2: *Regesten 900–983*, ed. C. Lübke, Berlin (1985).

Widukind of Corvey, *Res gestae Saxonicae*, ed. and German tr. A. Bauer and R. Rau, *Quellen zur Geschichte der sächsischen Kaiserzeit*, 2nd edn, Darmstadt (1977), pp. 1–183.

Secondary literature

Adamczyk, D. (2002), 'Orientalno-bałtycki system handlowy a proces kształtowania się Europy Wschodniej w IX i X w.', *Średniowiecze Polskie i Powszechne* 2: 63–88.

Adamczyk, D. (2007), 'Od dirhemów do fenigów. Reorientacja bałtyckiego systemu handlowego na przełomie X i XI w.', *Średniowiecze Polskie i Powszechne* 4: 15–27.

Adamczyk, D. (2012), 'Krise oder Stabilisierung? Die politischen Folgen der Verschiebung der Silberströme für die Herrschaftsbildung im östlichen Europa an der Wende vom 10. zum 11. Jahrhundert', *Przegląd Historyczny* 130: 1–26.

Adamczyk, D. (2013), 'Kruszec, moneta, tranzyt czy "hybryda", czyli częścią jakiego systemu handlowego były ziemie Polski południowej w X wieku?', in P. Boroń (ed.), *Argenti fossores et alii. Znaczenie gospodarcze wschodnich części Górnego Śląska i zachodnich krańców Małopolski w późnej fazie wczesnego średniowiecza (X–XII wiek)*, Wrocław, pp. 197–202.

Adamczyk, D. (2014a), *Silber und Macht. Fernhandel, Tribute und die piastische Herrschaftsbildung in nordosteuropäischer Perspektive (800–1100)*, Wiesbaden.

Adamczyk, D. (2014b), 'Trzecia fala napływu arabskiego srebra a powstanie "państwa" piastowskiego', *Wiadomości Numizmatyczne* 58: 33–53.

Adamczyk, D. (2015a), 'Koniunkturalne cykle czy strukturalne załamania? Sieci redystrybucji srebra a fluktuacje w jego imporcie do Europy Środkowej i Wschodniej w IX–XI wieku', in B. Paszkiewicz (ed.), *Moneta czasów kryzysu – moneta czasów pomyślności. XV Ogólnopolska Sesja Numizmatyczna w Nowej Soli, Muzeum Miejskie 2013*, Nowa Sól, pp. 95–118.

Adamczyk, D. (2015b), 'Czy bez Mahometa nie byłoby Mieszka I. i Bolesława I.? Arabski system handlowy a ekonomia polityczna społeczeństw Europy Środkowo-Wschodniej w X wieku', *Historia Slavorum Occidentis* 1: 19–33.

Adamczyk, D. (2020), *Monetarisierungsmomente, Kommerzialisierungszonen oder fiskalische Währungslandschaften? Edelmetalle, Silberverteilungsnetzwerke und Gesellschaften in Ostmitteleuropa (800–1200)*, Wiesbaden.

Andrałojć, M. *et al.* (2005), *Wczesnośredniowieczny skarb z Kąpieli gm. Czerniejewo, woj. Wielkopolskie*, Poznań.

Andrałojć, M. *et al.* (2011), *Odkrycia skarbów wczesnośredniowiecznych z terenu Wielkopolski: kontekst archeologiczny znalezisk*, Poznań.

Andrzejewska, A. and U. Stankiewicz (2009), 'Wczesnośredniowieczne grodzisko w Trzciance, gm. Janów, pow. Sokółka', *Podlaskie Zeszyty Archeologiczne* 5: 137–47.

Auch, M. *et al.* (2012), 'Osadnictwo wczesnośredniowieczne na stanowisku Janów Pomorski 1', in M. Bogucki and B. Jurkiewicz (eds), *Janów Pomorski. Stan. 1. Wyniki ratowniczych badań archeologicznych w latach 2007–2008*, 3 vols, Elbląg, vol. 2, pp. 23–232.

Bartczak, A. (1996), 'The early medieval silver hoard of Ciechanów in the light of oriental coins', *Wiadomości Numizmatyczne* 40: 43–59.

Bartczak, A. (1999), 'Islamic dirhams from the Góra Strękowa hoard', *Notae Numismaticae* 3: 263–90.

Biborski, M. *et al.* (2010), 'Sword parts from a Viking Age emporium of Truso in Prussia', *Waffen- und Kostümkunde. Zeitschrift für Waffen- und Kleidungsgeschichte* 52: 19–70.

Biermann, F. (2013), 'Neue völkerwanderungs- und slawenzeitliche Münzfunde aus Brandenburg und ihre wirtschaftsgeschichtliche Aussage', in M. Bogucki and M. Rębkowski (eds), *Economies, Monetisation and Society in the West Slavic Lands* AD *800–1200*, Szczecin, pp. 223–37.

Biermann, F. (2016), 'North-western Slavic strongholds of the 8th–10th centuries AD', in N. Christie and H. Herold (eds), *Fortified Settlements in Early Medieval Europe: Defended Communities of the 8th–10th Centuries*, Oxford, pp. 85–94.

Bogucki, M. (2012), 'Monety wczesnośredniowieczne', in M. Bogucki and B. Jurkiewicz (eds), *Janów Pomorski. Stan. 1. Wyniki ratowniczych badań archeologicznych w latach 2007–2008*, 3 vols, Elbląg, vol. 3, pp. 30–9.

Bogucki, M. and B. Jurkiewicz (eds) (2012), *Janów Pomorski. Stan. 1. Wyniki ratowniczych badań archeologicznych w latach 2007–2008*, vol. 1: *Od paleolitu do wczesnego okresu wędrówek ludów*; vol. 2: *Od późnego okresu wędrówek ludów do nowożytności*; vol. 3: *Analizy*, Elbląg.

Bogucki, M. and D. Malarczyk (2014), 'Wczesnośredniowieczny skarb monet ze Srebrnego Wzgórza w Wolinie z 2. połowy X w.', in B. M. Stanisławski and W. Filipowiak (eds), *Wolin średniowieczny*, 2 vols, Warsaw, vol. 2, pp. 291–317.

Brzostowicz, M. (1993), 'Wczesnośredniowieczne grodzisko w Spławiu, gm. Kołaczkowo, woj. Poznańskie. Wstępne podsumowanie wyników badań ratowniczych z lat 1991–1992', *Wielkopolskie Sprawozdania Archeologiczne* 2: 115–32.

Brzostowicz, M. and A. Stempin (eds) (2009), *Tu powstała Polska: katalog wystawy stałej w Muzeum Archeologicznym w Poznaniu*, Poznań.

Buko, A. (2008), *The Archaeology of Early Medieval Poland. Discoveries – Hypotheses – Interpretations*, Leiden.

Callmer, J. (1987), 'The archaeology of Kiev to the end of the earliest urban phase', *Harvard Ukrainian Studies* 11: 323–64.

Cnotliwy, E. (2014), 'Umocnienia obronne wczesnośredniowiecznego Wolina', in B. M. Stanisławski and W. Filipowiak (eds), *Wolin średniowieczny*, 2 vols, Warsaw, vol. 2, pp. 197–277.

Czapkiewicz, M. and F. Kmietowicz (1960), *Skarb monet arabskich z okolic Drohiczyna nad Bugiem*, Cracow.

Czapkiewicz, M. *et al.* (1964), *Skarb monet arabskich z Klukowicz*, Warsaw.

Czapkiewicz, M. *et al.* (1988), 'Arabische Münzen aus einer frühmittelalterlichen Handwerker- und Handelssiedlung in Janów Pomorski, Gem. Elbląg', *Folia Orientalia* 25: 157–69.

Dobrovol'skii, I. G. *et al.* (1991), *Graffiti na vostochnykh monetakh: drevniaia Rus' i sopredel'nye strany*, Leningrad.

Dulinicz, M. (2000), 'Mazowsze w X wieku', in H. Samsonowicz (ed.), *Ziemie polskie w X wieku i ich znaczenie w kształtowaniu się nowej mapy Europy*, Cracow, pp. 199–220.

Dulinicz, M. (2008), 'Forschungen zu den Herrschaftszentren des 10. bis 11. Jahrhunderts in Polen', in J. Henning (ed.), *Europa im 10. Jahrhundert: Archäologie einer Aufbruchszeit*, Mainz, pp. 147–60.

Filipowiak, W. (1988), 'Handel und Handelsplätze an der Ostseeküste Westpommerns', in M. Müller-Wille (ed.), *Oldenburg – Wolin – Staraja Ladoga – Novgorod – Kiev: Handel und Handelsverbindungen im südlichen und östlichen Ostseeraum während des frühen Mittelalters*, Mainz [= *Bericht der Römisch-Germanischen Kommission* 69], pp. 690–719.

Filipowiak, W. (2000), 'Wollin: ein frühmittelalterliches Zentrum an der Ostsee', in A. Wieczorek and H.-M. Hinz (eds), *Europas Mitte um 1000*, Stuttgart, pp. 152–5.

Gorjunova, V. M. (2001), 'Technologietransfer im Töpferhandwerk. Westslawischer Einfluß auf die frühe Drehscheibenware in Novgorod', in M. Müller-Wille *et al.* (eds), *Novgorod: das mittelalterliche Zentrum und sein Umland im Norden Russlands*, Neumünster, pp. 323–47.

Gumowski, M. (1958–9), 'Moneta arabska w Polsce IX i X wieku', *Zapiski Historyczne* 24: 7–61.

Horoszko, G. (2014), 'Monety wczesnośredniowieczne z badań archeologicznych w Wolinie', in B. M. Stanisławski and W. Filipowiak (eds), *Wolin średniowieczny*, 2 vols, Warsaw, vol. 2, pp. 277–90.

Jankowiak, M. (2015), 'Wer brachte im 10. Jahrhundert die Dirhems in die polnischen Gebiete und warum', in D. Adamczyk and N. Kersken (eds), *Fernhändler, Dynasten, Kleriker: die piastische Herrschaft in kontinentalen Beziehungsgeflechten vom 10. bis zum frühen 13. Jahrhundert*, Wiesbaden, pp. 41–54.

Kara, M. (2009), *Najstarsze państwo Piastów – rezultat przełomu czy kontynuacji? Studium archeologiczne*, Poznań.

Kleingärtner, S. (2014), *Die frühe Phase der Urbanisierung an der südlichen Ostseeküste im ersten nachchristlichen Jahrtausend*, Neumünster.

Kmietowicz, A. (1994), 'Wczesnośredniowieczny skarb srebrny Dzierżnica II: Uwagi o historii znaleziska i jego części orientalnej', *Wiadomości Numizmatyczne* 38: 161–7.

Kovalev, R. K. and A. C. Kaelin (2007), 'Circulation of Arab silver in medieval Afro-Eurasia: preliminary observations', *History Compass* 5: 560–80.

Kubiak, W. (1956), 'Zagadnienie "odważników handlowych" u Ibrahima ibn Jakuba', *Slavia Antiqua* 5: 368–76.

Lewczuk, M. (2015), 'Wędkarze oddali srebrne arabskie monety i dostali nagrody "za obywatelską postawę"', *Bezprawnik.pl* (30 November 2015), bezprawnik.pl/wedkarze-monety-znalezne/ (accessed 27 July 2020).

Liwoch, R. (2013) 'Skarby zachodnioruskie doby przedmongolskiej', *Materiały Archeologiczne* 39: 7—31.

Łosiński, W. (1990), 'W sprawie rozwoju gospodarki towarowo-pieniężnej na ziemiach polskich we wczesnym średniowieczu w kontekście dziejów obrotu pieniężnego w strefie nadbałtyckiej', *Archeologia Polski* 35: 289–309.

Łosiński, W. (1991), 'W sprawie rozwoju gospodarki towarowo-pieniężnej II', *Archeologia Polski* 36: 235–64.

Mühle, E. (1987), 'Die Anfänge Kievs (bis ca. 980) in archäologischer Sicht. Ein Forschungsbericht', *Jahrbücher für Geschichte Osteuropas* 35: 80–101.

'Niezwykłe znalezisko' (n.d.), *Muzeum Regionalne w Szczecinku*, www.muzeum.szczecinek.pl/niezwykłe-znalezisko.html (last accessed 24 June 2020).

Noonan, T. S. (1988), 'The impact of the silver crisis in Islam upon Novgorod's trade with the Baltic', in M. Müller-Wille (ed.), *Oldenburg – Wolin – Staraja Ladoga – Novgorod – Kiev*, Mainz [= *Bericht der Römisch-Germanischen Kommission* 69], pp. 411–47.

Noonan, T. S. (1992), 'Dirham hoards from medieval Lithuania', *Journal of Baltic Studies* 23: 395–414.

Nowakiewicz, T. (2003), 'Ozdoby i srebro siekane z wczesnośredniowiecznego skarbu srebrnego z Ciechanowa', *Studia Galindzkie* 1: 261–317.

PSW 2 = Kiersnowski, R. and T. Kiersnowska (1959), *Wczesnośredniowieczne skarby srebrne z Pomorza. Materiały*, Warsaw.

PSW 3 = Gupieniec, A. *et al.* (1965), *Wczesnośredniowieczne skarby srebrne z Polski Środkowej, Mazowsza i Podlasia. Materiały*, Wrocław.

PSW 4 = Haisig, M. *et al.* (1966), *Wczesnośredniowieczne skarby srebrne z Małopolski, Śląska, Warmii i Mazur. Materiały*, Wrocław.

Rębkowski, M. (2010), 'The Pomeranian towns and the state of the first Piasts: the case of Szczecin and Kołobrzeg', *Acta praehistorica et archaeologica* 42: 9–17.

Ścibior, J. M. (2008), 'Zespół monet arabskich: dirhemów znalezionych w Trzciance, pow. Sokółka', *Podlaskie Zeszyty Archeologiczne* 4: 210–22.

Sindbæk, S. (2007), 'Networks and nodal points: the emergence of towns in early Viking Age Scandinavia', *Antiquity* 81: 119–32.

Stanisławski, B. M. (2013), *Jómswikingowie z Wolina-Jómsborga: studium przenikania kultury skandynawskiej na ziemie polskie*, Wrocław.

Stanisławski, B. M. and W. Filipowiak (eds) (2013–14), *Wolin średniowieczny*, 2 vols, Warsaw.

Steuer, H. (1987), 'Der Handel der Wikingerzeit zwischen Nord- und Westeuropa aufgrund archäologischer Zeugnisse', in K. Düwel *et al.* (eds), *Untersuchungen zu Handel und Verkehr der vor- und frühgeschichtlichen Zeit in Mittel- und Nordeuropa*, vol. 4: *Der Handel der Karolinger- und Wikingerzeit*, Göttingen, pp. 113–97.

Suchodolski, S. and D. Malarczyk (2007), 'Die Zustromwege der Dirhams nach Polen', in M. Andersen *et al.* (eds), *Magister Monetae: Studies in Honour of Jörgen Steen Jensen*, Copenhagen, pp. 93–100.

Wehner, D. (2010), 'Grundzüge der Herrschaftsentwicklung am Fernhandelsplatz Wollin vom 8. bis 12. nachchristlichen Jahrhundert', in A. Paroń *et al.* (eds), *Potestas et communitas: Interdisziplinäre Beiträge zu Wesen und Darstellung von Herrschaftsverhältnissen im Mittelalter östlich der Elbe*, Wrocław; Warsaw, pp. 345–56.

154 *Dariusz Adamczyk*

Wróblewski, W. (2001), 'U źródeł kasztelanii liwskiej: wczesnośredniowieczne struktury osadnicze w dorzeczu Liwca', in B. Bryńczak and P. Urbańczyk (eds), *Najstarsze dzieje Podlasia w świetle źródeł archeologicznych*, Siedlce, pp. 205–28.

Wrzesińska, A. and J. Wrzesiński (2006), 'Odważniki z wczesnośredniowiecznego stanowiska w Dziekanowicach', in M. Dworaczek *et al.* (eds), *Świat Słowian wczesnego średniowiecza*, Szczecin; Wrocław, pp. 341–58.

Zaborski, A. (2008), 'Bilans i przyszłość badań nad tekstem Ibrahima Ibn Jakuba', in A. Zaborski (ed.), *Ibrahim Ibn Jakub i Tadeusz Kowalski w sześćdziesiątą rocznicę edycji*, Cracow, pp. 25–73.

8 Coin circulation in early Rus and the dynamics of the *druzhina*s

Viacheslav S. Kuleshov[1]

Most recent works on the emergence and development of the early Rus polity place exchanges between Rus leaders and other groupings centre stage – whether military, diplomatic or commercial.[2] One reason for this lies in the sources at our disposal: this is the type of evidence to be found in the ninth- and tenth-century Arab, Latin and Byzantine written sources scholars use to re-construct the events and realia of early Rus history. However, there is another rich seam of evidence in the form of the hoards of Islamic Kufic silver dirhams found on Rus lands. This awaits full investigation for what the circulation of the coins can tell us about the early period. Despite some excellent studies,[3] numismatics has failed to have the impact it deserves on recent historiography concerning the development of the early Rus polity and remains relatively unknown in wider historical circles.

Between the second half of the eighth and the first decades of the eleventh centuries, silver coins were imported into the lands of Rus in vast quantities. During this period, in addition to those issued by the Abbasid caliphate in Baghdad and its core lands in Iran and Iraq, dirhams were being struck at over a hundred mints across a vast territory: from North Africa, Egypt and Yemen to Syria, Central Asia and the Transcaucasus. The coins found in Rus come mainly from two of these regions – the Transcaucasus and southern Caspian, and Central Asia – and their typology underwent significant changes in this period. This was predominantly in response to events within the caliphate, but we also see surges in regional outputs triggered by local episodes. We can date changes in coin types with a fair degree of accuracy, since the legends of most Islamic coins give the date after the denomination and the name of the mint. The groups of issues in circulation at any one time thus offer markers of the various phases of silver inflows which, in turn, can shed light on trading between the Rus and those issuing monetary silver.

This chapter aims to summarise the main evidence on how silver minting in the Islamic world changed between the eighth and the early eleventh centuries and to present a chronology of monetary circulation in early Rus, drawing on data collected while studying the dynamics of the hoards' typology and the sequencing of their coins.[4] To help the reader unfamiliar with the major and minor Islamic dynasties minting coins in this period, and the names of key mints, a pocket dictionary of the former and list of the latter are offered in Appendices 8.1 and 8.2 at the end of the chapter.

Silver minting in the Islamic world (eighth to early eleventh centuries)

The urban centres of the caliphate were linked by an almost worldwide web of land and sea routes ranging east from India and south China, west to the Maghreb and al-Andalus, south to Ethiopia and east Africa and, to the north, the lands of the Khazars, the Rus, the *Saqaliba* (Slavs) and, in southern Siberia, the land of the Turks. Individual traders made their way 'from west to east and from east to west',[5] while caravans with thousands of camels and hundreds of escorts set off along trunk roads carrying mail and assorted wares to remote cities of the Islamic world, or bringing to the cities of the central caliphal lands elite goods from all the world: slaves, tax revenues paid in coin and, of course, information about the cultures, peoples and politics of the inhabited world, and tales of journeys made and curiosities encountered. By the first half of the ninth century this system of commercial links was already regarded as up-and-running, and functioning well.[6]

Building on the tripartite division of Abbasid coins, first proposed by Michael Bates (see Table 8.1),[7] one can talk in terms of five basic periods of monetary activity in the Islamic lands in the eighth to early eleventh centuries: Pre-Abbasid/Umayyad (late seventh to early eighth centuries); Early Abbasid; Middle Abbasid; Late Abbasid; and Post-Abbasid (945 to early eleventh century).

Each of these periods has its own characteristics in terms of the coins' inscriptions and designs, as well as distribution-patterns in the issue of gold and silver coins. The gold dinar's canonical weight was 4.25g, while that of the silver dirham was 2.97g. The fineness and high assay standard of both remained virtually unchanged throughout the Umayyad and Abbasid periods, setting aside minor reservations and some regional exceptions.[8] This was crucial for stabilising the finance system of the caliphate up to the opening decades of the tenth century. One consequence was the unrestricted issuing of local coins by autonomous and semi-autonomous rulers for general circulation between them. In every corner of the caliphate and beyond its borders, coins were in circulation from every mint then operating and from most of the various local dynasties in power.

The Abbasid caliphate was the greatest state of its day. Admittedly, signs of decline can be detected virtually from the time of its formation in the mid-eighth century, and a series of upheavals and losses detracted from its political and administrative weight. North Africa fell to Aghlabid rule in the ninth century and so, for a while, did Egypt and parts of Syria-Palestine to the Tulunids. The Dulafids took over the Jibal, the Saffarids ruled Fars, while Transoxania and Khorasan came under the Samanids. Meanwhile, religious movements stirred up by Shi'ite preachers were active in the Caspian region.

Table 8.1 Abbasid coin typology and caliphal reigns (until the collapse of Abbasid authority in Baghdad)

Typology	Period	AD	AH	Caliph
Early Abbasid	750–833 (AH 132–218)	749–54	132–6	al-Saffah
		754–75	136–58	al-Mansur
		775–85	158–69	al-Mahdi
		785–6	169–70	al-Hadi
		786–809	170–93	Harun al-Rashid
		809–13	193–8	al-Amin
		813–33	198–218	al-Ma'mun
Middle Abbasid	833–92 (AH 218–78)	833–42	218–27	al-Mu'tasim
		842–7	227–32	al-Wathiq
		847–61	232–47	al-Mutawakkil
		861–2	247–8	al-Muntasir
		862–6	248–52	al-Musta'in
		866–9	252–5	al-Mu'tazz
		869–70	255–6	al-Muhtadi
		870–92	256–79	al-Mu'tamid
Late Abbasid	892–945 (AH 279–334)	892–902	279–89	al-Mu'tadid
		902–8	289–95	al-Muktafi
		908–32	295–320	al-Muqtadir
		932–4	320–2	al-Qahir
		934–40	322–9	al-Radi
		940–4	329–33	al-Mutaqqi
		944–6	333–4	al-Mustakfi

For all that, up until the first third of the tenth century they had still not brought down the Baghdad caliphate. In fact, its power, authority and economic resources were still at their peak and the system of minting and circulating coins reflects this.

It is worth looking a little more closely at what was going on in the regions of most direct relevance to Rus, and at a highly significant shift in the balance of output between mints in the central caliphal lands – Iraq and Iran. Towards the end of the ninth century, Early and Middle Abbasid issues were circulating in roughly equal proportions. The coins struck between 750 and the 820s were high-quality dirhams of many different types, which offer us a great deal of information. The dominant issues are the ones from the time of Harun al-Rashid and his sons al-Amin and al-Ma'mun. The issues dominating the Middle Abbasid period, from the 830s to the 880s, are those of al-Mutawakkil, al-Muntasir and al-Musta'in. The coins are comparatively badly struck and astonishingly uniform in type.

Things changed quite rapidly from the last years of the ninth century onwards. We shall consider below the Samanids' striking of their own silver coins. But first we must note the major reform carried out by Caliph al-Mu'tadid in 892, which changed the style of epigraphy on both gold and silver coins. Since the manufacture of coin dies was centralised and concentrated in a single workshop, the innovation soon spread across the vast swathes of the caliphate, and the characteristics of Late Abbasid coins took shape. The coins of earlier periods, especially the lowest-quality pieces of the ninth century, began to drop out of circulation. They were used as raw material for the new reformed coins.

In this Late Abbasid period, something like 50 mints were in operation in the caliphate's central lands, in areas stretching from Fars and Jibal to Syria and Egypt, and from Lower Mesopotamia to the southern Caucasus. The most important centres of production, turning out coins without interruption, were the capital cities of Baghdad ('City of peace', Madinat al-Salam) and Samarra ('He who sees it is delighted', Surra man ra'a), as well as the cities of Basra, Kufa and Wasit. Slightly more than a thousand varieties of silver dirhams have been identified, along with several hundred dinar types.

Not that all was quiet on the political plane. In the 930s the Shi'i Daylamite dynasty of the Buyids was on the rise, establishing itself in the regions of Fars and Jibal. The Buyids expanded into Iraq and had truly imperial ambitions, with their leader Adud al-Dawla demanding that the Abbasid caliph al-Mustakfi should proclaim him *shahanshah* ('king of kings'). The upshot was their conquest of the central regions of the caliphate as far as the borders of Syria and Upper Mesopotamia and the end of effective Abbasid statehood in 945. From this time on, the Buyids replaced the Abbasids as the real power, 'taking on' the Abbasid inheritance, as it were. This had an effect on coin production. Work did not halt at all the old mints, but dirhams bearing the names of numerous Buyid rulers soon became the mainstay of the money supply, replacing Late Abbasid dirhams. Their silver and gold issues continued into the first years of the eleventh century and the start of the so-called 'silver crisis'.

Khorasan and Central Asia

In the 880s, Ya'qub ibn al-Layth al-Saffar, the founder of the new dynasty of the Saffarids, consolidated his hold over Khorasan. His very first silver coins were struck in Panjshir, a district rich in silver mines. Ya'qub's successors established themselves in the cities of wealthy Fars. For more than a quarter of a century they were rivals of the Abbasid caliphs and their commanders, and in the 890s and 900s they were rivals of the Samanids of Transoxania, too. Most of their coin types were struck in the Fars cities of Shiraz, Jannaba and Arrajan and circulated in the eastern provinces of the caliphate.

The 'Saffarid precedent' had a significant influence on the development of by far the most massive coin output in the entire history of the early medieval Islamic world, an output that completely changed the dynamics of its monetary circulation at the beginning of the tenth century: that of the Samanids (Table 8.2). They emerged in the ninth century as sub-governors for the Tahirids of Samarqand, Fergana, al-Shash (Tashkent) and Herat; by 875, they had consolidated their rule and Nasr I was invested as Abbasid

Table 8.2 Coin typology and reign dates of the Samanids, independent emirs in Transoxania

Typology	Period (AD)	Period (AH)	Rulers
Early Samanid[1]	895–943	282–332	Nasr I (864–92) Isma'il I (892–907) Ahmad II (907–14) Nasr II (914–43)
Middle Samanid	944–76	333–66	Nuh I (943–54) Ibrahim ibn Ahmad (947) [rival claimant] Abd al-Malik I (954–61) Mansur I (961–76)
Late Samanid	977–99	367–89	Nuh II (976–97) Mansur II (997–9) Abd al-Malik II (999–1000)

Note
1 Roughly contemporaneous with the late Abbasid period.

governor of the province of Transoxania; and by 892, they had united under the rule of Nasr's brother, Isma'il I, who received investiture from the new Abbasid caliph, al-Mu'tadid. Within two years, Isma'il had developed his own silver coinage in Samarqand and al-Shash. Over the next 30 years, output grew exponentially, reaching levels never seen before, especially from the 900s, when the Samanids established their suzerainty over the parts of Tokharistan that were rich in silver – Balkh, Andaraba and Ma'din (literally 'mine'), under the rule of a local dynasty, the Banijurids, and their governors. By the 920s, the commonest dirhams by far were those struck for Isma'il I, Ahmad II and Nasr II. Coin striking carried on until the Late Samanid period, when their polity began to wane, breaking up altogether under pressure from the Qarakhanids and Ghaznavid Turks. Treachery played a part in this: in the early 980s, the Turkic military commanders and vassals of the Samanids in Khorasan, the Simjurids, turned against their masters. All these goings-on have left a clear mark in the coinage.

Besides the regular issues of the Saffarids, Banijurids, Samanids and Late Abbasids in the towns and provinces of the Islamic world, all manner of military commanders and rebels aimed for possession of coin mints. We know of silver coins struck in Nishapur by the Tahirid general Rafi' ibn Harthama and the rebel Layla b. Nu'man, who was defeated by the Samanids; in Shiraz by the Saffarid supporter Subkara; in Andaraba by the Banijurids' enemy, Sa'id ibn Shu'ayb; and in al-Muhammadiyah (Rayy) by the Su'luqid governor Muhammad b. Ali.

Periodisation of the main Islamic coin groups found in Rus

While numismatists have made significant progress in describing and classifying early Islamic coins, Bauer's somewhat gloomy assessment of the state of play in Russia – 'eastern numismatics [have] yet to be written' – holds as true today as in the pre-war period when he was writing.[9] Elsewhere we now have corpuses of coin types and regions,[10] as well as analytical overviews[11] and reference works.[12] This gives us a much wider and more reliable base than Bauer and Vasmer had for studying the history of coin striking and the circulation of money in the early medieval Islamic world.

Dirhams that found their way into Rus at various stages were issued by the dynasties, tribes or groups shown in Table 8.3.[13]

As noted above, most significant for our study are the tenth-century silver dirhams issued by the Samanid rulers of Central Asia,[14] starting with the interim group of Abbasid-Samanid type (892–5, AH 279–81) and continuing from 895/6 (AH 282) with coins minted with the names of the Samanid rulers (see Table 8.2). In the late period, we also have the distinctive issues struck by the Simjurids.[15]

The main Samanid mints were in their principal urban centres of Samarqand, Bukhara, Merv, Nishapur and Balkh, and there were also important mints at the silver mines of al-Shash [Tashkent], Andaraba and Maʿdin. The dirhams produced there were conveyed by caravan from Khwarazm to the markets of northern and eastern Europe by way of Khazaria and Bulgar, straddling the Lower and the Middle Volga respectively.

Dirhams from the issue types shown in Table 8.4 have been found in Russia.

There are also finds of the various series of imitative coins. These include Khazar imitations of Abbasid dirhams, and also Volga Bulgar imitations of Samanid coins. The latter were issued in their principal town of Bulgar as well as in Suvar (another of their settlements); and even when Bulgar dynasts started to issue dirhams with their own names and authority-symbols, they continued to imitate Samanid dirhams.[16]

Coin circulation periods in mid-eighth- to early eleventh-century Rus

The earliest archaeological evidence for dirhams being imported into Rus is from the mid- to late eighth century and comes from four main regions: the northern Caucasus (Dagestan, Chechnya and northern Ossetia); the upper reaches of the Donets (Verkhniy Saltov to the north-east of Kharkhiv and the Netaylovka burial grounds on the opposite bank, as well as a number of hillforts in the Khazar-Slav border regions); the lower reaches of the Volkhov (including Staraia Ladoga's Zemlianoe fortress); and the wider and more culturally varied region encompassing the Middle Volga and the Kama. Judging by the dozen or so hoards found in the northern Caucasus and along the Upper Donets, the coins in circulation there were closely linked to the Transcaucasus and the caliphate's central and Caspian provinces. Coins circulating in Khazaria in the late eighth and early ninth centuries appear to be linked to Staraia Ladoga and the Volkhov region and indeed to northern Rus in general.[17] Coins were brought to the Volga-Kama region mainly by caravan from Central Asia.[18]

Table 8.3 Dirhams arriving in Rus

Region where minted	Pre-Abbasid late C7–early C8	Early Abbasid 750–833	Middle Abbasid 833–892	Late Abbasid 892–945	Post-Abbasid 945–early C11
General	Sasanians (drachms) Umayyads[1]	– – – – – – Abbasids – – – – – – – – – –			– – – –
Eastern Persia Transoxania Khwarazm	rebel allies of the Abbasids[2]	– – – – Saffarids and their contemporaries – – – –			
			– – – Samanids and their vassals – – –		
					Khwarazm Shahs (Afrighids of Kath / Ma'munids of Gurganj) Qarakhanids
Iraq Jazira	Umayyad governors of the eastern provinces (al-Mashriq)[3]			Abbasid vasals	Hamdanids Marwanids Uqaylids
Transcaucasus Western Persia	ispahbads of Tabaristan (Dabuyids)	Abbasid governors of Tabaristan[4]	Alids Dulafids	– – – – Buyids – – – –	
				Sajids	Sallarids Ziyarids
Egypt Syria			Tulunids		
North Africa		Abbasid governors of Ifriqiyya Idrisids and their contemporaries Aghlabids			
Spain		Umayyads of Spain			

Notes
1 Klat (2002); Kuleshov (2009), table 2.
2 Wurtzel (1978).
3 Kolesnikov (1998).
4 For their coins, see Malek (2004).

Table 8.4 Dirham issue types found in Rus

Type	Most complete sequences	Smaller series showing a discernible pattern
Pre-Abbasid	Umayyad	Sasanian (*drachms*) Umayyad governors of the eastern provinces (al-Mashriq)
Early Abbasid	Early Abbasid Abbasid governors of Ifriqiyya Abbasid governors of Tabaristan	Idrisid Aghlabid
Middle Abbasid		Saffarid
Late Abbasid	Samanid and their vassals	Banijurid and other Samanid vassals
Post-Abbasid	Buyid (later tenth century) Ziyarid	Late Abbasid Sharwan Shahs Uqaylid Marwanid Qarakhanid

Nearly all coin finds from the second half of the eighth century come in small quantities from burials or cultural settlement layers. It is only from the early ninth century onwards that we start to find actual coin hoards being deposited in eastern and northern Europe, as well as on the southern Baltic coast. By analysing the pattern of coins in our ninth-century hoards, and sequencing them according to the ratios of precisely dated issues and the coin *tpqs* they contain, we can identify the stages of early coin circulation in Rus shown in Table 8.5.[19]

A similar analysis of tenth-century hoard patterns, where the sheer quantity of silver is incomparably greater than in the ninth-century hoards, shows the stages displayed in Table 8.6.

It is worth considering Stage E in slightly more detail (see Table 8.7); it is represented by a large number of coin hoards and is enriched by the eventful numismatic history of the Samanid state and the Volga Bulgars, and by developments in Rus. The Samanids from the time of Isma'il I onwards were intent on enlarging their domain at the expense of various petty dynasties in Central Asia and gaining recognition of their right to rulership. Receiving grandiose documents, gifts and robes of honour from the caliph in Baghdad were important means of gaining recognition, but Isma'il saw that multiple advantages would accrue to him from issuing coins on a massive scale. The emir could thereby gain legitimacy through minting them in his own name, while at the same time avowing loyalty to the caliph through mentioning him on the coins, too. Furthermore, at a more practical level, the issuing of a reliable coinage could improve the level of order in his realm and render it more amenable to tax-collection. Isma'il seems to have regularised the system

Table 8.5 Analysis of eighth- and ninth-century coins found in Rus

Stage	Sub-stages	Approximate hoard dates	Time-span (years)	Caliphal coins circulating	Other types of coins found (dirhams unless otherwise stated)
A		750s–80s	~ 30–5	c. 725–75	Sasanian (drachms) Umayyad Early Abbasid
B		780s–800s	~ 20–5	c. 775–800	Abbasid governors of Ifriqiyya Abbasid governors of Tabaristan
C[1]		800s–50		c. 800–47 (end of al-Wathiq's rule)	Early Abbasid (Harun al-Rashid, al-Amin and al-Ma'mun) Khazar imitations (2nd quarter of the ninth century; Stage C2 only)
	C1	800s–20s	~ 40–5		
	C2	830–40s			
D		850–905		847–c. 892 (al-Mutawakkil's rule to the end of the Middle Abbasid period)	Middle Abbasid 'blank-flan' (i.e. not struck with die, or struck with worn die) dirhams Khazar imitations (2nd half of the ninth century) Saffarid / Banijurid coins (Stage D2 only)
	D1	850–70s	~ 45–50		
	D2	880s–900s			

Note
1 Some large hoards or those with independently dated contexts can be sub-divided, as can collections containing Khazar imitations from the second quarter of the ninth century (in the case of Stage C) and Saffarid and Banijurid coins (in the case of Stage D).

Table 8.6 Analysis of tenth-century coins found in Rus

Stage	Approximate hoard dates	Time-span (years)	Samanid coins circulating	Other types of coins found (dirhams unless otherwise stated)
E	895–955	~ 50–5	c. 892–943 (reigns of Isma'il I, Ahmad II and Nasr II)	Early Volga Bulgar imitations Late Abbasid Saffarid Sajid Early Buyid (pre-945)
F	945–79	~ 25–30	c. 943–76 (opening stages of the late period; reigns of Nuh I, Abd al-Malik I and Mansur I)	Buyid (post-945) Volga Bulgar (including emirs Mika'il ibn Ja'far, Abdallah ibn Mikhail, Talib ibn Ahmad) Hamdanid Sallarid Late Wajihid (including those of Muhammad and Umar, sons of the dynasty's founder Yusuf ibn Wajih) Julandid

(Continued)

Table 8.6 (Cont.)

Stage	Approximate hoard dates	Time-span (years)	Samanid coins circulating	Other types of coins found (dirhams unless otherwise stated)
F	945–79	~ 25–30	*c.* 943–76	Khwarazm Shah Ahmad ibn Muhammad (Iraqids of Kath) [AH 348 type only] Samanid vassal issues of Tokharistan ('oversize dirhams') Non-Islamic coins: from the Indian mint of Kabul (Ohinda) / Byzantine *miliaresia*
G	969–1004	~ 25–30	*c.* 961–97 (reigns of Mansur I and Nuh II, including the vassal mints of the Simjurids and Khorasan governors)	Ziyarid Bawanids of Tabaristan Late Buyid Volga Bulgar (Mu'min ibn Ahmad at Suvar and Mu'min ibn al-Hasan at Bulgar) [also bracteates[1]] Non-Islamic coins: Byzantine *miliaresia* of Basil II and Constantine VIII (976–1028) / western deniers
H	994–1025	~ 20–5		Marwanid Uqaylid 'Type A' (finds from Rus and the Baltic region) Late Ziyarid Khwarazm Shahs (Ma'munids of Gurganj) ['Type B' finds from Volga Bulgaria] Qarakhanid Non-Islamic coins: Byzantine *miliaresia* from the reign of Basil II and Constantine VIII and western deniers begin to dominate
J	1015–70s	~ 60		Islamic coin imports into Rus cease altogether at the start of Stage J, although coins from earlier stages and fragmented coins remained in circulation as bullion and also as decorative pendants amidst the western deniers; the terminus for this stage is quite blurred

Note
1 One-sided silver coins.

of weights and measures in his realm, judging by the stone weights bearing his name that have been found.[20] He and his successors instituted an effective bureaucracy, putting competent – often scholarly – officials in charge of its departments. The upshot was prosperity, fuelled by trading, in which slaves were a particularly valuable commodity. This was, however, no proof against struggles for the succession to the emirate at Bukhara. Rival members of the

Samanid dynasty struck their own coins as a mark of legitimacy,[21] while looking to Turkish commanders and their war-bands for support. They also had to face down the Buyids to the west, especially after the Buyids' conquest of Baghdad in 945, and their insecurity is registered by the grandiose styling of their coins.[22] Turbulence at the top eventually upset key functions such as tax-collection and this seems to be registered in a falling-off in the quantity and quality of dirhams minted from the 960s onwards.

Neither the Volga Bulgars nor the Rus can have been left unaffected by the Samanids' vicissitudes. The commercial – and cultural – orientation of the Bulgars is registered by the sizeable number of coins struck in imitation of the Samanids' dirhams, as also by the design of the coins issued by Bulgar rulers in their own names: Mika'il ibn Ja'far, for example. There is no such firm evidence that imitative dirhams were struck to the west of Volga Bulgaria, but the Rus' commercial reliance on the inflow of silver coins from the Samanids is plain enough. It can hardly be a coincidence that Prince Sviatoslav Igorevich launched his expedition south-eastwards and devastated Khazar urban centres in the 960s, at a time when silver was ceasing to arrive in significant quantities from the Samanid mints. His campaign, datable to *c.* 966, was spectacularly successful in putting paid to Khazaria as a major

Table 8.7 More detailed breakdown of Stage E

Stage	Approximate dates	Time-span (years)	Latest issues (dirhams unless otherwise stated)
E1a	895–908	~ 14	Samanid (Isma'il I), minted at al-Shash and Samarqand Saffarid Eastern European 'ugly' imitations of the types found in the Klukowicze and Pogorel'shchina hoards
E1b	909–14	~ 6	Samanid (Ahmad II) and his vassals in Tokharistan and eastern Transoxania Issues from al-Shash, Samarqand, Andaraba, Balkh and a dozen other minor mints
E1c	915–24	~ 10	Samanid (Nasr II) Issues from al-Shash, Samarqand and the vassal mints of Tokharistan and eastern Transoxania
E2	925–45	~ 20	Samanid (Nasr II's dirhams replace those of Isma'il I and Ahmad II) Volga Bulgar imitations of Samanid coins bearing the names of the first Muslim ruler of Volga Bulgaria, al-Amir Yaltawar (Almış Elteber), and the later ruler Mika'il ibn Ja'far are well represented (the latter not before the end of the 930s)[1]

Note
1 Rispling (1990).

power, but it could do nothing to revitalise the influx of silver from the mints and mines of the Samanids further east.

Trade and the earliest Rus *druzhina*s

Before moving on from the chronology of coin circulation in Rus to consider the trading activities of its various centres, we should briefly consider the term *druzhina* (literally, a company or retinue). Arguments over whether the term 'state' is appropriate or adequate for describing the political development of Rus between the eighth and tenth centuries, and what the particular features of that early polity were, have led to diametrically opposing views: from representing early Rus as a feudal or quasi-feudal state on the one hand, to the complete dismissal of any hints of a state and the downright 'primitivising' of its society on the other.[23] However, there is greater scholarly agreement over the key role of the *druzhina* in the establishment and development of the early Rus economy: both in the opening period, when *druzhina*s consisted of arms-bearing traders; and in the later period, when princely *druzhina*s came to the fore. The existence and material culture of the early *druzhina*s is also vividly represented by archaeological finds from the ninth and tenth centuries.[24] It thus seems more useful to consider trade between local *druzhina*s and particular centres of power, rather than the long-distance trade relations of the emergent Rus polity as a whole.

By aligning the dynamics of coin circulation (using the contents, typology and distribution-patterns of coin finds)[25] with what we know of events in Rus from the eighth to the beginning of the eleventh centuries, we can suggest the following chronology of economic activity and commercial interaction between the Rus *druzhina*s and settled communities.

Stage 1: Staraia Ladoga and Khazaria (750s–800s; coin circulation Stages A and B)

Dirhams were circulating at the settlement in Staraia Ladoga and along the northern Volkhov, and thus in what would eventually become political centres of Rus, as well as in those of its neighbours. This was connected with the circulation of such coins in Khazaria and the Slav-Khazar borderlands, and marks the beginning of the arrival of Islamic coins into the Baltic region. The members of the earliest Rus *druzhina*s started to trade with some parts of the Islamic world, primarily by way of the Khazar khaganate, whose traders acted as intermediaries.

Stage 2: Rus expansion along the riverways (810–90s; coin circulation Stages C and D)

Coins started to circulate around the settlements and encampments of arms-bearing traders along the river routes and portages of the forest zones of northern and eastern Europe – in the river basins of the Western Dvina, Upper Dnieper, Neman, Msta, Mologa, Upper Volga and Upper Oka. This series of networks of trading enterprises and waterways criss-crossed the entire forest zone; it linked the Rus settlements and *druzhina* centres with Khazaria, Volga Bulgaria and the Kama region and, according to the Arabic geographers of the ninth and early tenth centuries, reached on across the Caspian – to Tabaristan and the central provinces of the caliphate.

Stage 3: Kiev and Volga Bulgar (900–40s; coin circulation Stage E)

This is the era of Riurik (late ninth century) and of Oleg and Igor; from around the end of the ninth century onwards, it saw the establishment of a new ruling dynasty in Kiev, the Riurikids. Hoards from this earliest phase of Kievan Rus are characteristic of this stage of coin circulation, with Volga Bulgaria seemingly now functioning as the main trading partner. There is a marked falling-off of direct trade with centres in the caliphate, shown by the lack of significant quantities of Late Abbasid dirhams in the hoards.

Stage 4: Novgorod, Gnezdovo and new axes (950s–70s; coin circulation Stage F)

This stage covers coin circulation during the reigns of Princess Olga and her son Sviatoslav Igorevich. Characteristic hoards come from Novgorod at the time of its foundation, the Novgorodian hinterland and the settlement at Gnezdovo, which was the precursor to Smolensk. As in the previous stage, contacts with Volga Bulgaria were fundamental to Rus trade with the outside world. However, a number of changes in coin circulation indicate the development of new axes: with Byzantium, especially following the Russo-Byzantine treaty of 944 and the baptism of Princess Olga in Constantinople, probably in 957; and with the region to the south of the Caspian, after the removal in the late 960s of the 'Khazar obstacle' to direct trade there. This was a significant factor in the sudden and massive output of silver coins from the mints of the Ziyarids in the 970s.

Stage 5: axes to the east, south and west (980s–1010s; coin circulation Stages G and H)

Stage 5 marks the reign of Vladimir Sviatoslavich, when a network of wide-ranging and multi-faceted relationships between the various Rus *druzhina*s and early urban centres was established. This took three main directions: east and south-east towards Volga Bulgaria, the Caspian basin and the western Transcaucasus; south to Byzantium; and now – for the first time on a really sizeable scale – west, to the markets of central and western Europe. The first of these axes is signalled most clearly by coinage from the Uqaylid and Marwanid emirates in Upper Mesopotamia and Asia Minor, wherein the principality of Tmutarakan may have played a key role in developing trade links, taking on the role of Khazar-ruled Tamatarkha (S-m-krts).

A rather more precise chronology of the coins circulating in early Rus should help us to understand the dynamics of trading in the region. It is hoped that the framework suggested above may offer a more detailed picture of the early Rus' trade with the outside world, making possible further investigation into their geographical ties and the role of the *druzhina*s in this trade.

Appendix 8.1 Major and minor Islamic dynasties whose dirhams reached Rus: a pocket dictionary[1]

Dynasty/tribe/ governorships	Region	Dates active AD (AH)	Brief description	Main centres, mints and coinage
Abbasids	Caliphate or dar al-Islam	750–945 (132–334)	Meccan clan descended from the Prophet's uncle al-Abbas, giving them legitimacy in Sunni orthodox eyes that the Umayyads lacked. Faced frequent revolts in the first century of their rule from the descendants of the 2 sons of Ali, whose followers (the Shi'a) felt that they certainly had a better claim to the caliphate. Steadily lost territories as local groupings broke away from their control. Abbasid power in Baghdad collapsed in 945 during the reign of al-Mustakfi, when their territories came under Buyid control, but the Abbasids remained as nominal caliphs. After the Mongol sack of Baghdad in 1258, moved to Aleppo and then Cairo (1261–1517)	Initially centred in Kufa; in 762 al-Mansur moved the capital from Damascus and established Baghdad, near the Sasanian capital Ctesiphon

Basra and Kufa until 763/4 (AH 147); thereafter Baghdad (Madinat al-Salam) and Rayy (al-Muhammadiya), with others being al-Abbasiya, Ifriqiyya, Balkh, al-Shash, Samarqand, Isfahan, al-Rafiqah and Sistan (Zaranj)

Middle and Late period: most common mint is Madinat al-Salam, with others being Basra, Samarra (Surra man ra'a), Shiraz and Wasit

Early Abbasid dirhams pre-762/3 (AH 145) have a common type but show an increasing variation by mint and by year thereafter. Middle and Late Abbasid dirhams are once again standardised and fairly uniform across the caliphate, apart from around the turbulent rule of al-Mu'tamid (870–92) |
| Abbasids (rebel allies of) | | 744/5–754/5 | The Abbasid revolt of the black banners against Umayyad rule gained momentum slowly. Led by Abu Muslim, it climaxed in the mid-740s. The Abbasid al-Saffah was elected caliph in 749 (AH 132) | Over a dozen mints struck dirhams, including Jayy and Merv

Coins started to be struck from 744/5 (AH 127) onwards, with brief slogans proclaiming the sectarian doctrines of the various groups in addition to the usual Umayyad inscription. Not all supported al-Saffah and some factions continued to strike their own coins until 754/5 (AH 137) |

Abbasid governors of Ifriqiyya (North Africa)		Last effective governor d. 787	Member of the Muhallabid family appointed governor of Ifriqiyya in 768, marking the beginning of nearly 3 decades of Muhallabid rule there; last governor was appointed in 797, before the Aghlabid dynasty was established in 800	After the Muslim conquest, *drachms* of Sasanian type continued to be issued with local Abbasid governors' names, mainly in Arabic, until *c.* 808/9, when they were replaced by standard dirhams with Arabic inscriptions
Abbasid governors of Tabaristan	Tabaristan	761–808/9		
Aghlabids	Ifriqiyya, Algeria, Sicily	800–909 (184–296)	Sunni dynasty of amirs originally from Khorasan, whose founder had served in the Abbasid army; granted the province of Ifriqiyya by Harun al-Rashid for annual tribute of 40,000 dinars; independent rulers under nominal suzerainty of the caliph; overthrown by the Fatimids	Centre at Kairouan (al-Qayrawan) and main mints were al-Abbasiya and Ifriqiyya; also Sicily. Coins followed Abbasid models, notably the western Abbasid style of al-Abbasiya and Ifriqiyya
Alids of Tabaristan	Tabaristan	864–900, 914–28	Local Shi'i rulers in Amul and Gurgan. The first and most powerful Zaydi emirate was active in Tabaristan between 864 and 928; it was interrupted by Samanid occupation in 900 but restored in 914 by another Alid branch	Amul and Gurgan
Banijurids (Abu Dawudids)	Tokharistan (eastern Khorasan)	*c.* 848–*c.* 908 (*c.* 233–*c.* 295)	A line of minor local rulers and vassals of the Samanids, probably of Iranian origin	Balkh, with most coins struck at Andaraba and Panjhir. Coinage was spurred by their ownership of the Panjshir valley and adjoining regions

(Continued)

Appendix 8.1 (Cont.)

Dynasty/tribe/ governorships	Region	Dates active AD (AH)	Brief description	Main centres, mints and coinage
Bawandids (ispahbads of Tabaristan)	Tabaristan highlands and Gilan	665–1349 (45–750)	Longest lived of the petty Caspian Shiʿi dynasties and rivals for power with the Qarinids; vassals of the Buyids	Firrim Coins were only struck in 2 periods: silver from 353 to the 380s (debased after 370); and gold only from 494 to 560
Buyids (Buwayhids)	Most of north, west and southern Iran and Iraq	932–1062 (320–454)	Daylamite Shiʿi dynasty originally made up of 3 principalities (southern and western Persia, and Iraq) which were united in the late tenth century. The most powerful and far-reaching of the independent emirates to emerge in the east as the Abbasid caliphate weakened (along with the Ziyarids and Samanids), the Buyids assumed real power in Baghdad, exerting influence over the Abbasids while pledging allegiance to them. Weakened by factionalism and threatened by the Oghuz and then the Seljuq Turks, who roused Sunni feeling against the Buyids. Baghdad was lost to the Seljuqs in 1055, although Fars held out for 7 more years	The main Buyid amir was based in either Baghdad or Shiraz. Over 60 mints, including in: Iraq: Baghdad, Basra, Wasit, Kufa Western Iran: Hamadan, Mah al-Kufa Khuzistan: Suq al-Ahwaz, Tustar min al-Ahwaz, Ram-Hurmuz Fars: Shiraz, Siraf, Fasa Kirman: Bardasir, Jiruft Central Iran: Isfahan, Qazvin, al-Muhammadiya Tabaristan: Amul, Gurgan
Dabuyids (Dabwayhids) (ispahbads of Tabaristan)	Tabaristan, Gilan, Ruyan	c. 640–761 (c. 19–144)	Local dynasty of ispahbads (local princes who governed for the Sasanian emperors) who claimed Sasanian descent. Zoroastrians who never accepted Islam. Ruled until the Abbasid invasion (758/9) and conquest (761) of the region	Sari Began to issue drachms of Sasanian type in 711/12 (AH 93) in reaction to the new Muslim dirhams. Tabaristan series coins were half the standard Sasanian drachm weight at c. 2.08g and may have been known as tabari dirhams

Dulafids	Jibal (central and western Iran)	Early C9–897 (early C3–284)	Arab Sunni dynasty who served as Abbasid governors of Jibal; briefly independent until defeated by the Abbasids, who took Jibal back into direct control	Capital at Karaj (between the mints of Isfahan and Hamadan)
Hamdanids	Northern Syria and the Jazira (Upper Mesopotamia)	906–1004 (293–394)	Arab Shi'i dynasty who rose to power as Abbasid governors of Mosul, becoming increasingly self-sufficient; seized Aleppo in 947, establishing a second branch there. Period of fierce jihad against the Byzantines and artistic flourishing under Saif al-Dawla; driven out of Mosul by the Buyids at the end of the tenth century, but reinstalled as their governors there	Capitals and main mints at Aleppo and Mosul, also Nasibin (in the eastern territories); Syrian mints less common. Silver coinage of variable quality, better struck at eastern than at western mints (as was Abbasid coinage)
Idrisids	Morocco	789–985 (172–375)	Arab Zaydi Shi'i dynasty, whose founder Idris I had to flee the Hijaz after participating in the Alid uprising against the Abbasids in 786 (AH 169). Several Berber (Amazigh, pl. Imazighen) chiefs in northern Morocco pledged allegiance, but the dynasty later fragmented and fell prey to Berber foes and the Fatimids	Walila, later Fez. More than 20 mints, the earliest ones being Tudgha and Walila, later Fez and Wazaqqur
Idrisids, contemporaries of	Southern Morocco	789–828 (172–213)	A number of local rulers, including the Kharijites of Tudgha and others mostly of the Sufri and Ibadi sects, struck coins during the time of Idris I and Idris II	Tudgha

(Continued)

Dynasty/tribe/ governorships	Region	Dates active AD (AH)	Brief description	Main centres, mints and coinage
Ispahbads of Tabaristan (see Bawandids; Dabuyids)				
Julandids (al-Julanda)	Oman	Mid-C10 (mid-C4)	Originally descendants of the Azd tribe from Yemen who arrived in Oman in pre-Islamic times. The first imams of the Ibadi sect of Islam, they were one of the first minor dynasties to break away from Abbasid control in 753 (AH 135). Ruled briefly on the Iranian side of the Persian Gulf	Huzu (near modern Bandar Lengeh on the Iranian coast of the Persian Gulf); most coins were struck at Huzu
Khwarazm Shahs (Iraqids of Kath)	Khwarazm	Pre-Islamic times to 995 (385)	Sunni Persianate dynasty who converted to Islam in the late eighth/early ninth century; in various periods under the suzerainty of the Sasanians, Hephthalites, Göktürks, Umayyads and Samanids; overthrown by the Ma'munids in 995	Based on the right bank of the Oxus at Kath; main mint was Khwarazm
Khwarazm Shahs (Ma'munids of Gurganj)	Khwarazm	995–1017 (385–408)	Local Khwarazmian family who overthrew the Iraqids of Kath; Gurganj (on the left bank of the Oxus) became increasingly important in the tenth century as emporium for the caravan trade up the Volga to Rus; under nominal Samanid suzerainty; in 1017 the Ghaznavids in Khorasan seized Khwarazm	Kath and Gurganj (Urgench); minted coins at Bukhara, Farwan, Kath, Khwarazm, Nisa and Jurjaniya
Marwanids	Diyar Bakr	983–1085 (372–478)	Shi'i dynasty of Kurdish origin who exploited the Buyids' decline to oust the Hamdanids from Diyar Bakr (the northern province of the Jazira) c. 990/1, going on to hold Mosul and threaten Baghdad; recognised their powerful neighbours the Tahirids and Uqaylids, as well as the caliph; overthrown by the Seljuqs in 1085	Mayyafariqin and Amid, minting also at al-Jazira

	Dates	Territory	Description	Mints
Qarakhanids (Ilek-Khans or Ilig-Khans)	922–1212 (283–609)	Transoxania, Fergana, Semirechye (modern south-eastern Kazakhstan) and eastern Turkestan	Turkish dynasty possibly originally from the Qarluq confederation who converted to Sunni Islam in the mid-tenth century and were attracted into Transoxania by the Samanids' decline. Loosely structured with 2 khanates: west (based in Samarqand) and east (in Kashgar)	Samarqand and Kashgar Some 60 mints, principal among which were Bukhara, Uzkand, Balasaghun (Quz-Ordu or Quz-Ulush), Akhsikath, Tashkent, Saghaniyan, Taraz
Saffarids	861–1003 (247–393) (continued as *maliks* of Sistan until 1537)	Sistan, but expanded into Persia and eastern Afghanistan	Sunni Persianate dynasty; one of the semi-independent or independent Iranian kingdoms – including the Tahirids, Samanids and Buyids – which began to appear on the fringes of the declining Abbasid caliphate. Conquered by the Seljuqs in 1048	Two dynasties: the Laythids 861/2 – 910/11 (AH 247–98) (Yaʿqub to al-Muʿaddal b. Ali) with Fars, Shiraz and Panjhir the most common mints; and the Khalafids 923/4 – c. 1003 (AH 311–90s) throughout Sistan, but Zaranj was the main mint
Sajids	889–929 (276–312)	Azerbaijan and extended to parts of Armenia	Sunni line of autonomous caliphal governors of Soghdian descent, never independent of Baghdad; the murder of the last governor led to the region being taken over by various Daylami and Kurdish tribes	Bardhaʿa (Barda) is the most common mint, with others being Ardabil, Adharbayjan and Arminiyya
Sallarids [Musafirids]	Pre-916– c. 1090 (Pre-304– c. 483)	Daylam, expanding eastwards after the collapse of the Sajid governors into Azerbaijan, Arran and parts of eastern Armenia	Native Shiʿi Iranian dynasty with 2 branches ruling from Tarom and Ardabil. Came under pressure from the Buyids, among others, as well as intense factional in-fighting, becoming vassals of the Seljuqs in 1043	Tarom and Ardabil

(Continued)

Appendix 8.1 (Cont.)

Dynasty/tribe/governorships	Region	Dates active AD (AH)	Brief description	Main centres, mints and coinage
Samanids	Khorasan and Transoxania, with increasing suzerainty over Khwarazm, the lands of the Upper Oxus and Sistan while rivalling the Buyids in Persia	819–1005 (204–395)	One of the major independent Sunni Persianate dynasties; had previously ruled as governors under the Abbasid caliphate, the Tahirids or both. Awarded Khorasan in 900 by the caliph in gratitude for their defeat of the Saffarids	Mints reflect changing geography of the kingdom: Balkh, Bukhara, Samarqand and al-Shash are most common for silver; others include Andaraba, Maʿdan, Farwan and Nishapur. Silver mines in eastern Khorasan and Badakhshan. A branch of the Samanids ruled at Akhsikath in the Fergana valley, and minted their own coins
Sasanians [Sasanids]	Persia and Central Asia	224–651	Pre-Islamic Persian dynasty	Capital at Ctesiphon. Main currency was the silver *drachm*; over 50 mints, of which the most common were Basra, Bishapur, Darab-jird and Sijistan (Sistan). Early Islamic silver coinage adopted Sasanian models (notably the silver *drachm*) and was struck from the death of Yazdigerd III in 651 until the early 700s (with subsidiary series in Tabaristan and eastern Sistan almost to the end of the eighth century)
Sharwan Shahs [Khaqanids/Shirvanshahs]	Shirvan (eastern Transcaucasus)	799–early C17 (183–early C11)	Title may go back to Sasanian times; governors of Armenia, Azerbaijan, Arran, Shirvan and Darband (Bab al-Abwab)	Al-Yazidiyya

Simjurids	Khorasan/Quhistan	913–1002 (300–92)	Governors in Khorasan and feudatories in Quhistan; Turkish military slaves of the Samanids who rose to prominence when the Samanids drove out the Saffarids and occupied Sistan	Nishapur and Herat
Tahirids	Khorasan	821–91 (205–78)	Abbasid Governors in Khorasan, who rose to favour as commanders in the caliphal army and ruled from Nishapur as a hereditary line of governors; driven out by the Saffarids	Main mint Samarqand
Tulunids	Egypt and Syria	868–905 (254–92)	Dynasty of Turkish origin established by the Abbasid governor of Egypt who extended his power into Palestine and Syria; became the first independent dynasty to rule Islamic Egypt, as well as much of Syria, until the Abbasids restored the region to their direct rule	Capital at Fustat (near Cairo) with mints at Damascus (Dimashq) and al-Rafiqah (Raqqa) Tulunid silver is rare; gold struck at Misr (Fustat)
Umayyads	Caliphate or *dar al-Islam*	661–750 (41–132)	Dynasty of caliphs originally governors in Syria. Two distinct lines within the clan of Umayya: the first 3 caliphs were Sufyanids; the remaining 11, Marwanids	Some 100 mints recorded, of which Wasit and Damascus were the main silver ones. Other common mints included Ardashir Khurra, Basra, Darabjird, Istakhr, Kirman, Merv (Marw) and Sabur Umayyad caliphs introduced a reformed silver coinage in AH 79, starting out at c. 2.85g and rising to c. 2.97g by the 710s (AH 90s)

(Continued)

Appendix 8.1 (Cont.)

Dynasty/tribe/ governorships	Region	Dates active AD (AH)	Brief description	Main centres, mints and coinage
Umayyads of Spain	al–Andalus (the Iberian peninsula apart from the Christian kingdoms of the north) and north-west Africa	756–1031 (138–422)	From 711 (AH 92), Arab and Berber (Amazigh, pl. Imazighen) troops drove the Visigoths out of the Iberian peninsula. The area was ruled by a succession of Arab governors from the east under the Umayyads of Syria. In 756 (AH 138), Abd al-Rahman I – one of the few Umayyads to avoid slaughter during the Abbasid revolution – founded an emirate, becoming independent dynasts after the Abbasids took over from the Umayyads; from 927 (AH 316) start to style themselves caliphs	Ruled from Cordoba and Seville. All coins bear the mint name al-Andalus (presumably Cordoba) from 316–35 and again from 365 to the end of the dynasty. From 336–64 coins were minted at the nearby palace compound of Madinat al-Zahra (just outside Cordoba). Also dirhams from Madinat Fas (Fez in Morocco) from the late 370s until 402. Until 928 (AH 316), coinage was mostly anonymous; thereafter, the name of the ruler was added
Umayyad governors of the eastern provinces (al-Mashriq)	Kufa: controlled northern Iran, Iraq, Azerbaijan (until AH 94), Jibal, lands to the south/south-east of the Caspian Basra: controlled southern and eastern Iran, southern Iraq, the Gulf provinces of Khuzistan, Fars and Kirman; Khorasan and Sijistan[2]	661–750	A major administrative district, fairly autonomous of Damascus; immensely powerful governors controlled this eastern province (the lands of the former Sasanian empire) which made up nearly half the Umayyad territories; based in Basra and Kufa, unified from 670/1 (AH 50)	Basra and Kufa

Uqaylids	Jazira and northern Syria (at the greatest extent, stretching almost from Baghdad to Aleppo)	c. 990–1169 (c. 380–564)	Shiʿi Bedouin north Arab dynasty, originally dependants of the Hamdanids then vassals of the Buyids; later torn between the Fatimids (natural Shiʿi allies) and the Sunni Seljuqs, but territorial advantages in the latter; ended as Seljuq governors of Mosul	Nasibin and al-Mawsil; later issues from Ukbara; several regional branches of the dynasty issue coins
Wajihids	Oman	C10 (C5)	Arab dynasty, originally Abbasid governors of the region	Suhar
Ziyarids	Tabaristan and Gurgan (Jurjan) province	931–c. 1090 (319–c. 483)	Sunni Iranian dynasty originating in Gilan; at times independent, at others acknowledged Samanid or Buyid suzerainty (as part of the Samanid–Buyid struggle for northern Persia); later vassals of the Ghaznavids and then Seljuqs. Founded by a soldier of fortune in the caliphal army, descended from the royal clan of Gilan, who seized much of northern Persia after the revolt of a Samanid general, stretching his territories as far as Isfahan and Hamadan, but after his murder his territories contracted; his brother retained the eastern Caspian region	Amul, Gugan and Sariya (Sari) in Tabaristan, al-Hawsam in Gilan

Notes
1 For further details, see Album (2011); Bosworth (1996).
2 Bates (1986), pp. 237–8.

Appendix 8.2 Mint names

Mint name	Current/more familiar name
Transcaucasus and Western Persian lands	
Adharbayjan	Ardabil
Amul	Amol
Bardasir	Kerman (capital city of Kirman)
Firrim, Pirrim	stronghold in the Elburz Mountains, exact location unknown
Gurgan	Gorgan
Jiruft	Jiroft (south-west of Bam)
Madinat Jayy	Isfahan
Mah al-Kufa	Dinawar (to the north-east of Kermanshah in western Iran)
al-Muhammadiya	Rayy, Rey
Ram-Hurmuz	Ramhormoz, Samangan
Suq al-Ahwaz	Ahvaz
Tustar min al- Ahwaz	Shushtar (south-western Persia)
Eastern Persian lands, Transoxania and Khwarazm	
Andaraba	Andarab
al-Banjhir, Panjhir	in the Panjshir valley (*c.* 150km north of Kabul)
Marw al-Shahijan	Merv
al-Shash	Tashkent
Uzkand	Uzgen
Egypt and Syria	
Dimashq	Damascus
Halab	Aleppo
al-Mawsil	Mosul
al-Rafiqah	Raqqa
Iraq and Jazira	
al-Basrah	Basra
al-Kufah	Kufa
Madinat al-Salam	Baghdad
Nasibin	Nusaybin, Nisibis
Surra man ra'a	Samarra
Al-Andalus and North Africa	
Fas	Fez, Fès
Madinat al-Zahra	Cordoba
al-Qayrawan	Kairouan

Notes

1 This is an extended version of the paper on 'Islamic coins in Russian Viking-Age hoards' delivered at the 2015 International Medieval Congress in Leeds (9 July 2015), under the aegis of DfS. I should like to thank Julia Zarubinska-Toepritz for her help in translating into English the Russian version published as Kuleshov (2016).
2 Franklin and Shepard (1996); Machinskii (2009); Mel'nikova (ed.) (2011); Petrukhin (1995); Petrukhin (2013); Shinakov (2009); Tolochko (2015).
3 V. V. Grigoriev (1844) and P. S. Saveliev (1846) provided a rationale for the systematic study of early medieval Rus hoards; this was brilliantly taken up in the 1920s and 1930s by R. R. Vasmer (1933) and N. P. Bauer (2014) and, more recently, by Thomas Noonan and A. V. Fomin: on Noonan's work, see the special review by Kovalev and Rispling (2002); see also Fomin (1984); Fomin (1992). Others who have picked up the baton include V. L. Ianin (1956), S. A. Ianina (1956, 1962, 1963), V. V. Kropotkin (1968, 1969, 1971) and Roman Kovalev (2011, 2015; Kovalev *et al.* 1997).
4 Sections of this chronology have already been published: Kuleshov (2011a); Kuleshov (2015). See also the synthesis by Kuleshov (2012) and the contribution by V. S. Kuleshov and A. A. Gomzin to Leontiev and Nosov (2012), pp. 387–93; there are valuable amendments to Kuleshov (2011a) in Shchavelev and Fetisov (2014).
5 Ibn Khurradadhbih, *Kitab al-masalik*, ed. de Goeje, p. 153.
6 A likely product of this ambiance, for all the uncertainty about its date and authorship, is the text entitled 'Concerning clear-sightedness in business' (*Al-Tabassur bi-l-tijara*): Pellat, 'Gahiziana'.
7 Bates (1996).
8 On variations to silver dirham weights found in Scandinavia, see Jankowiak (2019), pp. 16–19.
9 Bauer (2014), p. 84.
10 Lowick (1996); Treadwell (2001); Klat (2002); Malek (2004); Shams Ishraq (2010); Vardanyan (2011); Vardanyan (2013).
11 Miles (1975); Heidemann (2010).
12 Diler (2009); Album (2011).
13 Kuleshov (2011b).
14 See Barthold (1900); Negmatov (1978).
15 On their coins, see Begovatov and Bugarchev (2013).
16 Franklin and Shepard (1996), p. 63.
17 Nosov (1976); Kirpichnikov (1995).
18 Kuleshov (2012). Our knowledge of the distribution of Sasanian *drachms* and Umayyad dirhams during this early minting period is, of course, governed by diagnostic variants in the composition of the known coin sets registering circulation in the central and eastern provinces of the caliphate in the eighth to early ninth century.
19 See Jankowiak in this volume.
20 Frye (1975), pp. 138, 140. On the Samanids, see also Treadwell (forthcoming).
21 Frye (1975), p. 141.
22 Frye (1975), p. 151.
23 A useful survey can be found in Dvornichenko (2014).
24 For the latest synthesis, see Makarov (2012).
25 See the maps and lists of hoards found in Rus, prepared by V. S. Kuleshov and A. A. Gomin, in Leontiev and Nosov (2012), pp. 387–93.

Bibliography

Primary sources

Ibn Khurradadhbih, *Kitab al-masalik*, ed. and French tr. M. J. de Goeje, *Kitab al-masalik wa-al-mamalik (Liber viarum et regnorum)*, BGA 6, Leiden (1889).

Pellat, C. (1954), 'Gahiziana, I: Le *Kitab al-Tabassur bi-l-tiğara* attribué à Ğahiz', *Arabica* 1(2): 153–65.

Secondary literature

Album, S. (2011), *A Checklist of Islamic Coins*, 3rd edn, Santa Rosa, CA.

Barthold, W. (1900), *Turkestan v epokhu mongol'skogo nashestviia*, vol. 2: *Issledovaniie*, St Petersburg.

Bates, M. L. (1986), 'History, geography and numismatics in the first century of Islamic coinage', *Revue Suisse de Numismatique* 65: 231–62.

Bates, M. L. (1996), 'The ʿAbbasid coinage system, 833–946', unpublished paper presented at the Annual Meeting of The Middle East Studies Association, 1996.

Bauer, N. P. (2014), *Istoriia drevnerusskikh denezhnykh system, IX v.–1535 g.*, Moscow.

Begovatov, E. A. and A. I. Bugarchev (2013), 'Monety dinastii Simdzhuridov', *Numizmaticheskie chteniia 2013 goda* (Moscow): 42–7.

Bosworth, C. E. (1996), *The New Islamic Dynasties: A Chronological and Genealogical Manual*, Edinburgh.

Busse, H. (1975), 'Iran under the Buyids', in R. Frye (ed.), *The Cambridge History of Iran*, vol. 4: *The Period from the Arab Invasion to the Saljuqs*, Cambridge, pp. 250–304.

Diler, Ö. (2009), *Islamic mints [Islam darp yerleri]*, 3 vols, Istanbul.

Dvornichenko, A. I. (2014), *Zerkala i khimery. O vozniknovenii Drevnerusskogo gosudarstva*, St Petersburg.

Fomin, A. V. (1984), 'Obrashenie oblomkov kuficheskikh monet v Vostochnoi Evrope v X– nachle XI v.', *Numizmatika i epigrafika* 14: 133–8.

Fomin, A. V. (1992), 'Novgorodskiie klady kuficheskikh monet X v.', *Numizmatika, Bonistika, Faleristika. Issledovaniia i Materialy. Numizmaticheskii Sbornik* 9: 32–44.

Franklin, S. and J. Shepard (1996), *The Emergence of Rus, 750–1200*, London.

Frye, R. (1975), 'The Samanids', in R. Frye (ed.), *The Cambridge History of Iran*, vol. 4: *The Period from the Arab Invasion to the Saljuqs*, Cambridge, pp. 136–61.

Grigoriev, V. V. (1844), 'O kuficheskikh monetakh VIII, IX, X i otchasti VII i XI veka, nakhodimykh v Rossii i pribaltiiskikh stranakh, kak istochnikakh dlia drevneishei otechestvennoi istorii', *Zapiski Odesskogo obshchestva istorii i drevnostei* 1: 115–66.

Heidemann, S. (2010), 'Numismatics', in C. Robinson (ed.), *The New Cambridge History of Islam*, vol. 1: *The Formation of the Islamic World, Sixth to Eleventh Centuries*, Cambridge, pp. 648–63, 775–9.

Ianin, V. L. (1956), *Denezhno-vesovye sistemy russkogo srednevekov'ia: domongol'skii period*, Moscow.

Ianina, S. A. (1956), 'Nerevskii klad kuficheskikh monet X veka', *MIA* 55: 180–207.

Ianina, S. A. (1962), 'Novye dannye o monetnom chekane Volzhskoi Bolgarii X v.', *MIA* 111: 179–204.

Ianina, S. A. (1963), 'Vtoroi Nerevskii klad kuficheskikh monet X v.', *MIA* 117: 287–331.

Jankowiak, M. (2019), 'Silver fragmentation: reinterpreting the evidence of the hoards', in J. Kershaw *et al.* (eds), *Silver, Butter, Cloth: Monetary and Social Economies in the Viking Age*, Oxford, pp. 15–31.

Kirpichnikov, A. N. (1995), 'Ladoga VIII–X vv. i ee mezhdunarodnie sviazi', *Drevniaia Rus': novye issledovaniea* (St Petersburg) [= *Slaviano-russkiie drevnosti* 2]: 28–53.

Klat, M. G. (2002), *Catalogue of the Post-Reform Dirhams: The Umayyad Dynasty*, London.

Kolesnikov, A. I. (1998), *Denezhnoe khoziaistvo v Irane v VII veke*, Moscow.

Kovalev, R. K. (2011), 'The role of Khazaria and Volga Bulgaria in trade relations between the Near East and European Russia during the tenth through the early eleventh centuries (the numismatic evidence)', *Archivum Eurasiae Medii Aevi* 18: 43–155.

Kovalev, R. K. (2015), 'O roli Rusov i Volzhskikh Bulgar v importe severoiranskikh dirkhemov v Evropu vo vtoroi polovine X–nachale XI v.', *DG* 2015, pp. 95–143.

Kovalev, R. K. and G. Rispling (2002), 'Thomas S. Noonan: in memoriam (1938–2001)', *Revue numismatique* 158: 375–83.

Kovalev, R. K. *et al.* (1997), 'Viking-Age dirham hoards from eastern and northern Europe', *A Survey of Numismatic Research 1990–1995: International Association of Professional Numismatists Special Publication* 13, Berlin, pp. 751–9.

Kropotkin, V. V. (1968), 'Novye materialy po istorii denezhnogo obrashcheniia v Vostochnoi Evrope v kontse VIII–pervoi polovine X v.', in E. I. Krupnov (ed.), *Slaviane i Rus'*, Moscow, pp. 72–9.

Kropotkin, V. V. (1969), *Ekonomicheskie sviazi Vostochnoi Evropy v I tysiacheletii nashei ery*, Moscow.

Kropotkin, V. V. (1971), 'Novye nakhodki sasanidskikh i kuficheskikh monet v Vostochnoi Evrope', *Numizmatika i epigrafika* 9: 76–97.

Kuleshov, V. S. (2009), 'Periodizatsiia chekanki kuficheskikh dirkhamov v Khalifate Umayyadov (po dannym numizmaticheskikh istochnikov)', *Materialy i issledovaniia Otdela numizmatiki* 48 (St Petersburg): 86–97.

Kuleshov, V. S. (2011a), 'Khronologiia obrashcheniia monet Khalifata v Vostochnoi Evrope (VIII–IX vv.)', *XVI Vserossiiskaia numizmaticheskaia konferentsiia: tezisy dokladov i soobshchenii*, St Petersburg, pp. 46–8.

Kuleshov, V. S. (2011b), 'Novye dannye o kompozotsii Koz'iankovskogo klada', *Studia Numismatica Albaruthenica* 1 (Minsk): 79–93.

Kuleshov, V. S. (2012), 'Kompleks umayyadskikh monet Elmedskogo klada i ego vydaiushcheiesia istoriko-kul'turmoie znacheniie', *Trudy Kamskoi arkheologo-etnographicheskoi ekspedicii*, vol. 8: *Arkheologicheskie pamiatniki Povolzhia i Urala*, Perm, pp. 218–27.

Kuleshov, V. S. (2015), 'Khronologiia obrashcheniia islamskikh monet v Vostochnoi Evrope (konets IX–XI v.)', *Numizmaticheskie chteniia Gosudarstvennogo Istoricheskogo Muzeia 2015 goda* (Moscow): 73–6.

Kuleshov, V. S. (2016), 'Periodizatsiia monetnogo obrashcheniia serediny VIII–nachala XI v. v Vostochnoi Evrope i dinamika ekonomicheskikh sviazei drevneishikh russkikh druzhin', *Upravlencheskoe Konsul'tiravanie* 2: 169–79.

Leontiev, A. E. and E. N. Nosov (2012), 'Vostochnoevropeiskie puti soobshcheniia i torgovye sviazi v kontse VIII–X v.', in N. A. Makarov (ed.), *Rus' v IX–X vekakh: arkheologicheskaia panorama*, Vologda, pp. 382–401.

Lowick, N. (1996), *Early Abbasid Coinage: A Type Corpus 132–218 H/AD 750–833*, ed. E. Savage, London.

Machinskii, D. A. (2009), 'Nekotorye predposylki, dvizhushchie sily i istoricheskii kontekst slozheniia russkogo gosudarstva v seredine VIII–seredine XI veka', in B. S. Korotkevich *et al.* (eds), *Slozhenie russkoi gosudarstvennosti v kontekste rannesrednevekovoi istorii Starogo Sveta* [= *Trudy Gosudarstvennogo Ermitazha* 49], St Petersburg, pp. 460–538.

Makarov, N. A. (ed.) (2012), *Rus' v IX–X vekakh: arkheologicheskaia panorama*, Vologda.

Malek, H. M. (2004), *The Dabuyid Ispahbads and Early Abbasid Governors of Tabaristan: History and Numismatics*, London.

Mel'nikova, E. A. (ed.) (2011), *Drevniaia Rus' i Skandinaviia: izbrannye trudy*, Moscow.

Miles, G. C. (1975), 'Numismatics', in R. Frye (ed.), *The Cambridge History of Iran*, vol. 4: *The Period from the Arab Invasion to the Saljuqs*, Cambridge, pp. 364–77.

Negmatov, N. N. (1978), *Gosudarstvo Samanidov. Maverannakhr i Khorasan v IX–X vv.*, Dushanbe.

Nosov, E. N. (1976), 'Numizmaticheskie dannye o severnoi chasti baltiisko-volzhskogo puti kontsa VIII–X v.', *Vspomogatel'nyie istoricheskie distsipliny* 8 (Leningrad): 95–110.

Petrukhin, V. I. (1995), *Nachalo etnokul'turnoi istorii Rusi IX–XI vv.*, Smolensk; Moscow.

Petrukhin, V. I. (2013), *Rus' v IX–X vekakh: ot prizvaniia variagov do vybora very*, Moscow.

Rispling, G. (1990), 'The Volga Bulgarian imitative coinage of al-Amir Yaltawar ("Barman") and Mikail b. Jafar', in *SP*, pp. 275–82.

Saveliev, P. S. (1846), *Mukhammedanskaia numizmatika v otnoshenii k russkoi istorii*, vol. 1: *Topografiia kladov s vostochnymi monetami i izdeliiami VII, VIII, IX, X i XI veka v Rossii i pribaltiiskikh stranakh*, St Petersburg.

Shams Ishraq, A. (2010), *Silver Coinage of the Caliphs*, London.

Shchavelev, A. S. and A. A. Fetisov (2014), 'K istoricheskoi geografii Vostochnoi Evropy IX–nachala X veka. Karta kladov i konfiguratsiia torgovykh putei', in I. G. Konovalova and M. Akvilon (eds), *Istoricheskaia geografiia*, Moscow, pp. 7–53.

Shinakov, E. A. (2009), *Obrazovanie drevnerusskogo gosudarstva: sravnitel'no-istoricheskii aspekt*, 2nd edn, Moscow.

Tolochko, O. P. (2015), *Ocherki nachal'noi Rusi*, Kiev.

Treadwell, L. (2001), *Buyid Coinage: A Die Corpus (322–445 AH)*, Oxford.

Treadwell, L. (forthcoming), *A History of the Samanids: The First Islamic Dynasty of Central Asia*, Edinburgh.

Vardanyan, A. R. (2011), *Islamic Coins Struck in Historic Armenia*, vol. 1: *Arminiya, Arran (Madinat Arran), Barda'a, Dabil, Harunabad/al-Haruniya and Ma'din Bajunays. Early Abbasid Period (142–277 AH/759–891 AD)*, Yerevan.

Vardanyan, A. R. (2013), *The Coins as Evidence for the History of Armenia and Adharbayjan in the Xth Century AD*, Tübingen.

Vasmer (Fasmer), R. R. (1933), 'Ob izdanii novoi topografii nakhodok kuficheskikh monet v Vostochnoi Evrope', *Izvestiia Akademii Nauk SSSR* 6–7 (Leningrad): 473–84.

Wurtzel, C. (1978), 'The coinage of the revolutionaries in the late Umayyad period', *Museum Notes (American Numismatic Society)* 23: 161–99.

Part III

Gotland

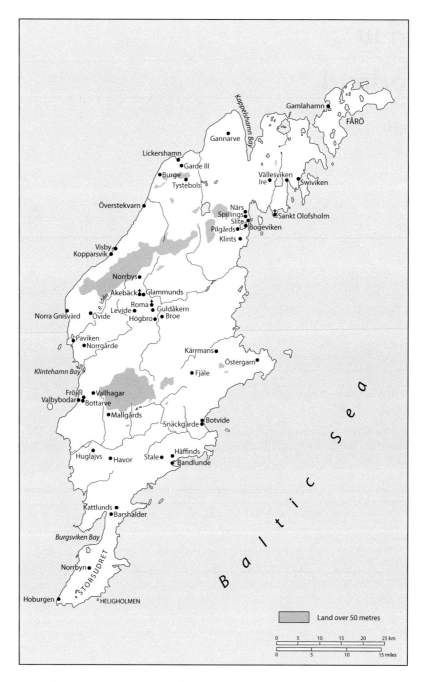

Map III.1 Gotland: geography and key locations.

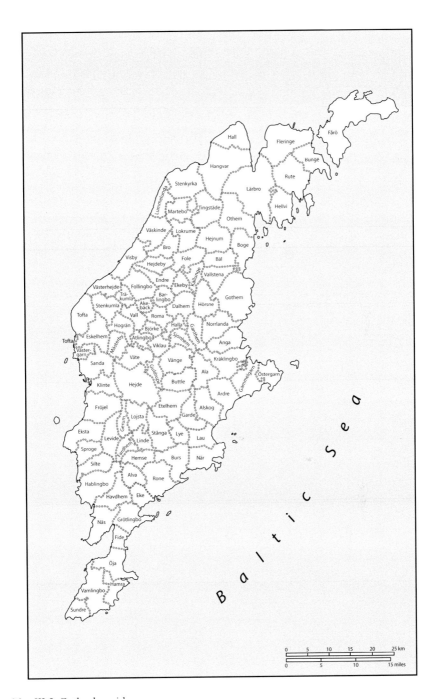

Map III.2 Gotland: parishes.

9 Hoards, silver, context and the Gotlandic alternative

Jacek Gruszczyński

The dearth of contemporary written sources about Gotland would suggest *ex silentio* that the island was of little importance to the early medieval political and economic dynamics of the Baltic zone. This situation is in stark contrast to the unparalleled abundance of Viking-Age precious metal finds on the island, principally hoards – by far the highest concentration of early medieval silver in Europe. This fact alone makes Gotland central to discussions on Viking-Age hoarding, economies and long-distance connections.

My doctoral research identified 866 finds of precious metal on Gotland in the published material,[1] of which 505 constitute hoards.[2] The following discussion is based on 347 of these hoards which fulfil three criteria: their coins can be fairly securely dated to between *c.* 800 and 1050, their locations can be determined with reasonable precision, and the weight of their silver is either known or can be securely reconstructed.

In analysing Gotland's hoards, one needs to ask two fundamental questions: why and how? Why was silver put in the ground and never reclaimed? And, since the Baltic zone has no sources of its own, how did it get there in the first place? However intriguing the why may be,[3] my focus below is on the how. Naturally, the reasons for importing silver and the mechanisms for circulating it are complex and varied. In this chapter I will examine just one aspect of this complicated issue: what factors led to the concentrations of silver deposits in Gotland, and the implications they have for our understanding of the movement of silver, people and goods. I will also briefly contrast the situation in Gotland with that in Pomerania and Svealand, showing that Gotlanders developed ways of dealing with silver that were quite different from those in other areas of the Baltic zone in the Viking Age.

Spatial analysis

Map 9.1 shows the distribution of Gotlandic hoards fulfilling our criteria. It is clear that the hoards are not randomly distributed, but form statistically significant clusters which are shown as dark-grey 'hot spots'. While in Pomerania and Svealand (Maps 9.2 and 9.3) it is possible to connect the

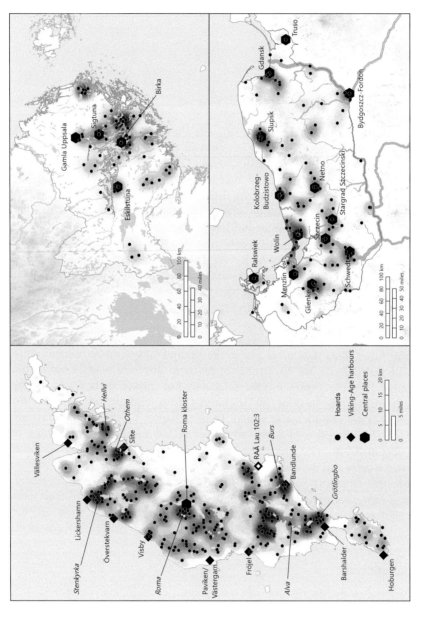

Maps 9.1, 9.2 and 9.3 Viking-Age hoards and harbour sites (landing places and central places) overlaid on kernel density heat maps of hoards from Gotland (left), Pomerania (top right) and Svealand (bottom right) (density classification by 9 equal intervals).

majority of hoard concentrations to some form of central place – be it emporium, stronghold or other high-status site – this is almost impossible on Gotland. The island's excavated settlements are few and far between, and they show little evidence of emporia-scale sites.

Guta Saga may hint at links between our hoards and places of social or economic importance on Gotland. It mentions a certain Avair Strabain of Alva parish, whose skilful negotiations brought about a treaty with Sweden.[4] It may be significant that Alva, home to this key player, is the location of a small but discrete hoard concentration. A much larger, denser cluster of hoards is found to the north-east of the island, in Hellvi parish. This is where the chapel built by Ormika of Hejnum was located, at Sankt Olofsholm, and the area is associated with a visit of the Norwegian king (and later saint) Olaf Haraldsson (1015–28), who is said to have stayed there a while.[5] If true, the young king may well have chosen a prosperous and prestigious area as his base. Another intensive cluster is located in the north-west, in Stenkyrka parish. Stenkyrka is associated in *Guta Saga* with Likkair Snielli ('the Wise'), who is said to have 'carried most authority at that time',[6] while the first church on Gotland was reportedly built by his son-in-law, Botair of Akebäck. It is worth noting that Akebäck lies in the western part of a hoard concentration centred around Roma. Like Avair, Likkair and Botair only appear in *Guta Saga* and their historicity is open to doubt. However, none of the hoards from the concentrations around Stenkyrka and Hellvi can be dated to the ninth century, and they are generally late tenth or early eleventh century: for the saga's author, these could thus have been important parishes in the not-so-distant past.

These associations are highly speculative. A slightly more solid indication of connections between our hoards and places of social and economic importance on the island may be traced in the proximity of the Stenkyrka concentration to the Viking-Age harbour at Lickershamn, which would have offered a crucial gateway for long-distance trade and elite contacts. A similar argument can be put forward for the hoard concentrations in Othem, Burs and Grötlingbo parishes. However, out of these only the harbour at Bandlunde in Burs parish has been excavated in any detail.[7]

One final concentration that requires mention here is the hoard cluster in the western part of Roma parish, centred only a few kilometres from the twelfth-century Cistercian monastery at Roma which is referred to as 'Sancta Maria de Gutnalia' in contemporary sources.[8] The name has been interpreted as deriving from a Latinised form of 'by the *Gutnalthing*' and is traditionally associated with the highest level of assembly on the island.[9] Although the exact location of the *Allthing* is the subject of debate, the area north of the monastery has yielded plentiful finds associated with trade and exchange, including weights, silver coins, fragments of copper alloy bars and ornaments.[10] Unfortunately, all the finds were made by metal detector and the site has yet to be excavated, leaving unclear the exact chronology, nature and character of one of the best candidates for a Gotlandic central place.

Regression analysis

Thus the association – however tentative – of hoards with possible loci of political power on Gotland remains elusive, and the reasons why hoard concentrations formed in some areas and not others becomes correspondingly complex. To investigate this, I analysed the information available on the context of silver discoveries on the island, including their association with contemporary settlements, earlier structures and settlements, burials and cemeteries, stone markers and picture stones, watery environments, metalworking workshops, harbours and landing places, historical and modern land use, and soil types. These factors were then combined into a regression model (see Appendix 9.1).

Infields

Firstly, and unsurprisingly, the model suggests that the formation and intensity of hoard concentrations is strongly associated with the productive landscape of infields, taken to be the arable fields and meadows pictured in the cadastral maps from *c.* 1700.[11] Some 56% of our Viking-Age hoards were associated with infields and a further 22% with pastureland; the remaining hoards were found outside the agricultural landscape, mostly in forests, bogs and lakes. Over three-quarters of the hoards were associated with areas of intensive agricultural production, and therefore with the most densely settled areas. The 22% found elsewhere are harder to explain, although one should not forget the importance of wood supply, stone quarrying and fishing to the Viking-Age population. The infields have also been subject to the most intensive cultivation over the past 300 years and this association between hoards and infields may be somewhat influenced by data bias, partly reflecting the reasons for the discovery of hoards in modern times rather than for their original deposition.

Harbours

The spatial and regression analysis highlighted, above all, the importance of relative ease of access to the largest possible number of harbours and, failing that, of relatively close proximity to at least one of them. Approximately fifty pre-Viking-Age and Viking-Age harbours (or rather landing places) and fishing villages dotted around the coastline of Gotland have been identified by Dan Carlsson, mainly through non-invasive archaeological surveys, and only a few have been excavated thus far.[12] Map 9.1 shows ten of these harbours for which we have archaeological evidence of Viking-Age activity, although this is mainly artefactual and not without interpretative problems. For example, scholars still struggle to agree on the nature of Viking-Age Visby, which only seems to have emerged as a harbour in the eleventh century and to have become an influential trading site no earlier than the

1200s.[13] Investigations at Västergarn face similar problems.[14] Despite the growing number of finds of dirhams, as well as German and English coins, suggesting that commercial activities were already underway in the early eleventh century, Västergarn's exact function and relationship with nearby Paviken in this period are still unclear. Chronology is not the only issue: the location of a harbour at Bogeviken divides opinion between the more traditional approach, placing it on the inner shore of the bay near the villages of Pilgårds and Boge, and Carlsson's well-argued suggestion that it lay in the centre of present-day Slite to the north-east.[15]

Despite these issues, it appears that Viking-Age Gotland had a relatively high number of landing places, even if the available evidence does not allow for parallels to be drawn with sites on the scale of the Baltic emporia. Only Paviken has a number of linear stone constructions leading into the water which might indicate some sort of harbour infrastructure, such as piers and jetties, although none of these features has yet been excavated to confirm their association with Viking-Age activity. Nevertheless, our few, partially excavated Viking-Age sites suggest that long-distance trade, craft production, non-ferrous metalworking and ship-building did take place at these locations throughout the Viking Age.[16]

Our map of hoard density and harbours with Viking-Age activity (Map 9.1) shows a general correspondence between the two. More exactly, the harbours lie at the extremities of these hoard concentrations, acting as potential 'gateways' for the silver to reach further inland. At the same time, the paucity of hoards in the eastern part of the island is underlined by the lack of harbours there: only two of our ten harbours showing evidence of Viking-Age activity lie on the east coast of Gotland.

The proximity of hoards to harbours helps explain the hoard concentrations in the coastal parishes of Stenkyrka, Othem, Burs and Grötlingbo, and the dearth of silver deposits along the eastern coast, but not the concentrations further inland. The densest cluster in the south of the island – on the border between the parishes of Linde, Fardhem and Hemse – is almost equidistant to three of our harbours (Bandlunde, Barshalder and Fröjel), indicating some sort of relationship between the quantity of silver deposits and accessibility to a number of harbours. In fact, nearly all the concentrations inland are within *c.* 19km of at least two of our Viking-Age harbour sites, which undoubtedly served as entrepôts for silver to reach the island. Including accessibility to the largest possible number of harbours provides a much closer correlation with the hoard clusters. The only outlier is a concentration in Alskog parish, near the site at Botvide where a number of stone constructions, presumably slipways, have been discovered.[17] The name of a nearby field, Snäckgärde, could well offer a hint: 'snäck-' may derive from 'snekkia', a word often used to describe ships, particularly Viking-Age and medieval war ships.[18] Unfortunately, since Botvide has not been archaeologically investigated or dated, this potential landing site could not be included in our analysis.

Metalworking

The regression model provided clear confirmation of an association between hoard concentrations and the areas with the most abundant evidence for non-ferrous metalworking. There can be little doubt that some of the silver deposited in the ground was intended for remelting and moulding into other objects, mainly the ornaments so important for the overt expression of cultural identity and display of status that was vividly captured by Ibn Fadlan in his tenth-century *Risala*.[19] Ny Björn Gustafsson has recently identified eighty-nine sites associated with Viking-Age non-ferrous metalworking, which he divides into four subgroups based on the estimated intensity and quality of the metalworking remains: farms (fifty-one), workshops (fifteen), possible workshops (eleven) and harbours (six).[20]

It may be surprising, therefore, that only about a tenth of our hoards come from sites that can be associated in some way with metalworking. Nevertheless, these sites still clearly show the level to which non-ferrous metalworking was practised on farms in otherwise ordinary settlements. Nearly half of what are believed to be Viking-Age farms on the island show some signs of non-ferrous metalworking (77 out of 180),[21] and some 43% of these metalworking farms were also find spots for one hoard or more. The proportion of farms constituting find spots *and* showing signs of non-ferrous metalworking is almost double that for farms where hoards have been found, which is just over a quarter (see below).[22] My results are reinforced by a comparison of distances between hoards and the nearest metalworking sites, which shows that nearly half of all silver deposits on Gotland were located within 2.5km of a metalworking site. Thus metalworking could have been an important factor in hoard deposition, although it is difficult to determine whether hoards were deposited because of workshops, or whether metalworkers were attracted to areas abundant in silver, where work was to be had. But given that only seven hoards can be associated with dedicated workshops, whereas twenty-six were found in otherwise ordinary settlements, the second possibility seems more likely.

Settlements

It is widely believed that hoards on Gotland are closely connected with Viking-Age settlements,[23] although this opinion is not without its opponents.[24] In my review of the available sources, I was only able to make this association with confidence for some 15% of hoards (53 out of 347). One should bear in mind that this is partly due to a lack of archaeological investigation: of the 180 probable Viking-Age settlements on the island, 90% are known only from the artefactual evidence, recovered by metal-detector survey and often questionable. Excavations have tended to be confined to the hoard itself, with no record of any other features present. Even excavations that have extended beyond the immediate vicinity of the find spot have often failed to capture the archaeological context. For example, in 1977 an area of 58m^2 was excavated in 10cm spits at the find spot of Garde III, with each spit scanned using metal detectors to retrieve the metal finds; however, when the underlying sterile soil was reached in part of the trench, the final spit was left unexplored.[25] Similarly, the hoard surroundings were excavated at Mallgårds II in 1977 and two postholes exposed, which unfortunately were not investigated further.[26] Out of the thirty-four excavated hoard find spots on the island, eighteen produced no archaeological features and four only undated features: these sites can provide solely conjectural, *artefactual* evidence associating hoards with putative settlements, based mainly on the decontextualised objects retrieved through metal-detecting. Eleven of the excavated find spots produced structural remains and/or cut features, and thus better *contextual* evidence to link the hoards with broadly contemporary settlements. Depending on how strict one is with the data, there is archaeological evidence to associate between a third and just over half of the thirty-four excavated Gotlandic hoards with Viking-Age settlements.

Given these challenges, we should not completely disassociate hoards from settlements, but should probably accept that the true figure lies somewhere between 15% (obtained from the sources) and 56% (the most generous figure from the thirty-four excavated sites). Based on the data currently available, it is safe to assume that at least a quarter of Viking-Age settlements contained hoards: of the 180 settlements identified, forty-six contained a find spot – some with multiple finds – which fits comfortably within the proposed range. A few of the more extensive and detailed excavations, such as those at Spillings, Häffinds II and IV, Kattlunds II and Norrgårde, show that some hoards do seem to have been deposited within the footprint of what were probably Viking-Age buildings, although only at Spillings has a direct stratigraphic association between the deposits and the structure survived.[27]

Thus Gotland's hoards seem to have a moderate association with Viking-Age settlements, although not to the degree previously believed. Because the number of known Viking-Age settlements is low, this introduces a degree of uncertainty into the results' reliability, and our picture of Viking-Age settlement on the island is at best fragmentary. However, comparing distances between hoards and their nearest settlement reinforces the view of a moderate association between hoards and settlement sites: hoards seem to have been deposited in relative proximity to habitation, since 61% were found within a 2km radius of one of the 180 probable Viking-Age farms. The regression analysis also highlighted the statistical importance of the proximity to contemporary settlements for the formation of hoard concentrations. The proximity of hoards to settlements, combined with their relative absence from the settlements themselves, reinforces the correlation of silver deposits with the productive landscape noted above. This means that a significant number of hoards were associated with the Viking-Age fields rather than settlements themselves.

Soils

The association of hoards with farmland rather than settlements is further strengthened by a significant correlation between hoard concentrations and areas of marginal soil. Gustav Svedjemo has shown that there is a strong correlation between third- to sixth-century settlements and moraine soils, with up to 60% of stone house foundations to be found on these heavier soils and only 20% on sandy soils. In contrast, by around 1700 farms and fields tended to be situated on lighter, sandy and gravelly soils. His analysis of Viking-Age sites indicates that 56% of settlements were on moraine and silt and 35% on sandy soils, whilst by *c.* 1700 around 55% of fields (and 39% of farmsteads) were on moraine soils, and 30% of fields (and 41% of farmsteads) on sandy soils.[28] This suggests that the move to the lighter soils was already underway in the early medieval period.

Moraine and sandy soils, although dominant on Gotland, together make up only 62% of the island. By including less common soil types, we may gain a more rounded picture of soil-type preference on Gotland (Table 9.1). By studying changes in the preference for all types of soil over time (linear trends), it is possible to categorise them into two major groups: traditional soil types (which show a decreasing trend similar to moraine, which remains the main component of traditional soils) and marginal soil types (which show an increasing trend observed in sandy substrata, which make up most of the marginal soils). Once converted into density per km^2, thus evening out differences in soil-type area and distribution on the island, the overall density of hoards per km^2 is higher within marginal soils than in traditional ones, and this trend is far more noticeable in hoards whose exact location is known. When we apply the same method to settlements, the overall density of Viking-Age settlement also appears higher on marginal soils: the percentage difference in density per km^2 shows the distribution of Viking-Age settlements on Gotland was some 15% greater on marginal soils than on traditional ones. Since settlements were still overwhelmingly on the established, traditional soils, the regression and density calculations may suggest an intensive colonisation of marginal, less readily accessible soils, possibly triggered by a pressing need for new land in this period. This suggestion is compatible with the very rigid laws of inheritance and land purchase on Gotland, which effectively made division of family property impossible. The colonisation process is even more clearly represented by hoards. The percentage difference in density per km^2 of hoards deposited in less available, marginal soils was up to 59% higher than in traditional soils. In a sense hoards 'push' into the marginal lands much more intensively than Viking-Age settlements.

The importance of hoarding for land ownership

The association of silver deposits with marginal soils is particularly important for hoarding on Gotland where, I would argue, silver deposits can be

Table 9.1 Comparison of association of site types with traditional and marginal soils on Gotland[1]

	Traditional			Marginal			Percentage difference in density (traditional/marginal)
	Area or number	Proportion	Density/ km^2	Area or number	Proportion	Density/ km^2	
Soils							
	2,041km^2	66%		810km^2	26%		
Settlements							
3rd to 6th century AD	1,809	80%	**0.89**	440	20%	**0.54**	**49%**
Viking-Age	121	67%	**0.06**	55	31%	**0.07**	**15%**
Hoards							
Viking-Age (All)	217	63%	**0.11**	128	37%	**0.16**	**37%**
Viking-Age (Exact location)	127	59%	**0.06**	87	41%	**0.11**	**59%**

Note
1 Percentage difference calculated using the formula: $(|x-y|/((x+y)/2))*100\%$. Data on third- to sixth-century settlement sites was kindly made available to me by Gustaf Svedjemo.

perceived as important agents in land ownership and social structures. The importance of land integrity noted above and the provisions for its legal protection from misappropriation through neglect, inheritance, neighbourly disputes, sale or purchase – sale to non-Gotlanders was banned absolutely – feature heavily in *Guta Lag*, but nowhere more categorically than in Chapter 28, where we find such statements as 'no one may sell land unless pressing need arises' or 'land may never be bought out of the family'.[29] Although written in the thirteenth century, 'many alliterative phrases and some residual rhythmic passages' indicate that an earlier form of oral law underlies the known manuscripts,[30] and it is likely that many of the legal provisions may have their origin in the late Viking Age. Considering the importance of land to the Gotlanders and the widespread occurrence of unclaimed hoards on the island in the Viking Age, I would suggest that a great proportion of Gotlandic hoards may be associated with the land itself, and particularly with a settlement's productive landscape of field systems, as well as with the social and legal structures.[31]

An example of such symbolic association comes from *Svarfdæla Saga* written in the fourteenth century, although describing events that took place between 875 and 980:

Thorstein the Tumultuous now took control of the valley between mountain and fjord on the other side of the river. He went to the mountains and erected a boundary stake at the uppermost edge and broke a comb and threw the pieces on the ground. Afterwards he had silver buried in three places, a half mark in each place, and that strip of land is called Kamb. Thorstein named witnesses, made the valley his legal domicile, and gave it his name, calling it Svarfadardal.[32]

This fragment, frequently cited by scholars in the context of hoarding and boundaries,[33] indicates that the process of acquiring land involved not only staking one's claim to it by, literally, marking it out in the landscape, but also – and more importantly – by symbolically forging one's own personal bond with the land through offering up a private possession. Torun Zachrisson believes that deposition of personal objects and silver around the edges of his newly taken land was meant to bind Thorstein to the boundaries of his claim,[34] where his private possessions would act as symbolic guardians of the border zone in his stead. I would like to take this a step further, and would emphasise the key importance of Thorstein's confirmation of his claim with silver that was not intended to be retrieved; that is, hoarded silver. Zachrisson's study of Eddic poetry and folklore suggests that, in the Viking Age, precious metal was intimately associated with its owner:

> [. . .] it was a keeper and preserver of his happiness and wellbeing. By obtaining a treasure by force, one stole another person's wellbeing. Since happiness in older times was perceived as a limited resource, one not only stole the other person's treasure but also his or her wellbeing. This may be the reason why digging for treasure was considered to be a fatal act.[35]

By binding himself to his land through buried silver, an owner added a potent new layer of protection for his farm: any seizure of land thus claimed would, symbolically, be tantamount to an attempt on his life. This is particularly important on Gotland, where the majority of land divisions observed in the Viking Age are likely to have been well established. The process of forging a personal bond with newly acquired land became ever more important, since established farms and the rare new addition could really only change hands through inheritance or violent seizure; and the need for symbolic personal connection became ever more significant in the case of disputes, particularly in the increasingly crowded and relatively rare marginal soils. This suggests that the most intensive hoarding on Viking-Age Gotland, particularly of placed deposits, was focused on lands that were newly colonised, most probably in newly broken fields. This could well have intensified the need for the symbolic behaviour described in *Svarfdœla Saga* – or to appease the *genius loci*.

Chronology and changes in hoard distribution patterns

On Gotland the paucity of contemporary written sources makes it impossible to correlate chronological changes in hoard distribution patterns with historical events. Nevertheless, the networks that facilitated the import and redistribution of silver, as expressed by hoard concentrations and the factors determining their intensity, were not static. They reacted to wider political and, above all, economic circumstances, principally at times when major changes in the sources of silver can be identified (Map 9.4).

In the ninth century, a period dominated by the inflow of Abbasid silver, the distribution of silver on Gotland is confined to just three areas where more or less discrete concentrations can be observed. The southernmost group seems to be associated with the harbour of Bandlunde and an emerging inland concentration – centred around Hemse parish and extending south to Alva – could be related to the figure of Avair Strabain (above, n. 4). In addition, a very tentative grouping appears in Grötlingbo parish, perhaps linked to the harbour at Barshalder, but suggesting that southern Gotland may have already been supplied through more than one harbour in the ninth century. The second concentration, in the northern part of the island, is clearly focused in Othem parish and its harbour site of Slite. The area has not produced the largest number of hoards, but they are highly concentrated and, importantly, include the largest hoard ever found, Spillings. The third concentration of hoards is the most numerous, albeit very dispersed, and is focused in the central area of Roma, in all probability the site of the island's *Althing*. Hoard distribution suggests that the political centre of the island in this earliest period of silver inflow was supplied through Paviken, and possibly also Fröjel, although the breadcrumb trail leading inland from this

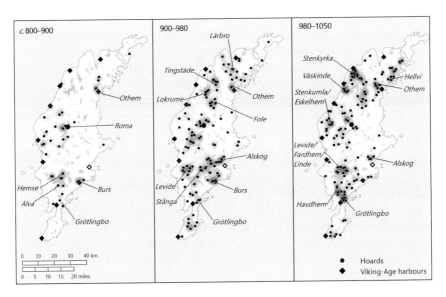

Map 9.4 Chronological changes in the distribution and concentrations of hoards on Gotland (density classification by 9 equal intervals).

harbour site is not so obvious. The location of silver deposits suggests that even in the ninth century Visby may have been a point of entry for silver to the island: certainly not the powerful trading centre it became in the eleventh century, but more likely a well-situated landing site through which the island's interior could be reached by silver merchants. A picture starts to emerge: although found more frequently than in Svealand or Pomerania in the earliest period of its influx, oriental silver was not yet widespread throughout Gotland; rather it was confined to areas of political importance – possibly the heartlands of the *tredingar*s – which were well connected with the outside world through a number of harbours and landing places.

Silver deposition explodes in Gotland with the introduction of Samanid silver between 900 and 980 and the metal seems to have become available throughout the island. We still find a hoard concentration at Roma, the island's political centre, although by the tenth century it seems to have arrived mainly via Fröjel in the south-west. On the basis of hoard evidence, Paviken's role in the acquisition and redistribution of silver seems to have diminished in this period. In the north, Othem's monopoly had also been broken and new harbours such as Vällesviken may have been responsible for some of the silver arriving in Lärbro parish.[36] It is also possible that other harbours may have been active in the safety of the wide bay centred on Klintehamn to the west, which also housed Fröjel and Paviken. Unfortunately, the archaeological evidence is too meagre to draw any firm conclusions. The growing availability of silver is highlighted by the emergence of three new hoard concentrations in the parishes of Fole, Lokrume and Tingstäde. This may have been connected to the formation of a political centre in the northernmost *tredingar* of the island – as the 'ting-' particle suggests – although how the silver reached these inland areas remains unclear. Most of the silver deposited between 900 and 980 appears to have been concentrated in the southern *tredingar*, in a number of smaller local groups. Like Slite in the north, Bandlunde still appears to have been heavily involved in funnelling silver from the coast to the more densely inhabited areas inland. However, we see a shift in depositions within southern *tredingar*, away from the earlier concentrations around Alva and Hemse towards an area slightly further north, which runs between the parishes of Levide, Stånga and Alskog. The apparent prosperity of southern Gotland was certainly boosted by proximity to several harbours: Fröjel, Grötlingbo, Hoburgen and a possible but unverified harbour at Botvide.[37]

After 980 the hoarding pattern changes again with the introduction of European silver, although well-established concentrations at Roma and Othem continue to thrive. Previously prominent harbours such as Fröjel and Bandlunde seem to lose their importance, and Barshalder takes centre stage in the southern part of the island, with Visby becoming more active as a conduit for silver going to Roma. A new concentration of hoards arrives on the map in Stenkulma and Eskelhem parishes, between Visby and Paviken; but since Paviken was in decline, this silver may have been routed through Västergarn, which emerged at the beginning of the eleventh century but ultimately failed to rival the future dominance of Visby. The most striking change triggered by the arrival of European silver is the rise of the north-western part of the island, primarily Väskinde and Stenkyrka parishes, most likely supplied by harbour sites at Överstekvarn and Lickershamn. Both Stenkyrka and another new hoard concentration in Hellvi are traditionally associated with the arrival of Christianity on the island, and the conversion of important local figures such as Ormika and Likkair Snielli. It may be no coincidence that in this period the centre of hoard concentration in Roma moves towards Akebäck, which *Guta Saga* associates with Botair, builder of the first Gotlandic church. Although Gotlanders were certainly familiar with Christianity before 980, the influx of European Christian coinage may have accelerated popular acceptance of the new faith.

Conclusion

On the basis of the early thirteenth-century *Guta Saga*, some Gotlandic hoard concentrations can tentatively be associated with regions of social and possibly also political importance – although not with individual sites. But this can only be an educated guess, since there is little archaeological evidence to identify any political central places with confidence. The one exception may be the concentration of hoards found in the western part of Roma parish, where the Gotlandic *Althing* is believed to have assembled at a site near the medieval Roma Abbey. Unfortunately, this area has yet to be excavated and investigations have been by metal-detector survey only. The general absence of evidence for centralised political power on the island is combined with another peculiarly Gotlandic feature: the abundance of harbours, or rather landing places,[38] at least eleven of which may have been active in the Viking Age. Again, most are known only from metal-detector surveys, and from cartographic or linguistic analysis. Rare excavations at Paviken and Fröjel, and to a lesser degree at Bandlunde and Västergarn, have provided archaeological evidence for long-distance trade and craft production, but none of the Gotlandic harbour sites could be described as large international emporia on the scale of Birka or Wolin. Moreover, those Gotlandic Viking-Age harbours that might be considered the closest parallels to Pomerania and Svealand's central places are generally located on the fringes of hoard concentrations, and not at their centres like their continental counterparts. There is also no evidence to link them with any political structures. Based on an analysis of cadastral maps from the beginning of the eighteenth century, Carlsson argues that Gotland's harbours were divided into a number of small plots which belonged to different farms located inland.[39] They were most likely collectively owned by farmers – possibly elite, well-to-do ones – and they seem to have served merely as 'gateways' facilitating the flow of silver and other goods into the island's interior, especially into regions where true political power was located. This may also explain why silver distribution is so different on Gotland. The multitude of sites through which silver reached the island – none of which seems to have at any point gained the upper hand, unlike Birka or Wolin which dominated their respective regions – was the result and an expression of the comparatively democratic political structure of island society, as our archaeological and written sources suggest. It was probably also influenced by the topography of the island: there were no major rivers that would structure access to the interior, as found in Pomerania, for example.

The traditional theory among historians is that Gotland was an egalitarian peasant society based on several distinctive features,[40] such as farms of equal size without landed estates and political autonomy, and with an autonomous law that, despite nominal submission to the Swedish crown, made no mention of royal power.[41] This view has been challenged mainly by scholars from mainland Sweden, who argue that Gotlanders lived and acted within a socially stratified framework that was profoundly Germano-Norse.[42] The archaeological site most often used to support this argument is the Högbro (Broe) cemetery in Halla parish, whose 700 or so graves include rich burials interpreted as belonging to those of elite status. However, Ny Björn Gustafsson has recently and convincingly argued that these graves date to the Vendel Period, and similar social stratification should not necessarily be assumed for the Viking Age.[43] Gotlandic burials in the Viking Age tended to be fairly standard, with graves lacking the more extravagant features found on the Swedish mainland, features that are generally assumed to have signalled social stratification and hierarchical superiority. Tryggve Siltberg provides extensive evidence for the egalitarian mentality of the Gotlanders. The most illustrative, although late, example is the legend of a local chief named Takstainarn in Lärbro, a legend later attributed to a certain Vigen in Grötlingbo, who was murdered by his fellow farmers for attempting to coerce the local priest and take sole charge.[44] An analysis of historical land divisions and (admittedly few) settlement sites led Kenneth Jonsson and Majvor Östergren to conclude that there is little evidence of landed estates or a socio-political elite.[45] Spatial and regression analyses show that Gotlandic hoards are distributed throughout areas settled in the Viking Age, which could imply that a large section of the population had uniform access to silver.[46] This is not to say that Gotlandic society did not have some who were 'more equal than others', thanks to economic resourcefulness or military capability. But the legal requirement to maintain the integrity of landholdings, alongside restrictive inheritance and land purchase rules, prevented any individual from amassing large estates and political power.

All of this may have increased the need for mercantile or military ventures beyond the island, as in the case of shared inheritance: when male inheritors came of age, one of them was 'to take his scrip and his scales and each have responsibility for himself, if they no longer wish to be together'.[47] The abundance of hoards on Gotland suggests that a good proportion of the proceeds from such socially forced enterprises returned to the island in the form of silver. And Gotlanders would seem to have used this silver for ritual purposes more frequently than is found elsewhere: permanent deposits, aimed at securing and reinforcing personal or kin-group links with the land, are certainly scarcer on the Baltic mainland.[48]

Central places in Pomerania and Svealand, including emporia, were associated with more or less centralised and hierarchical power structures,[49] an affiliation that offered protection for their trade. On Gotland, such protection may instead have been provided by 'the interdependence of groups and communities, rather than by coercive power'.[50] I believe, therefore, that Gotland lacked the political structures that would have enabled emporium-class trading ports to emerge. The Gotlanders evolved an alternative approach which bypassed the need for central places, since the system of decentralised, collectively run harbours and landing sites could supply them with extraordinary amounts of silver. The large number and density of these sites on an island located strategically in the middle of the Baltic, with ease of access to long-distance trade in silver, slaves and other high-value goods, was facilitated by a more democratic social structure than in areas where central places developed.

Appendix 9.1 Determining the combination of explanatory variables underlying Gotlandic hoard deposition

The regression modelling method was designed to determine what combination of explanatory variables could best explain the factors underlying observed Gotlandic hoard deposition, and how statistically significant each factor might be.[51] A linear model would not have been suitable for our data (the density of hoards expressed as the number of finds within a defined area), since it assumes a dependent variable (the observations one wants to explain) which is continuous and normally distributed. But by using a generalised linear model (GLM), the Poisson distribution, we were able to relax these assumptions and to consider cases where the dependent variable is non-normal and in particular has a discrete distribution.[52] GLMs are based on the exponential family of distributions and are thus most suitable for modelling the number of times an event occurs, in this case hoard depositions.[53] They provide a global model of the variable or process one is trying to understand and create a single regression equation to represent that process. In other words, they model the dependent variable (in this case hoards) in terms of its relationships to a set of explanatory (independent) variables.

Table 9.2 summarises the Gotlandic GLM regression model. Because the Poisson distribution belongs to the exponential family and the explanatory variables are expressed in different units, most relevant comparison can be made by using the values of statistical significance (*p*-values, listed under 'Significance' in Table 9.2): the smaller the *p*-value, the higher the statistical

Table 9.2 Summary of the Gotlandic GLM regression model

Explained (dependent) variable: number of hoards

Explanatory (independent) variables:

	Significance	Code
Number of harbours	0.00006	***
Distance from harbour	0.02366	*
Proximity to contemporary settlement	0.00403	**
Traditional soil	0.03523	*
Marginal soil	0.00509	**
Infields	0.000003	***
Number of sites with evidence for non-ferrous metalwork	0.00818	**
Significance codes:	'***' 0.001	'**' 0.01
	'*' 0.05	'.' 0.1

Goodness-of-fit parameters:

(Dispersion parameter for Poisson family taken to be 1)	
Null deviance:	444.66 on 113 degrees of freedom
Residual deviance:	105.81 on 106 degrees of freedom
AIC (Akaike information criterion):	361.49
Pearson's chi-squared test (χ^2):	0.4869341

significance of a variable as a predictor of the observed hoard concentrations. These values correspond with the significance codes in the next column, e.g. *** denotes statistical significance of below 0.001, which means that the confidence level of an explanatory variable in the model is over 99.999%.

Notes

1　Including *SGW*, vol. 2; *HV*; *CNS*, vol. 1 (Gotland), pts 1 (Akebäck–Atlingbo), 2 (Bäl–Buttle), 3 (Dalhem–Etelhem), 4 (Fardhem–Fröjel); Hammarberg *et al.* (1989); Brather (1995–6); *WKG*, vol. 4; an unpublished database of oriental coins by Gert Rispling, who kindly made it available to me; entries in FMIS; and 106 reports by ArkeoDok, Arendus and Länsmuseet på Gotland (Gotland Museum). I owe Per Widerström a debt of gratitude for his help in obtaining most of the reports.
2　The number of hoards on Gotland is often given as between 700 and 800, based on different definitions of what constitutes a hoard. Numismatists tend to consider that assemblages of coins qualify; this can be five, ten or even more, although the number is not always specified: Noonan (1994), p. 221; Kilger (2008); Zachrisson (1998); Kovalev (2011). Others include stray finds of large ornaments such as bangles, arm- and neck-rings, but without clearly defining the degree of completeness or the minimum size or weight needed to qualify: *MSoS*, p. 16. The most widely

accepted definition of a hoard, one that reduces the possibility of confusing intentionally hidden or accidentally lost objects, is that it must consist of more than a single item: Oras (2012), p. 65. In this chapter I follow Wilhelm von Brunn in considering a hoard to be a find of at least two objects, discovered at a single place and time, signifying a form of material wealth which was disposed of deliberately for reasons known and important to the hoarder: Brunn (1968), vol. 1, p. 236.

3 Gruszczyński (2016).
4 GS, pp. 6–7; on what little is known of this treaty between Gotland and Sweden, *ibid.*, pp. xxxiii–xxxvi; the historicity of Avair cannot be proved, but it is possible that the passage echoes oral tales or poetry concerning a much-respected heathen: *ibid.*, p. xxxv.
5 GS, p. 9; on the visit of St Olaf, *ibid.*, pp. xxxvi–xl.
6 GS, p. 9.
7 See Widerström in this volume.
8 Lagerlöf and Svahnström (1966), pp. 203–5.
9 Gustafsson (2013a), p. 38; Östergren (2004).
10 Myrberg (2009); RAÄ site identification number Roma 85:1; see also Kilger in this volume.
11 These maps show the countryside before the agricultural revolution of the nineteenth and twentieth centuries, and the infields were probably in similar use during the Viking Age; see also Svedjemo in this volume.
12 Carlsson (1999), p. 115; Carlsson (2008a), p. 21–2. See also Carlsson in this volume.
13 Roslund (2001); see also Widerström in this volume.
14 Carlsson (2011); Kilger *et al.* (2015).
15 Carlsson (2009), pp. 90–102.
16 On Bandlunde: Brandt (2002), although the interpretation of the site-layout is problematic (see Widerström in this volume); on Fröjel: Carlsson (2008b); on Paviken: *DKV*; Karn (2013); Karn (2014).
17 RAÄ Lau 102:3.
18 GS, pp. 56–7; Olsson (1971–2), pp. 180, 187–9.
19 IbnF², p. 46.
20 Gustafsson (2013a), p. 47; Gustafsson (2013b), p. 4. See also Gustafsson in this volume.
21 I identified 180 contemporary Viking-Age settlement sites through the review of 688 fully and 538 partially excavated sites in Gotland listed in FMIS combined with the study of published materials: *WKG*; Gustafsson (2013b); *LD* (which highlights the source-critical aspects of FMIS on pp. 16–18).
22 This impression is further reinforced by statistical comparison (using Band Collection Statistics in ArcGIS) of the density of sites with evidence of metalworking and density of silver deposits, which gives a relatively strong correlation coefficient of 0.6.
23 This has been the case since the pioneering doctoral dissertation of Majvor Östergren, published in 1989: *MSoS*.
24 Zachrisson (1998), pp. 119–20; *LD*, p. 114; see also Svedjemo in this volume.
25 *MSoS*, pp. 149–50; *WKG*, vol. 4, pp. 663–4.
26 *MSoS*, pp. 120–2; *WKG*, vol. 4, p. 502.
27 On Spillings: Östergren (2009); Widerström (2009); on Häffinds II: *WKG*, vol. 4, pp. 87–94; on Häffinds IV: Brisholm and Rispling (1986); Östergren *et al.* (1991); *WKG*, vol. 4, pp. 87–94; on Kattlunds II: *SGW*, vol. 2, nos 201, 205, 207, 214; Hammarberg *et al.* (1989), no. 64; *HV*, nos 19, 131, 139, 384; *WKG*, vol. 4, pp. 283–4; Jonsson and Östergren (1989), pp. 90–7; ArkeoDok (2011), p. 5; on Norrgårde: *SGW*, vol. 2, no. 457; *WKG*, vol. 4, p. 612.
28 *LD*, p. 177; see also Svedjemo in this volume.

29 *GL*, pp. 41–3.
30 *GL*, pp. xxiv–xxv.
31 Viking-Age hoards in Uppland and Gästrikland have been associated with the holding of allodial lands: Zachrisson (1998), p. 218.
32 *Svarfdæla saga*, pp. 161–2.
33 See, for example, Eggers (1940), p. 30; *HV*, p. 161; Zachrisson (1998), p. 199.
34 It should be noted that the *Saga* does not explicitly state that the silver Thorstein had buried was on the boundary of his newly taken land.
35 Zachrisson (1998), p. 221.
36 Or nearby Kappelshamn: see Carlsson in this volume. At the time of writing, in 2016, I was unable to secure published sources to confirm that Kappelshamn was active in the Viking Age. Since then I have ascertained that indeed Kappelshamn, as well as Swiviken in the neighbouring Rute parish, participated in the silver influx into Viking-Age Gotland: see Gruszczyński (2019).
37 RAÄ Lau 102:3.
38 These harbours have been identified by the pioneering research of Dan Carlsson. It is not impossible that similar sites existed in other regions along the Baltic coast, but no similar research has been undertaken outside Gotland.
39 Carlsson (1999), p. 123; Carlsson (2011), p. 28; see also Gustafsson and Carlsson in this volume.
40 Siltberg (2012), pp. 221–2.
41 See *GS*; *GL*.
42 See Gustafsson (2013a), p. 42 for references.
43 Gustafsson (2013a), p. 43.
44 Siltberg (2012), pp. 220, 222.
45 Jonsson and Östergren (1990), p. 146.
46 See, for example, *MSoS*, pp. 26–7; Jonsson and Östergren (1990), pp. 146–7.
47 *GL*, ch. 20, p. 27.
48 Some 57% of hoards on Gotland can be categorised thus, as opposed to 44% in Svealand and 37% in Pomerania, although it should be noted that these deposits comprise respectively only 12%, 9% and 4% of silver by weight: Gruszczyński (2016), fig. 6.2.
49 Written sources associate Birka and Sigtuna with royal power, exercised either directly or through representatives: Rimb*VA*, ch. 11, pp. 40–3; Ad*GH*, IV.29(28), pp. 472–5. We have no proof of a royal or princely power in Wolin, but the sources provide some evidence for self-government (Thietmar, *Chronicon*, VI.33(24), pp. 278–9) and the emporium is thought to have been a Wolinian political centre. Other Pomeranian central places were located at or were themselves strongholds, political or symbolic centres of their respective *civitates* (Lübke, 2001, p. 385). Truso and Ralswiek are exceptions, although even they are only some 5km from the nearest stronghold, whose elites may have offered protection in exchange for commercial goods. Hauke Jöns (2006, p. 100) suggested a similar set-up for Menzlin, which was also around 5km from the stronghold in Grüttow. Although this has been contested by Donat Wehner (2010, p. 258) on chronological grounds – Grüttow was established at the end of the eighth century, whereas Menzlin emerged at the start of the century – Wehner admits that 'no sign of self-government has been found on the site [Menzlin] so far: the possibility of dependence on authorities beyond the trading place of Menzlin is therefore not at all far-fetched'.
50 Sindbæk (2008), p. 155.
51 My thanks to Daniel Lunn at Oxford's Department of Statistics for his help in developing the modelling method, which was calculated in RStudio.
52 *ISM* (2002a), p. 1.
53 *ISM* (2002b), p. 14.

Bibliography

Primary sources

Svarfdœla saga, tr. F. J. Heinemann, 'The saga of the people of Svarfadardal', in *The Complete Sagas of Icelanders, Including 49 Tales*, ed. V. Hreinsson *et al.*, 5 vols, Reykjavik (1997), vol. 4, pp. 149–92.

Secondary literature

ArkeoDok (2011), *Rapport över efterundersökning med metalldetektor vid fyndplats för silverskatt, RAÄ 246 och 188, Uddvide 1:20, Grötlingbo socken, Gotland. Projekt Ett plundrat kulturarv. Rapport ArkeoDok 2011:51. Lst. Dnr. 431-1721-09*, Visby.

Brandt, B. (2002), 'Bandlundeviken: a Viking trading centre on Gotland?' in G. Burenhult (ed.), *Remote Sensing*, vol. 2: *Archaeological Investigations and Remote Sensing Case Studies*, Hässleholm, pp. 243–311.

Brather, S. (1995–6), 'Frühmittelalterliche Dirham-Schatzfunde in Europa. Probleme ihrer wirtschaftsgeschichtlichen Interpretation aus archäologischer Perspektive', *Zeitschrift für Archäologie des Mittelalters* 23–4: 73–153.

Brisholm, K. and G. Rispling (1986), 'Gotländskt myntfynd utgrävt i orört skick', *Svensk numismatisk tidskrift* 1986(1): 4–7.

Brunn, W. A. von (1968), *Mitteldeutsche Hortfunde der jüngeren Bronzezeit*, 2 vols, Berlin.

Carlsson, D. (1999), 'Harbours and farms on Gotland', in N. Blomkvist and S.-O. Lindquist (eds), *Europeans or Not? Local Level Strategies on the Baltic Rim 1100–1400 AD*, Visby, pp. 115–24.

Carlsson, D. (2008a), *Hamnar och fiskelägen i Sundre under vikingatid–medeltid*, ArkeoDok Rapport 2008:9, Visby.

Carlsson, D. (2008b), '"Ridanæs": a Viking Age port of trade at Fröjel, Gotland', in *VW*, pp. 131–4.

Carlsson, D. (2009), 'Owner missing? The hoard, the farm and the community', in *SH*, pp. 65–107.

Carlsson, D. (2011), *Vikingatidens Västergarn: en komplicerad historia*, ArkeoDok Skrifter 3, Stockholm.

Eggers, H. J. (1940), *Das römische Einfuhrgut in Pommern, Beiheft zum Erwerbungs- und Forschungsbericht* [= *Baltische Studien* 42: 1–35], Stettin.

Gruszczyński, J. (2016), 'Comparative study of archaeological contexts of silver hoards c. 800–1050 in northern and central Europe', unpublished DPhil dissertation, Oxford.

Gruszczyński, J. (2019), *Silver, Hoards and Containers: The Archaeological and Historical Context of Silver Coin Deposits in the Baltic c. 800–1050*, Abingdon.

Gustafsson, N. B. (2013a), *Casting Identities in Central Seclusion: Aspects of Non-Ferrous Metalworking and Society on Gotland in the Early Medieval Period*, Stockholm.

Gustafsson, N. B. (2013b), 'In the wake of the hoards: glimpses of non-ferrous metalworking through the finds of the Gotland hoard projects', *Fv* 108: 1–11.

Hammarberg, I. *et al.* (1989), *Byzantine Coins Found in Sweden*, CNS n.s. 2, Stockholm; London.

ISM (2002a), 'Introduction to generalized linear models', *Introduction to Statistical Modelling*, IAUL/Statistics, University of Oxford, Trinity 2002, stats.ox.ac.uk/pub/bdr/IAUL/ModellingLecture5.pdf (accessed 15 December 2019).

ISM (2002b), 'Applications of generalized linear models', *Introduction to Statistical Model-ling*, IAUL/Statistics, University of Oxford, Trinity 2002, stats.ox.ac.uk/pub/bdr/IAUL/ModellingLecture6.pdf (accessed 15 December 2019).

Jöns, H. (2006), 'Zur Rekonstruktion der historischen Topographie und Infrastruktur des Handelsplatzes Menzlin an der Peene', *Jahrbuch der Bodendenkmalpflege in Mecklen-burg-Vorpommern* 53: 81–109.

Jonsson, K. and M. Östergren (1989), 'Vikingatida silverskatter: nya forskningsrön på skilda sätt', *GA* 61: 79–98.

Jonsson, K. and M. Östergren (1990), 'The Gotland hoard project and the Stumle hoard: an insight into the affairs of a Gotlandic "farman"', in *SP*, pp. 145–58.

Karn, A. (2013), *Paviken 2013. Rapport över 2013 års utgrävning av den vikingatida hamn-platsen Paviken, Västergarns socken*, Rapport Arrendus 2014:8, Visby.

Karn, A. (2014), *Paviken 2014. Arkeologisk undersökning, Stora Mafrids 5:12, Västergarn socken, Region Gotland, Gotlands län*, Rapport Arrendus 2014:27,Visby.

Kilger, C. (2008), 'Kaupang from afar: aspects of the interpretation of dirham finds in northern and eastern Europe between the late 8th and early 10th centuries', in *ME*, pp. 199–252.

Kilger, C. *et al.* (2015), 'Mynt och bebyggelse: bebyggelseutvecklingen inom Väster-garnsvallen ur ett numismatiskt perspektiv', in T. Talvio and M. Wijk (eds), *Myntstu-dier: Festskrift till Kenneth Jonsson*, Stockholm, pp. 141–56.

Kovalev, R. K. (2011), 'Khazaria and Volga Bulgaria as intermediaries in trade relations between the Islamic Near East and the Rus' lands during the tenth to early eleventh centuries: The numismatic evidence – Part I', *Archivum Eurasiae Medii Aevi* 18: 43–155.

Lagerlöf, E. and G. Svahnström (1966), *Gotlands kyrkor: en vägledning*, Stockholm.

Lübke, C. (2001), 'The Polabian alternative: paganism between Christian kingdoms', in P. Urbańczyk (ed.), *Europe around the Year 1000*, Warsaw, pp. 379–89.

Myrberg, N. (2009), 'An island in the middle of an island: on cult, laws and authority in Viking Age Gotland', in E. Regner *et al.* (eds), *From Ephesos to Dalecarlia: Reflections on Body, Space and Time in Medieval and Early Modern Europe*, SSA 48, Stockholm, pp. 101–8.

Noonan, T. S. (1994), 'The Vikings in the east: coins and commerce', in B. Ambrosiani and H. Clarke (eds), *Developments around the Baltic and the North Sea in the Viking Age*, Stockholm, pp. 215–36.

Olsson, I. (1971–2), 'Snäck-namn på Gotland', *Fv* 66–7: 180–208.

Oras, E. (2012), 'Importance of terms: What is a wealth deposit?', *Papers from the Institute of Archaeology* 22: 61–82.

Östergren, M. (2004), 'Det gotländska alltinget och cistercienserklostret i Roma', in *Gotland vikingaön* [= *GA* 76]: 40–5.

Östergren, M. (2009), 'Spillings: the largest Viking Age silver hoard in the world', in *SH*, pp. 11–40.

Östergren, M. *et al.* (1991), 'Coin finds from Bandlundeviken: a Viking-Age harbour on Gotland', *NNÅ* 1985–6: 33–52.

Roslund, M. (2001), 'Gutar, främlingar och den förblindande vikingatiden: om staden Visbys tidigaste datering', in A. Andrén *et al.* (eds), *Från stad till land: en medeltidsarkeo-logisk resa tillägnad Hans Andersson*, Stockholm, pp. 241–51.

Siltberg, T. (2012), 'The conception of an egalitarian Gotlandic peasant society', in M. Scholz *et al.* (eds), *The Image of the Baltic: A Festschrift for Nils Blomkvist*, Visby, pp. 203–28.

Sindbæk, S. M. (2008), 'Local and long-distance exchange', in *VW*, pp. 150–8.

Wehner, D. (2010), 'The hinterland of the early medieval trading places Wolin and Menzlin: a comparison', in B. Ludowici *et al.* (eds), *Trade and Communication Networks of the First Millennium* AD *in the Northern Part of Central Europe: Central Places, Beach Markets, Landing Places and Trading Centres*, Hanover, pp. 258–66.

Widerström, P. (2009), 'Spillings farm: the home of a rich Viking in the Northeast of Gotland', in *SH*, pp. 41–63.

Zachrisson, T. (1998), *Gård, gräns, gravfält: sammanhang kring ädelmetalldepåer och runstenar från vikingatid och tidig medeltid i Uppland och Gästrikland*, SSA 15, Stockholm.

10 Hoards and their archaeological context

Three case studies from Gotland

Majvor Östergren

Gotland is famous for its Viking-Age silver hoards,[1] although our knowledge of the 750 or so found on the island to date remains incomplete since very few find spots have been excavated. Despite their intrinsic value, it is first and foremost the hoards' context that can offer us information about Viking-Age society, trading and raiding. Sadly, excavations require resources, and these are scarce on Gotland – even when the cultural heritage in question is of international importance. The island's silver hoards are truly world class, although not yet on UNESCO's World Heritage List. Viking-Age coins are not found to the same extent even in their countries of origin, where old coins tended to be recalled before new ones were issued. In Scandinavia, however, coins did not have a face value: instead they were valued by weight and silver content, often using scales and balances, and could therefore be in circulation for long periods of time. More than 260,000 Viking-Age silver coins have been found in Sweden; of these, around two-thirds – more than 170,000 – come from hoards on Gotland. It is therefore regrettable that so few excavations have been carried out. Perhaps it is simply a problem of over-abundance: Gotland's Viking-Age silver hoards are so common that, despite their value for international scholarship, it is easy to become blasé. Couple this with the amount of work and high costs involved in excavating a site and it is easy to see why new discoveries are sometimes more of a burden than an asset.

The silver hoard from Stale in Rone parish, found in April 2012, illustrates the problem. It is the largest hoard to contain western coins ever found in Scandinavia, consisting of more than 6,300 coins in a copper vessel. The hoard was found completely intact under the plough layer of a field by the archaeologist Jonas Paulsson during a routine metal-detector survey. Per Widerström and I oversaw its removal, plastered in its entirety, after which the Länsstyrelsen (County Administrative Board) took over. Yet five years later, most of the coins remain unclassified while work to preserve them has only just begun. The site has still not been excavated. No excavation is planned.

The case studies

Almost thirty years ago, in my doctoral thesis on Viking-Age silver hoards as indicators of settlement, I argued that Gotland's hoards had a spatial connection to the remains of Viking-Age settlements, especially dwelling houses. This conclusion was based on metal-detector surveys of about eighty find spots.[2] Since then I have revised my opinion. Viking-Age silver hoards seem to be linked not only to dwelling houses, but also to workshops, storehouses and smithies: only a very few appear to have no connection at all to contemporary settlement remains.[3] However, more find spots need archaeological excavation before firm conclusions can be drawn, especially those with few Viking-Age or earlier finds apart from the hoard itself. My study also noted that Gotlandic farms were not static in the Roman Iron Age: farmers cultivated the same fields and meadows, but their buildings moved, probably reflecting changes in land use and ownership. It was only during the middle ages that farms became more static, parish churches were built and roads became permanent.[4]

This chapter presents three case studies of find spots that have been excavated. By international and even Swedish standards, the excavated areas are not particularly extensive, but in the context of Gotland, the excavations are comparatively large. The three sites are Burge in Lummelunda parish, Gannarve in Hall parish and Spillings in Othem parish. At the end of the chapter, I shall briefly describe two further find spots with, it would appear, different contexts.

Burge in Lummelunda parish

In the summer of 1967, the farmer Per-Anders Croon ploughed up a bronze vessel in which a silver hoard had been deposited. The hoard (Burge I, SHM 28830) consisted of 3,100 coins, three bracelets, a large number of ingots and bars, including several of Russian type, as well as some pieces of silver. At 10.4kg, at the time it was the largest hoard found on the island and was dated to post-1143. In 1972, during the excavation of the find spot, a second silver hoard (Burge II, RAÄ 102) was found scattered in a field 180m north-east of the original site, close to the current farm buildings. The area was investigated using a metal detector after a single coin was found on the surface. The second hoard contained 102 coins and is dated to post-1017.

The excavations

Excavations began in 1970 and lasted for ten years, led for most of the period by Lena Thunmark-Nylén. They covered an area of some 1,000m² and were carefully documented. Although a full report has yet to be published, a brief report was issued in 2014.[5] The length of the excavations and lack of a comprehensive dig report complicate matters somewhat.

The main hoard (SHM 28830, tpq 1143)

The main hoard was located inside the remains of two overlying houses, positioned in the middle of both and at roughly the original floor level of the later house (Figure 10.1). It does not appear to have been buried but rather hidden under a bench or the like, of which no trace remained. The houses have been dated to the late Viking Age or early middle ages from the artefacts excavated there and from radiocarbon dating of a posthole (see Appendix in this volume, no. 56). In the meadow next to the archaeological site lie the foundations of four more medieval houses, two of which have also been excavated.[6]

The artefacts found at Burge were particularly rich. In addition to the main silver hoard, they included a Roman *denarius*, some fifteen Gotlandic coins from the 1100s, a penannular brooch, ten heart-shaped silver belt mounts and eight oblate spheroid iron weights with bronze shells. The large number of bronze finds included several animal-head and oval brooches from different periods of the Viking Age, as well as a dozen pins, needle holders and sewing needles, finger-rings, various types of fittings, the chape from a sword scabbard, fish hooks, chain links and wire. Among the iron objects were padlocks and keys, arrowheads, spurs, axes, sickles and scythes, hinges, a hammer head, fire steel and cauldron hook, around fifty knives, spikes, needles, hooks, chain links, buckles and buckle pins, wedges, awls, chisels, horse shoes and rings, as well as hundreds of nails, rivets and sheet metal. Bone objects included a flute, combs, needles and spindle whorls. Furthermore, twenty-seven glass beads were found together with pieces of

Figure 10.1 The main hoard from Burge (detail), discovered in 1967 and weighing 10.4kg. Courtesy SHM.

glass, rock crystal lenses, a piece of amber, pottery, soapstone, resin and more than a hundred complete and broken pieces of whetstones, two sandstone moulds, grindstones, a crucible fragment, slag, unburned bone and daub.

The second hoard (RAÄ 102, tpq 1017)

After the chance discovery of a second Viking-Age silver hoard on the farm in July 1972, Thunmark-Nylén investigated using a metal detector and then excavated an area of 27m² down to the sterile soil. She unearthed eighty-seven silver coins as well as a stone structure, the nature of which could not be determined. The farm's owner had apparently ploughed up and removed large amounts of stone from the area, and phosphate mapping of the fields showed high values in exactly this spot. In autumn 1984, I re-examined the two find spots using a metal detector. Despite poor conditions at both locations, I found two coins and a bronze brooch pin at the site of the main hoard, and an additional fifteen coins at the secondary hoard site; taken together with the earlier finds of a fragment of a copper sheet and three pieces of copper alloy melts, this suggests a cluster of settlement-related finds.[7]

Thus it would appear that the main hoard was stored in a contemporary building, part of a farm complex with at least five houses dating to the late Viking and early medieval period. The foundations of four of the houses have been preserved in a meadow which has never been cultivated, and this farm complex was probably the site of Burge farm in the middle ages. Since the building containing the main hoard seems to have lacked a hearth, it can hardly have been a dwelling. The structure was rectangular, measuring about 17m by 7m, with paired, usually stone-lined, postholes and wattle and daub walls. Some wood remnants were found in the postholes, and radiocarbon analysis dates them to the Viking Age (Appendix, no. 56). The floor consisted of a mixture of gravel and clay, and the entrance to the building was on its long, eastern side facing the meadow and the rest of the farm complex. Gravel paths ran between the buildings. Among the four foundations in the meadow there are examples both of houses of earthfast post construction and of houses with stone sills.

Burge farm has been located in virtually the same place for at least a thousand – and probably closer to two thousand – years, only moving around by a few hundred metres in all this time.[8] The site of the medieval farm is next to the modern farm buildings and the two silver hoards show that Burge has its roots in the Viking Age. In an adjacent field there are also the remnants of ploughed-over house foundations from the early Iron Age. From the start, the inhabitants of Burge chose a good settlement site, and the reason for the occasional shifts was probably to do with new building techniques and changes in land use.

Gannarve in Hall parish

Four silver hoards were found at Gannarve in the 1920s, all within a space of only about 100m² and all during cultivation, ploughing and other agricultural work. The largest (Gannarve I, SHM 17747, *tpq* 1120) was unearthed in 1924, although stray coins have been found since. It contained 1,240 coins, three finger-rings and 119 pieces of silver. The three smaller hoards (Gannarve II, *tpq* 934/5; Gannarve III, *tpq* 938/9; and Gannarve IV, *tpq* 991) comprised twenty-three Islamic coins (II), fourteen Islamic coins (III), and forty-nine German coins and twenty-three pieces of silver (IV), although their exact find spots are unknown. In addition, a large number of mainly bronze, iron and bone settlement-related objects from the site have been submitted to the authorities. Noteworthy is a glass linen smoother (Figure 10.3), used for luxury fabrics. Again, we lack the exact find spots and only know that they were found within the same 100m² area.

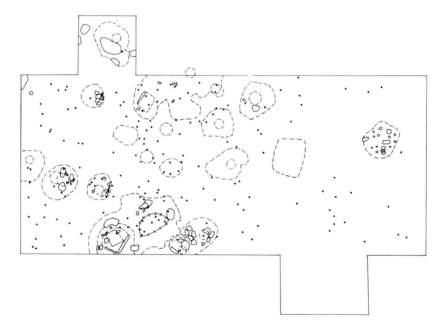

Figure 10.2 Plan of the excavated area at Gannarve, showing postholes, hearths and metal object finds (represented as dots). From *SoB*, fig. 19.

The excavations

I have twice undertaken a metal-detector survey of the site, in 1977 and 1982, finding remnants of the largest hoard along with a quantity of predominantly bronze and iron settlement objects. As part of my doctoral thesis, I followed this up in May and June 1983 by excavating 94m² of the site, together with Magnus Elfwendahl.[9]

Figure 10.3 Glass linen smoother, used for luxury fabrics such as silk, found in the 1920s at Gannarve.

Courtesy RAGU; photo: Lennart Rubbestad.

The excavations revealed the remains of at least two houses that overlay each other, and the twenty-four features that we uncovered included three hearths and thirteen postholes. The houses were of wood, probably in post-and-plank technique with internal roof-supporting posts: some of the postholes contained pine residues. The rich find materials and radiocarbon analysis of both wood and charcoal place the buildings in the tenth to twelfth centuries (Appendix, nos 38–41). Some of the finds also pre-date the Viking Age, including two oval brooches from the 600s which were found outside but close to the investigated area.[10]

Excluding rivets, nails and unidentified iron fragments, more than 300 objects were found. Among them were two stray silver coins, one English minted for Æthelred II, the second from Gotland, dated to the period 1140–1210/20.[11] Artefacts included two spherical weights, twenty-nine pieces of jewellery or dress accessories, nine comb fragments, part of a lock and four iron keys, eighty-one pottery pieces and thirty-two household tools, among them bone needles, spindle whorls and sewing needles, and two fabric smoothers made of glass and iron. Other everyday finds included ten smaller iron tools, parts of a bridle, a bone skate, the point of a fish spear, fish hooks, arrowheads, thirty-five complete or broken iron knives, a sword chape, fifty whetstones (both complete and fragmented), four beads, an axe, pieces of iron slag, two mould fragments, five pieces of copper alloy melts and twenty-two of bronze sheet and plate.

The excavations showed that the silver hoard was originally hidden inside the building or buildings, and that both hoard and building(s) were probably from the last phase of settlement on the site. Nine of the datable bronze objects are eleventh or twelfth century. The deposited silver seems to have been situated at about the same level as the original floor, and some of the stray finds indicate that there were also older houses in the area.

The bone material was analysed by the osteoarchaeologist Berit Sigvallius. It shows that Gannarve seems to have been an ordinary farm with a traditional economy, where cattle played the biggest role, followed by sheep or goats, and then pigs. Trapping birds and fishing were both important activities, although hunting does not seem to have played a major role. Cattle were used both for milking and meat; sheep for their wool and also for meat.[12]

The rich find material indicates that there was metalworking on the farm, and that its inhabitants led lives that were neither isolated nor primitive. There are a range of what can best be termed as luxury items. For example, a glass fabric smoother implies that precious textiles such as silk were imported and used. A piece of a Latvian set of chain ornaments suggests foreign contacts – if not directly, then at least indirectly – and the same goes for the silver hoards and the single English coin that was found in a posthole.

The site where the four hoards were found is probably where Gannarve farm was located from the late Bronze Age (*c.* 1100–500 BC) perhaps until around 1150 AD, a period of more than 1,600 years. Directly adjacent to the excavated area is a late Bronze-Age *skeppssättning* and a third- to sixth-century *kämpgrav*, stone walls and burial mound. The settlement area is located just east of a still partially preserved prehistoric road that runs from north to south.

Perhaps as early as the mid-1100s the site was abandoned and the farm moved a few hundred metres to the east, possibly in two stages, where it has remained ever since. This is typical of farms on Gotland, with a gradual shifting of the buildings over the centuries for a variety of reasons, including soil fertility and land use, the transfer of common land into private ownership, and the construction of new, permanent roads. This came to an end in the middle ages, when farms became more fixed, usually adjacent to the historic road network; and as with Gannarve, they sometimes ended up on Iron-Age grave fields which lay on the borders between infield and outfield.[13]

Spillings in Othem parish

Our third case study is the find spot of the Viking-Age silver hoard at Spillings farm: discovered in July 1999 and dated to after 871, it was excavated between 1999 and 2007. This is the largest hoard on Gotland and the largest known and under study worldwide. It weighed 67kg and contained 486 bangles and bracelets, twenty-five finger-rings, about eighty bars and a vast quantity of spiral rings and other cut silver, as well as more than 14,300 mostly Islamic, mostly fragmented coins.[14] The handling of the Spillings hoard is a good example of how important cooperation between different authorities is in a case like this. A find of this calibre – dubbed 'the world's largest Viking-Age silver hoard' – requires efficient organisation and successful partnerships.[15]

The finds and find spots

The hoard was unearthed by pure chance. A television team were filming a programme on the looting of ancient monuments on Gotland and were interviewing the archaeologist Jonas Ström in a field at Spillings farm, where the landowner had reported his discovery of Viking-Age bronze objects and Islamic silver coins to the authorities. Kenneth Jonsson, Professor of Numismatics at Stockholm University, happened to be on Gotland at the time and took part in the interview. Shortly after filming had wrapped up, the first characteristic signal was heard from the metal detector indicating the presence of silver in the ploughed soil. They sent for back-up from the Gotland Museum and the area was cordoned off; as the museum director at the time, I had the privilege of being on the spot. We immediately sent a report to the Länsstyrelsen, which has responsibility for registering newly discovered ancient monuments, and which grants permission for excavations. The County Custodian of Antiquities, Lennart Edlund, was swiftly on the scene to conduct a primary inspection.

It was soon clear that this was an unusually large and remarkable find, and that excavations would take time. To avoid the risk of looting, we decided to lift the find at once, with a team of archaeologists working by day to isolate the find and security guards watching over it by night. We also decided to make the excavations open to the general public: this was obviously an archaeological sensation, a significant part of Gotland's cultural heritage and a unique occasion, and we wanted the general public to feel involved. So instead of trying to keep the find a secret, the local media and public were invited on guided tours and to follow the excavation work. This met with a tremendous response: the number of visitors that first weekend totalled 2,000!

We later established that the hoard consisted of two deposits, which lay beyond reach of the plough some 3m from each other. Both were in the shape of a square, about 40–45cm by 50cm in size, with slightly rounded corners. The silver had clearly been stored in sacks made of fabric, pelt or hide, but no traces of these remained. Of the total 67kg deposited, twenty-seven were in the first deposit and forty in the second. The smaller of the deposits was in poor shape. Many of the objects had been corroded by a chemical process which had transformed their outer surfaces to a lilac-coloured silver chloride, making them extremely fragile. Once the conservation had been completed, we realised that this damage had been done by salt, and the conservators felt that it was probably the containers that had caused the problems, rather than the surrounding soil (Figure 10.4). Because of the fragility of its artefacts, the smaller deposition was mainly

Figure 10.4 Part of the Spillings hoard: salt damage can clearly be seen (left), as can the bund-
ling of bangles and spiral rings into units weighing 200g (one mark of silver).

Courtesy Gotland Museum; photo: Göran Ström.

excavated on site. The larger deposit was more compact and better preserved.
It was plaster jacketed and lifted in its entirety.

Both deposits were examined more closely in the museum's laboratory during
the winter of 1999/2000, under Jonas Ström's direction. The examination can
best be described as an archaeological excavation in miniature, and a record –
primarily photographic – was taken throughout. The more advanced preservation
operations were taken care of in Stockholm by the RAÄ and the curator at the
Royal Coin Cabinet. A lot of the material had been bundled together into equal
units of weight, corresponding well with the Viking-Age weight system, where
one mark of silver was equal to 200g. Most of the artefacts had never been used,
while a few were quite worn. The jewellery is mainly of Gotlandic production,
probably using Islamic silver coins as raw material.

In 2002, work started on classifying the Islamic coins from the hoard. This
was undertaken in partnership with the Royal Coin Cabinet's Gert Rispling
and just over 5,000, or a third, of the coins have been classified. They came
from both deposits, albeit mainly from the second since the silver was in better
condition. This analysis indicated that they probably shared a common origin.
The dating, place of minting and, in percentage terms, relative distribution of
the various coin types were practically identical, showing that the deposits were
in all likelihood part of one and the same hoard. The hoard had probably been
split on site before being placed beneath the floor, 3m apart.[16]

New knowledge

Ninth-century silver hoards were thought to be both fewer and much smaller than tenth-century ones until the Spillings find: but this view has now been turned upside down. The hoard also sheds new light on Islamic coinage before 870/1: it is clear that between 833 and 870 this was far more extensive than scholars had previously believed. In addition, some 200 coins are imitations (roughly 1.55% of the total hoard or 4.4% of those coins that have been identified). Apart from the ancient Greek coinage in Crimea, they represent the first coins to be struck on what is now the territory of Russia, according to Gert Rispling.[17] The coins in the Spillings hoard come from widely scattered mints: among the coins classified so far, we have examples from sixty-nine different mints located in what are now fifteen European, Asian and African countries.

Some of the coins are sensational. A prime example is the 'Moses coin' (Figure 10.5). This bears a unique inscription, *Musa rasul Allah*, which is Arabic for 'Moses is God's messenger'. It was most likely struck by a convert to Judaism and the words are a direct parallel to 'Mohammed is God's messenger' in the Islamic creed, the standard inscription on Islamic coins. The inscription on the Moses coin is thus astounding. The most likely explanation is that the coin is not Islamic, but an imitation minted in the Khazar khaganate. Several written sources, both Arabic and Hebrew, testify to the fact that the khagan and some of his people converted to Judaism around 800, yet despite numerous excavations, no archaeological evidence has been found in Russia to confirm these claims. The Moses coin in the Spillings hoard is therefore the first artefact that links

1cm

Figure 10.5 The 'Moses coin'.
Courtesy Kungliga Myntkabinett; photo: Kenneth Jonsson.

Judaism to the Khazars. This makes the coin of paramount significance to numismatic and historical research.[18]

Further excavations

At an early stage, our metal-detector survey indicated yet another large deposit of precious metal a mere 1.5m from the second silver hoard. A 2m by 2m trial trench was dug, reaching down to the plough depth. This revealed a deposit with a vast quantity of scrap-metal of bronze – some complete but, above all, broken pieces of bangles, costume pins, bracelets, necklaces, excess metal waste, bars and mounts, many of which had been melted together to form a large 'cake'. The total weight of the bronze would later prove to be over 20kg, and all the objects seem to have been manufactured in the Baltic region. The excavation also uncovered many wooden remnants, several iron rivets and iron mounts, as well as an ingenious locking device with a large piece of ironwork, about 10cm by 50cm in size – all presumably the remains of a chest. The bronze deposit was left in situ until more comprehensive investigations of the find spot could be undertaken.

Six weeks of excavations were carried out in early summer 2000. Under the auspices of the Gotland Museum and directed by Per Widerström, they were co-funded by the government and private sponsorship; archaeology students from the local university also took part. The excavations established that both the silver hoards and bronze deposit had been placed in an existing

Figure 10.6 Some of the Viking-Age bronze objects found at Spillings.
Courtesy Gotland Museum; photo: Raymond Hejdström.

building, directly beneath floorboards that rested on a single layer of stones and sand (Figure 10.7).[19] This building had no hearth and was probably some kind of utility building, perhaps a warehouse or store: radiocarbon dating shows that it was in use in the Vendel Period and Viking Age, although this is an imprecise method and we cannot be sure that the building was in continuous use from the sixth century on (Appendix, nos 30–3).

The bronze deposit was uncovered, encapsulated in plaster and transported to the museum's laboratory, where the plaster jacket was carefully removed (Figure 10.8). The chest that emerged may have been an import from the east, since it was made of spruce, an uncommon wood on Viking-Age Gotland. After radiocarbon dating, it appears the chest is from the seventh century – much older than the objects stored in it.[20] It is surprising that bronze objects should have been stored in a wooden chest with robust ironwork and lock, while the silver seems to have been stored in much simpler and more perishable containers. The chest probably contained raw material for bronze casting.

At the same time as excavating the hoard building, the archaeologists started searching for other – above all contemporaneous – farm structures, using trial trenches of no more than 1m².[21] One of these, north of the find spot, exposed

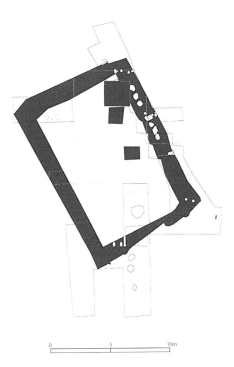

Figure 10.7 The foundations of the building at Spillings in which the silver hoards and bronze deposit were found.

Plan: Per Widerström.

Figure 10.8 Excavating the bronze deposit at Spillings: the relatively well-preserved iron
chest mounts can be seen (left).
Courtesy Gotland Museum; photo: Raymond Hejdström.

the remnants of what may have been a dwelling house, some 5.5m wide. The
house had posts dug into the ground, propped up by stones, and a floor made of
a compacted layer of clay. Two hearths were uncovered, a mere metre apart,
both built of standing and horizontal limestone slabs. Wood had been preserved
in the postholes and radiocarbon dating put the house in the Viking Age.[22]
A third building was found 25m east of the hoard. Since none of the postholes
contained wood, they could not be dated. However, the building was probably at
least a century later than the hoard, judging from two types of pottery discovered
there. West of the hoard site, medieval coins and pottery were found and a trial
trench exposed a hearth base containing a lump of slag as well as large quantities
of burned clay.[23] North-east of the hoard site, in a bordering field, traces of
another possible settlement were discovered by metal-detecting. The finds would
imply that the two settlements existed side by side – possibly indicating not one
but two Viking-Age farms. However, no further investigations have been carried
out in this field.

The field with the hoards

Before the land reforms of 1873–6, the field belonged to Närs farm – a
neighbouring farm of Spillings – and was Närs' largest, possibly oldest and

most significant field. Another hoard was uncovered on Närs farm in 1843, dated to the 950s. It contained 141 coins, and might very well have been discovered in the same field. All of the coins were Islamic, except one, which was Byzantine. The abandoned settlement in the field with the hoards was probably the earlier site of Närs farm. Spillings and Närs farms are situated just north of Bogeviken, probably one of Gotland's most important and best-sheltered Viking-Age harbours, and another such harbour was situated in Slite, a settled area close to both the hoard find spot and Bogeviken.[24]

The entire field where the hoards were found was surveyed with a metal detector between 1999 and 2001. Most of the artefacts retrieved are of precious metal: it would be far too costly to preserve the enormous quantities of iron objects. The field has also been phosphate surveyed. The surveys show continuous settlement on the site over the course of a thousand years, right up to the seventeenth century, and the areas producing the greatest quantity of metal objects also produce the highest phosphate content:[25] the farm must have been situated at the same place through the centuries, with new houses gradually replacing old ones in the same yard.

Some 700 objects have been retrieved in total; although they were spread over both fields, they were concentrated in two areas at a distance of 50–60m from each other. Just over ninety of these were Viking-Age silver coins, of which the vast majority – almost eighty – were Islamic, the rest being English, German, Byzantine and Swedish. Few, if any, can be connected to the silver hoard: they are either stray finds, or the remains of hoards previously discovered at the site.[26] Although coins that have been dropped by accident are common at Viking-Age settlements on Gotland, in this case they are so numerous that logically most of them must be remnants of a previously uncovered hoard. Some of them, for example, might well be the remains of the hoard unearthed at Närs in 1843. Nor can we discount the fact that an unreported hoard might have been unearthed there, even as early as the middle ages, given the continuity of settlement in the Viking Age and medieval period. Of the non-Viking-Age coins, about fifteen were medieval.

Apart from the coins, the finds are mostly of complete or broken pieces of jewellery. Several artefacts indicate that metalwork took place at the site, including raw materials such as rods and cut silver, as well as numerous crucibles, casting cones and discarded objects, mainly of copper and bronze, but also of silver. Their distribution gives us a clear picture of where the dwelling house, utility buildings and workshops were located, although the site's continuous settlement over nearly a millennium does complicate matters. Excavations in 2005 uncovered a Viking-Age grave, and there may well have been further graves in the area, from which some of the objects might have come, but which have been churned up by the plough.[27]

Conclusions

This chapter has presented three case studies of excavated find spots of Viking-Age silver hoards on Gotland. In all three, farms have been occupying roughly the same place for at least a thousand years, with evidence of earlier buildings on or close to present-day farms. All three have produced rich archaeological material. However, silver hoards can have different contexts and there is a need for more comprehensive work in this area, particularly where hoards have been found in places with few or no characteristic settlement objects. What do these hoards add up to? Metal-detector surveys have revealed many Viking-Age settlement remains in the fields on Gotland, far more than the seventeenth-century farms recorded by the cadastral maps.[28]

To conclude, I shall briefly compare the three case studies with two excavated find spots where the find material is sparse, apart from the hoard. In spring 1989, the find spot of a Viking-Age silver hoard at Kattlunds in Grötlingbo parish was looted by individuals equipped with metal detectors. The hoard was originally discovered in 1866 (SHM 3484, *tpq* 1018) and contained about 1,100 coins and 126 pieces of silver. The discovery of the looting led me to excavate the site, examining an area of 158m[2].[29] In addition to 119 Viking-Age silver coins and a number of silver pieces, only a few bronze settlement objects were uncovered, including the head of a Viking-Age pin and half a glass bead. However, twelve sturdy postholes were found, belonging to a wooden building measuring about 15m by 5m. The spread of the coins showed that the hoard had originally been hidden inside its walls. Remarkably, no pottery was found, or any signs of a fireplace – although the remains of a cobbled surface in the northern part of the house might indicate the location of an oven or hearth. After photographing the excavated area, it was backfilled, since we lacked the financial resources to continue and the aim of the excavation – to check the looted find spot for a silver hoard – had been fulfilled. However, this left the postholes unexcavated and no radiocarbon analysis of the charcoal samples could be made. A fresh excavation of the site might enable us to understand the chronological connections between the building and the hoard.

In 1905, a silver hoard of nearly 700 Islamic silver coins and two spiral arm-rings was found during ploughing in Norrgårde in Sanda parish (SHM 12,622, *tpq* 859/60). In 1985, I investigated the site with a metal detector and found additional coins; and in the following spring, I excavated some 53m[2] of the site. This exposed a small feature which I interpreted as a possible hearth, and two rows of charcoal-filled pits at right angles to one another.[30] Only a very few bronze settlement objects were found: two pieces of sheet metal and a simple arm-ring, dated to the second half of the eighth century. However, several iron tools were also uncovered, which can probably be linked to a workshop, along with iron slag. It is possible that the rows with charcoal pits were within a wooden building which burned down.

The two hoards from Kattlunds and Norrgårde represent find spots where key questions about the connection between Viking-Age hoards and buildings remain unanswered, and the lack of archaeological evidence is frustrating. On the other hand, our three main case studies (Burge, Gannarve and Spillings) all show a picture of farms occupying roughly the same place throughout the centuries and they offer rich archaeological material. Gotland's silver hoards seem to have a variety of contexts – more specifically, different kinds of settlements and buildings. Only fresh investigations and more detailed analysis can help clarify the subject and do justice to the hoards and their full historical and cultural significance.

Notes

1 Most Gotlandic hoards contain purely silver, although gold has been found in sixty-four of the *c.* 750 discovered to date.
2 *MSoS*.
3 Östergren (2004), p. 43.
4 *MSoS*, pp. 235–40.
5 This was commissioned by the Riksantikvarieämbetet and the Gotland Museum and its author, Johan Norderäng, worked in cooperation with Thunmark-Nylén: Norderäng (2014).
6 *WKG*, vol. 3.2, pp. 477–8; Norderäng (2014); *MSoS*, pp. 125–7. See also the chapter by Widerström in this volume.
7 *MSoS*, pp. 126–7.
8 *MSoS*, p. 195, fig. 182.38.
9 *SoB*; *MSoS*, pp. 104–5.
10 *SoB*, p 50.
11 Jonsson (1986).
12 Jonsson (1986).
13 *MSoS*, pp. 217–26.
14 *SH*, esp. Widerström (2009); Östergren (2009).
15 Key players working on the Spillings hoard include Gotland Museum, the island's Länsstyrelsen (County Administrative Board), Gotland University, RAÄ, SHM, the Kungliga Myntkabinettet (Royal Coin Cabinet) and the Stockholm Numismatic Institute.
16 Östergren (2009), pp. 22–4.
17 Rispling (2004), p 125.
18 Östergren (2009), pp. 28–31.
19 Widerström (2009).
20 Östergren (2009), p. 32.
21 Widerström (2009), pp. 50–2.
22 Widerström (2009), p. 50; Appendix, no. 31.
23 Widerström (2009), p. 52.
24 Carlsson (2009), pp. 90–102.
25 Widerström (2009), p. 53.
26 Östergren (2009), pp. 34–6.
27 Widerström (2009), pp. 57–8.
28 These were undertaken as part of the *Ett plundrat kulturarv* project ('A looted cultural heritage'): Hellqvist and Östergren (2011).
29 Jonsson and Östergren (1989), pp. 90–6.
30 *MSoS*, pp. 44–5, 143–5. For radiocarbon dating of the hearth and pits, see Appendix, nos 62–5.

Bibliography

Carlsson, D. (2009), 'Owner missing? The hoard, the farm and the community', in *SH*, pp. 65–107.

Hellqvist, M.-L. and M. Östergren (2011), *Ett plundrat kulturarv. Att motverka och förebygga plundring av fornlämningar* (Länsstyrelsen Gotlands län, Rapport 30 November 2011), Visby.

Jonsson, K. (1986), 'Myntfynden', in *SoB*, pp. 78–82.

Jonsson, K. and M. Östergren (1989), 'Vikingatida silverskatter: nya forskningsrön på skilda sätt', *GA* 61: 79–98.

Norderäng, J. (2014), *Rapportsammanställning för arkeologisk undersökning år 1967 & 1969–1979, RAGU. RAÄ-nr Lummelunda 93:1, Burge 1:10 (idag Burge 1:69), Lumme-lunda socken, Gotland* (RAÄ dnr 3.4.2–46–2015), Visby.

Östergren, M. (2004), *Under plogen. Mallgårds i Levide sn. En studie inom ramen för forskning-sprojektet 'Fornlämningar i odlingslandskapet'*, Fårö Konsult Arkeologiska Skrifter 1, Visby.

Östergren, M. (2009), 'Spillings: the largest Viking Age silver hoard in the world', in *SH*, pp. 11–40.

Rispling, G. (2004), 'Spännande mynt i Spillingsskatten', *GA* 76: 123–32.

Widerström, P. (2009), 'Spillings farm: the home of a rich Viking in the northeast of Gotland', in *SH*, pp. 41–63.

11 Gotland

Silver island

Dan Carlsson

Situated in the middle of the Baltic, a meeting point between east and west, Gotland has a tremendously rich heritage from the Viking Age. In spite of its small size – the island is about 170km from north to south and 50km from east to west – more than 700 silver hoards have been found around Gotland, and almost every year a new hoard comes to light. The hoards are spread fairly evenly across the island, except for forest areas where there has never been any settlement, and archaeological investigations show that more or less every farm on Gotland has at least one Viking-Age silver hoard.

Some two-thirds of all Viking-Age hoards found in Sweden are from Gotland and consist mainly of silver coins. In all some 170,000 coins have been discovered: most are of Arabic origin, but there are also pieces from Germany, England, Denmark, Byzantium and many other places. Besides coins, many hoards also include silver and gold jewellery, as well as numerous examples of arm-rings, finger-rings and different kinds of brooches. Many hoards also contain scrap silver, obviously intended for melting down and manufacturing into new objects. It should also be noted that silver was not the only metal to reach the island from outside. Most objects used in daily life were made of either iron or bronze – base metals not found on the island – not to mention glass, amber, antler and slate, which also had to be imported. A good example of this is one of the hoards found at Spillings in Othem parish, which consists of some 20kg of bronze waste, partly melted down for reuse.[1]

The reason for this extraordinary wealth on Viking-Age Gotland was its position in the Baltic Sea: situated halfway between the Swedish mainland and the Baltic coast, it was a meeting place between east and west and a middleman in east–west trade. The relatively even distribution of the island's hoards shows a society in which most farms took part in this highly lucrative trade.[2] There are no signs of early kings on medieval Gotland and the evidence points to a society built on farms and farmers, although, of course, some farmers had more to say than others.

In spite of the island's position in east–west trade and consequent exposure to foreign customs and religious influences, Gotland very much had its own culture, not least in the use of female jewellery. All over the Viking world the oval brooch was commonplace. But Gotland's women wore box-shaped and animal-head brooches not encountered anywhere else in Scandinavia, and many other types of dress and jewellery can only be found on Gotland. This separate culture can be explained to a large extent by its long history of isolation, since such islands tend to develop their own unique cultural blend. Yet Gotland's Viking-Age history is primarily a story of eastern connections. It had little to do with mainland Sweden at that time – despite Wulfstan's statement that Gotland was 'subject to the Svear'[3] – and seems to have had closer ties to the areas along the eastern shore of the Baltic,[4] and still further east, down to the Black Sea and on to the Caspian.

The affluence of Viking-Age Gotland continued well into the middle ages, when Visby become one of the leading towns in the Hanseatic League, a centre on the trade route between Novgorod and western Europe. However, Gotland gradually lost its position as a Baltic hub, with ships no longer needing to stop in Visby to load supplies, and the conquest of Gotland by the Danish king Valdemar IV Atterdag in 1361 marked the end of the island's heyday. Gotland was reduced to a minor economic player and faced two hard centuries.

Harbours and trade

The influx of silver and other foreign goods clearly required a well-developed and functioning network, as well as ports and probably also marketplaces (Map 11.1). It should be noted that major manufacturing apparently went hand in hand with the large-scale importing of metals, antler, glass and other materials, and was largely concentrated around harbour locations or marketplaces. However, most farms could undertake basic metalwork, as shown for instance by materials found at the deserted farm at Fjäle in Ala parish and by other studies of farm sites. The harbour was, in other words, a node between the island's longstanding community and the outside world. It was here that they bought the goods that could not be produced at the farm; from here they set off on their trading expeditions to other parts; and here they met with foreign merchants.

As we have seen, the very even spatial distribution of silver hoards across the island implies that almost every farmer took part in trade in one way or another, which in turn leads to the conclusion that there must have been many harbours along the Gotlandic coast, not just one or two. A recent, 10-year research project under my direction has given us a good sense of the island's harbours. We aimed to analyse and describe the number of harbours and trading places, and their structure, development, spatial organisation and development, between roughly 600 and 1000 AD, and this involved coastal field surveys as well as minor – and in some cases, more extensive – excavations.

The project's starting point was to study archives and old maps of the coastal region. Three criteria were decisive in locating possible harbours: the presence of early medieval burials or grave fields situated close to the coast; a shore protected from strong winds; and a distinctive cultural landscape, as shown on the eighteenth- and nineteenth-century cadastral maps. The distinguishing

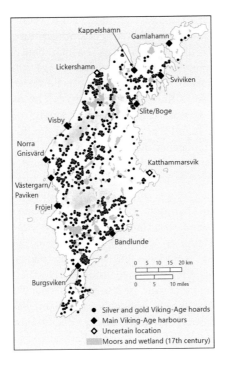

Map 11.1 Gotland's Viking-Age hoards and harbours.

marks could include, for example, roads that meet at a certain point on the coast, or agricultural land (cultivated fields and meadows) located close to the coast but with no farm in reasonable distance. Having identified possible harbour locations, the next steps involved phosphate mapping of these locations and the excavation of some 10 key places along the coast that showed signs of activity ranging from the Roman Iron Age to the early middle ages, but with their centre of gravity in the Viking Age.

Our investigations revealed some 60 locations along Gotland's coast showing signs of Viking-Age activity. Most are, for the time being, merely 'possible' harbours, and excavations have only been carried out at a handful. We cannot be certain that they all have the same character: they could range from small fishing camps to larger trading places, and some may have nothing to do with Viking-Age harbour developments at all. Our methodology also means that some harbours are yet to be detected. For instance, there are surprisingly few harbours on the east coast of the island, which probably reflects the problems in identifying them: the east has a far gentler shelf than the west, with a greater number of beaches, making it more difficult to identify precise harbour spots.

The sheer number of landing places identified suggests that Viking-Age Gotland was primarily about small, farm-based fishing harbours. Fishing was clearly of great importance, as was seal hunting, but there are also traces of manufacturing as well as trade. In most cases these Viking-Age fishing settlements can be linked to the seventeenth-century fishing settlements found on the island's oldest farm maps, which date back to 1693–1703, showing direct continuity between the Viking-Age settlements and today's fishing settlements – much as today's farms can be traced back to the Viking Age and, in many cases, to the Roman Iron Age. The main change along the coast is that the harbours and buildings have moved outwards, towards the water's edge, as the island has seen a gradual uplift of some 2–3m per thousand years since the last ice age.

In addition to the many farm-based fishing harbours, we found a number of ports or central harbours that seem to have been much larger and to have had a far broader function: not only ports and trading centres, but also places of manufacture. Of the harbours that could be substantiated, eight could be termed ports, in the sense that they served a much larger area than just one or two farms. In addition to a far broader range of activities, especially in trade and crafts, these may have been meeting places for Gotlanders and outsiders. The Viking-Age ports we know of today are Visby, Paviken/ Västergarn, Fröjel, the inner part of Burgsviken bay, Bandlunde, Bogeviken and Kappelshamn. We should probably add Gamlahamn on Fårö to this group of central harbours; and there was probably another one somewhere near Östergarn, although such a central harbour has yet to be found in eastern Gotland.

Harbours have always been fundamental for Gotlanders, and this was so in the Viking Age. The archaeological survey of harbours, whether smaller, farm-based landing places or central ports, shows an interesting spatial distribution pattern and sheds light on their functions, both internal and external. I will illustrate this with three examples: two small local landing places which served as fishing harbours for a few farms, Swiviken and Norra Gnisvärd; and one of Gotland's central harbours on the west coast – Fröjel – which served as an international meeting place.

Swiviken in Rute parish

Swiviken is a typical example of a farm-based harbour or landing place (Figure 11.1).[5] Today called Lergravsviken, it is located in Rute parish in northern Gotland. The innermost part of the bay has become silted up, but during the Viking Age it extended considerably further inland, as can be seen on late seventeenth-century maps. To the west there is a markedly flat area that slopes down to the former shoreline: this was given over to arable or grassland in the late 1600s, and remains arable today. A small burial ground with at least four graves lies next to this; based on the height above sea level, these graves are probably from the Viking Age. To the west, at least six *slipskårestenar* lie level with the Viking-Age shoreline. The area has produced a number of stray finds of beads, most probably from a destroyed grave; and

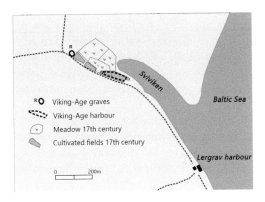

Figure 11.1 Swiviken: a typical Viking-Age landing place.

there is anecdotal evidence of wooden piles next to the bay's western shore, which could have been jetties or piers.

Phosphate mapping of the area around the bay revealed relatively high values within an area of approximately 0.5ha on the west side. Subsequent excavations there gave clear indications of Viking-Age activity at the site: postholes, marked cultural layers, plenty of bones and a number of other objects. Among the latter were a lock large enough for a coffer or another type of lockable storage space, two loom weights, a piece of hardware from a coffin or a door, a well-preserved bronze pendant and a beautifully decorated bronze plaque. The excavations also revealed numerous postholes close to the bay, signalling a number of huts, and the artefacts included a large number of fish bones – only to be expected, given the nature of the site. Alongside these findings emerged a fairly extensive range of ceramics which, taken together with the other finds, indicate that Swiviken had been a harbour from the Viking Age up to the middle ages, and only later moved to the position shown on maps from the 1690s on.

The old map of the area gives an interesting picture of the various farms that owned land adjacent to our Viking-Age harbour site and thus might be linked to its activities. There appear to have been four such farms – Stora and Lilla Valla, Alvans and Puttersjaus – all located close together and separated from the bay by hills. The land at the harbour site is clearly divided between the four farms. It follows that these four farms, or their predecessors, used and owned this small fishing harbour in the Viking Age. The seventeenth-century map also shows that by then the fishing huts were located further into the bay, although still on the same side, a move presumably caused by silting up and uplift.

One of the most interesting finds was of a quarter of an Arabic coin dated to the reign of the Abbasid caliph al-Amin (809–13). Other studies of Viking-Age harbours and farmsteads on Gotland have shown regular finds of coins, even in small fishing settlements. It would seem that coins were used in everyday trading on the island, and were not something that only turned up in silver hoards.

Norra Gnisvärd in Tofta parish

The second example of this kind of minor landing place or harbour is to be found on the west coast of Gotland, some 15km south of Visby and around 500m north of the fishing village of Gnisvärd in Tofta parish. Just inland from the current beach lies the former bay, today a wetland, some 2–3m above sea level.[6] This is flanked by two grave fields, one to the north and one to the south, with a typical Gotlandic picture stone of later type (700–1100 AD) standing, in its original location, adjacent to the southern grave field.

The northern burial ground has nine visible graves, but archaeological excavations in 1966 and 1986 revealed ample evidence of early Viking-Age graves below the surface. One of these, a woman's, contained a box brooch, two bronze pins and three iron knives. A second grave, which has been completely destroyed by a gravel pit, contained a sword and spear in addition to the remains of a skeleton. The southern grave field consists of 55 graves and the picture stone mentioned above. It lies around 6m above sea level and has not been excavated, although it can be dated to the Roman Iron Age. There is also a third burial ground, located about 300m east of the harbour site on a marked elevation; its 12 graves have yet to be studied.

Phosphate mapping was carried out in the area between the northern and southern grave fields, adjacent to the former bay, as a first step towards locating the harbour settlement. This gave consistently low values, with a relatively small area of some 40m^2 showing markedly higher values, close to the southern grave field. Based on this and spatial analysis, limited excavations were carried out to find any traces of settlement. These yielded rich and diverse find materials, in terms of structures and objects, and also graves invisible on the surface.

Building remains were primarily in the form of a dozen postholes, most of which were stone framed. In one of the trenches there was a clear floor horizon: a layer 2.5m wide and several inches thick with soil that contained carbon, flint, burnt and unburnt pieces of bone and clay, herring vertebrae, highly corroded nails and iron pieces. Four Arabic silver coins, two dating from the early or mid-ninth century, were also discovered and radiocarbon dating of the floor gave the age of the house as AD 875 ± 70 years – consistent with the age of these coins. The total of 68 broadly ranged finds does not include the large amounts of bone, coal, flint and suchlike that were also unearthed. Particularly noteworthy are the relatively large quantities of fish bones and flint, in addition to traditional settlement materials such as nails, iron rods and ceramics. The settlement can be dated based on the find material, primarily the four Arabic coins and four radiocarbon datings: the former range from AD 754–64 to AD 866/7, the latter from AD 710 and AD 875 ± 70 years, indicating that the settlement was in use in the Viking Age.[7]

Three graves were found in the south-eastern part of the survey area, some 20m north of the southern grave field and completely invisible from above ground. Two have been examined, while the third remains unexcavated with only the cranium visible in the excavation trench. All three skeletons are lying in the same direction and appear contemporaneous. Grave 1 contains a man in the supine position, approximately 65cm below the surface, with his head to the north-northeast and his legs and arms lying alongside his body. This well-preserved skeleton was in a coffin- or boat-shaped stone frame. The man was quite tall, some 1.80m high, with a heavily corroded knife at his left hip and a similarly badly corroded belt buckle above his right. In the case of of the ground Grave 2, the skeleton of a young woman was revealed only 20–25cm below the surface of the ground, lying on her back with her legs straight, arms slightly bent and her head to the north-northeast. Her skull had been partially peeled away, most probably by earlier ploughing. Aged between 15 and 20, she had been buried with a typical set of late Vendel-Period jewellery, including a necklace made up of 152 beads, mostly glass but some of limestone. Other ornaments included 15 fish-head pendants, two animal-head brooches and, at the right temple, a dress pin, all made of bronze. On her left arm she wore three arm-rings, two of bronze and one of iron, and a limestone spindle whorl lay at her right femur.

It would thus seem that Gnisvärd was active as a harbour in the late Vendel Period and early Viking Age, but that its importance declined as the bay became cut off from the sea with rising land levels. The harbour's layout – with an inlet to the north-west, a settlement area inland from the bay and to the south, and burial sites flanking the bay to the north and south – is similar to many other landing places on Gotland. As at Swiviken, coin finds attest the widespread use of silver and coins throughout Gotland as early as the ninth century. Arabic and later western coins are commonly found at settlements, landing places and also in many graves. Silver and coins were a common commodity, as our next example from Fröjel clearly shows.

Fröjel: Viking port

Fröjel is one of Gotland's best-explored central harbour sites: a trade and manufacturing hub located on the west coast some 40km south of Visby (Figure 11.2). More than 10 years of research and excavation have yielded large quantities of varied material which can help us to understand Viking-Age trade and handicraft production on Gotland, despite the fact that less than 2% of the port's surface area has been investigated to date.[8]

Layout and history

The trading centre is located just below and to the west of Fröjel Church, next to what was an inlet protected by an outlying island: the area is still called Holmen (the Swedish for 'islet'), even though today it forms part of the Gotlandic mainland. The harbour covers an area of about 10ha, bearing comparison with Birka, which measures around 7ha inside its ramparts. However, it should be noted that the cultural layers at Birka are far thicker than at Fröjel, although Fröjel seems to have been active for longer. The

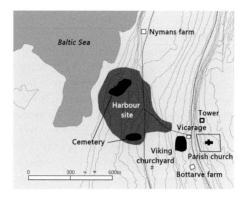

Figure 11.2 Fröjel: Viking port.

settled area extends eastwards from the former beach, virtually to the edge of the cliff on which today's parish church stands. The siting of Fröjel Church is, in itself, evidence of the harbour's importance, since most farms are to be found in Upper Fröjel, some 4km eastwards inland. In other words, the church is not at the centre of the parish, as is customary on Gotland, but is directly linked to the coast and to the harbour, suggesting both that the harbour was in use into the early middle ages, and that the site was of sufficient status for it to be considered a suitable place for the later parish church.

Fröjel started as a small fishing harbour sometime in the sixth or seventh century, linked to local farms. It evolved over the course of the Viking Age and early middle ages to become a permanently inhabited central point for trade and manufacturing, and by the eleventh and twelfth centuries it had become highly urbanised, with buildings divided into plots and rows in a grid pattern of streets. The oldest artefact to be found on the site is a late sixth-century brooch, probably from a ruined grave. The latest dating – to *c.* 1100 – comes from workshops to the east of the marketplace and from a churchyard (probably with a church alongside) situated just below the cliff where the later, twelfth-century parish church was built. The site was probably abandoned sometime during the twelfth century, when the strait leading into the port became too shallow thanks to a simultaneous land uplift and lowering of the water level. Smaller-scale activities carried on, however, and a basic harbour continued to function close to today's coastline until the mid-seventeenth century. Later still, Fröjel's inhabitants started to use the fishing harbour at Valbybodar, situated some 500m down the coast from the old rural port.

Despite the fact that we have clear indications of Viking-Age settlement and activities connected to trade, manufacturing and shipbuilding, we lack any secure evidence of jetties and the like in the port area. This is probably because the area is now arable land, and cultivation over several hundred years has wiped out many of the traces of jetties and other constructions connected to the harbour itself. This has also affected the cultural layer at the site, which is thin – rarely more than 0.5m deep – making it extremely difficult to see separate layers or any accumulation of material over time, let alone to separate different time periods from one another in the cultural layer. On the other hand, spatial changes over time are clearly visible: the site expanded greatly, from small beginnings close to the former beach, to a huge area covering some 10ha.

The materials excavated include around 35,000 registered objects, and help elucidate the site, the activities carried out there, the dating and its connections to the surrounding world. As might be expected, the main finds consist of animal bones, slag and flint, pointing to intense activity, especially in the production of artefacts. Thanks to the high calcium content of the soil – Gotland is essentially a limestone cliff in the ocean – bones and other organic material are well preserved, notably skeletons. Besides these materials, there are numerous traces of bone and antler crafting, bead making, metalworking and shipbuilding, as well as trading, in the form of coins, scales and weights, giving a clear indication of the function and significance of the place. Spatial distributions point to a concentration of certain activities in the central and northern parts of the settlement area, but with workshops more or less spread out across the whole area.

Craft working

Interesting material comes from one of the few workshops not to have been affected by cultivation. It was excavated in 2000.[9] Extensive traces of metalworking materials clearly reveal the building's function, including crucibles, moulds and melting furnaces. A detailed analysis of these materials has shown that various metals were used, particularly silver, but also gold and bronze, and that production went all the way from raw materials to finished products. Traces of extensive remelting and refining of silver, with the help of lead in hearths lined with bone ash, are frequently encountered on Viking-Age Gotland, but are far less common in Scandinavia as a whole. Gotlanders probably sought the highest concentration of silver in the raw metal before casting it into different types of arm-rings. This maximising of raw silver content must have been of great importance, since arm-rings played a significant role as a means of payment. Extensive finds of slag as well as semi-finished and other iron products, including iron bars, all testify to iron production on the site. Iron is by far the commonest metal at Fröjel, making up almost half the materials found, and it is likely that its production was a key activity. As already noted, iron is not found on Gotland in the sort of quantities needed and it must therefore have been imported, although as yet we have no indication as to where the people in Fröjel got their iron from.

About 600 beads have been found at the site: most of them are made of glass, but there are also beads made of amber, carnelian, amethyst, limestone, bronze and bone. An interesting material here is rock crystal (Figure 11.3). As with other raw materials, it does not exist on the island in significant quantities and so must have been imported. There are finds of finished objects such as beads and lenses, as well as of rock crystal in its raw form. Some of the beads were clearly made at Fröjel, judging by a number of cracked, unfinished beads drilled from both sides. Glass beads were clearly manufactured on site and huge amounts of waste and half-finished beads have been found there, alongside pieces of millefiori, probably originally imported from Italy.

Rock crystal lenses have been found in other parts of Sweden, such as at Sigtuna on the mainland and at Eketorp on the island of Öland, but the vast majority come from Gotland – some 77 finds in all. These include round and lenticular lenses, and Gotland's finds exceed those of Sweden, Norway and Denmark combined.[10] The Gotland lenses are also unique because of their silver mounting. Their ornamentation shows a strong Slavic influence, once more signalling extensive trade contacts between the island and eastern Europe during the Viking Age. The Gotland lenses have been found mainly in silver hoards and female graves from the late Viking Age and early middle ages, although a large number have also been found without a context. The largest concentrations are in the south of the island, with seven lenses excavated at Fröjel, as well as silver lens mountings. The Gotland lenses are likely to have been used as women's jewellery, but they might also have served as a magnifying glass, or as decorative stones on various ecclesiastical items.

├──────────────┤
1cm

Figure 11.3 One of the seven rock crystal lenses (with solder) excavated at Fröjel.
Photo: author.

It has been suggested that Gotland's concentration of rock crystal lenses indicates that lenses arrived on the island first, before spreading from there to the rest of Scandinavia. If Gotland had a kind of trading monopoly on lenses, this might explain why so many have been found there.[11] It could also be that silver-framed lenses were typical of Gotland.[12]

Workshop activity in Fröjel can clearly be seen from the large amounts of bone and antler waste. There are also extensive finds of finished artefacts such as combs, needles, spindle whorls, dice, weaving and decorated bone objects. Cattle bone may well have come from local animals, but antler had to be imported, since deer are not native to Gotland. Steve Ashby has investigated the origin of the bone and antler used in 15 combs found at Fröjel and has shown that most are made from the antlers of elk or red deer, suggesting that large antlers were the standard material used in comb-making at the site. The absence of reindeer contrasts with findings from elsewhere in Scandinavia, and implies that materials were not imported from a long distance, but were more likely to have come from the southern Baltic or south Scandinavia.[13]

Gotland's contacts with the outside world, and the importance of trade and manufacturing, are well reflected in the Fröjel find material. Of more than 150 coins found, most are German, but there are also Arabic, English and Danish examples. There are some strange copper coins from the late Roman Iron Age, probably imported as raw material. The coins were all stray finds, scattered across the excavated area, and do not represent a silver hoard. Typical of a manufacturing and trading site of this kind are weights and scales. In all, 21 pieces of scales and 45 weights dating to the Viking Age have been excavated. The weights are both of an earlier, octagonal kind, made of bronze, and later, round weights made of iron with a copper or lead shell.[14] Many other finds point to an extensive network of connections around the Baltic Sea and further east, including walrus ivory from the Arctic ocean, and jewellery from Novgorod, Karelia and the Baltic, together with a Resurrection egg from Kiev (Figure 11.4) and ecclesiastical book mountings and decorations, most probably from western Europe.

Although Fröjel was clearly a meeting place between Gotlanders and foreign merchants, the role of its workshops and craftsmen should not be underestimated: they are one of the enduring features of the site. Judging by the bone finds, the port was in fairly permanent use, even if activity probably diminished over winter, depending on the amount of ice in the Baltic.

Buildings

The Fröjel excavations cover $1,500m^2$, a fraction of the whole port; the trenches are quite widely spread; and only three areas have been investigated intensively. Despite this, hundreds of postholes and other structural features pointing to houses and buildings have been unearthed. The main problem has been putting these together to form a pattern of houses. It has been possible to identify only a few clear houses, which appear to be made of wood,

Figure 11.4 The glazed clay Resurrection egg (*Uppståndelseägg*) from Kiev found at Fröjel. Photo: Roland Hejdström.

supported by posts along the walls, and somewhere between 4m by 7m in size. But a certain pattern does seem to emerge: of a settlement in rows along narrow streets, as in many other Viking-Age harbours and trading places such as Birka and Hedeby. The rows of houses in Fröjel seem to run parallel to the coastline, with an ancient road running from north to south at the settlement's eastern edge.

Grave fields

At least three different grave fields are connected to the harbour and workshop site, ranging from the seventh to late eleventh centuries: one to the north (Figure 11.5), one to the south and a third to the east, which forms part of a late Viking-Age/medieval churchyard (the oldest part of the church is late twelfth century). Most of the burials are inhumation graves dug into the gravel and, given that the area has been arable land for centuries, there are likely to be more grave fields in the surrounding area which have yet to be discovered. The northern grave field is the largest, starting in the seventh century and remaining in use until the tenth. It was more or less built over by the harbour settlement in the tenth and eleventh centuries, with postholes penetrating through some of the older graves. The southern grave field dates mainly to the tenth and eleventh centuries, while the churchyard, further east, is from the eleventh and early twelfth centuries. Thus, in a way, we have a continuous line

Figure 11.5 The northern grave field at Fröjel.

of burials over a period of 400 to 500 years, but they show clear differences. In the northern grave field, 77 burials have been excavated, of which 42 are female and only 18 male; 12 could not be interpreted with certainty, and there were also a number of cremation graves for which gender could not be ascribed. Only nine graves have been investigated from the southern grave field, and these contained six men, one woman and two unknown.

The early Christian churchyard has been dated to the eleventh century by artefacts and radiocarbon datings and has been partially excavated. In all, 38 inhumation graves have been investigated in the northern sector of the churchyard, all proving to be of women or, in some cases, children. Trial trenches in the southern sector of the churchyard have revealed four male graves. There would appear to have been a clear division in the churchyard, with the north reserved for women and children, the south for men. This is in line with what has been found in other late Viking-Age churchyards on Gotland, such as those at Stånga, Garda, Havdhem and Burs.[15]

Individuals' health and origins

In all, some 150 graves have been investigated from the three different grave fields. Most are of mature individuals (aged between 40 and 59), but there

Figure 11.6 A well-preserved male skeleton from the northern grave field at Fröjel: around 1.80m tall and buried without any artefacts, he was found lying above the skeleton of a woman who was well equipped with typical Gotlandic brooches and beads, and facing in the opposite direction.

Photo: author.

are quite a few infants buried in the northern grave field. An analysis of 13 individuals from the northern grave field sheds light on their health – and by extension of the people of Fröjel in the Viking Age.[16] The analysis was of three men, eight women and two children, although the latter were newborns and thus not relevant to the study. Of the three men, one was adolescent and the other two adult; of the women, one was adolescent, five adult and two senescent. The individuals' heights were slightly greater than is expected for the period, but it has not been possible to calculate an average height for Fröjel's Viking-Age inhabitants.

Most of the bones showed signs of damage, including 46 examples of osteoarthritis, as well as osteomyelitis and Schmorl's nodes (indicative of degeneration of the spine). Somewhat unexpectedly, an example of Klippel-Feil Syndrome was found (where two or more cervical vertebrae grow together). Dental problems included cavities, tartar and periapical changes. Nine of the eleven adults were measured for osteoporosis and all showed good results, with a high bone density. Traces of an active lifestyle, in the form of large muscle attachment sites, were observed on the humerus, clavicle and tibia of some individuals, while two skeletons showed anomalies: bilateral asymmetry (a significant difference in size between the collarbones) on one, and changes to the tibia shaft in the other, with a flat cross section instead of the normal triangular shape. A number of fractures were noted and X-rayed: some had become infected, but had healed. One of the men also showed violent injuries to his legs, stab wounds to his back, shoulder blade and upper arm, and signs of having fended off attack on the two bones of his forearm. Most of the damage and wear and tear seen in the Fröjel material are to be expected in skeletal remains from this era, and are also found on Viking-Age skeletons from Birka and Fjälkinge, and medieval ones from Lund and Skara. One difference, however, is that deficiency diseases such as cribra orbitalia (a porosity of the skull behind the eyes, traditionally linked to anaemia) and enamel hypoplasia (thin, defective tooth enamel associated with, among other things, poor nutrition) were not observed at Fröjel, as they have been in Birka and Fjälkinge.

An illuminating study of the skeletons from the northern grave field at Fröjel uses DNA from male teeth to determine origin.[17] It investigated a male marker which is found in Baltic and Finnish regions, but which is largely absent in western Europe: Tat-C allele. Levels in male Gotlanders today are around 4.7%, and this is also the case in other parts of Sweden and in western Europe more generally. Southern Swedes show levels of 2.5% and male Icelanders, Danes, the Dutch and Belgians as low as 0.4%. However, the Finnish and Baltic regions today show far higher percentages: Finns, for example, can have values as high as 61.4%. Four out of our nine male skeletons from Fröjel (44%) exhibit elevated levels of Tat-C allele, suggesting their origins lay in the Baltic, or regions inhabited by the Finns or Rus.

Another study of the skeletons uses strontium isotope data from tooth enamel to determine the proportion of non-locals buried in Fröjel's grave fields. Samples from 60 adults were analysed for strontium isotope ratios, as were samples of archaeological fauna, to determine the local bioavailable strontium isotope baseline range. Individuals were deemed local if they fell within two standard deviations of the mean baseline data value: the study showed that 8 of the 60 individuals were not local to Fröjel and the authors conclude that they 'were likely from areas in northern Sweden or Norway'.[18]

The study of male DNA offers significant confirmation of what we already know from the find material: that Gotlanders had a clearly developed eastern network. Thus, it is not surprising that they had their own compound (known as the *Gutenhof*, *Gutagård* or *Gotskii dvor*) in the important city of Novgorod (*Holmgarðr*), in the same way that Novgorodians had their own church in the commercial town of Visby in the middle ages. Although Gotland served as a hub between east and west, an overview of the materials clearly shows that eastern contacts dominated: Gotlanders looked to the east far more than to the west from the Roman Iron Age right up until the end of the Viking Age, as the bronze hoard from Spillings shows. From around 975, however, judging by the number of coins found on the island from Germany, England and Denmark, Gotlanders started to orient themselves more towards the west. Nevertheless, the many indications of external contacts found at the harbour sites, not least Fröjel, do not mean such contacts were of paramount importance. Gotland, like most of Scandinavia at the time, was an essentially agrarian society and its inhabitants probably spent most of their time as farmers.

Notes

1 Östergren (2009), pp. 31–34; see also Östergren in this volume.
2 It should be noted here that settlement on Gotland mainly consisted of single farms, not villages or hamlets.
3 Bately, 'Wulfstan's voyage', p. 15. See also Jansson in this volume.
4 Present-day Finland, Estonia, Latvia and Lithuania.
5 Ahlqvist (1991).
6 Carlsson (1998), pp. 25–38.
7 For recalibrated dates, see Appendix in this volume, nos 57–61.
8 Carlsson (1999); Carlsson (2008).
9 See Gustafsson in this volume.
10 Antell (2009), p. 8.
11 Temple (2000), p. 44.
12 Antell (2009), p. 10.
13 Ashby (2015).
14 The earlier weights were cubo-octahedral and the later oblate spheroid in shape.
15 Westholm (1926).
16 Andersson (2013).
17 The study was undertaken by Professor Lars Beckman and Christina Heuck of Gotland University, but is unpublished.
18 Peschel *et al.* (2017), p. 175.

Bibliography

Primary sources

Bately, J., 'Wulfstan's voyage and his description of *Estland*: the text and the language of the text', in A. Englert and A. Trakadas (eds), *Wulfstan's Voyage: The Baltic Sea Region in the Early Viking Age as Seen from Shipboard*, Roskilde (2009), pp. 14–28.

Secondary literature

Ahlqvist, I. (1991), 'Sviviken. En delundersökning i projektet Gotländska hamn- och handelsplatser 600–1100-talet', unpublished BA thesis, Uppsala University.
Andersson, M. (2013), 'Hälsan i behåll? En studie av sjukdomsbilden i det vikingatida Fröjel, Gotland', unpublished BA thesis, Gotland University.
Antell, S. (2009), 'Gotlands linser under lupp. En studie av de gotländska linsernas funktion, utseende och fyndkontext', unpublished BA thesis, Gotland University.
Ashby, S. (2015), 'Biomolecular analysis of antler combs from Gotland, Sweden', unpublished report, University of York.
Carlsson, D. (1998), *Vikingahamnar: ett hotat kulturarv*, ArkeoDoks Skrifter 1, Visby.
Carlsson, D. (1999), *'Ridanäs': vikingahamnen i Fröjel*, ArkeoDoks Skrifter 2, Visby.

Carlsson, D. (2008), '"Ridanæs": a Viking Age port of trade at Fröjel, Gotland', in *VW*, pp. 131–4.

Östergren, M. (2009), 'Spillings: the largest Viking Age silver hoard in the world', in *SH*, pp. 11–40.

Peschel, E. *et al.* (2017), 'Who resided in Ridanäs? A study of mobility on a Viking Age trading port in Gotland, Sweden', *Journal of Archaeological Science: Reports* 13: 175–84.

Temple, R. (2000), 'Forntida gotländska linser', *GA* 72: 41–52.

Westholm, A. (1926), 'Gotländska kyrkogårdsfynd från brytningstiden mellan hedendom och kristendom', *Fv* 21: 104–14.

12 Silver hoards and society on Viking-Age Gotland

Some thoughts on the relationship between silver, long-distance trade and local communities

Christoph Kilger

Viking-Age silver hoards are a complex phenomenon, linking local histories and trajectories with distant geographies and global economies. During the Viking Age, Scandinavia was fuelled by exotic objects from across the early medieval world, stretching from Central Asia to western Europe. Foreign silver coins travelled within networks spanning vast distances, and were available in almost every corner of the Viking world. Some regions in northern Europe with many silver hoards proved extremely successful in these networks. On the island of Gotland alone more than 750 hoards have been recorded containing some 178,900 silver coins.[1] Even in global comparison, no other region has yielded so many coin and silver finds from the Viking period.

Studying the numismatic composition of hoards has contributed considerably to our understanding of the geography and rhythms of different silver currents: their sources, extent and magnitude.[2] Hoards can be seen as archives, storing information on engagements with the outer world. In this respect Gotland deserves special attention, because the island's community obtained silver from different parts of the known medieval world, unbroken over long periods of time. The hoarding record stretches throughout the Viking Age and up to 1150, a period of some 350 years, showing the island's resilience and its ability to regroup and reorganise its travel to changing destinations.

The meaning of silver and the question of its uses in Gotlandic society, as well as the hoarding phenomenon itself, have all been matters of debate for quite some time. There are two main approaches to explaining the meaning and use of silver. The first sees it as a means of exchange:[3] silver was the backbone of a developing economy and the hoards represent families' fortunes and savings in the Viking Age,[4] with the influx of dirhams in the tenth century perhaps triggering the development of a monetary, coin-based economy.[5] The second approach is to investigate the phenomenon of hoarding itself and to ask why the silver should have been left buried in the ground. Many different explanations have been put forward for this phenomenon: an un-retrieved hoard might signify an investment for the afterlife,[6] attest the social prestige of its owners,[7] represent a material metaphor for the dead[8] or be the ritual disposal of powerful objects that had accumulated complex biographies.[9] Common to all these interpretations is the view that the hoards – and by extension the silver – remained hidden in the ground because they did not play an integral part in economic life and thought.

Yet in fact silver was omnipresent on Gotland in the Viking Age, and it is found in different contexts and with a variety of meanings and uses. One example is provided by the huge number of Viking artefacts that have recently been documented by metal-detecting in the infields of the Cistercian monastery of Roma in the centre of the island. Among the finds are many dirham fragments and over 400 weights, mostly polyhedral.[10] The Roma material resembles the evidence of metal-rich sites from other parts of Scandinavia, such as the central places of Uppåkra in Scania, Sorte Muld on Bornholm or the well-known productive sites from Great Britain.[11] By the middle ages, Roma had become the general assembly site for the Gotland *Althing*. But the evidence suggests that it had taken on the central functions of a *Thing* site during the Viking Age, and was already then a public, crowded place where people from all parts of Gotland gathered and where silver was probably weighed and exchanged on many different occasions.

Given the general impression that silver was only used for purposes of hoarding on Gotland, the evidence from Roma offers a quite different scenario where silver was used on a daily basis. There is a tension in the material which the Roma evidence highlights: silver circulating above the ground, traded and exchanged, as opposed to silver hoarded and hidden in the soil. This ambiguity of silver in Gotlandic society will also frame the questions I will set out and discuss in this chapter. How did silver connect the networks overseas with the hoarding communities at home? What did silver mean at home? Why was it hoarded in such quantities, and what was the rationale behind this phenomenon? Based on my reading of the medieval *Guta Lag*, and especially the provisions regulating matters of inheritance and property in and between families, spouses and relatives, I will argue that there was a gendered relationship between movable wealth such as silver, the possession and inheritance of land, and the social fabric of Gotlandic society.[12]

Hoards and the farming communities

The presence of Viking-Age silver hoards in the rural landscape is a peculiar feature of Gotland. It is still a matter of debate how hoards are related to settlements, notably whether they were concealed under the floorboards of dwelling-houses, on farm complexes or in the cultivated areas of early settlements.[13] Few hoards have been excavated and few find circumstances have been archaeologically investigated. Indeed, the archaeological evidence of Viking-Age farms reveals a similar uncertainty, since few houses have been excavated and properly documented.[14] One area of research that awaits further investigation is the development of a methodology to delimit both the extent of

Viking-Age farms in the inhabited landscape and the topographical and geographic relationship between hoards and farms. There are also still challenges in tracking settlements by using metal-detecting or phosphate analysis. For instance, the metal-rich sites discovered through detecting have been variously identified as farmsteads, metal workshops or burial sites destroyed by ploughing.[15] But so far we lack a coherent empirical framework and analytical procedures for evaluating the fresh data. We also lack full publication of both the archaeological and the numismatic evidence. At this stage it is fair to say that we still do not know exactly what constituted the territorial domain of a settlement or how hoards related to farms during the Viking Age.

Another phenomenon often observed is the clustering of Viking hoards in the infields of modern farms. In a few instances it has been possible to study and compare the numismatic contents of these hoards. This was the case with the twin hoards discovered at Glammunds farm in Akebäck parish (Figure 12.1). Both date to the first half of the eleventh century and were discovered only 13 metres apart. Based on a comparison of their dating and composition, Kenneth Jonsson has argued that their proximity could be explained in terms of ownership and a close social relationship. Both hoards could represent the fortunes of a single family, involving two successive generations who lived together on a farm and who engaged in trading. Jonsson further suggests that the presence of twin hoards implies knowledge of trading and travelling within the family.

Figure 12.1 The infields of Glammunds farm: a typical Gotlandic find spot, the field was probably the site of one or more Viking-Age farms, and many earlier traces – including two picture stones – have been found close to the twelfth-century Romanesque church of Akebäck seen in the background.

Photo: author.

Unfortunately, the site at Glammunds has only been surveyed by metal-detector and has not been excavated. Later rescue surveys conducted in the same area discovered the remains of a third tenth-century hoard. It is not certain whether all three hoards relate to the same farm, according to Jonsson, but their presence within a confined area implies a long tradition of how to conduct the business of trading.[16] Besides Glammunds, there are further examples of the clustering of hoards.[17] Interestingly Jonsson's interpretation links the numismatic composition of hoards with their respective placement in the landscape. In this sense the clustering of hoards may be understood as a material expression of social cohesion and the transfer of knowledge within close social bonds. As such, hoards are not only the material outcome of trading, but they also embody the knowledge of where to travel and how to trade. Taking these thoughts as a point of departure, some more questions arise. If silver was regarded as a prized possession and a resource to exchange, what significance did it have within the domain of the Viking-Age farm and its household? What are the underlying mechanisms that link both of these dimensions?

Brothers abroad and brothers at home

There are contemporary sources on Gotland that tell of individuals who travelled abroad and their often tragic destinies. Some runestones dating to the tenth and eleventh centuries give us the names and accounts of those who participated in such expeditions, which often ranged far from the island. In some instances, the stones mention how the travellers were related. One famous example is the Pilgårds runestone (G 280) from Boge parish in north-eastern Gotland. The stone was raised in memory of Ravn, a member of an expedition to Rus, who died somewhere on the river Dnieper near the well-known rapids, one of which was called Aeifor. Altogether six individuals are mentioned, of whom four were brothers, and the inscription says:

> Brightly painted, this stone was raised by Hegbjarn and his brothers Rod-visl, Austain and Emund.
> They have raised stones in memory of Ravn south of Rufstain.
> They penetrated far into the Aeifor.
> Vivil was in command.[18]

The eleventh-century runestones from Sjonhem (G 134, G 135 and G136) offer another example. Raised by parents in commemoration of their three sons, two of whom died en route from Gotland, they recount the sons' fate. The inscription on G 134 (Figure 12.2) also mentions *i utfaru*, a contemporary expression for travelling abroad:

> Rodvisl and Rodälv had these stones raised in memory of their three sons.
> This stone in memory of Rodfos.

He was betrayed by the Wallachians on an outward journey.
God help Rodfos' soul.
May God betray those who betrayed him.

Taken together, the stones tell us that such expeditions were conducted by the male members of entire families – brothers and sons – who travelled overseas on joint enterprises.

In *Guta Lag* we again hear of brothers who were engaged in common undertakings, although this time in the role of possible heirs. The chapter regulating inheritance, which is one of the longest and most complex sections of the text, describes not only the different contexts of how and when property could be handed over; it also offers us glimpses of the web of kindred relations, rights and mutual obligations that existed between the members of families resident on the island's farms. We hear of *scyldir menn*, a family's closest male relatives, and *etar menn*, the male members of the clan who had to be consulted first on inheritance issues. We also hear of the *karl*, the older, male head of the family, and of his sons and daughters. At the

Figure 12.2 The eleventh-century Sjonhem runestone (G 134), referring to betrayal by *bla-kumen*, possibly Wallachians (Vlachs).

Photo: Berig (2008); licensed under CC BY-SA 3.0.

centre of all the concerns addressed by *Guta Lag* lies the farmstead, the *garþr*: how to keep it undivided and in the possession of those living there. Christine Peel, who has translated and written a commentary on the original text, concludes that the law was 'designed for a closed, self-governing, farming community, with a need to maintain estates at a viable size, despite the necessity of providing younger sons with a living and daughters with a dowry'.[19]

The chapter on inheritance starts with an account of the rights and obligations of brothers living on a farm. It states that if several brothers inherit on the death of their father, the farm should under no circumstances be divided before the youngest reaches maturity. The farm must be kept within the close family, and the sale of land to those outside the clan should only be contemplated in cases of dire need. Nor should the older brothers part from the youngest after their father's death. Yet there are no laws of succession as to who should take over as *karl*, and no main heir was determined in advance. Instead, the lawmakers ordain loyalty between the remaining male members of the family and offer flexible suggestions when matters of inheritance had to be settled.[20] One such suggestion, when farms became crowded with younger brothers squabbling over their inheritance, was to send them away on journeys. *Guta Lag* explicitly links these young men with the business of trading: when the youngest reaches maturity, at the age of fifteen, he takes 'his scrip and his scales'.[21] This probably means that he symbolically takes responsibility for himself by weighing out his portion. Although the expression *skiaupa ok scalar* is not entirely clear,[22] it presumably refers to the tools that allowed a young man to take up trading in his own right.[23] The farm offered a safe haven to which the travelling brothers could return and which could provide a base for their future expeditions.

The runestones and *Guta Lag* afford us glimpses of the island's social organisation. Taken together, they hint at the importance of closed kindred networks, run by their male members and linked to the farms. To keep the farm and its lands together, exchangeable property was needed, both to reconcile differing interests and to prevent potential conflict. The acquisition of silver through trading enabled the travelling brothers to raise their status and position within the family, and this may have been an advantage when matters of succession had to be settled. Another time when silver could well have been needed was during the negotiation of marriage alliances between families, when claims to land and property had to be balanced with the demands of family honour and reputation. If *Guta Lag* can be used as a source to investigate Viking-Age conditions, can it provide any clues as to why silver was hoarded and why the hoards remained in the ground? To answer these questions I want to continue my argument by presenting and discussing some aspects of the strict patrilocal rules of inheritance in the law, which prescribe that landed property should pass only to a farm's resident male heirs. A liminal situation for every farm would have been a wedding, when a bride from another farm stepped over the threshold and entered the domain of her husband's family.

Female inheritance and property

One issue that *Guta Lag* deals with in particular is that of women's property and inheritance rights. Women from distant farms who married into a family were explicitly excluded from inheriting and obtaining a share of the husband's property. In fact, Nils Blomkvist has concluded that married women were probably considered to be no more than guests in their new home.[24] However, a wife's status and security within her husband's family could be secured by different economic means.

Figure 12.3 Haimfylgi? The recently discovered Stale hoard from Rone parish on southern Gotland.[1]

Photo: author.

Note

1 Östergren (2015), pp. 36–7.

One was the *haimfylgi*, the dowry that followed a woman from her home and that she brought to the marriage (Figure 12.3).[25] Another was the *hogsl*, the bride price presented to her by the groom on the morning after the wedding. And a third means was the *iþ*, probably a sum paid to a widow as recognition for the work she had contributed to the farm during her marriage.[26] One aspect of *Guta Lag*'s provisions on female inheritance which is barely mentioned or discussed in the literature, however, is the detailed instructions on how to deal with property assigned to and owned by married women. As we shall see, these provisions show that a married woman's property was of considerable importance to both families.

The property of an heiress (*erfilytia*) – that which she rightfully could claim as her own possessions – could be inherited by either branch of the family so long as her bloodline was still alive. However, the situation changed when her bloodline died out. In that case, her property could be reclaimed by the farm from which she had been married. This happened when there were two successive male generations descended from her, but not a third. Then her property would probably have reverted to the 'spear side'; that is, to her father's family.[27] However, when there were three successive male generations descended from her, the property remained with the farm; that is, with her husband's family. These provisions imply that a woman's property was regarded as untouchable and a division of her possessions between the families after her death was not negotiable.[28] In a subsequent provision, it is ordained that the property a wife takes into the marriage from her farm can also be taken out again by her. This happened when her husband died and she became a widow.

The questions to ask are: why was there such detailed provision on this issue, and why was a woman's property regarded as something not open to negotiation, at least for three generations after her death? One conceivable answer is that neither landed property nor movable stock was owned individually; rather, it was collectively owned by a clan. Thus, from a gendered perspective one might argue that although movable property, especially the dowry (*haimfylgi*), was considered to be a woman's property, it was not necessarily owned by the bride herself, but by her kin and her bloodline on her father's side. If we accept that *Guta Lag* and its inheritance provisions reflect the customs of earlier periods, such as the Viking Age, some of the hoards that remained buried in the ground can be seen as unclaimed properties, tokens of a lasting contract between families and farms. A further reading of the text prompts us to develop this conclusion further. This principle was also valid for the bride price and other assets owned by a woman who was married into another clan. A woman's possessions handed over to the husband's clan during the wedding could have been regarded as her family's pledge. They were considered to be untouchable as long as her bloodline – the kin on her father's side – could lay legal claim to it.

A similar explanation for why hoards remained buried in the ground has been suggested by Mats Burström. However, his interpretation implies a slightly different logic from the one presented here. Burström argues that the huge inflow of silver to Gotland was conditioned by a scarcity of land on the island by the Viking Age.[29] The lack of land, and consequent difficulty in establishing new farms, led to a system of bridewealth which was controlled by senior men and which effectively limited access to land. In this context Burström stresses the importance of silver as bride price. Young men were forced to obtain silver from abroad in order to be part of the game. This led to a raised matrimonial age, which in turn considerably delayed them taking over the farm. Burström's model offers a compelling explanation why silver became so important in Gotlandic society and why young men sought their fortunes abroad. However, Burström considers silver to have only prestige value which, once buried in the ground, was not convertible. Silver was transferred to the bride's family in a public ceremony during the wedding, in order to confirm the bridegroom's status. The silver was then hoarded on the bride's farm. Sealed off from further circulation, it remained in the ground as a symbolic token of a successful wedding transaction and as a confirmation of the status of the bride's family. By burying it, the silver became enclosed within a socially binding sphere which prohibited its further circulation. A conversion into the sphere of exchange would have caused a serious loss of prestige for the owners.

In contrast to Burström's model, I would argue that silver was hoarded precisely because it had come to assume the various qualities of money, regardless of whether it was buried or circulated above ground. At some point silver had assumed bargaining power: it became a means of value, saving and also security. Social and landed relations in Gotland society seem to have been intertwined to such a degree that access to movable stock was of paramount importance. Seen in this context, silver proved a vital resource. The patrilocal inheritance system as outlined by *Guta Lag* helps explain why hoards remained in the ground and why Gotlanders were forced to seek their fortunes abroad. Obtaining silver in such quantities and the phenomenon of hoarding seem intimately linked to the negotiation of inheritance matters in farming communities at home. In this respect hoards attest not only inflows of silver, but also a web of social relations criss-crossing the island.

Conclusions

This chapter has discussed aspects of the interconnectedness between Gotlandic society, trade and exchange in the Viking Age. One of the keys to the success of Viking Gotlanders in their encounters and interactions with the outside world was the stability of their own social structures and institutions. These institutions not only made these time-consuming and risky ventures possible; they also nourished the need and desire to bring home movable wealth such as silver. It has been argued that silver at some point intersected with ideas of ownership and property in a kin-based society.

When silver started to appear in huge quantities, in its capacity as movable wealth it became an important asset and stimulus in the great game of land. Family ties, inheritance rules and above all marriages between farms and clans offered diverse opportunities and reasons for using silver. This mix of circumstances was the driver for Gotland's engagement with the outside world. From this perspective, individual hoards represent a material record of exchanges, trading expeditions and relations beyond Gotland, as well as offering us knowledge of the 'companies' who undertook these journeys. But equally importantly, hoards are also archives telling us about the individual histories of farms and families. The peculiar inheritance system on Gotland, which provides insights into the important issues around control over and access to land, was probably one of the driving forces behind all the travel and seeking of fortunes abroad.

A system based on kinship may have provided the reservoir of knowledge and stable social structure needed to sustain travel abroad on such a scale. It lay behind the brothers who feature on the runestones and in *Guta Lag*, and it was probably responsible for the flow of commodities and coins to the farms. As argued above, the hoards themselves can be understood both as the material outcome of these contacts and networks and as the property and wealth of individuals. One fascinating aspect is to look at some of the silver hoards as gendered property: the possessions of young women who were married to distant farms. Their composition may show the importance of kinship in the development of a bridewealth system based on silver in the late ninth century.

Silver became a new means for allocating movable wealth between families and farms on the island and, in so doing, it paved the way for the success of Gotland's long-distance trading networks. Yet important as silver was for the Gotlanders travelling overseas, whether to trade or raid, it was the role it played in channelling knowledge and resources on the island that transformed society profoundly. In that sense, silver was not only a dynamic means of exchange for travellers returning there; it also had a socially enhancing effect by facilitating alliances between families and the pooling of different networks.

Hoards and settlements on Gotland are interrelated in many ways, and this relationship affects how we analyse hoard size and content, since this tells us not only about Viking-Age Gotlanders' ventures overseas, but also about the relationships between farms and families at home. The same goes for the analysis of silver inflows to Gotland, and for assessing silver's uses and circulation on Gotland. Even though my interpretation of the social organisation of farms rests on later medieval sources, it should open up new ways to approach the social fabric that lay behind Gotlandic trading networks. However, the interpretation offered here, viewing silver hoards as dowries, offers only one possible explanation. The mindset and the range of ideas behind the hoarding phenomenon remain a challenge to explore.

Notes

1 For the latest update on the total number of coins in finds from Gotland and else-where in Sweden, see Jonsson (2015). The threat of looting led the municipal authorities on Gotland to launch a rescue project in 2008 to recover material

from known hoards: Hellqvist and Östergren (2011). Previously unknown and undisturbed hoards were discovered during this fieldwork. The project ended in 2011 and awaits full publication. As a result, the estimated number of *c.* 750 hoards is likely to be adjusted.

2 For example, Noonan (1990); Brather (1995–6); Kovalev and Kaelin (2007); Kilger (2008); Adamczyk (2014); Jankowiak (2015).

3 Jonsson and Östergren (1990).

4 Odebäck (2009).

5 Jonsson (2010).

6 Thunmark-Nylén (1986).

7 Burström (1993).

8 Myrberg (2009).

9 Myrberg Burström (2015).

10 Östergren (2016); Gustafsson and Östergren (2017), p. 98, Tab. 1: altogether 435 weights, of which 277 (64%) are cubo-octahedral. Since 2017 more weights have been detected which are not included in this number.

11 Blackburn (2003).

12 From her analysis of the structure and language, and by comparing it with the provisions of other provincial laws from the Swedish mainland, Christine Peel argues convincingly that the earliest manuscript text of *Guta Lag* was compiled in the early thirteenth century (*GL*, pp. xxxvi–xxxix). If this is correct, the last known hoards to be buried on Gotland in the mid-twelfth century were deposited there only a couple of generations before the laws were written down.

13 *MSoS*; for a different view see Carlsson (2010); *LD*, pp. 113–14.

14 *WKG*, vol. 3.2, pp. 473–84.

15 See Östergren, Carlsson, Gustafsson and Svedjemo in this volume.

16 Jonsson and Östergren (1990); Jonsson (2010), pp. 12–14.

17 See Svedjemo in this volume.

18 For traveller runestones from Gotland, see Westholm (2009), pp. 122–9.

19 *GL*, p. xxvi.

20 Blomkvist (2010), pp. 108–11.

21 *GL*, p. 27.

22 *GL*, p. 113.

23 Altogether more than 50 scales and 400 weights were documented on Gotland by Lena Thunmark-Nylén in 2006: *WKG*, vol. 3.1, pp. 338–9, with more found in the years since (see above, n. 10). Weighing equipment has also been found in Viking-Age and medieval harbours on Gotland: Östergren (1983); Kilger *et al.* (2015), pp. 76, 83.

24 See Blomkvist (2010), p. 112, where he argues that the patrilocal regime in force on farms is key to understanding Gotland's social fabric. As argued here, this also has far-reaching consequences for our comprehension of the hoarding phenomenon.

25 *GL*, p. 119.

26 *GL*, pp. 119–20.

27 *GL*, pp. 114–15.

28 *GL*, pp. 116–19.

29 Burström (1993), p. 34.

Bibliography

Adamczyk, D. (2014), *Silber und Macht. Fernhandel, Tribute und die piastische Herrschaftsbildung in nordosteuropäischer Perspektive (800–1100)*, Wiesbaden.

Blackburn, M. (2003), '"Productive" sites and the pattern of coin loss in England, 600–1180', in T. Pestell and K. Ulmschneider (eds), *Markets in Early Medieval Europe: Trading and 'Productive' Sites, 650–850*, Bollington, pp. 20–36.

Blomkvist, N. (2010), 'Folk och gårdar på medeltidens Gotland: en nyckelfråga för Östersjöforskningen', in *Från Gutabygd: årsskrift för den gotländska hembygdsrörelsen*, Visby, pp. 61–126.

Brather, S. (1995–6), 'Frühmittelalterliche Dirham-Schatzfunde in Europa. Probleme ihrer wirtschaftsgeschichtlichen Interpretation aus archäologischer Perspektive', *Zeitschrift für Archäologie des Mittelalters*: 23–4: 73–153.

Burström, M. (1993), 'Silver as bridewealth: an interpretation of Viking Age silver hoards on Gotland', *Current Swedish Archaeology* 1: 33–7.

Carlsson, D. (2010), 'Skatter, gårdar och landskap: vikingatidens Gotland', *Myntstudier* 2010(1): 6–10.

Gustafsson, N. B. and M. Östergren (2017), 'Weights and values in the Gotlandic heartland', *Lund Archaeological Review* 23: 95–105.

Hellqvist, M.-L. and M. Östergren (2011), *Ett plundrat kulturarv. Att motverka och förebygga plundring av fornlämningar* (Länsstyrelsen Gotlands län, Rapport 30 November 2011), Visby.

Jankowiak, M. (2015), 'Wer brachte im 10. Jahrhundert die Dirhems in die polnischen Gebiete und warum?' in D. Adamczyk and N. Kersken (eds), *Fernhändler, Dynasten, Kleriker: die piastische Herrschaft in kontinentalen Beziehungsgeflechten vom 10. bis zum frühen 13. Jahrhundert*, Wiesbaden, pp. 41–54.

Jonsson, K. (2010), 'Myntcirkulationen på Gotland i belysning av skattfyndprojektet', *Myntstudier* 2010(1): 10–15.

Jonsson, K. (2015), 'Viking-Age coins found in Sweden', in L. Larsson *et al.* (eds), *Small Things, Wide Horizons: Studies in Honour of Birgitta Hårdh*, Oxford, pp. 51–7.

Jonsson, K. and M. Östergren (1990), 'The Gotland hoard project and the Stumle hoard: an insight into the affairs of a Gotlandic "farman"', in *SP*, pp. 145–58.

Kilger, C. (2008), 'Kaupang from afar: aspects of the interpretation of dirham finds in northern and eastern Europe between the late 8th and early 10th centuries', in *ME*, pp. 199–252.

Kilger, C. *et al.* (2015), 'Mynt och bebyggelse: bebyggelseutvecklingen inom Västergarnsvallen ur ett numismatiskt perspektiv', in T. Talvio and M. Wijk (eds), *Myntstudier: Festskrift till Kenneth Jonsson*, Stockholm, pp. 141–56.

Kovalev, R. K. and A. C. Kaelin (2007), 'Circulation of Arab silver in medieval Afro-Eurasia: preliminary observations', *History Compass* 5: 560–80.

Myrberg [Burström], N. (2009), 'The hoarded dead: late Iron Age silver hoards as graves', in I.-M. Back Danielsson *et al.* (eds), *Döda personers sällskap: gravmaterialens identiteter och kulturella uttryck*, SSA 47, Stockholm, pp. 131–45.

Myrberg Burström, N. (2015), 'Things of quality: possessions and animated objects in the Scandinavian Viking Age', in A. Klevnäs and C. Hedenstierna-Jonson (eds), *Own and Be Owned: Archaeological Approaches to the Concepts of Possession*, SSA 62, Stockholm, pp. 23–48.

Noonan, T. S. (1990), 'Dirham exports to the Baltic in the Viking Age: some preliminary observations', in *SP*, pp. 251–7.

Odebäck, K. (2009), 'Familje- och släktskatter under äldre vikingatid', *Myntstudier* 2009 (2): 9–25.

Östergren, M. (1983), 'Bandlundviken i Burs sn – en vikingatida hamnplats', *GA* 55: 119–21.

Östergren, M. (2015), 'An unlikely story: about looting, trials and Viking Age silver treasures on Gotland', in T. Talvio and M. Wijk (eds), *Myntstudier: Festskrift till Kenneth Jonsson*, Stockholm, pp. 26–38.

Östergren, M. (2016), '"Rudera effter Steenhuus och andra monumenter": om Roma som central ort för landet Gotland', in E. Selin and C. Emdén (eds), *Roma kloster och cistercienserna*, Visby, pp. 39–64.

Thunmark-Nylén, L. (1986), 'Hedningar, kristna och silverskatter', *GA* 58: 23–44.

Westholm, G. (2009), 'Gotland and the surrounding world', in *SH*, pp. 109–52.

13 From the foreign to the familiar

The arrival and circulation of silver in Gotlandic society

Ny Björn Gustafsson

Early medieval Gotland and its silver has been an issue of enduring interest since the dawn of antiquarian research in Scandinavia. Both coins and non-numismatic silver have regularly been recovered from most parts of the island, to an extent unparalleled in Scandinavia. Unfortunately, only a minority of these finds have been scientifically excavated: most were unearthed by farmers working their land and are, at best, accompanied by vague notes about the find location and context. This has hindered a closer understanding of the hoards and the society that left them behind, regardless of whether the finds can be connected to known or assumed hoards, workshops or settlements. The original context has normally been obliterated by farming, as a single turn of the plough is often enough to alter and obscure centuries of cultural deposits. Yet the silver, and a great wealth of other finds, would not have come to light had it not been for the farming. Gotland is a predominately rural province which has seen very little of the infrastructural and urban development that normally triggers archaeological excavations in other parts of Scandinavia. Thus, it was not until the 1970s that silver finds on the island began to be included in research models, instead of simply being seen as treasure that had been hidden away in troubled times and never recovered.

Modern research has shown that Gotlandic silver hoards were, and are, much more than uncollected savings deposits. In her doctoral thesis, Majvor Östergren convincingly pointed to a connection between Viking-Age settlements and a number of silver hoards.[1] Even though the settlements in her study had all been damaged by farming, they could still be identified through clusters of settlement-related finds recovered by metal-detecting. Östergren's observations have repeatedly been confirmed through the excavation of sites where in situ settlement remains have been preserved below ploughing depth.[2] Torun Zachrisson has shown that silver was also deposited in and along features that accentuated and defined boundaries, for example stone walls and cairns.[3] It has also been suggested that some silver finds represent scrap metal stocks and reflect extensive local production of metal artefacts.[4] The current view can thus be said to have moved away from an initial interpretation of silver as wealth hidden away and meant to be retrieved by individuals who failed to do so, to an 'all of the above' stance which recognises that there is not one single, universal explanation for the phenomenon.

Trading and raiding: sources of silver

Unlike the deposition of silver, its accumulation on Gotland has generally been attributed to two major sources: trading and raiding. These two reasons have a long tradition in Scandinavian research and have intermittently been favoured by scholars.[5] However, most modern studies tend to merge the two into an opportunistic system where local contexts decided whether a group traded or raided.[6] The northern European slave trade, often mentioned but rarely analysed in-depth, is a good example of where the two merged, since raids were essential to acquire sellable 'merchandise'.[7]

The Viking-Age influx of silver to Scandinavia, and Gotland, is often divided into two phases: the first, which began in the late eighth century, largely consists of eastern coins,[8] while the second, which started in the late tenth century, was mainly characterised by western European ones.[9] Many hoards also include large portions of non-numismatic silver in various stages of fractioning, from solid ingots to minute shavings,[10] making it clear that silver bullion played an important role in the Gotlandic economy. The value of bullion is determined by its intrinsic value (its quality relative to its quantity). Thus, confirming both quality and quantity is critical in bullion-based economies. For the latter, a rich and growing body of material finds aid our understanding: weights and scales for weighing silver – and other goods – are common in most parts of Gotland.[11] Establishing quality was a more demanding task. Nicks, pecks and bends both on coins and non-numismatic silver indicate that basic examination by observing colour and testing plasticity was common. A trained eye can, to some extent, estimate the level of debasement from the colour of a freshly cut surface. Similarly, it is roughly possible to feel if a silver object is made from purer or more debased silver by bending it. But a more precise determination of silver quality demands chemical analysis: fire assaying. As with test-nicking and bending, there is rich evidence for fire assaying (also known as cupellation) throughout the Norse cultural sphere. The method appears to have been fairly standardised: silver of unknown purity was melted, together with lead, at a very high temperature and with oxygen added. Under such circumstances the lead oxidises into litharge, into which the base metals dissolve, separating them from the silver. This process can produce silver of very high purity and has remained more or less unchanged for several millennia.[12] Analysis using this method is simple, but depends on weighing implements – silver of unknown quality is weighed both before and after cupellation. The difference in weight constitutes the level of debasement.

Thanks to Anders Söderberg's pioneering work on small-scale Viking-Age cupellation in Sweden, we have a good notion of how widespread it was.[13] Fire assaying took place at a number of emporia and trading sites in present-day

Sweden, Gotland included.[14] It was normally carried out in small ceramic discs that became highly vitrified on the inside during the cupellation process, in contrast to crucibles where vitrification occurs on the outside. These discs are typically found in fragments and when reassembly is possible, a scar-like depression in the middle is commonly seen: presumably it was made by the purified silver, which was broken off after cupellation and submitted to a second weighing.

Early Gotlandic metalworking

As noted above, much of the rich archaeological record from Gotland is based on chance finds recovered during farming. This holds true for finds from graves and settlements alike. Even though the number of properly excavated and documented contexts on the island has risen considerably over the past decades, it is still extremely low compared with most areas of the Swedish mainland. Conversely, there is a long tradition of metal-detecting on Gotland, whereas it has been limited elsewhere. However, a pilot study on the mainland, pairing metal-detector survey of ploughed-over find contexts with excavation, has shown that the vast majority of finds at such sites lie in the ploughing layer and above potentially unaffected remains of floors and postholes.[15] This suggests that the clusters of finds identified by metal-detection on Gotland offer a good indication as to the nature of the undisturbed contexts.

Given the condition of archaeology on the island, this is often as good as it gets; archaeometallurgy, in particular, has long suffered from a lack of properly excavated and documented contexts. Thus despite the fact that Gotland was culturally distinct from mainland Scandinavia – as seen, for example, through a rich array of insular jewellery[16] – few sites are known that could indisputably be connected to non-ferrous metalworking. It is normally necessary to rely on compiling key artefact types recovered at potential settlements, such as slag, technical ceramics, scrap metal, spillages and miscasts. Slag and technical ceramics in particular have no value and are of limited potential for re-use. They are thus unlikely to have moved very far from their original point of deposition and can be used as key indicators of early metalworking.[17] Of these, plano-convex slag cakes are typical of the debris left by iron working, while ceramic casting moulds indicate non-ferrous metalworking. However, the slag cakes' source value is undermined by the fact that they look the same right up until the early modern period, and thus cannot exclusively be dated to the early middle ages without radiocarbon analysis. The use of clay casting moulds, on the other hand, largely came to an end during the twelfth century, as did rural bronze casting. They are therefore a much better indicator of early metalworking. Unfortunately, their porous nature makes them acutely liable to fracturing; and since moulds, unlike hearth linings, do not normally contain a high percentage of metal, they are more or less impossible to find through metal-detecting.[18] Until the summer of 2000, for example, only a single

Gotlandic site had yielded substantial numbers of clay casting mould fragments: the cave at Stora Förvar on Stora Karlsö, an island off Gotland's west coast.[19] This changed in 2000, when the best preserved early medieval metal workshop on the island was excavated, at the Fröjel harbour settlement on Gotland's west coast.

A sole survivor: the Fröjel workshop

The Fröjel workshop came to light during excavations by the Fröjel Discovery Programme. Initially there was nothing to single the site out, apart from the fact that it lay in a meadow untouched by ploughing and where a stone sill was partly visible above ground.[20] Two trenches were laid out over an area that included the sill and *c.* 42m^2 was fully excavated. The building measured *c.* 5.5m by 4m and was characterised by a modest amount of debris from various crafts, such as bone-, antler- and glass-working.[21] In the building's north-western part, the excavators uncovered what was later established to be remains of a cupellation hearth and a casting hearth. Taken together, these served to identify the building as a workshop. The debris from other crafts showed that it was not exclusively used for metalworking. Instead, it appears to have been a multi-purpose building and as such it fits quite well into a pan-Scandinavian pattern.[22] The casting hearth was of a common design, sunk into the floor and filled with various bits of debris, such as two intact crucibles and 960g of fragmented casting moulds. An even greater discovery was made 1.5m from the casting hearth, in the form of a cupellation hearth for silver. Like the casting hearth, it had been filled with soil mixed with debris, in particular fragments of litharge-soaked bone ash hearth lining. Given the overall shortage of casting moulds on Gotland, the Fröjel fragments offer a number of crucial insights into contemporary non-ferrous metalworking, since a large number of the mould fragments carry imprints of the objects cast in them. But the moulds' true importance comes from being part of a contextual entity, together with the remains of the cupellation hearth and the crucibles. Through these mundane-looking fragments, it is possible to follow silver through its transformation at the hands of local metalworkers: from incoming, foreign metal of unknown quality to proofed silver bullion. This then underwent another transformation, as the mould fragments show, into native Gotlandic jewellery. At least four different types of object that are regularly found in silver hoards on the island were cast in the workshop; mainly bangles but also a penannular brooch.[23] Elemental analyses have shown that the silver melted in the crucibles and cast in the moulds corresponds to that of the cupellation hearth.[24]

A possible, but unfortunately lost, parallel to the Fröjel workshop may have been located at Bandlunde on the south-eastern coast, where a Viking-Age harbour settlement was partly destroyed by farming in the 1950s. Besides five silver hoards, dating from the tenth century to around 1100, the site has also yielded a miscast silver bangle of Stenberger's Type Ab.2.[25] It could just be a stray piece of hack-silver, but it could also indicate that the site housed a workshop producing Gotlandic jewellery. The piece was found in the middle of a field ploughed almost down to the natural sand,[26] thus irreversibly destroying most of the settlement deposits.

Cupellation in a world of change

The general presumption that coins were melted and cast into ingots and other objects has a long tradition in Scandinavian research. The process itself is seldom visible through finds, but batches of half-molten coins have been recorded.[27] In the earlier Viking Age, when Carolingian and Islamic coins dominated, it appears as if no proofing by cupellation or physical testing was needed.[28] Until the second half of the tenth century, coins generally maintained a high and consistent level of silver, although rapid debasement has been observed thereafter.[29] Once Scandinavian rulers started to strike their own coinage in the eleventh century, finds and written accounts point to deliberate debasement: first in Norway during the reign of Harald Hardrada (1046–66), and later in Denmark towards the end of Sven Estridsen's long reign (1047–74).[30] Based on the finds, the Fröjel workshop can probably be dated to the later part of the eleventh century. In addition, a radiocarbon sample from charcoal in the cupellation hearth indicates a probable dating of between 970 and 1160 (see Appendix in this volume, no. 20). By this time, mainland Scandinavia had for the most part left Viking-Age socio-cultural norms behind, but on Gotland they lingered.[31] Native coinage is seen as a key indicator of such socio-cultural change.[32] It was introduced on Gotland in the mid-twelfth century, but until then a bullion-based economy seems to have predominated. Large-scale use of cupellation becomes more understandable in light of this, in answer to the influx of unverified, possibly debased, minted silver issued west and south-west of the Baltic Sea. Among bullion-inclined Gotlanders, who regarded quality above royal affirmation, cupellation was a convenient way to solve an evident shortage. Recent analyses also show that Scandinavian filigree jewellery tends to have a higher silver content than cast jewellery. The silver content in filigree objects is also notably higher than in contemporary coins, while they display a similar pattern for the occurrence of other trace elements such as gold and bismuth. This would indicate that the silver intended for filigree jewellery was cupellated.[33] Since Gotlanders had far-ranging economic ties with areas that were employing organised debasement, they simply could not avoid debased silver.

It should be noted that even though few actual remains of cupellation debris have been found on Gotland (or the Swedish mainland), there is a find type that might be connected to more extensive cupellation: the plano-convex silver cakes, sometimes referred to as *göt* (casts), that form part of a number of late hoards (see Figure 13.1).[34]

Figure 13.1 Cupellated silver cakes from the Övide hoard in Eskelhem; the largest measures
            74mm across.
Photo: author.

The shape of these silver cakes – with a convex, often blemished underside
and an even, flat upper face – corresponds well to the shape at the bottom of
a cupellation hearth. Eleven cake fragments, both large and small, were
recently recovered as part of a late hoard found at Övide in Eskelhem on
western Gotland.[35] Three were submitted to micro x-ray fluorescence
analysis, and all three yielded a high silver content of around 98–99%.[36]
Despite this, the fragments feature testing nicks, as do many other complete
specimens. This would indicate that the cakes in themselves were not seen as
trusted bullion. This find type is not exclusive to Gotlandic hoards: similar
cakes are known from hoards on the Swedish mainland and Norwegian
single finds.[37]

The eleventh century saw another, profound change: Gotland began to
open up to foreign traders. Prior to that, the insular society seems to have
distanced itself from the surrounding world. This seclusion is clearly visible
through the material culture, in particular the design of jewellery and local
varieties of pan-Scandinavian art styles.[38] However, the eleventh century
appears to have brought a departure from established norms. A passage in the

medieval *stadslag* (town law) of Visby recalls events that were by then several centuries in the past. The sole surviving copy, a fourteenth-century Low German edition, states that when

> the people in Gotland of various tongues assembled together, they swore peace, that there should be for ever all round the land eight fathoms [*c.* 14.4m] inland of free foreshore [...] so that every one might be able thereon the better to land his goods.

Eventually, the law continues, hostility arose between the islanders and foreigners as the town grew. Social unrest escalated and it took the intervention of Henry the Lion, Duke of Saxony and Bavaria, to resolve it.[39] This intervention, the Artlenburg Privilege, dates to 1161 and was primarily meant to settle issues between the Gotlanders and the many German inhabitants of Visby. The *stadslag* goes on to remind us of a similar privilege issued by the duke's grandfather, Emperor Lothar III, who had ruled thirty years earlier.

However, the archaeological records show that people 'of various tongues' had arrived on Gotland even earlier. This is mainly indicated by the presence of East Slav ceramics which, in the course of the eleventh century, increased dramatically at certain harbour settlements on Gotland.[40] These harbours are themselves an indication of a rising number of foreign visitors. Until the end of the tenth century, the island's coast was characterised by many smaller landing sites at favourable locations.[41] From the beginning of the eleventh century, a number of these developed into harbours which were frequented by a more multi-ethnic clientele – people of 'various tongues'. Visby and Fröjel belong to this group, and possibly also the settlement at Bandlunde noted above. Favourable conditions for wood preservation at a fourth harbour site, the Paviken/Västergarn complex situated on the west coast between Fröjel and Visby, have enabled sampling for dendrochronological analysis. This has shown that timbers from an excavated jetty were felled around 1015, and those from a second, more substantial structure around 1050.[42] It is probably not far-fetched to assume that these larger harbours acted as bridgeheads for foreign influences at both the social and material level, although the two are effectively inseparable. Such trends and minor alterations to the general material culture can already be seen at smaller, earlier local landing sites.[43] Since larger harbours allowed for considerably higher numbers of non-Gotlanders, this exposure would have increased drastically in the course of the eleventh century. To understand these changes and what went before, we must glance at the foundations of early medieval society on Gotland as seen through the written sources and scholarly interpretation.

Political organisation on early medieval Gotland

Even from a Scandinavian perspective, written sources for early medieval Gotland are scarce and say little. This has led to some creative interpretation of – and at times outright speculation on – various aspects of society then. From around 1200, the number of extant written sources increases considerably. Most notable is *Guta Lag*. Surviving copies date from the fourteenth century, but features and wording in a number of clauses suggest that it encompasses an older, oral tradition.[44] The law's appendix, commonly referred to as *Guta Saga*, has long been used as a primary source for medieval Gotland, as it touches upon earlier pagan cults, the advent of Christianity, migrations and its political organisation. Apart from *Guta Lag*, most of our other written sources date from after the watershed in Gotland's history: the cataclysmic decades of the mid-fourteenth century. This was when the Black Death of 1350 and the Danish invasion of 1361 sent the insular society into a demographic and economic decline, from which it took three hundred years to recover. It has been argued that the picture of society painted by our later sources has little in common with that of the pre-cataclysmic period.[45] A particular feature of this later society was low social stratification compared with the Scandinavian mainland, leading to one of the prevalent views of early medieval Gotland: that it was an autonomous and egalitarian farmers' 'republic'.[46]

Based on these written accounts, Gotland is thought to have been divided into twenty local assemblies (*Things*), each overseen by an elected judge who collected taxes as well as administering the law, and whom most scholars consider to be the *seniores* or elders mentioned in a number of medieval sources.[47] There may have been two further administrative divisions of the island – sixths (*siettungar*) and ridings (*tredingar*) – each with their own judges. All these units are believed to have been subordinate to a supreme *Thing* (known as the Landsting, *Gutnalthing* or *Althing*), whose membership was drawn from the local assembly judges, and which constituted the highest political and judicial assembly on Gotland. An early fifteenth-century German version of *Guta Lag* offers grounds for the traditional assumption that the *Gutnalthing* met at Roma, in the centre of the island, presided over by the 'judge of the land', the island's highest official.[48] Recent archaeological finds may support this assumption, with Viking-Age weights, coins, hack-silver and metalworking debris unearthed in quantities not found elsewhere on the island, hinting at regular, sizeable gatherings rather than permanent settlement.[49]

Bridgeheads and the need for control

At this point, we should address the evident resilience of a native culture on the island. As noted above, a distinctively local version of the pan-Scandinavian material culture persisted on Gotland throughout the Viking Age and well into the twelfth century. As with all cultural expression, it inevitably underwent changes; but while the dominant features of its mainland Scandinavian counterpart all but disappeared during the eleventh century, the insular Gotlandic version survived long into the next. This shift in the material culture throughout the Norse cultural sphere has been connected to the advent of Christianity,[50] with Scandinavian dress – notably women's paired oval brooches – being linked to pre-Christian practices. However, Gotland refutes this argument, since late animal-head brooches, the local version of paired brooches, have repeatedly been found in churchyard graves, an indisputably Christian setting.[51] Thus the essence of insular material culture lingered on Gotland – signalling an important and widespread preference for the traditional.

When the island opened up to foreign traders, it also exposed itself to the impact of foreign influences. This could be another reason why larger harbours were developed: not primarily for foreigners' benefit, but because they allowed the Gotlanders to maximise trade on their own terms. A more recent example of such an arrangement can be found in the Canton system, where westerners wishing to trade with China were strictly allotted quarters to prevent them from interacting with the local populace.[52] A number of the larger Gotlandic harbours display similar, extant traces of demarcation. In Fröjel, for example, a roughly semi-circular cropmark encompasses the part of the settlement area closest to the sea. It probably indicates the presence of an in-filled demarcation ditch.[53] A similar feature can still be observed in the current system of streets in Visby: a number of them clearly run in a semi-circular shape encompassing the part of the town closest to the old harbour bay.[54] If these constitute physical traces of attempts to regulate interaction between Gotlanders and non-Gotlanders, they are unlikely to have been local initiatives; they are more likely to have been dug on the instructions of a higher island authority. Seventeenth-century taxation records also show that the division of land at some of these former harbour areas was much more complex than in other areas along the coast. At Fröjel and Västergarn, for example, some of the land was owned by farms from other parts of the island. This might represent traces of an older system, where individual farms engaged in and benefited from trade by owning shares in harbours.[55] It has been suggested that the larger harbours belonged to the *siettungar*,[56] although the geography of Fröjel and Paviken/Västergarn poses a challenge to this, since they both belonged to the same *siettung*.[57]

Gotland between bullion and coinage

The place of silver in late Viking-Age Gotlandic society would therefore appear more complex than it might at first seem. This was a society largely governed by tradition. The archaeological record shows a clear desire to demonstrate a specific Gotlandic identity – thousands of extant pieces of insular dress jewellery are testimony to this. At the same time, pressure from the outside increased. *Guta Saga* tells of foreign kings fighting to gain control over the island; according to the text, this was resolved by a voluntary and loose protective alliance with the Svear of mainland Sweden.[58] Yet this bond does not appear to have gone beyond practical, economic matters: it did not result in any evident cultural changes on Gotland, but rather the opposite.

Instead, the real challenge must have come when people of other cultural and social backgrounds started to arrive on Gotland around 1000. The Gotlanders' response seems to have been to control the visitors by only allowing them to stay in special economic zones:[59] the designated harbour areas where their influence – and trade goods – could be controlled. Given the Gotlanders' preference for silver bullion, it is hardly surprising that the Fröjel workshop was situated at some distance from the harbour area, outside the possible demarcation ditch. It was most probably operated locally, targeting the Gotlandic market by producing insular objects of proven value. In her work on the production of silver bangles on the island, Lena Thunmark notes the occurrence of cruciform marks on the insides of several of the heaviest Stenberger's Type Ab.3 bangles. She connects these with crosses found on silver coins, and suggests that they could be interpreted as a quality mark, asserting the purity of the silver in the bangle.[60] Anders Söderberg comes to a similar conclusion, pointing out that Viking-Age Scandinavia's bullion economy encompassed the monetary ideals of weight and purity, and lacked only a standardised unit whose quality was underwritten by kingly authority.[61] Like Thunmark, he suggests that the cruciform bangle markings were an attempt to hallmark value using a commonly accepted symbol. Despite the fact that only a small fraction of Gotlandic silver jewellery bears such hypothetical hallmarks, nicks and other traces of physical testing are very uncommon on complete pieces. It could be that the objects were in themselves an affirmation of their value. When metalworkers at Fröjel used purified silver to cast Stenberger's Type Ab.2 and Ab.3 bangles, they may have been following commonly agreed norms on the quality of silver from which these objects were cast. Such a practice would certainly be in line with Söderberg's discussion on affirmed standards, but the decision could hardly have been up to the individual metalworker. As with the construction and delimitation of larger harbours noted above, such instructions are likely only to have come from the highest authority on the island, the *Gutnalthing*. But whether or not this was the case, no system or common agreement is foolproof.

Tricking the system: on extant forgeries

Where a sanctioned economic standard exists, individuals will try to override or exploit it, and early medieval Gotland was no exception. Indeed, the whole system of testing – whether physical or by fire assay – bears witness to this. Despite attempts to broaden the discussion on nicking, pecking and bending beyond the purely technical,[62] it is unlikely that such methods originally developed in an environment of mutual trust. Testing and small-scale fire assaying developed because they were needed. Accordingly, there are a number of Gotlandic finds that can, in effect, be branded as counterfeits. One of the most glaring examples is a straightened-out bangle from Tystebols in Stenkyrka on north-western Gotland.[63] At first glance

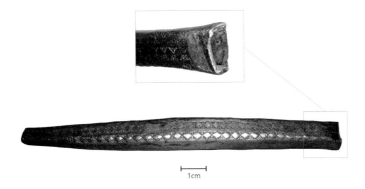

1cm

Figure 13.2 Counterfeit bangle from Tystebols in Stenkyrka, with close-up showing the hidden copper-alloy core.

Photo: author.

there is little to reveal its true nature, other than a somewhat rough outline. The front face is covered by geometrical ornaments and punctuated triangles,[64] and one end has been severed. The cut-off end shows clear marks of hammering and it is quite possible that it was when someone started to hammer it out that the first suspicions as to the bangle's validity arose. The cross-section of the severed end will have left no further room for doubt – it has a solid inner core of copper alloy, covered in silver (see Figure 13.2).

It is clear that this forgery was primarily targeted at Gotland and its economy, since it mimics – indirectly, but quite clearly – a common and trusted insular design. The Tystebols counterfeit does not display a single nick, peck or similar sign of testing, although this would not have made any difference, since the outer layer of silver is thick enough to allow nicking without revealing the core. Thus, while the number of known Gotlandic counterfeits is small, it is quite possible that an unrecorded number of forgeries remain undetected in museum collections.

Perhaps it is in the light of such forgeries that we should see the hypothetical hallmarked crosses on heavier bangles – as an extra measure of safety and assurance from the metalworkers when they transformed and incorporated foreign silver into familiar, socially accepted, objects of value.

Notes

1 *MSoS.*
2 Thunmark-Nylén (1983); *SoB*; Brandt (2002).
3 Zachrisson (1998), p. 121.
4 Gustafsson (2013b), p. 4.
5 See, for example, *HV*; Sawyer (1982), p. 125.
6 Samson (1991).

7   Brink (2012), p. 85.
8   Noonan (1990); Sawyer (1982), p. 124.
9   Jonsson (2004).
10 *SGW*.
11 *WKG*, vol. 3.1, p. 338.
12 Bayley and Eckstein (1997).
13 Söderberg (2004); Söderberg (2011).
14 On the harbour settlement in Fröjel, see Gustafsson (2013a), p. 151.
15 Svensson and Söderberg (2009).
16 Rydh (1919); A. Carlsson (1983); *WKG*, vol. 3.1, esp. pp. 19–126, 156–242.
17 Gustafsson (2013b).
18 Gustafsson (2013c).
19 Örjestad and Almgren-Aiken (2008).
20 Dahlström and Eriksson (2002).
21 See also Carlsson in this volume.
22 Gustafsson (2011).
23 Gustafsson and Söderberg (2007).
24 Wojnar-Johansson (2005a); Wojnar-Johansson (2005b).
25 *MSoS*, p. 187.
26 Brandt (2002), p. 248.
27 Blackburn (2008), p. 32.
28 Archibald (2011), p. 61. For an overview of other possible reasons for test marks on precious metals in the Viking Age, see Kershaw (2019), pp. 241–4; see also Kershaw (2014).
29 Eniosova (2012), p. 269.
30 Gullbekk (2000); Gullbekk (2011), p. 96; Elfver (2007).
31 Thunmark-Nylén (2007).
32 Myrberg (2008).
33 Eniosova (2012), p. 271.
34 *SGW*, vol. 1, p. 231; Nylén (1969).
35 *tpq* 1131; Langhammer (2013).
36 Thuresson (2012).
37 University of Oslo Museum inventory no. C56911.
38 Gustafsson (2013a). See also Jansson in this volume.
39 *Codices*, ed. Schlyter, p. 21; tr. Twiss, p. 387.
40 Roslund (2001).
41 Carlsson (1987); Carlsson (1998); Carlsson (2008).
42 Carlsson (2011), p. 150; the dates have been adjusted by an addition of nine years, following Bartholin (1998).
43 Gustafsson (2013a), p. 111.
44 *SL*, vol. 4, p. lxxii; see also *GL*, pp. xiv–xxi.
45 Blomkvist (2010), p. 72.
46 Siltberg (2012).
47 Björkander (1898), p. 32; Yrwing (1978), p. 89.
48 The oldest account naming the twenty local *Thing*s appeared in 1412: Yrwing (1978), p. 86. However, the *Gutnalthing* is first mentioned in chapter 2 of *Guta Saga*, which may imply that this assembly was already well established by the Viking Age, a hypothesis that is supported by recent findings: Östergren (2013).
49 Östergren (2013); see also Gruszczyński in this volume.
50 Hayeur Smith (2005), p. 83.
51 *WKG*, vol. 3.2, p. 608.
52 Hellman (2015). There are also similarities with the Rus in Constantinople: in the accord of 907, the Byzantines accepted the Rus' terms – including food,

supplies and unlimited baths when in *Tsargrad* – but responded with the proviso that the Rus should only dwell to the north of the Golden Horn, in the St Mamas quarter: *PVL*, p. 17; *RPC*, p. 65.

53 Carlsson (1999), p. 39.
54 Lundberg (1944), p. 49; Westholm (1989), p. 83.
55 Carlsson (2011), p. 28.
56 *DKV*, p. 121.
57 Carlsson (2011), p. 14.
58 *GS*, p. 7.
59 Kalmring (2016).
60 Thunmark (1974), pp. 32–3.
61 Söderberg (2011), p. 24.
62 Kilger (2006).
63 Inventory no. SHM 16835, acquired by the Swedish History Museum in 1921 and said to have been found together with a set of folding scales, two oblate spheroid weights and a coil of metal wire.
64 In the same fashion as Stenberger's bangle type Ab.1 – cf. *SGW*, vol. 1, pp. 104–7.

Bibliography

Primary sources

Codices, ed. C. J. Schlyter, *Codices iuris Visbyensis urbici et maritimi / Wisby stadslag och sjörätt* [= *Corpus iuris Sueo-Gotorum antiqui / Samling af Sweriges gamla lagar* 8], Lund (1853); tr. T. Twiss, in *The Black Book of the Admiralty, with an Appendix*, vol. 4, London (1876; repr. Cambridge, 2013), pp. 385–414.

Secondary literature

Archibald, M. (2011), 'Testing', in *CH*, pp. 51–64.
Bartholin, T. S. (1998), 'Dendrokronologiens tilforlidelighed', *Fv* 93: 141–2.
Bayley, J. and K. Eckstein (1997), 'Silver refining: production, recycling, assaying', in A. Sinclair *et al.* (eds), *Archaeological Sciences 1995*, Oxford, pp. 107–11.
Björkander, A. (1898), *Till Visby stads äldsta historia: ett kritiskt bidrag*, Uppsala.
Blackburn, M. (2008), 'The coin-finds', in *ME*, pp. 29–74.
Blomkvist, N. (2010), 'Folk och gårdar på medeltidens Gotland: en nyckelfråga för Östersjöforskningen', in *Från Gutabygd: årsskrift för den gotländska hembygdsrörelsen*, Visby, pp. 61–126.
Brandt, B. (2002), 'Bandlundviken: a Viking trading centre on Gotland', in G. Burenhult (ed.), *Remote Sensing*, vol. 2: *Archaeological Investigations and Remote Sensing Case Studies*, Hässleholm, pp. 243–311.
Brink, S. (2012), *Vikingarnas slavar: den nordiska träldomen under yngre järnålder och äldsta medeltid*, Stockholm.
Carlsson, A. (1983), *Djurhuvudformiga spännen och gotländsk vikingatid*, SSA 5, Stockholm.
Carlsson, D. (1987), 'Äldre hamnar: ett hotat kulturarv', *Fv* 82: 6–18.
Carlsson, D. (1998), *Vikingahamnar: ett hotat kulturarv*, ArkeoDoks Skrifter 1, Visby.
Carlsson, D. (1999), *'Ridanäs': vikingahamnen i Fröjel*, ArkeoDoks Skrifter 2, Visby.
Carlsson, D. (2008), 'Medeltidens dolda landskap: att spåra fiskelägen i Sundre', *GA* 80: 13–28.

Carlsson, D. (2011), *Vikingatidens Västergarn: en komplicerad historia*, ArkeoDoks Skrifter 3, Visby.

Dahlström, C. and T. Eriksson (2002), *Rapport från utgrävningen av den vikingatida hamn-och handelsplatsen Fröjel, Gotland 2000* (Fröjel Discovery Programme Dnr 220–1955–00), Högskolan på Gotland, Visby.

Elfver, F. (2007), 'General debasement during the reign of Svend Estridsen? The coin-age of Lund *c.* 1035–1050 and some metal analyses', in U. Fransson *et al.* (eds), *Cultural Interaction between East and West: Archaeology, Artefacts and Human Contacts in Northern Europe*, SSA 44, Stockholm, pp. 212–16.

Eniosova, N. V. (2012), 'Tracing the routes of silver procurement to the early urban centre Gnezdovo in the 10th/early 11th century', in T. Bendeguz (ed.), *Die Archäologie der frühen Ungarn: Chronologie, Technologie und Methodik*, Mainz, pp. 261–76.

Gullbekk, S. H. (2000), 'Myntforringelse i Danmark og innføring av monopolmynt under Sven Estridsen (1047–74)', *NNÅ* 1994–6: 111–29.

Gullbekk, S. H. (2011), 'Norway: commodity money, silver and coins', in *SEMSS*, pp. 93–111.

Gustafsson, N. B. (2011), 'Beyond Wayland: thoughts on early medieval metal work-shops in Scandinavia', *Historical Metallurgy* 45: 20–31.

Gustafsson, N. B. (2013a), *Casting Identities in Central Seclusion: Aspects of Non-Ferrous Metalworking and Society on Gotland in the Early Medieval Period*, Stockholm.

Gustafsson, N. B. (2013b), 'In the wake of the hoards: glimpses of non-ferrous metal-working through the finds of the Gotland hoard projects', *Fv* 108: 1–11.

Gustafsson, N. B. (2013c), 'Scrutinizing copper and bronze slag on Gotland: on the making and dismantling of a category of archaeometallurgical finds', *Journal of Nordic Archaeological Science* 18: 49–53.

Gustafsson, N. B. and A. Söderberg (2007), 'En senvikingatida silververkstad i Fröjel', *GA* 79: 99–110.

Hayeur Smith, M. (2005), 'Breaking the mould: a re-evaluation of Viking Age mould-making techniques for oval brooches', in R. O. Bork (ed.), *De Re Metallica: The Uses of Metal in the Middle Ages*, Aldershot, pp. 81–99.

Hellman, L. (2015), *Navigating the Foreign Quarters: Everyday Life of the Swedish East India Company Employees in Canton and Macao 1730–1830*, Stockholm.

Jonsson, K. (2004), 'Västerländska vikingatida mynt', *GA* 76: 27–32.

Kalmring, S. (2016), 'Early northern towns as special economic zones', in L. Holmquist *et al.* (eds), *New Aspects on Viking-Age Urbanism, c. AD 750–1100*, Stockholm, pp. 11–21.

Kershaw, J. (2014), 'Viking-Age silver in north-west England: hoards and single-finds', in S. E. Harding *et al.* (eds), *In Search of Vikings: Interdisciplinary Approaches to the Scandinavian Heritage of North-West England*, Boca Raton, FL, pp. 149–64.

Kershaw, J. (2019), 'Gold as a means of exchange in Scandinavian England', in J. Kershaw *et al.* (eds), *Silver, Butter, Cloth: Monetary and Social Economies in the Viking Age*, Oxford, pp. 227–50.

Kilger, C. (2006), 'Silver handling traditions during the Viking Age: some observations and thoughts on the phenomenon of pecking and bending', in B. Cook and G. Williams (eds), *Coinage and History in the North-Sea World, c. AD 500–1250*, Leiden, pp. 449–65.

Langhammer, D. (2013), *Arkeologisk undersökning av ett skattfynd i Övide, Eskelhem socken Övide 2:1, Eskelhem socken, Gotland* (Länsstyrelsen Gotlands län dnr 431–2358–12), Gotland Museum, Visby.

Lundberg, E. (1944), 'Staden och dess minnesmärken', in E. Lundberg, I. Andersson and J. Nihlén (eds), *Visbybilder: från forntid och hansevälde*, 2nd edn, Stockholm, pp. 11–160.

Myrberg, N. (2008), *Ett eget värde: Gotlands tidigaste myntning, ca 1140–1220*, Stockholm.

Noonan, T. S. (1990), 'Dirham export to the Baltic in the Viking Age: some preliminary observations', in *SP*, pp. 215–17.

Nylén, E. (1969), 'Gotlands största silverskatt funnen vid Burge i Lummelunda: fyndet, dess smycken och bitsilver', *GA* 41: 7–46.

Örjestad, J. and E. Almgren-Aiken (2008), *Arkeologisk undersökning boplatslämningar på Stora Karlsö, sammanställning över arkeologiska undersökningar vid Stora Förvar och Norderhamnsområdet mellan 1973–1981* (RAÄ dnr 321–2322–2008), Länsmuseet på Gotland, Visby.

Östergren, M. (2013), *Rapport över arkeologisk undersökning inom fastigheten Roma kloster 2:1, Gotland 2011, 2012 och 2013*, Fårö Konsult Rapport 2013:2, Ava, Fårö.

Roslund, M. (2001), 'Gutar, främlingar och den förblindande vikingatiden: om staden Visbys tidigaste datering', in A. Andrén *et al.* (eds), *Från stad till land: en medeltidsarkeologisk resa tillägnad Hans Andersson*, Stockholm, pp. 241–51.

Rydh, H. (1919), *Dosformiga spännen från vikingatiden*, Stockholm.

Samson, R. (1991), 'Fighting with silver: rethinking trading, raiding and hoarding', in R. Samson (ed.), *Social Approaches to Viking Studies*, Glasgow, pp. 123–33.

Sawyer, P. H. (1982), *Kings and Vikings: Scandinavia and Europe AD 700–1100*, London.

Siltberg, T. (2012), 'The conception of an egalitarian Gotlandic peasant society', in M. Scholz *et al.* (eds), *The Image of the Baltic*, Visby, pp. 302–28.

Söderberg, A. (2004), 'Metallurgic ceramics as a key to Viking Age workshop organisation', *Journal of Nordic Archaeological Science* 14: 115–24.

Söderberg, A. (2011), 'Eyvind Skáldaspillir's silver: refining and standards in pre-monetary economies in the light of finds from Sigtuna and Gotland', *Situne Dei* 2011: 5–34.

Svensson, H. and B. Söderberg (2009), 'Dumpad kunskap? Om metallsökning och uppdragsarkeologins villkor', *Fv* 104: 131–6.

Thunmark [Thunmark-Nylén], L. (1974), 'Stämplar på gotländskt vikingasilver', *GA* 46: 15–34.

Thunmark-Nylén, L. (1983), 'Burge i Lummelunda: gårdsplats och skattplats', in *GoV*, pp. 49–58.

Thunmark-Nylén, L. (2007), 'On chronology: *Die Wikingerzeit Gotlands* and some method-problems', in U. Fransson *et al.* (eds), *Cultural Interaction between East and West: Archaeology, Artefacts and Human Contacts in Northern Europe*, SSA 44, Stockholm, pp. 358–65.

Thuresson, K. (2012), *Analysrapport. Analys Av Silvergöt* (Dnr 415–3993–2012), Enheten för konserveringsvetenskap, Visby.

Westholm, G. (1989), 'Visby: bönders hamn och handelsplats: Visbysamhällets uppkomst och utbredning under förhistorisk tid och äldsta medeltid', in *Visby: staden och omlandet 2* (Rapport RAÄ och SHM. Medeltidsstaden 72), Stockholm, pp. 49–114.

Wojnar-Johansson, M. (2005a), *Analys av två fragment av kupellationshärdväggar, RC 6:3 och 57/238*, Arkeologiska Forskningslaboratoriet Uppdragsrapport 19, Stockholm.

Wojnar-Johansson, M. (2005b), *Analys av en degel och två fragment av gjutformar från Fröjel, Gotland*, Arkeologiska Forskningslaboratoriet Uppdragsrapport 29, Stockholm.

Yrwing, H. (1978), *Gotlands Medeltid*, Visby.

Zachrisson, T. (1998), *Gård, gräns, gravfält: sammanhang kring ädelmetalldepåer och runstenar från vikingatid och tidig medeltid i Uppland och Gästrikland*, SSA 15, Stockholm.

14 Was there life before death?

The Viking settlements on Gotland

Per Widerström

Archaeological evidence from Gotland suggests that, during some periods of the island's history, all the islanders did was die, while in others, all they did was live! The Viking Age is one of those periods when death predominates: we find many graves, but only a handful of known, investigated settlements. Inevitably, we tend to form our view of life on Viking-Age Gotland from its death rituals. In an attempt to redress the balance, this chapter summarises the current archaeological evidence of Gotlandic Viking-Age settlements and houses, scant as it is.

Our knowledge of Iron-Age and Migration-Period farms on Gotland is good, when the most typical building was the three-aisled longhouse, around 20–30m in length, with wide stone walls or at least stone foundations. Around 1,800 of these are still present and visible in the landscape.[1] A number of typologies and classifications of these buildings, and of the farms and villages in which they were found, have emerged since the 1930s and a lively discussion continues to this day. In stark contrast, we know of only a handful of Viking-Age buildings and farms. The archaeological evidence for this period is overwhelmingly made up of graves. This is partly because Viking-Age settlements tend to be on land that is still cultivated today; in contrast, the older farms are on meadows that, by and large, have escaped damage from historic but mostly modern ploughing. However, it is also partly the nature of Viking-Age buildings: the few known examples have far less substantial structural elements than their predecessors, and their locations can only be interpreted from objects and artefacts, usually recovered during archaeological metal-detecting campaigns.[2]

In the absence of settlement evidence, researchers have turned to the less direct, but more abundant, burial evidence. For example, the idea of multi-household farms has been suggested by Anders Carlsson and Martin Rundkvist, based on grave fields which suggest that all members of a community were interred together.[3] However, there is evidence that some social divisions did exist. At the extensive grave field at Barshalder in the southern part of the island, a more complex situation is found: 'the highest level of burial investment is found in the smallest clusters. This indicates that wealthy lineages and/or the holders of important offices had separate burial plots'. Rundkvist also argues that these graves, most of which were 'handsomely furnished', may have been only for free people. Thus, estimates of farm size based on recorded burials may not accurately reflect the actual demography. Rundkvist also suggests that landowners were buried apart from ordinary farm inhabitants.[4]

It is fair to say that our view of how Gotlanders in the Viking Age lived their lives has been based predominantly on our knowledge of their rituals around death. From this point of view, every excavation of a Viking-Age house and its surroundings is of immense interest and importance. At present, so few Viking-Age buildings on Gotland are known that classification, or development of local or general typologies, has proved impossible. However, the few examples we have do allow us to discern some patterns.

Viking-Age houses on harbour sites

Bandlunde

At Bandlunde in Burs parish, on the south-eastern part of the island, an area of 1,580m^2 has been excavated.[5] This is sizeable by Gotlandic standards. The archaeologists in charge of the excavations have suggested that the site was a trading port, with shipbuilding as one of its main activities.[6] The excavated area contains a large number of postholes, which have been interpreted as belonging to several Viking-Age houses.[7] Although there are certainly traces of Viking-Age buildings at Bandlunde, the reconstructions have some unexplained gaps, including missing postholes. Of course, this could be due to later farming. However, in a number of the buildings some of the hearths or fireplaces also seem strangely positioned for functional dwellings. There are therefore too many uncertainties for the Bandlunde structures to be described as Viking-Age houses.

Despite the interpretative problems, the rich evidence from artefacts indicates intensive activity at the site. Among a long list of finds from the major excavations that took place between 1983 and 1985, there are 70 fragments of Islamic coins, considered to be stray finds, and two silver hoards. Iron rivets and nails were found in large quantities, alongside needles, tools and fishing equipment, knives and keys. Of the bronze artefacts retrieved, there are fittings, dress pins, brooches (including ring brooches), chains, over 100 weights,[8] tweezers and cauldron fragments. Rarer finds include a glass rod, raw amber, a lead weight and also beads, combs, potsherds and loom weights. The volume and variety of finds strengthens the idea of a permanent Viking settlement, notably part of a bone skate which hints that it was more than a summer camp.

One of the coin hoards found within the site at Bandlunde has a *tpq* of 934/5; the second, of silver bracelets, can be dated to somewhere between 950 and 1050; and a stray German coin to 1075–90. Two radiocarbon samples are mentioned in the excavation publication: both can only broadly place the site in the Viking Age after calibration (see Appendix in this volume, nos 18–19). Two further thermoluminescence analyses give a date of AD 930±70.[9] Taking all of this together with the dating provided by the artefacts, it is fair to say that the site was in use throughout the Viking Age.

Fröjel

Another harbour settlement with Viking-Age houses is well documented: Fröjel on the west coast of the island. The settlement area covers 6ha (or *c.* 15 acres) and only a very small part in the centre of the site has been excavated. Sections of several houses with support posts have been recorded. Two of them were large, measuring at least 10m by 6m, with one being supported by posts dug into the ground and surrounded by rocks; the other had a stone sill along its long walls.[10] Determining the age of these houses is difficult, as no radiocarbon datings are available and the artefacts retrieved cover a long period of time.

Another structure built on a stone sill has been found not far away, on the outskirts of the same settlement area, and has been identified as a silver workshop.[11] Radiocarbon dating indicates that the workshop was probably in use between 975 and 1154 (see Appendix, no. 20), and Ny Björn Gustafsson and Anders Söderberg have argued that the types of bracelet-moulds found there show that the workshop was active in the second half of the tenth century.[12] Postholes indicate that it was constructed on top of another building.[13]

Paviken

The trading port of Paviken is probably the best-known Viking-Age site on Gotland. It is situated on the island's west coast, about 30km south of Visby. The site has been subject to several archaeological investigations. Located on an inlet of the old *vik* (bay), around 2,000m^2 has been examined by archaeologists, including some 500m^2 that was investigated as a single open area in the 1960s. The excavations have revealed the remains of an important Viking-Age harbour.

The inhabitants of Paviken have been characterised as boat-builders, traders and fishermen. Tools for boat-building and -repair have been found, as has evidence of everyday activities, including fishing hooks, net sinkers (weights) and a leister (a pronged spear used for salmon). Some 300 pieces of amber and similar quantities of garnet, as well as glass melts and rods, and pieces of mosaic, bear witness to trade with more exotic parts.[14] Per Lundström and Jan Peder Lamm, who excavated there in the 1960s, concluded that the site's heyday was during the early Viking Age. However, a round, 7m-wide grave from the early Vendel Period, centrally placed in the settlement area, had been left untouched by later Viking settlers. Lundström and Lamm suggested that this grave, and its occupant, was respected by later generations and that it may have held the remains of the settlement's founder.[15]

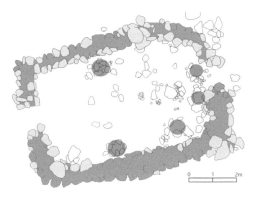

Figure 14.1 Viking-Age stone-wall house from Paviken.
Drawing: author (after Huttu 1996).

Two buildings have been uncovered at Paviken. The first was excavated in the mid-1990s (Figure 14.1), and has been dated to the Viking Age. Several internal features, possible postholes, were not deemed to represent roof-supporting posts, which in combination with stone foundations a metre in width led to the assumption that it was a house whose dominant feature was a roof with wooden gables.[16] The dating of this building to the Viking Age is by a single artefact: a tenth-century casting mould fragment.[17] A second house was found during excavations in 2014. It has a stone sill of about 8.5m long and 6m wide, upon which the wall must have been built, and a roof supported by two posts. The house has not been fully excavated, so the inner features remain largely unknown.[18] The stones used are slightly bigger than in the first building,[19] and the frame consists of just one line of stones. Apart from animal bones, not much has been found in the house. One of the posts has been radiocarbon dated to the tenth century (see Appendix, no. 37), although none of the artefacts retrieved support this dating; nor do they give an indication of the activities that took place there.[20]

Artefacts found during more recent excavations at Paviken do not change the picture of boat-building, trading and fishing suggested by earlier excavations. They do strengthen the impression that crafts were conducted on a large scale, not least through the finds of amber and garnets which hint at specialist workshops. However, it seems that Paviken may have been in use for somewhat longer than was initially believed, operating throughout the Viking Age before being abandoned and succeeded by the Västergarn complex.

Visby

Many towns along the Baltic and North Sea coasts claim to have been founded by the Vikings – so many that, were all the claims true, founding towns must have been one of the Vikings' main activities, despite a distinct lack of them back in their home countries. Visby is one of these Scandinavian towns believed to be of Viking origin, yet little is known about the town's early development, including on whose initiative it was founded and why. Some believe Visby grew organically, because of its location as a natural harbour; others suggest it was founded by a group of merchants, possibly Germans, Swedes or Rus. Who needed a town is also unclear: was its establishment driven by the administrative needs of the *Althing* in Roma, or were local merchants behind the initiative? Scholars have not even been able to agree on when Visby was founded, or when it became a town, with the ninth, tenth and eleventh centuries all offered as possibilities.

Despite all the question marks, there are some things we do know, thanks to skilful interpretation of the archaeological material. In the tenth century something happened at what was to become Visby: a new group of people entered the stage. And some of them, at least, stayed there until their graves were excavated in the twentieth century. With extensive cultural layers missing, it is the cemeteries that, somewhat paradoxically, reveal there was life on the site during the tenth century. Around Donners Plats, today an open square next to the old harbour, there are remains from what must once have been an extensive burial ground (Figure 14.2). Unfortunately, it is

Figure 14.2 Part of Visby's medieval quarter and the remains of a Viking-Age burial ground. Photo: author.

within what became the medieval metropolis of Visby, where little from the early middle ages has been preserved thanks to large thirteenth-century heavy stone houses built with basements. However, there are graves from the ninth, tenth and possibly also the eleventh century, including a small number of cremations, at the burial site close to Donners Plats; ritual elements indicate that these are early Viking Age.

Two types of Viking-Age houses have been identified in Visby: the first is of wattle and daub construction, with at least one example built on a wooden frame; the second is of small wooden post-and-plank construction. One of the latter type has been completely excavated and measures 3.5m by 3.5m.[21] The town's network of streets and alleys appears to have remained unchanged throughout the centuries, and was based on a system of plots with double rows of houses on a grid pattern of parallel streets. The excavated examples indicate that plots were between 7m and 14m wide. The later stone buildings followed the same plot system and were oriented along the same streets as the older, wooden buildings. From this, as with many other Viking-Age harbours, Visby would appear to have had a regulated plot system that stretched from the shore and a harbour. Seasonal fishing villages were arranged in the same style well into the modern era.[22]

Visby is likely to have started in the form of a small port and seasonal settlement used for fishing in the eighth and ninth centuries. The town has no significant cultural layers from before the eleventh century,[23] but there are plenty of graves with Viking-Age artefacts. Those who argue for Visby as a tenth-century town rely on radiocarbon datings, although these were generally made some time ago and are uncalibrated; they also have wide margins of uncertainty and are often used without reference to the original data. Recalibrated older radiocarbon samples date buildings to the eleventh century and other constructions to the 900s.[24]

Artefacts found in Visby are another good indicator of what types of activities went on there and when. Metalware suggests the end of the eleventh century as the point at which the settlement really took off, notably a convincing study of penannular, box and animal-head brooches.[25] The odd, earlier stray find can easily be explained as lost items from Visby's time as a fishing harbour. The fact that these are almost exclusively artefacts associated with men strengthens the idea that it was a seasonal rather than permanent settlement. Similar conclusions can be drawn from the dating of ceramic finds. The earliest Baltic ware pottery found in Visby comes from the mid-eleventh century, when there was an influx of such vessels from Rus. It is believed that through repeated contact with – and the physical presence of – the Rus, imported forms started to be copied by local potters.[26]

Thus, independently of one another, two major artefact categories point to the same conclusion. Visby's rare older cultural layers and artefacts testify to a permanent settlement from around 1050 onwards. Finds of individual objects datable to before 1000 can be explained simply by the place having long been used as one of the many seasonal fishing camps along the coast of Gotland.

Viking-Age farms

The sites at Bandlunde, Fröjel, Paviken and Visby have been interpreted as harbours and marketplaces, whose buildings are linked to a quasi-urban structure. Although the buildings at these harbour sites are of great interest, since we know so little about Viking houses on the island, they do not reveal much about daily life.

Fjäle

Far better for a case study of this kind is Fjäle, in Ala parish, where several buildings have been uncovered and excavated. Two of them – Buildings 4 and 5 – are believed to have been in use during the Viking Age. Building 4 measures 10.5m by 5.5m, and is thought to have had two floors, an access porch and a roof supported on posts cut into the bedrock.[27] Using uncalibrated radiocarbon dating and artefacts, Dan Carlsson has placed its construction in the mid-Vendel Period,[28] or early Viking Age.[29] This would suggest that the building functioned for at least 800 years, with posts simply being replaced when needed. Artefacts show that the house was in use during the Viking Age, but it is difficult to say whether it really dates from then, since the finds belong to the later part of the period and almost into the twelfth century.[30]

Building 5 was larger, measuring 15m by 7m. It has only been partly investigated, but judging by the layout of limestone fragments, it used to have a wooden sill. It is thought to have been a storage building, since it contained a lot of barley and was clearly separate from the main house. It was destroyed by fire.[31] Since we have accurately reported results from the original analysis, it is possible to recalibrate the radiocarbon dates. This shows that Building 5 was probably built in the Viking Age (Appendix, nos 52–5) and was slightly later than Building 4 (Appendix, nos 46–51). Although Building 5 contained carbonised barley, this was not sent for radiocarbon analysis. Perhaps the volumes were too small for the methods of the time, and the remains of the wooden posts were therefore chosen instead.

Spillings

In 1999 a huge silver hoard was found at Spillings farm near Slite in Othem parish, on the north-eastern part of the island. In the year following this sensational discovery, a more extensive excavation of the site was undertaken. It revealed traces of a building (Figure 14.3) in which three hoards had been tucked away: two of silver and one containing bronze artefacts (Figure 14.4). The evidence indicates that this was some kind of utility building, such as a warehouse; since no hearth has been found, it is unlikely to have been a dwelling house. The building is around 15m long and just over 10m wide. The excavated area of the building and hoards is some 150m^2, although further excavations in the immediate surroundings range from a number of 1m by 1m test pits to larger continuous areas and cover a further 160m^2.

The building probably had a wooden floor, beneath which there is a layer of rocks and sand, making the floor level and the ground well drained. Stone-free rectangular spaces break the continuity of the otherwise homogenous stone layer; these are where the hoards were deposited. Stones were removed to make room for the valuables, which were stashed away. The building had stone foundations, upon which the walls were built. On both sides of the stone foundations, several buried but still preserved wooden posts were uncovered. The posts on the outside were angled towards the centre of the building, while those on the inside were upright.

The angled posts around the house suggest either that the roof reached all the way down to the ground, or that the walls were buttressed by struts. The slope of the roof can be ascertained based on the angles at which the uncovered posts are standing. The framework was of pine, but the roofing material is unknown; possibly sedge, or a wooden roof of grooved boards or shingle. There are additional postholes in front of the south gable.[32] These may be the remains of an older building, or may have formed an attic or access balcony, as in the case of Fjäle's Building 4.

Dating the house is complex. In addition to artefacts, radiocarbon samples and the three hoards – two with silver and one with bronze – we also have stray finds from the building, although these are not particularly informative. Among the latter are beads from the postholes, which are likely to have ended up there while the building was still in use. The silver hoards have a *tpq* of 871, and it is likely that they were deposited under the floor of the Spillings building soon after that date.[33] Four radiocarbon dates from the building differ from each other. Wood from two of the posts may be from the Vendel Period or early

Figure 14.3 Part of the wall from the Spillings building; left: showing leaning posts on the outer side and upright posts inside; right: detail of a leaning post from the outer side.

Photo: author.

Figure 14.4 The bronze hoard from Spillings, with post in foreground.
Photo: author.

Viking Age. A burnt plank, interpreted as having fallen from the roof, is even earlier and has been dated to the Migration Period. And finally, wood shavings, believed to have come from woodworking once the building was no longer in use, are from the late Viking Age.[34]

Levide

A Viking-Age building in Vall parish was excavated in the early twentieth century. It was of wood and built on a stone sill that comprised stones laid out in three rows to form a total width of about 1m. In his excavation report from 1906 (Figure 14.5), the archaeologist Nils Lithberg noted:

> [. . .] a simple stone bed, on which the walls rest [. . .] the walls were constructed of wattle and daub, all held together by clay, which was charred. The house had a hearth and had burned down in the middle of the Viking Age. All traces of the building have now fallen victim to the plough.[35]

How large an area was excavated is not clear, and given the time of the excavations, no radiocarbon dating is available. However, the artefacts do

Figure 14.5 Nils Lithberg's sketch of the Viking-Age house from Levide, Vall parish.
Courtesy of ATA; from Lithberg (1906).

provide some evidence: according to Lena Thunmark-Nylén, the find materials are clearly Viking Age, although 'there are no objects that can be dated with certainty to the late Viking Age'.[36]

Burge

A collection of buildings from the late Viking Age have been excavated at Burge in Lummelunda parish (Figure 14.6). This complex was discovered thanks to the finding in 1967 of what was then the largest silver hoard (10.4kg) to be unearthed on the island. Six houses have been identified and excavated to a varying extent. Two of them, at the hoard find spot, lie on top of one another. This 'Silver Hoard' house, at 17m by 7m, is roughly the same size as the building at Spillings. The walls are constructed using upright posts, their bases set in postholes dug into the ground, and the roof was supported by paired posts. At the bottom of the postholes are flat stones. The function of these stones is unclear, but they are also found in the Spillings house; it is believed that they were meant to prevent the wood from rotting. Two building phases overlay one another and a wattle and daub wall from the later stage has been uncovered. At least three more buildings have been identified at the excavation site, making it six in total.[37] If the interpretation is correct, the 'North West Meadow' house was either a three-roomed building or a two-roomed building with a roofed but otherwise open area outside, similar to Building 4 at Fjäle.[38] To the east another building has been identified; however, judging from the excavation plan, this could very well be the remains of the same building.

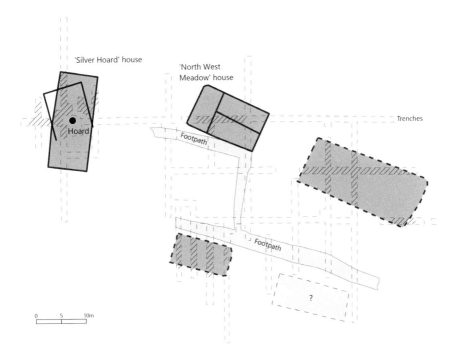

Figure 14.6 Burge farm; layout showing the 'Silver Hoard' house and 'North West Meadow' house.

Drawing: author (after a plan by Lena Thunmark-Nylén).

The excavations at Burge started in 1969 and are some of the most comprehensive to be undertaken at a Viking farm on Gotland. The total extent of the area investigated is hard to determine exactly, but the lead archaeologist believes it to be around 1,000m². The remains of a wooden post in the 'Silver Hoard' house were radiocarbon dated to the Viking Age, although the hoard seems to have been deposited around 1150 (see Appendix, no. 56).

The farm at Burge seems to have been a wealthy one. The artefacts, including the silver hoards, show traces of the good life; indeed, '*burgen*' is an old Swedish word for being rich. The more de luxe finds include jewellery and intact animal-head brooches, dress pins, fittings and finger-rings. Even rare rock crystal lenses, and a small, turquoise-coloured bottle, have been found. But there are also many objects that testify to daily life on a farm: weaving tablets, sewing needles, net sinkers, spindle whorls, antlers and other tools reveal a lot about the inhabitants' occupations. Everyday objects such as knives, beads, rivets, combs and keys have also been found in the layers surrounding the farm houses. Interestingly, the only weapons to be discovered are a scabbard ferrule and some arrowheads.[39] As the archaeologist in charge of the excavation describes it, 'Good soil, a good geographical position and good, hard-working people have – for those who follow – handed over one of the most interesting complexes in Gotlandic and Swedish archaeology'.[40]

Kattlunds

The remains of another building have been uncovered in excavations at Kattlunds in Grötlingbo parish. Twelve postholes supported the frame of a timber building, which measured some 15m by 5m.[41] This was also the find spot of a silver hoard (119 coins, *tpq* 1017), along with some other finds of interest, including a dress pin and half a glass bead.[42] No radiocarbon dating has been undertaken, although an area of 158m^2 has been investigated. This followed reports that the site had been looted by metal-detectorists: the landowner had noticed unusual holes in the ground and when the archaeologists arrived, they recorded around 200 empty holes. One was much bigger than the rest: it is thought that ploughing must have shattered a hoard, leaving the core intact, which would explain the greater size.

Gannarve

The situation at Gannarve in Hall parish is complex, with reports of finds throughout the 1920s and 1930s, in 1945, and again in the early 1980s. Some came to light during archaeological investigations; others were reported by the farmer. The main excavations were undertaken in 1930 and 1983, the latter covering an area of 94m^2. According to the lead archaeologist, there are two settlements on top of one another, forming two layers of finds. A post-built house unearthed in the top layer has Viking-style finds associated with it, although they cannot be firmly dated to the Viking Age. Radiocarbon analysis of the house remains shows that two of its posts have slightly different datings, but both are congruent with the artefactual evidence (see Appendix, nos 38–9).

Gannarve was discovered thanks to a silver hoard which drew the attention of the archaeologist Oscar Wennersten to the site. Significant quantities of silver from at least four hoards have since been discovered, indicating that this was a settlement in use throughout the Viking Age. Wennersten commented at the time:

> I have been advised of a discovery from Hall parish, consisting of a fragment of burnt daub that came up in the ruins of what appears to be a *kämpgrav*. And if I'm not mistaken, there are also Kufic and Saxon coins from the area. Just think if we have the remains of a tenth-century house there.[43]

His investigations did not find the remains of such a building. But the foundations of these stone houses are substantial, and Wennersten's description is unlikely to have been plucked out of thin air. What was recorded in the 1930s is probably not what was excavated in 1983.

Klints

In November 2002 an investigation was undertaken by Ann-Marie Pettersson at Klints, a farm in Othem parish (Figure 14.7). The landowner – who had an interest in local history, and had previously found and handed in Viking artefacts – had noticed objects in earth excavated during the development of a golf course. In 2007 more extensive excavations were undertaken and a Viking-Age building, measuring around 6m by 4.5m, was uncovered. It is thought to have been a storage building of sorts, with posts along the foundation trench. Thanks to good preservation of the wood, we know that it was built out of sturdy pine trees.[44] The house has been dated to 1044–50 by Hans Linderson of Lund University, using a complex combination of dendrochronology and radiocarbon dating.[45] Artefacts found at the ploughed-up site range from the Vendel Period to the late Viking Age, and even into the mid-twelfth century.[46] Dress pins and brooches have been discovered, as well as a chain, belt fittings, weights,[47] keys, arrowheads and the cast for part of a large brooch. Melted bronze indicates that some metalworking took place at the site.

Havor

One other interesting site is Havor in the parish of Hablingbo, which has several settlements of uncertain date: remains ranging from the Roman Iron Age to the early medieval period lie within a few hundred metres, sometimes on top of one another. The remains of one – possibly two – Vendel-Period houses have been found in a trench some 100m to the south-west of

Figure 14.7 Post from a house at Klints, Othem parish.
Photo: author.

a ringfort and Roman Iron-Age stone house foundations, with traces of a Viking-Age house on top.[48] Artefacts and postholes have also been found, but not in contexts that could be read as complete houses.

Vallhagar

A medieval – possibly late Viking-Age – house was also uncovered during the international post-war excavations at Vallhagar in Fröjel parish, a site best known for its early Iron-Age houses. The building measured 10.5m by 5m, and the excavations revealed stone-lined postholes: the remains of paired posts that supported the roof. In its latest phase the building had a stone sill.[49] It cannot be dated either by artefacts or by radiocarbon dating, and estimates of its age are based on comparative analysis only. It has been included here because it is frequently mentioned in the literature as a Gotlandic Viking house.

Suburbs of Visby

Periodic excavations have taken place just outside Visby for around 30 years. Although few Viking-Age buildings have come to light, two houses without any finds connected to them were uncovered in 2006. House 1 has a single aisle and measures 15m by 6m. It was built from four pairs of posts, with two additional posts in the gable sides. House 2 has three aisles with two roof-bearing post lines. It is believed originally to have had wall posts as well, but that these have been destroyed by agricultural activities. Radiocarbon dating shows that all the samples taken from within the buildings and around are Viking Age.[50] This makes it likely they are Viking buildings, although it is unclear what they were used for.

Kärrmans

Another farm on which signs of Viking settlement have been discovered is Kärrmans in Kräklingbo parish. The excavations covered 109m^2 and the artefacts show late Viking-Age characteristics. But as only two postholes are mentioned, it is hard to evaluate the nature and function of the building.[51]

Viking farms on the Swedish mainland

Our knowledge of Viking-Age settlement on the Swedish mainland has increased during the past 20 years. The dominant type of building, the three-aisled longhouse, remained little changed from previous eras, while units tended to be larger in agricultural areas than in woodland or mountains.[52] Viking-Age builders seem to have had a wide range of styles available to them, and construction methods varied. In Uppland, for example, three-aisled houses disappear in favour of framework houses with a single aisle. Houses could be built with either vertical or horizontal boards, or with wattle and daub walls, and sunken floors are also frequently found. Size and means of construction were very much up to local needs and conditions, with longhouses often divided into different areas, rooms or parts, which played different roles. Roof construction is a tough nut to crack, given the lack of evidence. Wood or straw is likely to have been in use. Some hogbacks (Figure 14.8) represent what are believed to be Scandinavian-style houses with shingle roofs – presumably made of wood – although it is difficult to tell whether this style was used in Scandinavia, too.

It is during the Viking Age that the number of buildings on a farm started to increase, although farm size continued to vary widely. Most had only two or three buildings: a main house, with living quarters and possibly also byres, and one or two additional buildings for storage or stabling. Really large farms, some with up to seven buildings, were few and far between, but their existence reflected 'large social differences among the landowning population in Scandinavia'.[53] A further change can be seen from around the tenth century on, with multi-functional buildings being replaced with more specialised ones – for housing animals, among other things – although specialised buildings are known throughout the Viking Age.[54] Some farms also had one or two pit houses: small buildings with sunken floors used as workshops. Moreover, from around 1000 there are signs that the number of stalls in a cowshed dropped, from around eight to fourteen animals per shed to between four and eight.[55]

The remains of one of the major Viking-Age settlements in Sweden, Birka, can be found on the island of Björkö in Lake Mälaren. There are

Figure 14.8 A hogback from Govan, Scotland: possibly the best image of Viking-Age roofing we have.

Photo: Johan Norderäng.

traces of timber framework houses without dug down posts, and by the first half of the tenth century there were already houses built on wooden sills. A hundred years later, stone sill buildings appear in Sigtuna, where they seem to be the rule rather than the exception.[56]

Radiocarbon dating: pluses and minuses

Radiocarbon dating has proved a great help in trying to understand the chronology of Viking-Age buildings, albeit not a particularly fine-tuned one, especially for sites that were in use over long periods of time. On the Swedish mainland, recent excavations have produced a lot of new information, helping to clarify our image of the Viking-Age farm. This is not the case on Gotland, where the most important investigations were undertaken in the 1960s and 1970s, before accelerator mass spectrometry was available. Fortunately, coins and other artefacts can sometimes fill this gap, the latter also being subjected to radiocarbon dating. However, knowledge of how radiocarbon dating works can sometimes be sketchy and some excavation reports lack specialist inputs, leading to faulty interpretation of the data.

Conclusion

Viking-Age farms on Gotland have not been nearly as well investigated as those on the Swedish mainland. Burge is the best example of an excavated farm and settlement area on the island, making it the most suitable for comparison with mainland farms, and it seems to fit the picture from there of larger, late Viking-Age farms. The Viking-Age buildings that have been excavated on Gotland tend to have stone foundations, a much earlier construction technique used in traditional *kämpgrav* houses. This technique fell out of favour long before the Viking Age in mainland Sweden, raising the question of whether stone foundations on Gotland reflect a re-use of older settlement sites, or whether Gotlanders maintained this building tradition. The farms at Spillings, Levide and Paviken appear to be purely Viking, with no artefacts found as yet to indicate previous settlement. Some of the Viking houses uncovered at Paviken had stone sills as foundations; but others were built using large stones (as at Spillings) or small stones (like Levide). The stone foundations discovered in Gannarve, close to the site of a tenth-century hoard, led the archaeologist to believe that this was a Viking-Age house. And at Burge and Spillings, according to the landowners, many rocks and stones had been removed over the years from the spots where the archaeological remains of early Viking-Age buildings were eventually located.

The lack of earlier artefacts at these sites, especially from the period when stone-wall houses were traditionally built, strengthens the idea that we are dealing with a Viking building type on Gotland rather than with the re-use of older foundations. It is more likely the re-use of a style, or a style that persisted much later than one might expect. By the late Viking Age, wooden posts dug straight down into the ground seem to have become the commoner technique. The postholes are sometimes strengthened by stones and quite a few of them have a flat, bottom stone, so as to prevent water from destroying the wood, or at least to slow the process down. Towards the end of the Viking Age, houses had wooden sills on a bed of stones, mainly limestone. The houses at Fjäle and Vallhagar, for example, had stone frames in parts of them. Pit houses with sunken floors, of the sort found on mainland Sweden, have not been discovered on Gotland.

The change that can be seen on the mainland in the size and composition of Viking farms cannot be seen on Gotland, for lack of evidence. But a comparison between the island's farms and its silver hoards – since by the late Viking Age, hoards are bigger but fewer in number – might indicate changes in both the settlement structure and distribution of wealth. Fewer people made more money, leading to a concentration of wealth and power in the hands of a decreasing number of individuals.

These changes are perhaps exemplified by the rise of Visby. If we believe *Guta Saga*, once established as a town at the present site and soon after the building of a church, Visby grew rapidly: from huts to a substantial stone settlement in the space of 200 years. It became a controlled area, supported by the local elite and attracting many to the island from the east, since Gotland was already by then an important link between east and west. For those who could raise tax revenue, Visby was a money maker. All that remains of the earlier wooden settlement is the Kopparsvik burial ground nearby, believed to have been in use throughout the tenth century, and perhaps from the ninth right into the eleventh.

Notes

1 See Svedjemo in this volume.
2 D. Carlsson (1983), p. 14; *LD*, p. 34.
3 A. Carlsson (1983), p. 36; Rundkvist (2003), p. 80.
4 Rundkvist (2003), p. 80.
5 Brandt (2002), p. 243.
6 Brandt (2002), p. 247.
7 Brandt (2002), p. 250.
8 Mainly of the earlier, polyhedral (cubo-octahedral) type, but some later spherical (oblate spheroid) weights were also found.
9 Brandt (2002), p. 255.
10 Carlsson (1999), p. 60.
11 See Gustafsson in this volume.
12 Gustafsson and Söderberg (2007), p. 105.
13 Gustafsson and Söderberg (2007), p. 110.
14 *DKV*, p. 115.
15 *DKV*, pp. 118–20.
16 Huttu (1996), p. 6.
17 Huttu (1996), p. 7.
18 Karn (2014), p. 33.
19 Huttu (1996), pp. 6–7.
20 Karn (2014), p. 77.

21   Westholm (1983), p. 399.
22   Westholm (1993), pp. 85–6.
23   Thunmark-Nylén (2004), p. 289.
24   Westholm (1983), p. 399. For a table of recalibrated radiocarbon datings for Gotland, see the Appendix at the end of this volume; and in particular, for Visby, Appendix, nos 1–17.
25   Thunmark-Nylén (2004), p. 288.
26   Roslund (2001), p. 175. See also Jansson in this volume.
27   For a plan of Building 4, see D. Carlsson (1983), pp. 18–19.
28   Carlsson (1979a) p. 135; Carlsson (1984), p. 145. See Appendix, nos 46–51.
29   Carlsson (1979b), p. 165.
30   The recalibrated dates, particularly within probability ranges registering highest peaks, are more in keeping with the artefactual evidence.
31   Carlsson (1979b), p. 166.
32   Widerström (2009), pp. 48–50.
33   Rispling (2004), p. 123. See also Östergren in this volume.
34   *WKG*, vol. 3.2, p. 701. See Appendix, nos 30–3.
35   Lithberg (1906).
36   *WKG*, vol. 3.2, p. 482.
37   Thunmark (1979), p. 152.
38   See above, n. 27.
39   Thunmark (1979), p. 157. For the Burge hoards, see Östergren in this volume.
40   Thunmark-Nylén (1983), p. 57.
41   Östergren and Jonsson (1989), p. 92.
42   Östergren and Jonsson (1989), p. 93.
43   Wennersten (1929). For the Gannarve hoards, see Östergren in this volume.
44   Carlsson and Jonsson (2008).
45   Linderson (2008).
46   Pettersson (2005), p. 14.
47   Including six oblate spheroid and two cubo-octahedral.
48   Manneke (2005), pp. 130–2.
49   Biörnstad (1955).
50   Wickman-Nydolf (2009). See also Appendix, nos 14–17.
51   Carlsson (1993), p. 26.
52   Fallgren (2008), p. 67.
53   Fallgren (2008), p. 69.
54   Myrdal (1999), p. 35.
55   Myrdal (1999), p. 39.
56   Rosberg (2009), p. 139.

Bibliography

Biörnstad, A. (1955), 'The Vallhagar buildings: building 8', in M. Stenberger (ed.), *Vallhagar: A Migration Period Settlement on Gotland, Sweden*, vol. 1, Copenhagen, pp. 154–6.

Brandt, B. (2002), 'Bandlundeviken: a Viking trading centre on Gotland?', in G. Burenhult (ed.), *Remote Sensing*, vol. 2: *Archaeological Investigations and Remote Sensing Case Studies*, Hässleholm, pp. 243–311.

Carlsson, A. (1983), *Djurhuvudformiga spännen och gotländsk vikingatid*, SSA 5, Stockholm.

Carlsson, D. (1979a), *Kulturlandskapets utveckling på Gotland [The Development of the Cultural Landscape on Gotland]*, Visby.

Carlsson, D. (1979b), 'Fjäle i Ala: vikingatida och tidigmedeltida huskonstruktioner', in W. Falck (ed.), *Arkeologi på Gotland*, Visby, pp. 163–8.

Carlsson, D. (1983), 'Bygd och gård på Gotland under vikingatiden', in *GoV*, pp. 11–23.

Carlsson, D. (1984), 'Change and continuity in the Iron Age settlement of Gotland', in K. Kristiansen (ed.), *Settlement and Economy in Later Scandinavian Prehistory*, Oxford, pp. 129–53.

Carlsson, D. (1993), 'Nyupptäckta fornlämningar i brandens spår', *GA* 65: 19–29.

Carlsson, D. (1999), *'Ridanäs': vikingahamnen i Fröjel*, ArkeoDoks Skrifter 2, Visby.

Carlsson, D. and K. Jonsson (2008), 'Utgrävningen av en skattfyndplats i Klints, Othem sn, Gotland', *Myntstudier* 2008(1): 1–8.

Fallgren, J.-H. (2008), 'Farm and village in the Viking Age', in *VW*, pp. 67–76.

Gustafsson, N. B. and A. Söderberg (2007), 'En senvikingatida silververkstad i Fröjel', *GA* 79: 99–110.

Huttu, J. (1996), 'Anläggning 1. Undersökning av ett hus i Paviken, Västergarn', unpublished BA thesis, Stockholm University.

Karn, A. (2014), *Paviken 2014: Arkeologisk undersökning, Stora Mafrids 5:12, Västergarn socken, Region Gotland, Gotlands län* (Rapport Arrendus 2014:27), Visby.

Linderson, H. (2008), *Dendrokronologisk analys av trästolpar vid arkeologisk utgrävning, Klints 1:16, Othem, Gotland* (Lunds universitet, Institutionen för kvartärgeologi Rapport 2008:49), Lund.

Lithberg, N. (1906), 'Letter from the excavation site to Oscar Almgren in Uppsala' (Antikvarisk-topografiska dossierer, Levide, Vall socken, Gotland, ATA), Stockholm.

Manneke, P. (2005), 'The excavations of Havor Ringfort and its environs', in E. Nylén *et al.* (eds), *The Havor Hoard: The Gold, the Bronzes, the Fort*, Stockholm, pp. 96–144.

Myrdal, J. (1999), 'Jordbrukets tillväxt 1000–1350', in J. Myrdal (ed.), *Det svenska jordbrukets historia*, vol. 2: *Jordbruket under feodalismen, 1000–1700*, Stockholm, pp. 19–110.

Östergren, M. and K. Jonsson (1989), 'Vikingatida silverskatter: nya forskningsrön på skilda sätt', *GA* 61: 79–98.

Pettersson, A.-M. (2005), *Arkeologisk efterundersökning: fyndplats för vikingatida silverskatt och boplatslämning. Klints 1:16 RAÄ 233 Othem socken Gotlands kommun* (Länsstyrelsens Gotlands län, dnr 431–5482–02), Visby.

Rispling, G. (2004), 'Spännande mynt i Spillingsskatten', in G. Westholm (ed.), *Gotland vikingaön* [= *GA* 76], pp. 123–32.

Rosberg, K. (2009), *Vikingatidens byggande i Mälardalen: ramverk och knuttimring*, Uppsala.

Roslund, M. (2001), *Gäster i huset: kulturell överföring mellan slaver och skandinaver 900 till*, Lund.

Rundkvist, M. (2003), *Barshalder, 1: A Cemetery in Grötlingbo and Fide Parishes, Gotland, Sweden, c. AD 1–1100 – Excavations and Finds 1826–1971*, Stockholm.

Thunmark [Thunmark-Nylén], L. (1979), 'Burget på Burge: en storgård på gränsen mellan heden och Kristen tid', in W. Falck (ed.), *Arkeologi på Gotland*, Visby, pp. 151–8.

Thunmark-Nylén, L. (1983), 'Burge i Lummelunda: gårdsplats och skattplats', in *GoV*, pp. 49–58.

Thunmark-Nylén, L. (2004), 'Visby: ett pussel med gamla och nya pusselbitar', *Fv* 99: 285–97.

Wennersten, O. V. (1929), 'Letter to Bengt Thordeman' (ATA, Stockholm, Inventory Number 5407/29).

Westholm, G. (1983), 'Boplatsen i Vi, nedanför klinten', in *GoV*, pp. 397–414.

Westholm, G. (1993), 'Visbysamhällets uppkomst: ett genmäle', *Fv* 88: 81–7.

Wickman-Nydolf, G. (2009), *Särskild undersökning, 'Stolphålshus i kv. Artilleriet 1:33', RAÄ 164 Artilleriet 1:33, Visby, Gotland* (Länsstyrelsen Gotlands län dnr 431-4748-05), Visby.

Widerström, P. (2009), 'Spillings farm: the home of a rich Viking in the northeast of Gotland', in *SH*, pp. 41–64.

15 Social structures and landscape

Gotland's silver hoards in the context of settlements

Gustaf Svedjemo

Archaeology on Gotland, in the minds of the general public and archaeologists alike, is almost synonymous with the island's Viking-Age silver. New hoards are discovered almost every year, finds that are often reported in the Scandinavian media and beyond. This chapter uses silver hoards and other data to study the island's settlement, landscape and social organisation, including some less well-known features and archaeological sources. Gotland's calcareous soil is excellent for preserving many types of buried features and artefacts, especially bone material, for example, and few Swedish regions offer such good conditions, making the island one of the most intensively researched areas in the country.

Aims and background

In the past four decades, the most widespread view of the island's settlement structure has been that villages never existed, and that solitary farmsteads housing nuclear families predominated from the Roman Iron Age on.[1] Gotland's settlement pattern throughout late antiquity and the middle ages had previously been thought to consist of both villages and solitary farms.[2] It was only in the late 1970s that villages 'disappear', probably under the influence of research from the Swedish mainland. The reason why the solitary farm hypothesis may have prevailed is because farms were listed individually in early modern cadastres and tax records: started by the Danish government, these continued after the Swedish takeover in the mid-seventeenth century. However, farms may have been listed this way because it was the individual farmers who were of interest as tax objects; it did not necessarily reflect their social organisation.

It is important to note that, except in a few regions, Swedish villages were never densely clustered: they were generally very small and are best compared to English hamlets.[3] For example, Jan-Henrik Fallgren estimates that the distance between Iron-Age farms on Öland was between 50m and 200m.[4] Another example from early seventeenth-century Uppland, using data from large-scale historical maps for around 850 villages, shows that some 35% had only two farms and 64% no more than three;[5] only 49 of these villages had seven or more farms, the largest recorded being 14.

However, using extensive study of physical settlement remains and historical maps, this chapter will show that villages did exist on Gotland – contrary to the prevailing view, and more or less in line with earlier research. Previous studies of settlement patterns and landscape utilisation were unable to incorporate the vast amount of data available for the entire island, and therefore analysed only small areas. This may have led to too generalised a picture, one that stressed continuity and did not pick up degrees of variation and change over time. Recent advances in GIS technology paired with the amount of archaeological and historical data now digitally accessible make more advanced and comprehensive analysis possible, covering most of the island and many different types of data. Thus, the overall objective of this chapter is to outline and discuss changes to settlement structures, landscape utilisation and social organisation on Gotland between 200 and 1700 AD.

Sources used in our analysis

We have good physical evidence for the early period, since houses on Gotland were built with sturdy stone walls between around 200 and 600 AD (Figure 15.1).[6] These stone house foundations are referred to in folklore as *kämpgrav* and around 1,800 remain visible in the landscape – almost half the 4,000 believed to have existed.[7] Gotlanders also used stone for much of their fencing in this period, protecting the infields from grazing cattle, and these stone walls are also partly preserved. All this is mapped and stored in FMIS, the Swedish geodatabase of heritage assets.[8]

Sweden also has a long tradition of large-scale mapping, which started in the early seventeenth century and covers some 90% of the populated areas, including provinces now lost.[9] The maps depict individual fields, meadows and other parcels of land in great detail, showing a relatively untouched historical landscape before land reforms and modern farming altered the physical landscape and farm structures.[10] Since most farms have been mapped on many occasions over the centuries, whether for taxation, land reform or other purposes, there are millions of good-quality maps in the various archives. For some years now they have been scanned and made available online by the Swedish National Land Survey (Lantmäteriet) and National Archives (Riksarkivet).[11] Some areas were never mapped – generally larger noble estates and church lands – and so there are gaps in most counties.[12] However, in the late seventeenth and early eighteenth centuries, every farm and every square inch of Gotland was surveyed and mapped at a scale of 1:8,000 (the GM1700 map series). There are no gaps in the data, and thus for this period we know what land each farm owned, field names, land use and much more. Historical map regression is also frequently used in Swedish landscape studies, since maps are snapshots depicting selected features at a given time, whereas the landscape is the result of development over time. By comparing maps from different periods, traces of past landscape use and older features and patterns can be revealed.[13]

Figure 15.1 Aerial photo of stone house foundations (*kämpgravar*) at Vallhagar, taken during the 1947 excavations.

Photo: Flying Officer Alstad, Royal Swedish Airforce; courtesy of ATA.

However, the main focus of this chapter is on the period between the third to sixth centuries and the twelfth century, when data for settlement studies is less readily available. The Vendel Period has left few settlement traces visible above ground,[14] but we do at least have the silver hoards for the Viking Age,[15] many of which may indicate farmsteads.[16] Majvor Östergren's argument that, with some rare exceptions, silver hoards were deposited on farmsteads, and most often within the farmhouses themselves, has been widely accepted. However, this may not be the case, as will be discussed below.

An estimated 750 find spots of Viking-Age silver have been recorded on Gotland to date.[17] Most were found in the nineteenth and early twentieth centuries, often during manual agricultural work, and precise locations were neither recorded nor described. This makes it hard to tell whether multiple finds from the same farm come from just one hoard or from several.[18] In the 1940s and 1950s, Mårten Stenberger published many of the find circumstances,[19] and this has since been supplemented and corrected. He mostly covers the larger hoards, since such finds are memorable, and stay in people's minds and local tradition. Many of Gotland's find spots are included in FMIS, but in an unstructured way, making them hard to retrieve.

Nearly all our silver hoards can be used to identify the extent of Viking-Age settlement and several studies have shown this.[20] But how many of the hoards are connected to – and found on – farmsteads is a key question for any detailed analysis of Viking-Age settlement patterns. Lena Thunmark-Nylén has made a compilation of all the known hoards based on their context and find spot topography.[21] Her survey contains numerous examples of silver hoards found in contexts that are unlikely to have been farmsteads, such as earlier graves, stone field boundary walls, bogs and wetlands. In all, Thunmark-Nylén lists around 45 such hoards: a relatively high number, given that most find circumstances are unclear.[22] Some finds of Viking-Age silver coins can be connected to coeval graves. According to Christoph Kilger, Arabic dirhams do not begin to appear in graves until the tenth century, and several graves containing dirhams have been excavated.[23] Nanouschka Myrberg has argued that some of the hoards can be seen as representations of the dead, constituting material obituaries that were deliberately composed and not just randomly gathered.[24]

Sites with late Viking-Age hoards tend to contain more secondary find material than early Viking-Age sites.[25] Thunmark-Nylén argues that because their purpose was primarily religious, the earlier silver hoards were not deposited on farmsteads, but rather beyond the farm. The silver was for the owner's use in the afterlife, according to 'Odin's Law' and as described in the Norse saga *Heimskringla*, and since the treasure was not meant to be recovered, it could be deposited anywhere.[26]

Other finds can, with reasonable confidence, be identified as offerings or cult deposits. Some hoards are reported to have been found in stone house foundations or other third- to sixth-century contexts. A passage in *Guta Lag* forbids the pagan worship of *stavgardar* (*stafgarþar*), and based on a study of Gotlandic place names related to or including the word *stavgard*, Ingemar Olsson suggests that these were Iron-Age dwelling sites later associated with a cult of ancestors.[27] The religious historian Torsten Blomkvist supports this interpretation, seeing a strong connection between *stavgardar*, *kämpgravar* and the Gotlandic picture stones, all of which he links to this ancestor cult.[28] Thus the finds of Viking-Age silver hoards that we know were discovered in *kämpgravar* are likely to have been ritual deposits connected to the cult of ancestors.[29]

This brief overview shows that Viking-Age silver hoards can be connected to various places and contexts, of which farmsteads are probably a common one. But how common? In her ground-breaking doctoral thesis, Östergren argued that silver hoards are nearly always found on Viking-Age farmsteads, defining a hoard as one large silver object – for example, a bracelet, arm- or neck-ring, or penannular brooch – or two to five coins, or more depending on the context.[30] Her conclusions were based on field observation and an analysis of secondary find material[31] from post-excavation surveys of 82 known silver hoard find spots. She concluded that 94% of these silver hoards were buried on Viking-Age farmsteads, most often inside a house.[32] There were some early counter-arguments, pointing out other contexts not connected to Viking-Age farmsteads,[33] and also more recent queries.[34]

Because find material from such surveys is open to interpretation, a fresh analysis was needed of known silver hoard find spots in FMIS and more recent reports. It was based on secondary find material from post-excavation surveys with metal detectors and descriptions of the topography and find circumstances. Over 300 such find spots were identified in FMIS, but many had not been surveyed and could not therefore be analysed. The analysis generated a geospatial database with 109 find spots which could be interpreted as being on Viking-Age farmsteads. Silver hoards found at harbour sites were not included. By extrapolation, around half of all known silver hoards could have been deposited on settlement sites, most likely farmsteads.[35]

As we have seen, Gotland has rich material remains from the Roman Iron Age onwards, as well as good historical maps, but the situation is different when it comes to written sources. In spite of the fact that Gotland – and especially Visby – played a leading role in the Baltic trade and that Visby was a major northern European city, very few written sources survive from before the sixteenth century. Tryggve Siltberg estimates that only around 100 medieval documents are preserved on Gotland, with possibly a further 3,000 or so concerning Gotland or Visby to be found in foreign archives.[36] From a European perspective, this is very slender. Except for a few special cases, written sources were therefore excluded from the analysis.

There is, however, another source available for Gotland in the middle ages: more than 100 medieval stone farmhouses, either still standing or whose more exact location is known from other sources. These are unique: no other Scandinavian region is known to have such stone-built farmhouses, using more or less the same techniques as for churches.

Villages in the third to sixth centuries

The exact position, size and orientation for most of the extant stone house foundations on Gotland are recorded in FMIS. A GIS algorithm was created drawing the houses to size and locating them correctly, which enabled both quantitative and visual spatial analysis. Farms were identified by drawing a circular buffer zone around each stone house foundation and grouping these into clusters where the circles intersected, based on a distance of 80m between their geometric centres. The layout of each cluster was sketched, often using stone-wall remains to help identify individual farms within the cluster. Finally, using greater geometric centre distances, we identified villages by grouping the farms into larger clusters (Figure 15.2).

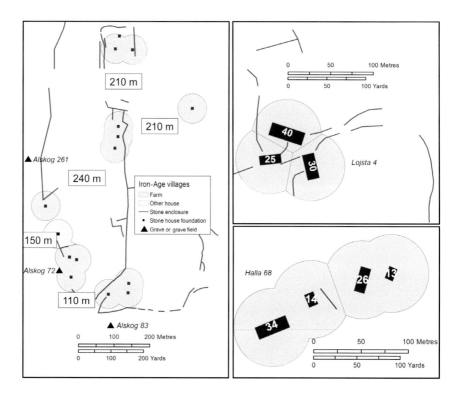

Figure 15.2 Identifying third- to sixth-century farms and villages; left: large, dispersed village recognisable from the stone walls that link it together; top right: compact village containing three farmhouses separated by stone walls; bottom right: small village of two farms, each with two buildings.

The results revealed that at least 60–65% of farms on Gotland were situated in villages during the third to sixth centuries: most villages contained only two farms, but 40% had three or more, with the largest having up to 12. Large villages were probably more numerous and possibly even bigger, but the removal of stone house foundations in more recent times means they can no longer be identified. The most famous village from this period is at Vallhagar. It contains around 10 farms and 24 identified, excavated stone house foundations, although it may originally have been larger: it is situated beside a modern field, where ploughing has likely destroyed the remains of several farms.[37]

A hierarchy was also identified among the farms analysed, with larger farms generally having more roofed space. It is estimated that around 100 larger farms once existed. They tend to be more numerous in areas that also contained most large farms in the early modern period, but are otherwise fairly evenly spread.

Villages in the early modern period

We know that villages still existed in the eighteenth century, since the land surveyors mapping the GM1700 cadastral maps noted whether farms were in 'village communities' (*byalag*) or 'solitary' (*enstaka*). Unfortunately, they did not note any village names, and listed farms as separate entities; and only around half of the farms are thus described, since not all surveyors used any such notation. Around 40% of the farms for which we have this information are said to be in village communities. The majority consist of two- or three-farm groupings, but villages with more than three farms are common, and the largest have seven.

The concept of villages persisted, and many groups of farms are known under a village name in ethnographic or historic sources. A study of farms whose names include positional information – for example, 'Österby' (eastern farm) or 'Medebys' (middle farm) – found that their names reflect their position within a group of farms, and not their location in the parish or vis-à-vis the church, although the author does not take the argument further and conclude that these were villages.[38] However, many of these groupings can be identified as villages by the criteria used in our present analysis.

Because of the richness of data in the GM1700 map series, we could take a different approach in spatial analysis to identify villages – both early ones and those still in existence in the eighteenth century. Because of the time needed to rectify all the scanned maps and vectorise the tens of thousands of land parcels mapped and described by the land surveyors, not all of the 92 parishes on Gotland could be analysed. However, more than half – 51 parishes – were included. Since the land belonging to each farm could be identified, the spatial extent of each farm could be mapped. Before the redistribution of land under the eighteenth- and nineteenth-century land reform acts (see n. 10), a farm's holdings could be quite scattered and mixed with land belonging to others. Farms with scattered land within a defined area were interpreted as belonging to a village, and each farm was coded using shading and lettering. As can be seen from Figure 15.3, the various farms' land parcels are mixed within a clearly defined village territory. The few parcels of land within the village territory belonging to other farms are probably the result of land transactions, marriage, inheritance and the like.

The 51 parishes analysed included around 60% of all farms on the island. In total 188 villages were identified, mostly smaller villages with two farms, but 40% were larger. Around 53% of farms in the parishes analysed were situated in a village. These included all but a few of the farms noted as being in a village community by the eighteenth-century land surveyors.

Viking-Age and medieval villages

Only around 70 of the 109 find spots identified via FMIS as Viking-Age farmsteads (above, p. 295) are situated within the 51 parishes included in our

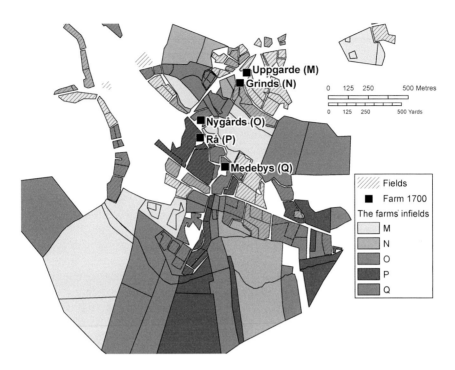

Figure 15.3 The infields of a village with five farms in Vallstena parish.

cartographic analysis. With such a small sample it is difficult to draw any reliable conclusions. However, in several places they tend to bunch together and coincide with early modern villages, all of which, not surprisingly, indicates the presence of Viking-Age villages in these spots, too.

When it comes to the middle ages, our sample is also very small. The largest village, Norrbyn in the parish of Vamlingbo, consisted of seven farms in 1703, of which five have traces of medieval stone houses. There are smaller villages with similar remains, for example in the parish of Anga. Since all but a handful of medieval stone farmhouses are found on farms known from later records, we can conclude that as a general rule the locations of farmsteads in the GM1700 cadastral maps are also valid for the late middle ages. However, we cannot extrapolate backwards and assume that every farm attested by the GM1700 map series also existed in the middle ages; or that every medieval farm remained in existence in 1700. The turbulent fourteenth and fifteenth centuries led to farms being deserted, primarily as the result of the Black Death, but also during other periods of plague and unrest, which affects the picture. But it is fairly safe to say that the vast majority of farmsteads found in the GM1700 map series had not moved since around the twelfth century. Thus, it is reasonable to conclude that villages also existed in the middle ages.

Changes in localisation and landscape utilisation

Our analysis points to a quite stable overall settlement structure for the whole of Gotland. Both villages and solitary farms are found in all periods, in very similar proportions during the third to sixth centuries and the early modern period. There is, however, one important difference: farms within villages are generally not situated in the same locations over time. The village territory seems to remain roughly the same, but farmsteads tend to move within that territory. One factor governing this is soil type. It has long been noted that third- to sixth-century settlements are on denser moraine soils, generally set low in the landscape near bogs and wetlands, while later farms are on sandy soils on higher ground.[39] This has not, however, been analysed on a large dataset before.

Map 15.1 shows the differences between the third to sixth centuries and 1700. The extent of the earlier landscape has been estimated by predictive modelling,[40] while that of 1700 is defined as the areas shown as fields and meadows on the GM1700 cadastral maps. As can be seen, most of the occupied landscape is the same. There are, however, areas that were settled in the earlier period and not later on, shown as black areas and dots, some

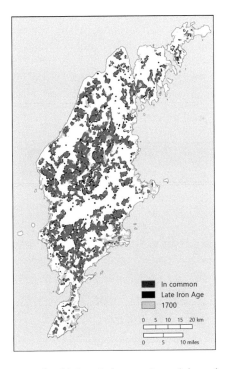

Map 15.1 Settlement areas in the third to sixth centuries and the early modern period.

quite far from any early modern farm. When these areas were abandoned is uncertain: they may have lasted until the crisis of the fourteenth century, like Fjäle farm in Ala parish.[41] There are also few traces of coastal settlement in the third to sixth centuries. Although it is clear that Gotlanders had connections with the European continent and the Roman empire in this period, the exact nature of these contacts and where they emanated from is presently unknown.

The coastal areas were extensively used by the early modern period and this may have begun during the Vendel Period or early Viking Age: this is when the first signs of Gotlandic trade appear, both on Gotland – in the form of many landing and harbour sites[42] – and in other parts of the Baltic rim. The settlement at Grobiņa in present-day Latvia shows clear traces of a Gotlandic presence, as do other places, with the earliest dating to the seventh century.[43] The first picture stones to depict ships with sails date from the early eighth century,[44] and they are most probably a sign of increasing maritime activity on the Baltic. That trade boomed during the Viking Age and the middle ages is attested by the silver hoards and medieval stone houses.

Other areas with only a limited degree of settlement during the third to sixth centuries are those with predominantly sandy soil. Moraine soils are much more common on the island, and these heavier soils were preferred by earlier settlers: the density of stone house foundations is more than double that found on sandy soils. Many of the larger areas settled extensively from the Vendel Period on have virtually only sandy soils.[45] One clear example of this is the island of Fårö, off Gotland's northern tip, where settlement shifted markedly from the western part, dominated by moraine soils, to the eastern part, dominated by sandy soils, between the third to sixth centuries and the early modern period (Map 15.2). This development is also visible on the island of Gotland proper, in such parishes as När, Näs and Hamra in the south and

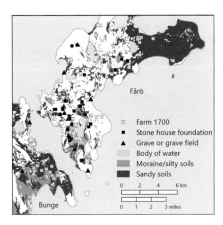

Map 15.2 The shift in settlement sites on the small island of Fårö between the third to sixth centuries and early modern period.

Bunge to the north, which are all dominated by sandy soils. Very few stone house foundations or other pre-Viking-Age remains are found here.

As Map 15.2 shows, areas with only patches of sandy soil were increasingly settled by the early modern period, with farms concentrated in the sandy areas. However, in areas with hardly any sandy soil, we see a mixture of late Iron-Age and early modern farms on moraine soils, but generally at some distance from each other.

The recent removal of house foundations by modern farming does, of course, skew the picture somewhat, but there is still a clear shift in the location of fields and settlement sites to sandy soils wherever possible from the third to sixth centuries on. The reason for this is not fully understood. Climate data shows that the third to sixth centuries were mostly warm and dry, but became wetter and colder towards the end of the period,[46] which may have forced settlements onto higher ground and, where possible, to soils with better drainage. But this is not the only explanation, and a shift in the agricultural economy may also have played a part. This seems to have started during the Vendel Period or Viking Age, since the find spots of silver hoards indicating Viking-Age settlements that have been analysed are more often found on or close to sandy soils than are third- to sixth-century settlements, and in this respect they resemble early modern settlements.

In parallel to this shift in the location of settlements between different periods, there are also several indications of a substantial decrease in the number of farms and population, which cannot be addressed in this chapter.[47]

Social organisation, production and trade

The fact that villages existed on Gotland, as in most parts of Scandinavia, is hardly surprising, since the island's development has much in common with the rest of the region. But Gotland is unique in some key respects. We have so far considered the long-term development of Gotland, but will focus for the rest of this chapter on the Viking Age and early middle ages. It is during this period that many of the settlement patterns seen in later eras were established in much of Scandinavia, as well as the formation of states and a feudal society. However, some of these processes and features may have had their roots in the third to sixth centuries.

No large private estates are known to have existed on Gotland. Even if society was stratified, no hierarchy with a ruling class, nobility and royal power ever emerged on the island to replace the old, kin-based system. The question of when such social organisation emerged in other parts of Scandinavia is hotly debated. Lotte Hedeager has suggested that the old, kin-based society in Denmark had been replaced by new allegiances to a royal ruler by the later Iron Age,[48] while Kent Andersson and Frands Herschend argue that this also involved the establishment of larger, dominant farms in north-western Europe and southern Scandinavia.[49] Such trends can be seen somewhat later in the Mälar region of Sweden. During the Migration and early Vendel Periods, large, elite-owned farms started to establish dominance there, according to Peter Bratt: large burial mounds, containing huge amounts of topsoil, were erected by these elites, which Bratt reasonably interprets as signalling that a central part of their political economy was based on control over labour and landed estates.[50] Some of these elites would develop into the nobility of medieval and later eras.

We see no evidence of such developments on Gotland, but rather a strengthening of social ties based on kin.[51] Kerstin Cassel interprets the clusters of stone house foundations to be village-like structures centred on kinship: larger farms do not signify a ruling class or dominant families, but simply the homes and production centres of different families.[52] According to Cassel, there was no central power: the island was divided up between small communities headed by local leading families. These families should not be seen as an aristocracy set apart from their communities, but rather as part of everyday society and production.[53] This interpretation tallies well with the archaeological and historical evidence from Gotland, and the results from our analysis presented above. The village may have continued to be a means of organising trade and production during the Viking Age and middle ages.

This is not to argue that a socio-economic elite failed to form on Gotland in the way that it did on the Swedish mainland; but on Gotland, their wealth and power was based on the emerging trade rather than on control of land, and thus they cannot be regarded as nobility. A study of areas in Scandinavia with only freehold land and no landed gentry during the Viking Age and middle ages shows that a high degree of trade was of major significance.[54] Olof Holm focuses on the county of Jämtland and uses Gotland as a reference area to confirm his results. Both show high levels of trade from the Viking Age on, and both were socio-economically stratified but not hierarchically structured, lacking large private estates.[55] According to Holm, one important reason for an area to be dominated by the landed gentry is favourable agricultural conditions; these existed on Gotland, yet no estates were formed. Holm argues that in areas where it was easier and more profitable to engage in trade, there were few incentives to develop large estates.[56] Although plausible, the strict rules governing the sale of land on Gotland should also be considered as a constraining factor in land acquisition and estate formation on the island.

Silver hoards in relation to farm and village size

As we have seen, even if only half of the silver hoards were actually deposited on farmsteads, nearly all of them were deposited in their vicinity and were connected to settlements, and are thus of interest to settlement studies. Many hoards include silver artefacts other than coins, such as bracelets, neck-rings, brooches and ingots. Although we lack a comprehensive compilation of the Gotlandic hoards and their composition, making it impossible to include every item of silver in our analysis, Kenneth Jonsson generously made available to us his database of all Viking-Age silver coins found on Gotland. An early study of the relationship between minted and un-minted silver in 48 Gotlandic hoards showed them to contain over 70% minted silver, and so there is little reason to doubt the results would differ significantly were all the silver to be included.[57] However, the results of some of the analyses that follow must be regarded as tentative.

We compiled a geodatabase with nearly all finds of five or more coins discovered so far, although some of the results from the latest surveys are not yet ready or have not yet been published, and were thus omitted.[58] The database contains around 360 hoards from almost 300 different farms. Because the exact location of the find spot is sometimes unknown, they are positioned at an aggregated farm level. To be able to analyse the silver hoards in the context of the villages identified via the GM1700 map series, a subset of the database was created with only the finds from those 51 parishes, which consisted of hoards from 180 farms. One hundred of these – some 55% – are situated within a village, which is in line with the fact that 53% of the farms are located in villages (above, p. 297). Hoards are thus not more common in villages than on solitary farms.

Sometimes people compare the size of the hoard to the size of the farm on whose land it was found, especially when it comes to the huge Spillings hoard.[59] Since Spillings is the smallest farm in Othem, they wonder how such a large hoard came to be found on such a small farm,[60] assuming a correlation between hoard size and farm size. To investigate this, correlation analyses were undertaken, using the number of coins to indicate hoard size, and for farm size either the *marklej* recorded in 1653,[61] the tax paid in 1747[62] or the acreage of the infields. All these measurements reflect, directly or indirectly, how much land a farm had. Regardless of which variable was used, no correlation was found between the number of coins and farm size when the relationship was tested on individual farms, and villages were disregarded: all the results were close to zero. However, if the farms in a village were treated as one unit, and the numbers for hoards, taxes and land were aggregated for the village, the correlation analyses turned out differently: both for villages and solitary farms, the correlation was between 30% and 40% for all measurements.

How should this be interpreted? Since the various measures of farm size to some extent reflect how much ground a farm or village covers, a high correlation is unsurprising and might be expected. What is more surprising is the total lack of correlation when villages are disregarded. I believe these results strengthen our village analyses and show that the villages identified via stone house foundations and the GM1700 map series were also relevant in the Viking Age. It also shows that size does matter to some degree, although not in all respects; and that the larger a farm or village was, the more silver coins were deposited on its land.

Silver hoards, medieval stone houses and the socio-economic elite

Map 15.3a–c shows, respectively, the density of Viking-Age silver coins, medieval stone houses and the largest eighteenth-century farms, all of which indicate where wealth and control of resources were concentrated: the homes of the socio-economic elite. The distribution of the hoards and medieval stone houses represent the heyday of Gotland's rich trading community, which lasted for some 400 to 500 years. Silver hoard find spots are spread over the entire island, but some concentrations can be seen, especially in the parish of Stenkyrka in the north-west, and in the south-east. The number of hoards decreases, but their size increases, at the end of the Viking Age, implying that trade became concentrated into fewer hands.[63]

Nowhere else in Scandinavia do we find medieval stone-built farmhouses and they indicate Gotland's wealth in the late middle ages. Some 175 are known, of which 62 still stand roofed or in ruins.[64] They are not connected to large estates, but to ordinary farms – quite a few of which are small scale when it comes to land.[65] The stone houses may well have been the homes of the leading traders who constituted Gotland's socio-economic elite.

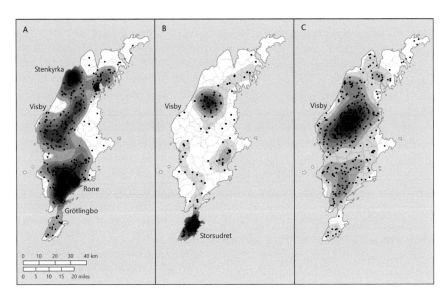

Map 15.3 Concentration of wealth and resources: (a) Density of coins found in Viking-Age silver hoards (with compensations made for two very large outliers: the Stale and Spillings hoards which contain four times the number of coins as the next largest hoard); (b) Density of known medieval stone houses on Gotland; (c) Density of tax amount of the 365 largest farms on Gotland (early eighteenth century).

Medieval stone houses are largely concentrated in two areas: to the north-east of Visby, and on Storsudret, at the southernmost tip of the island. Those around Visby were probably the homes of traders working via the town, while those in the south were probably built on the profits from the stone industry, which were considerable from the mid-eleventh century on.[66] Baptismal fonts and other artefacts made of sand- or limestone were major items of export and are found in abundance around the Baltic and in Denmark. They may well have come from Storsudret, the site of a great many medieval and early modern quarries.

The centre of gravity in the control of trade on the island shifted after the Viking Age, as Map 15.3 shows. This would suggest that the socio-economic elite was not made up of the same families over the centuries, although some clans may have lasted for quite a time. An example comes from the parish of Stenkyrka, where the concentration of silver hoards is high and where we have other evidence of trade and power from different eras. A runic inscription found in the parish, most likely from the mid-eleventh century, tells of Gotlandic traders dealing with furs 'in the south'.[67] In *Guta Saga*, a certain Likkair Snielli ('the Wise') from Stenkyrka is said to have 'carried most authority at that time', suggesting that he held the highest office on Gotland, Judge of the Land, and he is also said to have built one of the island's first churches.[68] One of the surviving copies of the Artlenburg Privilege from 1161 names the Gotlanders' representative as Lichnat,[69] and an elaborate gravestone in the parish church of Stenkyrka, dating to around 1200, over a man named 'Licauns' from 'Stenstufu' (Stone House), could well be his. Stenkyrka's harbour is also called Lickershamn, a form of the same name. All of these Likkairs, with different spellings in different sources, may not be the same man; but it is not inconceivable that they are from the same family, thus indicating that the parish of Stenkyrka was home to important and powerful men for a long period during the Viking Age and middle ages. However, there is no clear correlation between the richest agricultural districts in the eighteenth century (Map 15.3c) – those paying the most in tax – and the Viking-Age and medieval centres, even if there is a degree of overlap. These wealthy rural regions are the same today, even if drainage and cultivation of large tracts of the wetlands has altered the picture somewhat.[70]

Gotland's golden days came to an end once traders in the countryside were outmanoeuvred by those in Visby and elsewhere, and lost the lucrative transit trade. This process was underway by the late thirteenth century, and was followed by a collapse of trade during the upheavals of the fourteenth and fifteenth centuries, starting with the Black Death and the Danish invasion in 1361. This unstable political situation led to unrest: the island became a stronghold for pirates and a theatre for the power struggle between Danes and Swedes. Further invasions worsened the situation. The late middle ages proved to be a watershed in the island's history. The bases for Gotland's countryside elite vanished with the trade, and the once rich leading families started a downward journey. Without the large, aristocratic landed estates found elsewhere in Scandinavia, they had nothing to fall back on. Impoverishment and thus socio-economic levelling occurred, and the fairly egalitarian Gotlandic society of farmers that we meet in our historical sources was created. Of course, there were still rich and poor farmers, and a stratum of well-to-do farmers continued to exist, but the real riches were gone. And since villages never became established in the official records, over time they dissolved as a mean of social organisation, to be replaced by other forms of social bonds and ways of cooperating.

Conclusion

This chapter has shown that villages did exist on Gotland between 200 and 1700 and that changes in the island's social organisation and settlements were quite far-reaching in this period. The disturbances of the fourteenth and fifteenth centuries proved to be a watershed, one that had dire consequences for island society only touched upon here. Further research might better incorporate sources such as written records in foreign archives and gravestones, although this material has yet to be compiled. However, it could help to clarify the social organisation of Gotland's leading merchants and families, and this is an area I hope to return to in future.

Notes

1 See, for example, Carlsson (1979), pp. 146, 157; Lindquist *et al.* (1987), pp. 11, 187; *MSoS*, pp. 16, 193; Siltberg (1998), p. 78.
2 Lithberg (1915); Lithberg (1932); Nihlén and Boëthius (1933); Nerman (1963), p. 20; Fritzell (1972), p. 21.
3 Exceptions include the fully cultivated plains of Scania and Östergötland, and also Dalarna and some other areas, where villages could be large and more densely clustered, occasionally comprising more than 50 farms.
4 Fallgren (2006), p. 77.
5 The calculation is based on data from GEORG, a digital, online database of Sweden's oldest geometrical (map-based) cadastres, consisting of approximately 12,000 maps hosted by the National Archives (Riksarkivet): riksarkivet.se/geometriska.
6 This type of stone-walled house was also built on the island of Öland and the Norwegian region of Jæren at this time. Stone walls from the period are found in some other areas of Sweden.
7 *LD*, p. 107.
8 For FMIS, see Glossary. Around 20,000 locations are registered on Gotland, which makes it the Swedish county with by far the highest density of ancient remains, almost twice that of the runner-up.
9 Swedish large-scale maps also exist for territories which today belong to Finland, Russia, Estonia, Latvia, Germany and Poland.
10 Sweden passed major land reform acts, redistributing acreage among farmers to improve efficiency, in 1757, 1809 and 1827; these greatly altered the landscape and settlement structure in most parts of the country.
11 Available online from etjanster.lantmateriet.se/historiskakartor.

12 Svedjemo (2007).
13 Karsvall (2013).
14 The Vendel Period (600–800) is the least-researched period in Swedish history, according to John Ljungkvist (2013).
15 The Viking Age is generally defined in Sweden as 800–1050; however, on Gotland it extends to 1150, since this is when the depositing of silver hoards ceases.
16 The term 'silver hoard' is not really appropriate for many of these finds which only contain a single silver object. Östergren (2009, p. 11) mentions 700 precious metal hoards, but even if this number has increased to *c.* 750 since 2008, the relationship between hoards and settlements most probably still holds. See also Gruszczyński in this volume.
17 Majvor Östergren (e-mail correspondence with author, 4 January 2016).
18 The identification of different hoards is largely based on numismatic analysis; this important and very time-consuming work has been undertaken by Professor Kenneth Jonsson, but has yet to be published.
19 *SGW.*
20 Schnittger (1915), p. 243; Nihlén and Boëthius (1933), p. 16; Stenberger (1945), p. 18.
21 *WKG*, vol. 3.2, pp. 445–70.
22 *SGW*, vol. 1, p. 21.
23 Kilger (2008), p. 331.
24 Myrberg (2009), p. 141.
25 Östergren (1983).
26 Thunmark-Nylén (1986), p. 24; *WKG*, vol. 3.2, p. 463.
27 Olsson (1992).
28 T. Blomkvist (2002), p. 151.
29 *SGW*, vol. 1, mentions around 15 known cases of hoards found in what seem to be stone house foundations.
30 *MSoS*, p.16.
31 Finds not belonging to the hoards themselves, but retrieved in this case almost exclusively by metal-detector survey.
32 *MSoS.*
33 Westholm (1990); Zachrisson (1998), p. 119.
34 Andrén (2009), p. 42; see also Carlsson in this volume.
35 For a more detailed description of the analysis, see *LD*, p. 117.
36 E-mail correspondence with the author, 28 February 2014. Tryggve Siltberg is the former head of the Regional State Archive in Visby and one of the leading experts on Gotlandic written sources.
37 A very detailed description in English of the village and the excavations undertaken in the late 1940s can be found in Stenberger (ed.) (1955).
38 Lindquist (1981).
39 Arrhenius (1938), pp. 11–12; Moberg (1938), pp. 18–19; Lindquist (1979), p. 251.
40 See *LD*, pp. 95–108, for details.
41 Carlsson (1983).
42 Carlsson and Svedjemo (2006); see also Carlsson in this volume.
43 Nerman (1958); Gustin (2004), pp. 59–61; Gunnarsson (2012), p. 14.
44 Andreeff (forthcoming).
45 Gruszczyński (2016, p. 11) calculates that silver hoards are more commonly deposited on sandy soils, which he interprets as a way of securing newly colonised land. See also Gruszczyński in this volume.
46 For example, see Büntgen *et al.* (2011), fig. 4 on p. 581.
47 For an account of this see *LD*, pp. 31–53, 209–25.
48 Hedeager (1992), pp. 182–93, 238.

49 Andersson and Herschend (1997), pp. 94–5.
50 Bratt (2008), pp. 148, 157–62.
51 According to Kerstin Cassel's study of the Roman Iron Age on Gotland, although this is not a detailed study of the entire island: Cassel (1998), p. 126.
52 Cassel (1998), p. 161.
53 Cassel (1998), pp. 161, 167, 173, 181.
54 'Landed gentry' refers here to those with estates providing them with sufficient income for physical labour to be unnecessary.
55 Holm (2012).
56 Holm (2012), p. 164.
57 Lundström (1973), p. 16; the density map generated by Gruszczyński (2016, fig. 5), based on all the silver from 336 hoards, is very similar and seems to confirm this assumption.
58 Some hoards found at harbour sites, and the ones without a clear connection to any farm, were also excluded.
59 A hoard is normally named after the farm on whose land it was found.
60 Dan Carlsson (2009) notes that the Spillings hoard was found on land which in the early modern period belonged to the much larger Närs farm; however, he suggests that the hoard's size is more likely to reflect the location's proximity to the important landing and trading place of Slite.
61 An old Gotlandic farm assessment system, mentioned in *Guta Lag*: GL, p. 29 (tr.), 121–2 (comm.); *LD*, pp. 132–4.
62 This was the first time that tax had been calculated with precision for each farm. The correlation between the tax of 1747 and the *marklej* is 70%. The tax of 1747 was up to 75%, based on what was produced in the fields and meadows, and was calculated as an average for all farms on Gotland.
63 Östergren (2009), pp. 12–14.
64 Qviström (1995), p. 27.
65 *LD*, p. 196.
66 Landen (1997), p. 85.
67 G 207; Yrwing (1978), p. 104.
68 GS, p. 9; Fritzell (1972), p. 8. See also Gustafsson in this volume.
69 N. Blomkvist (2005), p. 418; on the Artlenburg Privilege, a trade and peace treaty between Henry the Lion and the Gotlanders, see also above, p. 305.
70 Around 90–95% of the very many, and sometimes very large, bogs and wetlands have been drained and cultivated since the late nineteenth century.

Bibliography

Andersson, K. and F. Herschend (1997), *Germanerna och rom*, Uppsala.
Andreeff, A. (forthcoming), *Stones and People: Viking Age Picture Stones from the Island of Gotland*, Gothenburg.
Andrén, A. (2009), 'Vem lät bygga kyrkorna på Gotland?' in M. Hellspong (ed.), *Saga och sed: Kungl. Gustav Adolfs akademiens årsbok 2009*, Uppsala, pp. 31–59.
Arrhenius, O. (1938), *Den Gotländska åkerjordens fosfathalt*, Stockholm.
Blomkvist, N. (2005), *The Discovery of the Baltic: The Reception of a Catholic World-System in the European North (AD 1075–1225)*, Leiden.
Blomkvist, T. (2002), *Från ritualiserad tradition till institutionaliserad religion: strategier för maktlegitimering på Gotland under järnålder och medeltid*, Uppsala.

Bratt, P. (2008), *Makt uttryckt i jord och sten: stora högar och maktstrukturer i Mälardalen under järnåldern*, SSA 46, Stockholm.

Büntgen, U. *et al.* (2011), '2500 years of European climate variability and human susceptibility', *Science* 331(6017): 578–82.

Carlsson, D. (1979), *Kulturlandskapets utveckling på Gotland: en studie av jordbruks- och bebyggelseförändringar under järnåldern*, Visby.

Carlsson, D. (1983), 'Fjäle i Ala: en gård på östra Gotland', in *GoV*, pp. 24–33.

Carlsson, D. (2009), '"Owner missing? The hoard, the farm and the community', in *SH*, pp. 65–107.

Carlsson, D. and G. Svedjemo (2006), *Gotländska hamn- och handelsplatser under perioden 600–1100 e. Kr.* (Länsstyrelsen Gotland, unpublished report).

Cassel, K. (1998), *Från grav till gård: romersk järnålder på Gotland*, SSA 16, Stockholm.

Fallgren, J.-H. (2006), *Kontinuitet och förändring: bebyggelse och samhälle på Öland 200–1300 e. Kr.*, Uppsala.

Fritzell, G. (1972), 'Tankar kring Gutesagan', *Gotländska Studier* 1: 11–46.

Gruszczyński, J. (2016), 'Viking-Age silver hoards in the Baltic zone: deposition and (non)retrieval', paper presented at the Medieval Archaeology Seminar, Institute of Archaeology, University of Oxford, 25 January 2016.

Gunnarsson, D. (2012), 'The Scandinavian settlement at Grobiṇa, Latvia: the connections between the settlement, the local population and Gotland', unpublished BA thesis, Gotland University.

Gustin, I. (2004), *Mellan gåva och marknad: handel, tillit och materiell kultur under vikingatid*, Stockholm.

Hedeager, L. (1992), *Danmarks jernalder: mellem stamme og stat*, Aarhus.

Holm, O. (2012), *Självägarområdenas egenart: Jämtland och andra områden i Skandinavien med småskaligt jordägande 900–1500*, Stockholm.

Karsvall, O. (2013), 'Retrogressiv metod: en översikt med exempel från historisk geografi och agrarhistoria', *Historisk tidskrift* 133: 411–35.

Kilger, C. (2008), 'Kombinationer av föremål: de vikingatida mittspännedepåerna', in K. Chilidis *et al.* (eds), *Facets of Archaeology: Essays in Honour of Lotte Hedeager on Her 60th Birthday*, Oslo, pp. 323–38.

Landen, A. (1997), 'Gotland centrum för medeltida stenexport', in E. Osvalds (ed.), *Medeltid*, Lund, pp. 81–93.

Lindquist, S.-O. (1979), 'Kartprojekten: regional markdatabas', in W. Falck *et al.* (eds), *Arkeologi på Gotland*, Visby, pp. 246–52.

Lindquist, S.-O. (1981), 'Sockenbildningen på Gotland: en korologisk studie', *GA* 53: 45–64.

Lindquist, S.-O. *et al.* (1987), *Vägen till kulturen på Gotland* [= *GA* 59], Visby.

Lithberg, N. (1915), 'Det gottländska bidlaget', *Fataburen: kulturhistorisk tidskrift* 1915: 41–8.

Lithberg, N. (1932), 'By och gård på Gotland', *GA* 4: 21–31.

Ljungkvist, J. (2013), 'Post-romersk globalisering: spåren av Bysans i Sverige 560–800 e. Kr.', in E. Weiberg *et al.* (eds), *Institutionens historier: en vänbok till Gullög Nordquist*, Uppsala, pp. 151–62.

Lundström, L. (1973), *Bitsilver och betalningsringar: studier i svenska depåfynd från vikingatiden påträffade mellan 1900 och 1970*, Stockholm.

Moberg, I. (1938), *Gotland um das Jahr 1700: eine kulturgeographische Kartenanalyse*, Stockholm.

Myrberg [Burström], N. (2009), 'The hoarded dead: late Iron Age silver hoards as graves', in I.-M. Back Danielsson *et al.* (eds), *Döda personers sällskap: gravmaterialens identiteter och kulturella uttryck*, SSA 47, Stockholm, pp. 131–45.

Nerman, B. (1958), *Grobin-Seeburg: Ausgrabungen und Funde*, Uppsala.

Nerman, B. (1963), 'Den gotländska utvandringen och sveaväldets expansion', in Å. G. Sjöberg (ed.), *Historia Kring Gotland*, Stockholm, pp. 15–26.

Nihlén, J. and G. Boëthius (1933), *Gotländska gårdar och byar under äldre järnåldern*, Stockholm.

Olsson, I. (1992), 'Stavgards-problemet: ännu en gång', *Fv* 87: 91–7.

Östergren, M. (1983), 'Silverskatternas fyndplatser: farmännens gårdar', in *GoV*, pp. 34–48.

Östergren, M. (2009), 'Spillings: the largest Viking Age silver hoard in the world', in *SH*, pp. 11–40.

Qviström, L. (1995), *Medeltida stenhus på Gotlands landsbygd*, Lund.

Schnittger, B. (1915), 'Silverskatten från Stora Sojdeby', *Fv* 10: 53–116, 189–246.

Siltberg, T. (1998), 'The Gotlandic farms in the late middle ages', in N. Blomkvist (ed.), *Culture Clash or Compromise? The Europeanisation of the Baltic Sea Area 1100–1400 AD*, Visby, pp. 65–90.

Stenberger, M. (1945), 'Gotlands silverålder', *GA* 17: 13–26.

Stenberger, M. (ed.) (1955), *Vallhagar: A Migration Period Settlement on Gotland, Sweden*, 2 vols, Copenhagen.

Svedjemo, G. (2007), *Ontology as Conceptual Schema When Modelling Historical Maps for Database Storage*, Linköping.

Thunmark-Nylén, L. (1986), 'Hedningar, kristna och silverskatter', *GA* 58: 23–44.

Westholm, G. (1990), 'Visby – Bönders hamn och handelsplats: en efterskrift', *META: medeltidsarkeologisk tidskrift* 1990(3): 16–34.

Yrwing, H. (1978), *Gotlands medeltid*, Visby.

Zachrisson, T. (1998), *Gård, gräns, gravfält: sammanhang kring ädelmetalldepåer och runstenar från vikingatid och tidig medeltid i Uppland och Gästrikland*, SSA 15, Stockholm.

Part IV

Comparisons

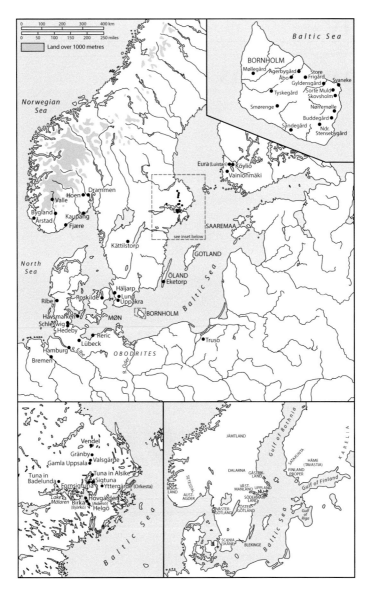

Map IV.1 Scandinavia.

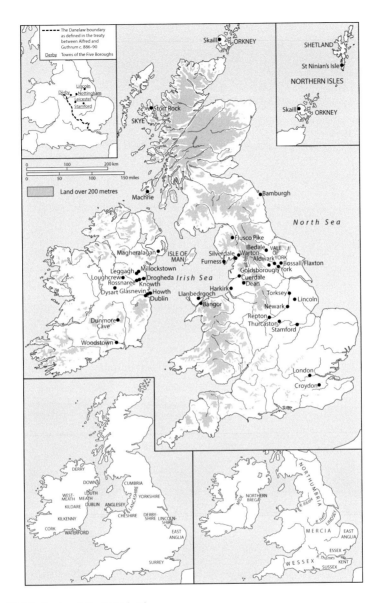

Map IV.2 Ireland and the British Isles.

16 Gotland viewed from the Swedish mainland

Ingmar Jansson

We often hear that 'Gotland is different', an island set apart by its nature, culture and history. This is true not least in the early and middle Viking Age, the focus of this chapter, when silver coins from the Islamic world were deposited there in larger numbers than anywhere else. And this affluence continued in the late Viking Age, when German and English coins replaced Islamic ones, and into the middle ages, when Gotlandic trade continued and Visby became a member of the Hanseatic League.[1] The difference between Gotland and the Swedish mainland is striking: 68,322 Islamic coins have been found on Gotland as against 13,820 on the mainland, excluding the 5,739 coins found on the island of Öland. There is no region of Gotland's size with a similar concentration of such coins.[2]

It seems clear that Gotland played an important role in the booming trade of the Viking Age. But how and why? It had no primary products of major importance, nor was its position in the middle of the Baltic an unmitigated advantage: in pre-modern times, water traffic tended to hug the coastline. For example, we have a thirteenth-century Danish description of the route from Blekinge to Estonia, both then in Danish hands. Known as 'King Valdemar's sailing route', it followed the Swedish coast northwards to Uppland, then went east via the Åland islands to the south coast of Finland before finally crossing the Gulf of Finland to Estonia. Of course, this was not the only route used between Denmark and Estonia, but it was a safe one, protected by archipelagos almost all the way.[3]

Viking-Age Gotland was part of the Scandinavian cultural area (see Map 16.1). This area was not homogeneous, but it was united by closely related North Germanic languages, a similar religion and, for example, stylised animal ornamentation. Within this area, Gotland shows the clearest differences, seen *inter alia* in women's jewellery. A common term for the Scandinavian cultural area excluding Gotland is 'mainland Scandinavia', which for the sake of convenience will be used here.

Gotland in the written sources

The first reasonably reliable source about the island is Wulfstan's account, included in the Old English translation of Orosius' *History* from the fifth

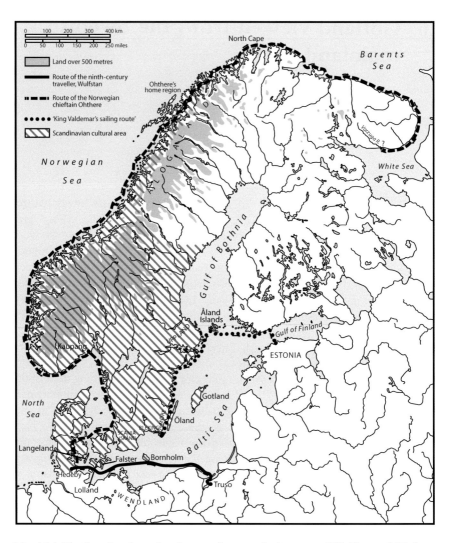

Map 16.1 The Scandinavian cultural area and routes: the journeys of Wulfstan and Ohthere, and 'King Valdemar's sailing route'.

century. The translation was commissioned by King Alfred of Wessex at the end of the ninth century, and has a description of northern Europe added to it which includes the accounts of two travellers: the Norwegian chieftain Ohthere, who sailed from northern Norway to the White Sea and south to Hedeby, and Wulfstan, probably an English trader, who journeyed from Hedeby to Truso, and said that:

> Wendland was on his starboard side, and on his port side were Langeland and Lolland and Falster and Skåne, and these lands are all subject (*or* belong) to Denmark [*hyrað to Denemearcan*]. And then the land of the *Burgendas* [Bornholm] was on our port side and they have their own king. Then after the land of the *Burgendas* there were on our port side these lands, which are called first island of the people of Blekinge and Möre and Øland [Öland] and Gotland [*Gotland*], and these lands are subject (*or* belong) to the Svear [*hyrað to Sweon*].[4]

This is virtually our only contemporary written source to mention Gotland in the early and middle Viking Age.[5] In the late Viking Age, runestones on the Scandinavian mainland record connections with Gotland. A man from Scania died there (DR 259) and another from Södermanland was killed on the island (Sö 174). One man from Uppland died at Boge on Gotland's east coast (U 375), while another two fell ill on the island – one 'when they took tribute' (**kialt**, *gjald*) (U 527; U 614) – and a picture stone was brought from Gotland to Uppland to serve as a memorial (U 414).[6] Some Gotlandic stones give us information about dealings overseas: a man died in the Dnieper rapids between Kiev and the Black Sea (G 280); another was 'betrayed' by *blakumen*, usually understood to be Vlachs to the west of the Black Sea, and his brother died **a: uitau**, perhaps at Ventspils (Windau) on the Latvian west coast (G 134; G 135); a fourth died in Novgorod (*Holmgardhr*) (G 220). We also have a trader, who 'sat in the south with skins' (**miþ: skinum**) and died at Ulvshale (probably a promontory on the island of Møn in Denmark) (G 207),[7] as well as a man killed by people from Lübeck (G 138).[8] Another stone records a man who 'had travelled to the west with *vikings*' (G 370), while a whetstone converted into a mould for casting simple ornaments has an intriguing inscription which suggests that two men, Ormika and Ulfhvatr [?], knew both the far west and the east: **krikiaʀ: iaursaliʀ (:) islat: serklat** (Greece [the Byzantine empire], Jerusalem, Iceland, Serkland [the Islamic world]) (G 216).[9]

Although the runic inscriptions offer clear evidence of Gotland's trading and military relations with the surrounding world in the eleventh century, neither the island nor its inhabitants appear in contemporary western or eastern sources. Most remarkable is Adam of Bremen's silence: written in the 1070s, his history of the archbishops of Hamburg-Bremen from the ninth century to his own time includes an extensive geographical description of the north.[10] Only from the twelfth century onwards does Gotland start to appear in Scandinavian as well as western and eastern sources. Among these late sources, some Norse narratives and one from Gotland itself deserve attention, because they refer to events in the Viking Age.

The former, written between the twelfth and fourteenth centuries, tell of four notable Norwegians who visited Gotland.[11] Three went there to raid or raise tribute: Olaf Tryggvason before he became king; the *jarl* Eric Hakonarson while in exile during Olaf Tryggvason's reign (995–1000); and Olaf Haraldsson (Saint Olaf) in his youth before becoming king in 1015, and again around 1030, on his return from exile in *Garðaríki* (Rus), receiving news from *Svía-veldi*, Denmark and Norway. The fourth was a relative of Olaf Haraldsson, Hallvard Vebjørnsson (Saint Hallvard), who visited the island as a merchant. Not the earliest but the best known of the Norse sources is Snorri Sturluson's *Heimskringla* composed around 1230. Included in his stories there are some stanzas of the court poets of Olaf Tryggvason, Eric Hakonarson and Olaf Haraldsson, which most researchers understand as genuine and therefore confirm some details in Snorri's stories. Olaf Tryggvason 'was dangerous to the life of the Gotar'; Eric Hakonarson 'had the coasts of Gotland raided far and wide'; and Olaf Haraldsson is praised for forcing 'the Gotland host to [pay] tribute (*at gjaldi*); the men did not dare to defend the nation's lands against you with the shield'.[12]

The Gotlandic source is *Guta Saga*, the earliest known history from eastern Scandinavia, probably composed in the thirteenth century and preserved as an attachment to *Guta Lag*, 'the Law of the Gotlanders'. In Chapter 2, before a story about Saint Olaf's missionary work on the island (not mentioned in Norse sources), we find:

> Many kings fought against Gotland while it was heathen; the Gotlanders [*gutar*], however, always held the victory and constantly protected their rights. Later the Gotlanders sent a large number of messengers to Sweden [*til Suiarikis*], but none of them could make peace before Avair Strabain of Alva parish. He made the first peace with the king of the Swedes [*suia kunung*] [...] Because he was wise and skilled in many things, just as the tales go about him, he entered into a binding treaty with the king of the Swedes. Sixty marks of silver in respect of each year is the Gotlanders' tax [*skattr*], divided so that the king of Sweden [*Suiarikis kunungr*] should have forty marks of silver out of the sixty, and the *jarl* twenty marks of silver [...] In this way, the Gotlanders submitted to the king of Sweden, of their own free will, in order that they might travel everywhere in Sweden [*Suiariki*] free and unhindered, exempt from toll and all other charges. Similarly the Swedes [*suiar*] also have the right to visit Gotland, without ban against trade in corn, or other prohibitions. The king was obliged to give the Gotlanders protection and assistance, if they should need it and request it. In addition the king, and likewise the *jarl*, should send messengers to the Gotlanders' general assembly [*gutnalþing*] and arrange for their tax to be collected there. The messengers in question

have a duty to proclaim the freedom of Gotlanders to visit all places overseas that belong to the king in Uppsala and, similarly, to such as have the right to travel here from that side.[13]

The Svear in the written sources

Thus the Svear are the first people to be mentioned in connection with Gotland, and the term appears in quite a few sources from early in the first millennium AD onwards. By the Viking Age, the name clearly refers to the people living in *Svethiudh*, 'the Svea people', the regions around Mälaren in east-central Sweden.[14]

Our first references to the Viking-Age Svear come from Frankish sources. The *Annales regni Francorum* mentions under the year 813 'Danish nobles who [...] had been in exile with the Swedes [*Sueones*]';[15] and in Einhard's *Life of Charlemagne*, written in the 830s, there is a description of 'an arm' of the 'Western Ocean' and the people living around this bay: 'The Danes [*Dani*] and the Swedes [*Sueones*], whom we call the Northmen [*Nortmanni*], occupy its northern shore and all its islands. The Slavs [*Sclavi*], the Esthonians [*Aisti*] and various other nations inhabit its southern shore'.[16]

The next mention is in the *Annales Bertiniani*, a continuation of the *Annales regni Francorum*. An embassy from the Byzantine emperor Theophilos travelled to the Frankish emperor Louis the Pious in 839. With them were 'some men who said they – meaning their whole people [*gens*] – were called Russians [*Rhos*] and had been sent to him by their king whose name was the Khagan [*Chaganus*] for the sake of friendship'. Theophilos asked Louis to arrange their journey home through his realm, because he did not want them to return via the dangerous route they had used to reach Constantinople. Louis found this story curious, and when he discovered that they belonged to the Svear (*gens Sueonum*), he suspected them of being spies and decided to detain them until he had established the truth.[17] This is the first well-dated mention of the *Rhos/Rus*, who appear in Byzantine and Islamic sources from the mid-ninth century onwards and later in East Slavic sources. Initially, the term seems to have referred to people from the north, later to the ruling class and the principality of Rus (*Rus'*), and finally also to the inhabitants of this realm more generally. It is commonly understood as stemming from the Balto-Finnic *Ruotsi/Rootsi*, the term for Svear/Swedes (now Sweden) which, in turn, seems to derive from the Old Swedish word *rodhr*, 'the act of rowing', a word which can also refer to 'a company of rowers' and 'a fairway or region characterised by rowing'. This has led to two interpretations of the ethnonym: that it refers to *vikings* and other seaborne groupings from the west, or to the coastal district of Uppland called *Roden* ('the *Rodhr*') in the middle ages and therefore to the Svear.[18]

It may seem strange that Louis was able to identify the *Rhos* as Svear, but an important background is found in our next Frankish source, *Vita Anskarii*. Here it is said that envoys from the Svear (*legati Sueonum*) came to Louis the

Pious and asked for priests, and Louis sent Ansgar, who had been on a mission to the Danes. Mid-journey, their ships were attacked by pirates (*pyratae*): Ansgar, his companion Witmar and the merchants travelling with them lost nearly everything. Forced to continue on foot, they finally reached a port of the Svea kingdom called Birka (*ad portum regni ipsorum, qui Birca dicitur*). Here they were received by the Svea king, Björn, who gave them permission to preach. Many were baptised, and Christian slaves who lived among them rejoiced at hearing God's word. Among the converted was Herigar, town prefect and king's counsellor (*praefectus vici et consiliarius regis*), who built a church on his ancestral property. After a year and a half Ansgar returned home and was appointed archbishop of a new see, Hamburg, with responsibility for the northernmost parts of the Frankish empire and for the Svear, Danes, Slavs and other peoples in the north. Another priest called Gauzbert was sent as bishop to the lands of the Svear (*ad partes* [...] *Sueonum*), where he was honourably received by the king and the people and built a church.[19]

All this happened around 830, but in the mid-840s things got worse. Hamburg was destroyed by pirates, and the Svea people became inflamed with fury, driving out Gauzbert and his companions.[20] In the early 850s Ansgar, now with his seat in Bremen, returned to Birka. The new king Olof gave Ansgar permission to resume his work only after the question had been approved by two assemblies (*placita*), one held at Birka and one in another part of the kingdom (*in altera parte regni*). Ansgar left a priest called Erimbert under the king's protection, and the king donated a plot in the town on which to build a chapel. The re-established Christian community seems to have still been in existence when Ansgar's successor Rimbert wrote *Vita Anskarii* in the 870s.[21]

Among the stories about Birka there is one mentioning a 'nearby fort', to which the inhabitants fled (*ad civitatem, quae iuxta erat, confugerunt*) when an exiled Svea king and Danes were approaching.[22] Another story, set in the years after Ansgar's second visit, concerns an expedition to the Curonians (*Cori*, living in present-day western Latvia and Lithuania), who 'had in former time been in subjection to the Swedes [*Sueonum principatui olim subiecta fuerat*], but had a long while since rebelled and refused to be in subjection'.[23] Knowing this, the Danes assemble a fleet and attack in order to plunder and subjugate the land. However, the Curonians gather in one of the five forts (*civitates*) of their kingdom (*regnum*), defeat the Danes and win gold, silver and rich spoils. When King Olof and the Svear learn of this, they collect a vast army and head to the Curonians' lands, capturing and plundering a town (*urbs*) called *Seeburg* before moving inland to another, *Apulia*. But here, both sides incur great losses and a stalemate is reached. Deeply distressed, the Svear cast lots and find their gods have deserted them. However, some merchants who remember Ansgar's teaching suggest that they should ask the Christian God for help. Again they cast lots and find Christ willing to come to their aid. Spirits revived, they attack *Apulia* once more and the Curonians soon sue for peace. They offer not only great riches, tribute (*census*) and hostages, but also to be subject to Svea rule (*imperium*) as before.[24]

Slightly later than Rimbert's *Vita Anskarii* is Wulfstan's account, mentioned above, but then we have around a century without contemporary written sources – if we set aside mentions of *Rhos/Rus*. However, Adam of Bremen, in his history of the Hamburg-Bremen archbishops, offers us some information about the tenth century, and one piece of information is generally deemed reliable: in 935–6 Archbishop Unni went to Birka, where with the king's consent he revived Ansgar's missionary work – and died.[25] From the 990s on a relatively large number of western sources mention the Svear and their kingdom, the most important of which is Adam of Bremen. Others include Scandinavian runic inscriptions from the late Viking Age, as well as silver coins struck in Sigtuna between around 995 and 1030 by Olof Skötkonung and Anund Jakob, calling themselves, *inter alia*, *REX AN SITUN*, 'king in Sigtuna', or *REX SWEVONUM*, 'king of the Svear'.[26] There are also many twelfth- and thirteenth-century Norse sources describing the Svear in the Viking Age, sometimes supported by skaldic poems. And, finally, we have an East Slavic source: the *Russian Primary Chronicle* from the early twelfth century, which under the year 862 tells how the *Rus'* – described as a Varangian tribe like the *Svie* (Svear) and *G"te* (Gutar) – were called in to rule by the 'Chuds, the Slavs, the Krivichians and the Ves".[27]

There are problems with all these sources. Ohthere's and Wulfstan's accounts are generally regarded as very reliable, as also is *Vita Anskarii*.[28] Still, the question stands: how much of Rimbert's information about Birka and the Svear is trustworthy? We can probably rely on the general outline,[29] but what about the many details in his description of Birka and the Svear? Could it be that his description is based not so much on factual knowledge as on general ideas about life among northern peoples? How should Latin terms such as *vicus*, *civitas*, *urbs* and *praefectus* be understood? It is also important to understand Wulfstan's words that Blekinge, Möre, Öland and Gotland '*hyrað to Sweon*'. He could be suggesting that these regions were dominated in some way by the Svear, but also that they were inhabited by people whom Wulfstan understood to be Svear.[30] I prefer the former interpretation: Wulfstan distinguishes the people of Bornholm as having their own king, which makes it reasonable to think that he had some sort of Svea dominion in mind.

Gotland: a tributary land of the Svea king?

According to *Guta Saga*, at their own initiative the Gotlanders had already reached agreement to pay a yearly tax to the Svea king and *jarl* in the pre-Christian period. Many accept this at face value, and Nils Blomkvist has advanced a general theory that in a transition from chiefdom to state, 'natural units' become integrated into 'multiregional polities' led by one of the constituent 'peers'. In northern Europe this occurs during the Viking Age, where a variant which Blomkvist terms 'network polities' emerges, organised

> along a system of sea and river routes, which are opening up for trade exchange between major civilisations, which would allow them access to the commodity flow with merchants visiting their emporia [...] The need for protecting trading centres and keeping sea lanes open and foreign merchants safe would be important causes for the formation of such a polity [...] the aim of military manifestations would be to establish, maintain or restore political control, rather than purely predatory activities.[31]

Blomkvist suggests that such 'network polities' typify the regions along the Russian riverways and around the Baltic from *c.* 800 onwards as a result of the expansion in long-distance trade and the emergence of proto-towns. The Norwegian kingdom and its *skattland* (tributary lands) in the late Viking Age and early middle ages exemplifies one such network; so does 'a Swedish network polity in the early Viking Age', Blomkvist argues, using the information given by *Vita Anskarii*, Wulfstan's account, the runestone U 614 (commemorating a man who fell ill 'when they took tribute on Gotland') and *Guta Saga*. He hints at the emergence of Rus being connected with the Svea-dominated polity, and sees the agreement between the Svear and the Curonians recorded in *Vita Anskarii* as 'the outline of a "skattland" contract from the 850s'.

There have been critical voices against interpretations of this kind. Peter Sawyer contends that *Guta Saga* should be seen as describing the situation in the thirteenth century and as wishful thinking about the past; even Ohthere's and Wulfstan's information about the Svear 'cannot be relied on'.[32] Sawyer also cautions against reliance on philological and archaeological sources to argue for a strong Svea realm, noting that: 'Linguistic and cultural unity did not imply political unity in Scandinavia any more than it did in England or Ireland'.[33] Such caution is prudent. After all, the Uppland runestone does not necessarily refer to regular tribute payments agreed between the Gotlanders and the Svea kingdom. It may equally well refer to an adventure similar to those of Olaf Tryggvason, Eric Hakonarson and Olaf Haraldsson: the latter was paid off by the Gotlanders with tribute. However, the sources adduced by Blomkvist could be hints of political organisation, especially if supported by philological and archaeological evidence.

Birka and Svea society

Birka can be identified with the settlement on the island of Björkö in Mälaren. We know of no other harbour in eastern Sweden with such wide-ranging trade in the early and middle Viking Age. There is evidence of smaller-scale crafts and exchange at several other sites, but the only places with more extensive traces are Helgö, 10km south-east of Birka, and Gamla Uppsala.[34]

Birka was a large (proto-)urban settlement surrounded by defence structures and burial grounds which existed during the early and middle Viking Age. It probably owed its foundation to some form of political power, and artefact finds offer ample evidence of crafts, as well as local and long-distance exchange with east and west. Eastern contacts were dominant in the later phases. The hillfort, mentioned in *Vita Anskarii*, shows no signs of having been inhabited, but in the final phase of Birka's existence there was a garrison outside its northern entrance: a large hall on an artificial terrace, it housed a group of warriors whose leader must have been a man of importance appointed by the king.[35]

Important source material comes from the graves, of which more than 1,100 have been excavated. The majority are cremations in mounds, usually of fairly standard size and with a burial rite similar to that found in the surrounding countryside but often with richer grave goods. There are also an unusually large number of inhumations, many in wooden chambers with exceptionally rich grave goods indicating high social status and long-distance connections. In the mid-Viking Age, men's garments often included elements which seem to imitate the ranking system at the imperial Byzantine court. This would indicate that they held positions in the retinue of the Svea king (Figure 16.1).[36]

The royal seat was obviously at Hovgården on the island of Adelsö, 3km north of Birka. Established at an early stage of Birka's existence (or earlier), the royal residence continued to be used several centuries after Birka was abandoned. It was located on a headland with a hall on the top (hidden by a thirteenth-century royal palace) and terraces for various kinds of buildings. The harbour was secured by defensive structures in the water (yet to be dated). The complex also features four big mounds and a '*Thing* mound' (a low, circular platform, not excavated). One big mound has been excavated, revealing an unusually rich, tenth-century cremation grave. To one side of the harbour there is a rune-inscribed boulder from the eleventh century (U 11), the only Swedish runestone mentioning a king: it was ordered for the king by Tolir, 'steward in *Rodhr* (**bry[t]i: i roþ**)'.[37] From the year 1200 on there is written evidence that Hovgården was the centre of a royal estate.[38]

It should be noted that Rimbert always speaks about 'the king of the Svear' (*rex Sueonum*). This and other expressions cited above indicate a larger realm than Birka. As I see it, the kingdom most probably embraced *Svethiudh* in the early and middle Viking Age and at times it had tributary lands, as Nils Blomkvist has suggested. The king no doubt had several manors besides Hovgården, including Gamla (Old) Uppsala some 4km north of Mälaren's northernmost bay in the Viking Age. *Ubsola* is mentioned by Adam of Bremen as a *templum nobilissimum*, where sacrifices were still performed in his time, sacrifices in which people from all provinces of *Sueonia* were obliged to

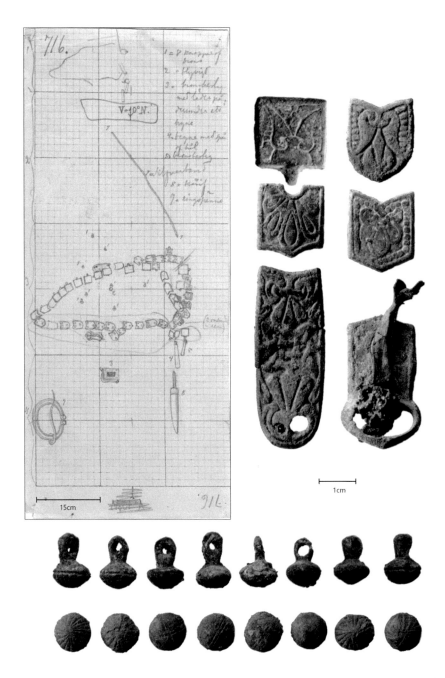

Figure 16.1 Inhumation grave at Birka (Bj 716) excavated by Hjalmar Stolpe in 1879: the man was buried in oriental-style dress decorated with silk, gold and silver wire – a tablet-woven silver braid is shown (7) on the plan above left; bronze buttons (1 and illustration bottom); bronze mounted belt with floral ornaments (illustration top right) and hanging purse (mount 3); a lead weight (2); and a Baltic-style penannular brooch with partial silver plating for his cloak (9).

Drawing: Hjalmar Stolpe (left), courtesy of ATA; photos: Nils Lagergren, SHM, courtesy of ATA.

participate.[39] Twelfth- and thirteenth-century Norse sources describe Uppsala as the ancient and most important royal seat, cult- and assembly place of the Svear, as well as the place of a winter market. It is also mentioned in various skaldic poems understood to be from around the year 1000 and later, as well as in *Ynglingatal*, a poem of disputed age about the Ynglinga kings of the Svear. In the early twelfth century Uppsala became a bishopric and, in 1164, the seat of the archbishop of Sweden, although it transferred to present-day Uppsala at the river mouth a hundred years later. The winter market at Gamla Uppsala is in all likelihood the one that was later held at Uppsala. Its name was Distingen, 'the assemblies of the goddesses *Diser*', revealing the market's pre-Christian roots as well as its connection with religious rites and assemblies. This was the most important market in medieval Sweden, with northern products such as iron and skins among the traded goods.[40]

All these written sources are problematic when it comes to defining Uppsala's role in the early and middle Viking Age.[41] However, archaeology shows that Gamla Uppsala was a site of exceptional importance long before the Viking Age. It was 'monumentalised' in the sixth and seventh centuries, when impressive burial mounds, plateaus and alignments of wooden posts were constructed. There is also an imposing '*Thing* mound' of uncertain age. On one of the plateaus stood a ceremonial hall some 50m in length, while on another were workshops. Although no monumental Viking-Age constructions have yet been found, settlement remains and graves show continued occupation, with crafts and exchange remaining important activities.[42]

There are many other sites around Mälaren with impressive grave mounds and settlement structures indicating the presence of a social elite. Fornsigtuna is a site closely resembling Hovgården and recorded as a royal manor from the 1170s on.[43] Other sites worth mentioning are the boat-grave cemeteries on the northern side of Mälaren, the best known being Valsgärde, 3km north of Gamla Uppsala, and Vendel, 30km further upstream. Some fifteen men were interred in boats in both places, richly equipped like the Birka chamber graves. The graves are spread in time from the early Vendel period to the late Viking Age – they seem to represent the leaders of two families with some sort of duty through fifteen generations.[44]

We face major problems interpreting these sites, since medieval characteristics do not necessarily indicate their function in the Viking Age. Distinguishing between kings and other kinds of chieftains and understanding their roles is also tricky.[45] However, the idea that the Mälar provinces of Uppland, Västmanland and Södermanland formed a more stable kingdom in the early and middle Viking Age gains support from their administrative divisions. By the middle ages, the smallest jurisdictional districts were called *hundari* throughout the three provinces, with the exception of Roden (the *Rodhr*, the coastal district of Uppland), where they were called *skiplagh*. Since the term *hundari* originally meant 'a host of a hundred men', and *skiplagh* meant 'a group responsible for a ship', both

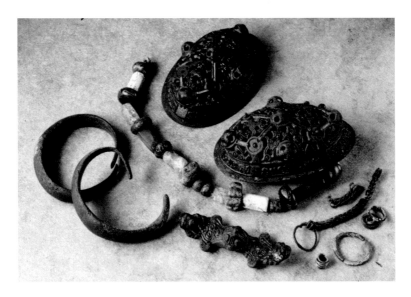

Figure 16.2 A characteristic set of middle Viking-Age female jewellery from mainland Scandinavia found in cremation grave no. 9, Gränby, Ärentuna parish, Uppland: two
oval brooches (*c.* 11cm in length), an equal-armed brooch (8.5cm), two arm-
rings, chain fragments and four small rings (all bronze); twenty-three beads,
mostly of glass but including a silver wire bead and eight prism-shaped ones
(three rock crystal, three white-burnt cornelian and two unburnt cornelian).

Courtesy of SHM; photo: Nils Lagergren, RAÄ-SHM, courtesy of ATA.

were obviously also used for the *ledung* (the naval levy).[46] An Uppland runestone
from the mid-eleventh century (U 212) mentions a man who 'made this
assembly place (**þinkstaþ**), and alone owned all this *hundari* (**hu-tari**)',[47] giving
us a *terminus ante quem* for the institution. Most probably its origins go back
considerably earlier, because place names have preserved an earlier term for these
districts: *hund*.[48] All of this implies a Svea realm comprising at least most of the
Mälar provinces in the earlier centuries. This does not mean that this realm was
always stable; that there was no competition between leaders on different levels.
But the source material seems to indicate that Svea society was characterised by
a considerable degree of continuity.

Gotland and Guta society

If we turn to Gotland, we find a very different picture. There is no place of
similar calibre to Birka, but instead a number of important harbours with trading
settlements spread along the coasts. The ninth and tenth centuries had a special
character: a transition between the earlier centuries, when we have only vague
indications of exchange at coastal harbours, and the eleventh and twelfth

centuries, when Visby developed into a significant town before becoming a member of the Hanseatic League. Other places such as Västergarn and Fröjel flourished for some time, but failed to keep pace with this development.

The most complex situation in the ninth and tenth centuries was probably that at Visby. There are several indications of harbour settlements and burial grounds both inside the medieval town wall and on the coast to the north and south. Of special interest here is the large cemetery at Kopparsvik south of the town where more than 330 graves have been excavated.[49] It has two distinct zones, with a mixed area in between: the northern zone is (almost) exclusively male, with often quite disorderly graves; the southern zone has both men and women. The two are of roughly equal size and date mainly to the tenth century, although the latest graves are early eleventh century and stray finds indicate that the burial ground was first used in the early Viking Age. The graves are entirely inhumations, which is almost unique on Gotland: burial grounds of this period usually contain a significant number of cremations.

Grave goods indicate that those buried in the southern zone were Gotlanders. There are some female brooches and other artefacts of mainland Scandinavian types, but in no case is there a full set of such brooches. Similar finds are known from a number of other places on Gotland, most of them in the vicinity of harbours.[50] Rather than indicating true mainland Scandinavians, they seem to indicate people with links to the Scandinavian world outside Gotland. It is more difficult to determine the origin of the men buried in the northern zone, since male outfits tend to be more 'international'. But in both zones, finds in the male graves are practically the same, with the exception that weapons are only found in the southern zone.

Two features should be highlighted: filed teeth and burial in prone position. Known from several places in the western Baltic, including Birka, and only found on male individuals, filed teeth are most commonly seen on Gotland, particularly in the northern zone of Kopparsvik. Burial in prone position, a rite spread in many cultures, is also especially common in the northern zone. Thirteen individuals with filed teeth or buried in prone position have undergone strontium isotope analysis, which revealed that three were probably from Gotland (two with filed teeth, one in prone position) while the others had grown up elsewhere.[51] The northern zone at Kopparsvik is, as far as I know, the only Scandinavian burial ground of this size to contain (almost) only men. All this, together with burial close to the shore, indicates that the people at Kopparsvik represent a specialised group of travellers: Gotlanders as well as foreigners.

The other harbour of special interest here is situated on the shore of Paviken, previously a lagoon-like bay and now an inland lake north of 'the town of Västergarn', a site with cultural layers from the early middle ages which seem to represent a town foundation that failed. There are several indications of early harbours around Paviken and one of them, Paviken I, is

Figure 16.3 A characteristic set of middle Viking-Age Gotlandic female jewellery from inhumation grave no. 18, Kopparsvik, south of Visby: two animal-head brooches (2–3),
a box-shaped brooch (1), a tool brooch (11) with chain for suspension of various
tools (12; there are places for five chains), a dress pin (4; usually a pair), three typical
Gotlandic pendants (6–8; sieve-shaped, spoon-shaped, tongue-shaped), an armring
(9), all of bronze although one with silver details (1) and one with gilding (8);
a silver coin (5; Roman *denarius*) turned into a pendant; fourteen beads (10), mostly
of glass but including two of amber, one of silver with filigree and one cubo-
octahedral of bronze.

Courtesy of Gotland Museum; photos: RAÄ; reproduced after *WKG*, vol. 1, Abb. 335a,
courtesy of Lena Thunmark-Nylén/ATA.

much discussed.[52] It consists of a 'productive' cultural layer, around 130m by 100m wide, at the mouth of the river Idån. An important part of the site was a boatyard. Other activities included iron working, the crafting of jewellery and antler objects, such as bronze pendants, glass beads, amber- and garnet-decorated ornaments and combs, and probably also large-scale preparation of hides and fleeces.[53] Trade is indicated by a large number of coins (with few exceptions, dirhams and mostly small fragments), hack-silver, weights and fragments of scales.

Who were the people living and working at Paviken I? Firstly, the site was clearly dominated by men. There are practically no indications of women or typically female crafts like textile production, although one or two of the excavated graves do seem to belong to women. The finds of female bronze jewellery should, in most cases, be interpreted as traces of jewellery production: two pendants have unperforated loops and are thus unfinished, and many fragments obviously represent scrap metal for use when casting new ornaments. Furthermore, many of the 200-odd beads as well as mosaic *tesserae* and glass waste are connected with bead production.

Secondly, there are few definite traces of Gotlandic culture and Gotlanders. It seems clear instead that at least some people came from mainland Scandinavia. The strongest indication of this is the graves. Directly connected with the settlement are around fifteen simple stone settings, five of which have been excavated. All contained cremations.[54] The most striking finds are the many boat rivets found in three graves. They either indicate that the dead had been cremated lying in a boat, or that boats or parts of boats had been used to build the funeral pyre. This is a burial rite probably unknown from other sites on Gotland,[55] but common in practically all other parts of Scandinavia, including among the 'Scandinavian diaspora' in western and eastern Europe. The richest grave contained a female outfit with Birka parallels. The two unfinished pendants mentioned above belong to mainland Scandinavian types, as do the beads.[56] They should therefore represent craft activities and goods for export.

Per Lundström first interpreted the site as a Svea emporium but later suggested that it was the central harbour for a district on Gotland. Lena Thunmark-Nylén has returned to Lundström's first interpretation, which could well be correct even if finds clearly pointing towards the Mälar region are not so numerous.[57] I would like to add that many of the craftsmen were probably Gotlanders who worked here temporarily and sold their products to travellers from mainland Scandinavia.[58]

That Paviken I was in use during the early and middle Viking Age is clear from the artefact finds, not least from the many weights found there. Half of these belong to types common in the early Viking Age, the other half to the standardised oblate spheroid and cubo-octahedral types of the middle and late Viking Age.[59] The activities ended around or soon after 1000, as indicated by an English coin from 991–7.[60]

Trade and crafts are not restricted to the coastal harbours on Gotland, but are spread throughout the island to a remarkable degree. This has long been obvious from accidental finds, but became clearer after Majvor Östergren's large-scale metal-detecting campaigns and trial excavations on silver hoard find sites. Twenty-five of the eighty-one inland sites investigated by Östergren up to 1989 yielded weights, mostly of the standardised types. More than forty places with weight finds are now known on Gotland. Indications of bronze, lead and iron working were found on more than half of Östergren's sites, and a few showed signs of silversmithing.[61] One important site investigated after 1989 is Guldåkern in Roma parish in the very centre of Gotland, where 429 weights have been found, mostly of the standardised types mentioned above. Other finds are 285 Viking-Age silver coins, mostly dirhams and mostly small fragments, as well as hack-silver and traces of bronze, silver and gold working. Written sources and place names suggest this was the site of Gotland's general assembly, *Gutnalthing*, and the site clearly functioned as a market, probably in connection with its legal role.[62]

Most scholars believe that *Guta Lag* and *Guta Saga* give a fair idea of Guta society in the Viking Age: no king or other kind of ruler and no explicit hierarchy among the farmers. Many Gotlandic merchants were *farmannabönder* ('travelling farmers'), based on their farms. The only known office was that of *domare* ('judge') who presided at the various *Thing*s. There are no signs of manors such as the ones found in the Mälar provinces. There are graves that stand out as unusually rich and comparable to elite graves in mainland Scandinavia, for example at Broe, situated south of the *Gutnalthing*, and Slite, probably related to harbours around Bogeviken.[63] But a more salient fact is the general richness of Gotlandic graves. There are no big mounds or other prominent burial structures.

Gotland is in many ways more akin to mainland Finland and the eastern Baltic, where graves often show general affluence and it is difficult to pinpoint individual burial grounds or graves as belonging to a higher level of a social hierarchy. Examples include the remarkable inhumation cemeteries in the parishes of Eura and Köyliö in Satakunta;[64] the ordinary, but unusually rich, cremation cemetery at Vainionmäki in Laitila, Finland Proper;[65] and the cremation cemeteries on the island of Saaremaa in Estonia.[66]

Gutar and Svear around the Baltic

There are many traces of Guta and Svea connections with the Baltic region in the early and middle Viking Age. The former are easier to trace, given the distinctiveness of many Gotlandic artefacts, and are known on practically all shores of the Baltic – usually not in large numbers, but enough to indicate contacts.[67] They are almost always in places where mainland Scandinavian finds have also been made. The largest number of Gotlandic artefacts comes from the south-eastern Baltic: between the Gulfs of Riga and Gdańsk.[68]

A noteworthy place is Grobiṇa (Grobin), situated on a small river in Latvian Curonia about 10km from the sea with a lagoon-like lake in between. Three burial grounds containing cremations with Gotlandic and mainland Scandinavian artefacts from the seventh to the ninth centuries were excavated by Birger Nerman in 1929-30: two with mounds (one large with *c.* 430 registered mounds and one small, totalling thirty-two excavated mounds); and one in a ploughed field without any preserved superstructures (114 excavated graves). Between the burial grounds lies a hillfort with adjacent open settlements. About 44km south-east of Grobiṇa there is a larger, more impressive hillfort at Apuolė in Lithuanian Curonia, generally identified with the *Apulia* mentioned in *Vita Anskarii*. Nerman excavated here in 1931, and the most remarkable finds were the many arrowheads of Scandinavian Viking-Age type on the outer slope of the rampart. Nerman concluded that Grobiṇa was *Seeburg* ('the sea or lake fort') mentioned in *Vita Anskarii*, and that it had been founded as a Svea garrison and had developed into a town where Gutar were active as merchants. He interpreted the mound burial grounds as belonging to the Svear and the one without superstructures to the Gutar.[69]

Nerman's writings have had a strong influence on our understanding of Scandinavian–Baltic relations. His identification of Grobiṇa with *Seeburg* is plausible in many ways; and the numerous Scandinavian arrowheads found at Apuolė seem to confirm *Vita Anskarii*'s story – although they could also be the result of other Scandinavian assaults. Nevertheless, many of Nerman's interpretations are open to question.[70] He had a strong belief in the historicity of the Old English poem 'Beowulf' and the Norse sagas mentioning mighty Svea kings: these written sources, together with *Vita Anskarii*, formed the basis for his interpretations of Grobiṇa. He worked these out in the early 1930s and held to them in his later years. It should be noted that Vendel- and Viking-Age archaeological material was much better known for the Mälar region and Gotland than for southern Scandinavia when he was first writing, and that Birka and Hedeby were the only Scandinavian parallels to Grobiṇa readily to hand. It seems strange that Nerman did not consider the eastern Baltic parallels, for example Apuolė, although they are better ones: unlike Birka and Hedeby, their hillforts were to a large extent inhabited.[71]

Nerman's ideas about a strong and stable Svea kingdom, already covering large parts of the Swedish mainland as well as Gotland and Curonia in the early Vendel Period, have been strongly criticised, although somewhat similar interpretations have also been put forward in recent years.[72] Further, his identification of Gutar and Svear as two separate groups in Grobiṇa's population cannot be upheld. None of the female graves contains a complete set of either Gotlandic or mainland Scandinavian jewellery. Excavations undertaken after Nerman have revealed typically Gotlandic elements in the large mound burial ground, the most remarkable find being a picture stone of early Vendel-Period type.[73] Nerman did not discuss the possibility that the mainland Scandinavian elements were connected with Scandinavian regions further to the south, and he underestimated the Baltic elements in Grobiņa's culture. Besides typically Baltic artefacts, it can be noted that the Scandinavian jewellery partly represents local variants unknown on Gotland and elsewhere in Scandinavia (Figure 16.4).[74]

The selection of artefacts to accompany the dead in the graves corresponds largely to Gotlandic and mainland Scandinavian traditions. However, deposition of the cremated remains in a pit, used in all three burial grounds, is known on Gotland but very seldom found in other parts of Scandinavia in the Vendel and Viking periods. Burial under flat ground is characteristic neither of Gotland nor of mainland Scandinavia. As a rule, the burial grounds are characterised by mounds or low, mound-like stone settings (and on Gotland, practically only stone settings are found). When superstructures are missing, one can usually suspect that they have been cleared away during farming activities.[75] This may also be the case at Grobiņa. Nerman's findings do not contain any clear indications of trade. His interpretation of the Gutar as merchants is obviously based on a preconceived idea of Gotland's role in the Baltic.

The fieldwork conducted after Nerman is only partly published. Several burial grounds with similar finds are known in the region. Excavations have been undertaken in the hillfort at Grobiņa. The thick cultural layer shows that it was in use long before and after the 'Scandinavian phase' (i.e. *c.* seventh to ninth centuries), and Scandinavian artefacts are not prominent.[76] One grave in

1cm

Figure 16.4 Early Viking-Age female bronze brooches from cremation grave no. III in the cemetery without any preserved superstructures at Grobiņa, Latvia: two beak-shaped brooches and a box-shaped brooch, the beak-shaped brooches and per-haps also the box-shaped brooch representing local eastern Baltic variants.

Courtesy of The National History Museum of Latvia, Riga; photo: Hulda Andersson, SHM, courtesy of ATA.

the large mound burial ground has yielded fragments of two dirhams from 816–22. There are also four hoards with dirhams and one more grave with a single dirham known from the Grobiņa region.[77] Thus indications of international exchange seem to appear at the end of, or perhaps after, the 'Scandinavian phase'. Grobiņa was obviously not an emporium of the kind we know from, for example, Birka.[78] It seems rather to represent an immigration of Gotlanders and other Scandinavians – why and how is still an open question.

If we move south to the region of Elbląg in the Polish part of Baltic Prussia, we find a comparable but more complex situation (Map 16.2). One burial ground with cremation pits at Pole Nowomiejskie (Elbing-Neustädterfeld) has yielded a similar blend of Gotlandic, mainland Scandinavian and local artefacts, including local variants of mainland Scandinavian and Gotlandic jewellery. It seems reasonable to think that there are Prussian influences behind some aspects of Grobiņa's burial traditions, for instance cremation pits. Other sites in the Elbląg region have also yielded Scandinavian and Scandinavian-like finds.[79]

Wulfstan's geographical information makes it clear that his destination, Truso, was situated at Elbląg, and in the 1980s a settlement was found that in all probability is the place: Janów Pomorski, 7km south-east of Pole Nowomiejskie.[80] This is clearly an emporium of international significance: a large, 'productive' settlement with numerous finds of Scandinavian type as well as coins, scales, weights and other artefacts indicating long-distance connections in the early and middle Viking Age. Mainland Scandinavian artefacts are prominent but not Gotlandic ones.[81] Oriental artefacts (cornelian and rock crystal beads, belt mounts) have parallels at Birka but hardly any on Gotland.[82]

About 100km north-east of Elbląg, near Mokhovoe (Wiskiauten) on the Sambian peninsula in Kaliningrad *oblast'*, there is a well-known burial ground in Kaup forest. A prominent part consists of ordinary-sized mounds from the early and, above all, middle Viking Age, many with artefacts of Scandinavian type but also of local type.[83] Most of the mounds cover cremations, sometimes with the remains deposited in a pit, but usually spread as a layer. This, together with the inventory of the richest mounds, gives the burial ground a stronger Scandinavian character than those at Grobiņa and Elbląg. The finds are mostly of mainland Scandinavian character, but Gotlandic types are also represented. For example, two female graves have a pair of oval brooches combined with a box brooch and a tool brooch of Gotlandic type.[84]

Birger Nerman, who undertook excavations in Kaup forest in 1932, interpreted the site as a Svea colony, an opinion usually taken up by later researchers.[85] The interpretation may come close to the truth, although it is difficult, as usual, to single out definite 'Svea' elements, and there are also south Scandinavian elements. Coins, scales and weights have been found in a number of graves from the middle Viking Age. Several years of geophysical investigations and excavations around Kaup have revealed settlement remains from the 'Scandinavian phase'. Some finds indicate crafts, including amber

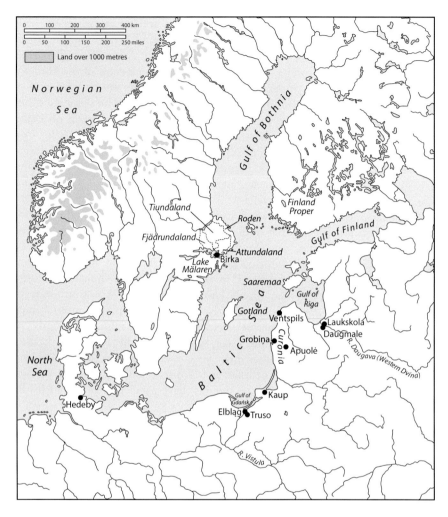

Map 16.2 Some find spots around the Baltic.

working, and at least one artefact is of Scandinavian type. However, Mokhovoe was obviously not an emporium as earlier believed, but a site with a minor role in international exchange.[86]

Mention must be made of the 'Prussian phenomenon'. There is a remarkable concentration of early dirham hoards and single finds of dirhams at Truso and elsewhere in Baltic Prussia. But no hoard has a *tpq* of later than 828, and no dirhams (or other contemporary coins) are later than the 850s. Nevertheless, there are many finds of scales and weights of the standardised mid-Viking-Age types, generally understood as used for weighing precious metal. There are similar discrepancies in other places and areas, but the Prussian phenomenon is the most extreme and hardest to understand. How could a place like Truso – and Baltic Prussia as a whole – be so different in its attitude to silver?[87]

The Daugava (Western Dvina), which empties into the Gulf of Riga, has no doubt been used for long-distance communications through the ages, but it seems that it only developed into a prominent trade route in the tenth century. There are single finds of mainland Scandinavian artefacts dated to the late Vendel and early Viking Age along the river, including two small oval brooches of late Vendel-Period types strongly connected with the Mälar region and Åland.[88] When we come to the late tenth and early eleventh century we find many graves with the characteristic blend of mainland Scandinavian, Gotlandic and Gotlandic-like artefacts, the former being most numerous. The graves have rich inventories dominated by local artefacts, and as a rule the western artefacts should be taken to indicate western contacts rather than buried westerners. However, one female grave has a complete set of Gotlandic jewellery, although none has a complete mainland Scandinavian set. The largest cemetery with Scandinavian artefacts (and with the complete Gotlandic set) is Salaspils Laukskola about 30km up the river. A hillfort with adjacent open settlements situated on the opposite bank, Daugmale, can be characterised as an emporium in the late Viking Age.[89]

On Gotland itself there are finds from mainland Scandinavia, Finland and the eastern Baltic. Graves with mainland Scandinavian female jewellery can usually best be explained as indicating mainland Scandinavian connections, as discussed above. The same goes, with one exception, for jewellery of eastern Baltic types. A remarkable find of eastern Baltic (mostly Curonian) bronze jewellery is the large hoard of scrap metal found in association with the silver hoards from Spillings. Eastern Baltic artefacts have also been found in mainland Scandinavia, mostly eastern Sweden.[90]

An important feature concerning the non-Gotlandic bronze jewellery found on Gotland is that many finds, like the Spillings hoard, obviously represent scrap metal, collected by craftsmen for casting new ornaments, and others are well-preserved, unfinished ornaments: the pin attachment of several brooches and the suspension loop of several pendants, in both cases of mainland Scandinavian types, have not been bored through, meaning that they cannot have been used (cf. above, p. 329). These pieces were obviously kept by the craftsmen as models for casting new ornaments. There are also two Baltic-type dress pins where the suspension loop has not been bored through. The known number of unfinished ornaments is large in comparison with the number of finished ornaments on Gotland, implying that the island's craftsmen made jewellery for sale to people living on both sides of the Baltic.[91]

Pottery is important for considering Gotland's contacts overseas. Scandinavian pottery – both mainland Scandinavian and Gotlandic – is coarse and simple. Foreign pottery of better quality is known, especially in southern but also in eastern Scandinavia, where Helgö and Birka stand out as the richest places with ceramics from the west, south and east.[92] Western finds are small in number but varied, with examples known from Uppland beyond Birka and Helgö, and one from Gotland.[93] A larger group comes from the Slavic regions to the south of the Baltic, with some finds in the Mälar region and Östergötland, as well as in Paviken I and the old town of Visby on Gotland.[94] A third group is Balto-Finnic ware, usually of high quality, characteristic of Finland, Estonia and partly also Latvia, with finds spread across Åland to the Mälar provinces and Gästrikland, but not to the south and not to Gotland.[95] Considerable efforts have been made to establish the origin of individual pots with laboratory analysis, and there are indications that some Slavic and Balto-Finnic pots were produced locally in eastern Scandinavia, presumably by potters coming from the south and east.[96]

Gutar and Svear beyond the Baltic

Gotlandic artefacts from the early Viking Age seem to be totally lacking further east, and artefacts from the mid-Viking Age are extremely few and seem to date from a late part of the period. A simple animal-head brooch comes from Staraia Ladoga (similar to Figure 16.3, no. 2), and a pseudo-penannular brooch, originally quite magnificent, from a Finnic cemetery near Murom in the Upper Volga basin (Figure 16.5). The first is a female brooch, the latter a male brooch. A third find is the well-known sword from a rich cremation grave in one of the biggest mounds at Gnezdovo on the Upper Dnieper (Figure 16.6). The sword blade is of ordinary type, perhaps from western Europe, but the hilt is decorated with animal and other ornaments with close parallels to Gotlandic female jewellery. The find association with an oval brooch and an equal-armed brooch indicates that those buried in the mound had connections with eastern mainland Scandinavia. Where the owner acquired the sword cannot be determined.[97]

In contrast, mainland Scandinavian artefacts are abundant, found in settlements, graves and hoards throughout the lands of Rus – in political and economic centres and also in some rural regions. Most finds must have belonged to migrants or immigrants from mainland Scandinavia, or to individuals closely connected with people from that area, and a closer study of the artefact types, selection of grave goods and burial rites indicates especially close connections with the Mälar provinces and surrounding

Figure 16.5 Middle Viking-Age pseudo-penannular bronze brooch from the Podbolot'e cemetery near Murom in the Upper Volga region (*c.* 9cm diameter): the two empty square frames on the hoop and the empty frame on the rhomboid plate above the pin would probably have contained filigree decoration.

Courtesy of Murom History and Art Museum; photos: bought from Eerik Laid in 1929, courtesy of ATA.

regions, including Åland. For example, iron amulets such as Thor's hammer rings are characteristic of the Mälar area but very rare on Gotland.[98] The easternmost finds of Scandinavian artefacts come from Volga Bulgaria and thereabouts, and an equal-armed brooch from the mid-Viking Age found in Bulgar (of the same type as in Figure 16.2) is especially characteristic of eastern Sweden.[99] It should be noted that artefacts from mainland Finland are more common in eastern Europe than are Gotlandic artefacts.[100]

When we turn to artefacts of eastern origin found in Scandinavia, Gotland is remarkably poor in those of materials other than silver.[101] For example, glass and cornelian beads of oriental origin (i.e. from the eastern parts of the caliphate and adjacent regions) dating from the very beginning of the Viking Age are known from northern Iran and the Caucasus, from around the Don, the Middle Volga and the Kama, as well as from Staraia Ladoga, Åland, the Mälar region and a few other places in Scandinavia, but not from Gotland. Later cornelian and rock crystal beads of oriental origin form a conspicuous element in finds from the early and middle Viking Age in Rus and mainland Scandinavia, especially the Mälar region and Åland, but on Gotland they date with few exceptions to the late Viking Age and the twelfth century, when such beads were not worn any longer in mainland Scandinavia. Before then, Gotlanders very much stuck to beads produced on the island.[102]

Other finds are oriental belts characteristic of the eastern caliphal lands, the Eurasian steppes and Volga Bulgaria, richly decorated with bronze or sometimes silver mounts. Such belt fittings appear in the Baltic region in the early Viking

Figure 16.6 The middle Viking-Age Gnezdovo sword (length 92cm), with Gotlandic animal
ornamentation on the gilt bronze hilt.

Courtesy of Smolensk State Museum-Preserve; photo: Sergei I. Kainov.

Age, and in the middle Viking Age they form a conspicuous element in Rus, Åland and eastern Sweden. From Gotland, only two mid-Viking-Age mounts are known to me: from Paviken I and the harbour at Bandlunde on the east coast. But again, the picture changes in the late Viking Age and the twelfth century – when such belts become more numerous on Gotland than anywhere else around the Baltic. There is also evidence that oriental belt mounts were now being produced on the island.[103]

Finally, some words about pottery. Among the Slavic slow wheel-turned pottery there seem to be not only West Slavic vessels from the southern Baltic but also some East Slavic vessels from north-west Rus, found at Birka and dated to the mid-Viking Age. No such pottery is known on Gotland.[104] Handmade pottery of so-called Ladoga-type, characteristic of north-western Rus, has also been found at Birka and some other places in Uppland and on Åland.[105] And a Volga Bulgar clay jug has been found at Birka,[106] as well as a group of high-quality pottery coming from around the Black Sea, the steppes or beyond.[107] No pottery of these sorts is recorded from other Scandinavian regions.[108]

Instead of conclusions

The wealth of Gotland is a riddle. No region can compete when it comes to the sheer quantity of silver from the early and middle Viking Age. But why is Gotland so poor in other kinds of eastern goods, while other parts of Scandinavia – especially the Svea region around Lake Mälaren – are so relatively rich? And why are Gutar almost invisible beyond the Baltic?

Part of the answer is obviously that the Gutar with their distinctive culture deliberately rejected foreign goods (although they gradually changed their attitude in the late Viking Age). Could it also be that the travelling Gutar were merchants and craftsmen who did not take their women with them and settle in the east?[109] Could the traded goods be of a kind that did not leave clear traces in the archaeological material – like slaves?[110] Could instead piracy lie behind the hoarding of silver, either in the way that Gotland was often attacked by *vikings*,[111] or that the Gutar themselves were successful *vikings*?[112] Were there different traditions in different regions underlying the hoarding, for example religious ideas?[113] Or was silver not so actively used on Gotland and therefore deposited in hoards?[114]

I leave the questions open, but I think there is not one single answer. And I think the overall amount of silver cannot be taken as a true measurement of a region's wealth and importance in international trade in the Viking Age. The Svear – and also other people - in many ways competed successfully with the Gutar.

Addendum

After completing this chapter, I received information from Dr Tamara A. Pushkina (Moscow) and Dr Petr E. Sorokin (St Petersburg) about a fourth artefact of Gotlandic type found in Rus: a fish-head pendant found on the Troitskii site in Novgorod. It is made of bronze sheet and is *c.* 5cm long, according to the scale on the published photographs. It was found in a layer dated by dendrochronology to the end of the tenth/beginning of the eleventh century.[115] Bronze-sheet pendants of this type (type 1) are characteristic of the ninth and tenth centuries, and the length indicates that the Novgorod specimen is late.[116]

Notes

1 Periodisation in this chapter varies slightly from the rest of the volume: Vendel Period (mid-sixth century to second half of the eighth century); early Viking Age (second half of the eighth century to second half of the ninth); middle Viking Age (second half of the ninth century to 970s/980s); late Viking Age (970s/980s to around 1100); middle ages (around 1100 to early sixteenth century).
2 Coin statistics from Professor Kenneth Jonsson (personal communication). The number of Sasanian *drachm*s, arriving with the Islamic coins, is 220, of which 112 have been found on Gotland. Coin finds in Uppland and Södermanland: Jonsson (2011).
3 Westerdahl (1990).
4 Bately, 'Wulfstan', p. 15 (inserts in square brackets, here and below, by the author). The Svear also appear in the geographical description of northern Europe and in Ohthere's account (*Sweon* and *Sweoland* respectively): Bately, 'Ohthere', pp. 44, 46.
5 A much-discussed source is the Old English poem 'Beowulf' – dated to between the eighth and tenth centuries but containing elements related to the Migration Period – in which Beowulf, king of the *Geatas*, crosses the sea to help the Danes but wars with the *Sweonas* (Svear). The *Geatas* have usually been identified with the Götar (in present-day Västergötland and Östergötland), but Bo Gräslund (2018) argues, quite convincingly, for the Gutar and claims that the poem is based on an east Scandinavian poem from the sixth century. For philological discussions of the names Gutar, Götar and Goths, see Andersson (1998a, 1998b, 2009, pp. 15–20).
6 Snædal Brink and Jansson (1983b); *Samnordisk runtextdatabas* (with English translations).
7 *Skinn* can denote furs but also fleeces and hides; cf. above, p. 329.
8 This was the Slavic trading place Old Lübeck, precursor to the German Hanseatic town in the south-western Baltic.
9 Snædal Brink and Jansson (1983a), although G 370, found in 1988, is missing from this; *Samnordisk runtextdatabas*. G 280 mentions **aifur**, obviously the rapid *Aeifor* in *DAI* ch. 9, pp. 58–9 and a stone or rock called **ru[f]stain**. When *viking* is written with a lower-case *v*, it is used in the meaning known from the written sources: 'sea-roving warrior'.
10 When Adam writes about *Gothi*, he usually means the Götar but in some cases the Goths and, according to Nyberg (1984, pp. 316–17), in one case the Gutar: Ad*GH* III.73, pp. 424–7; Adam, *Gesta*, tr. Svenberg, p. 198, Bok IV, Introduction B. This identification seems doubtful - the passage contains in principle nothing more than the name *Gothi*.
11 My thanks are due to Professor François-Xavier Dillmann, Versailles, for discussions.

12 *Óláfs saga Tryggvasonar* chs 25, 89: *HKr*[1], vol. 1, pp. 255, 337; tr. *HKr*[3], vol. 1, pp. 158, 211; *Óláfs saga Helga* chs 7, 182, 192: *HKr*[1], vol. 2, pp. 9, 331–2, 343–4; tr. *HKr*[3], vol. 2, pp. 7, 222, 230; close translation of the stanzas from *Poetry from the Kings' Sagas*, ed. Whaley, pp. 393, 461–2, 749. *GoV*, pp. 415–80 contains commentaries and Swedish translations of the various sources mentioning Gotland up to 1161, as well as the relevant chapters in *Heimskringla*. Saint Hallvard's visit to Gotland is mentioned in a Latin source: Henriksen (2011). Another Latin source, probably from the second half of the twelfth century, contains a more extensive account of Olaf Haraldsson's '*pyratica*' in the Baltic: *Historia Norwegie* ch. 18, pp. 100–1.

13 *GS*, pp. 6–7. For the date: *GS*, pp. xlix–liii.

14 Today a lake, Mälaren was then a bay of the Baltic Sea. *Svethiudh* covered mainly Uppland, Södermanland and Västmanland. On the etymology of Svear: Andersson (2004, 2009, pp. 12–15); Nyman (2005). Note the difference between *Svethiudh* and *Sviariki*, 'the Svea realm'. Early mentions of Svear are Tacitus in 98 AD and Jordanes in the mid-sixth century: Tacitus describes their military strength (*Germania* chs 44–5), Jordanes their fur trade (*Getica* III.21).

15 *Annales regni Francorum* s.a. 813, ed. Kurze, p. 139; tr. Scholtz and Rogers, p. 96.

16 Einhard, *Life of Charlemagne* ch. 12, ed. Holder-Egger, p. 15; tr. Thorpe, p. 67 (who incorrectly gives eastern instead of southern shore).

17 *Annales Bertiniani* s.a. 839, ed. Grat *et al.*, pp. 30–1; tr. Nelson, p. 44. For discussions, see Shepard (1995); Franklin and Shepard (1996), pp. 29–42; Garipzanov (2006).

18 For the first explanation, see Ekbo (2000); Falk (1981); for the second Andersson (2001, 2007). Historians and archaeologists have usually used the first explanation, e.g. Mel'nikova and Petrukhin (1990–1). Place-name scholars prefer the second. Schramm (2002), pp. 105–7, questions the link *Ruotsi/Rootsi-'rodhr'*.

19 Rimb*VA* chs 9–14, pp. 38–51.

20 Rimb*VA* chs 16–17, pp. 50–3.

21 Rimb*VA* chs 25–8, 33, pp. 82–93, 102–5.

22 Rimb*VA* ch. 19, pp. 56–65; once in this story, the fort is called *urbs*.

23 Rimb*VA* ch. 30, p. 94; Robinson (tr.), *Ansgar*, p. 97.

24 Rimb*VA* ch. 30, pp. 94–101.

25 Ad*GH* I.60(62)–62(64), pp. 230–3.

26 B. Malmer (2010), catalogue pp. 125–31, 295–8.

27 *PVL* s.a. 862, pp. 13, 149; *RPC*, pp. 59–60. These were 'tribes' living in the north-western part of what became the principality of Rus, with 'the Slavs' (*Slovene*) settled around Novgorod.

28 Knibbs (2011) claims, however, that *Vita Anskarii* is partly built on forged documents created by both Ansgar and Rimbert in order to strengthen Hamburg-Bremen in ecclesiastical conflicts. Criticism of Knibbs: Janson (2014).

29 Cf. Winroth (2012, pp. 105–10), who acknowledges Knibbs' conclusions but summarises Hamburg-Bremen's mission as told in *Vita Anskarii*. He also accepts the vague, stereotypical information in the anonymous *Vita Rimberti* about Rimbert's mission to the *Sueones* (*Vita Rimberti* ch. 20, p. 96; cf. Ad*GH* I.40, p. 212). The Swedish translators are more cautious: Adam, *Gesta*, tr. Svenberg, p. 262 n. 99; Hallencreutz and Odelman (1986), p. 116.

30 This latter meaning is preferred by Sawyer (2007), pp. 137–8; see also Sawyer (2005). It can be supported by Wulfstan's words that Witland in the south-eastern corner of the Baltic 'is subject to [or belongs to] the Ests'. Here another verb is used with the same dual meaning (*belimpeð to*), and the continuation

shows that the Ests and Estland did not form a political unity: Bately, 'Wulfstan', pp. 15–16, comm. pp. 18, 25.

31 Blomkvist (2011), p. 170. Blomkvist develops his argument on pp. 168–76.
32 Sawyer (1982), pp. 18–19.
33 Sawyer (2005), p. 168.
34 Birka: Ambrosiani (2016b). Helgö: general information Clarke and Lamm (2017); the coin finds and the absence of standardised oblate spheroid and cubo-octahedral weights indicate that large-scale trading ended with the early Viking Age: Hovén (1986); B. Malmer (1986); Kyhlberg (1980), pp. 177–97; activities had started long before the Viking Age. Gamla Uppsala: see below, n. 42. Evidence of crafts from other places: Jansson (1981), pp. 6–7, fig. 6; Dunér and Vinberg (2008), pp. 125–43, fig. 95e–h; Sahlén (2016); Beronius Jörpeland *et al.* (eds) (2017), pp. 407–20.
35 Holmquist Olausson (2002), pp. 159–63; Hedenstierna-Jonson *et al.* (2013), pp. 291–8. See also below, n. 71.
36 Hägg (2016). On the graves and grave finds: *Birka I–V*.
37 *Rodhr* is usually understood as referring to Uppland's coastal district, see above, p. 319, but there are also other explanations: Källström (2015).
38 For archaeology: Thordeman (1920); Rydh (1936); Brunstedt (1996); Ambrosiani (2016a); for written sources: Ferm *et al.* (1992), pp. 227–8. The document from 1200 says *mansio regia Alsnu*, and *Alsnu/Alsnö* is the name used in the thirteenth- and fourteenth-century documents (in later centuries distorted to *Adelsö*). *Hovgården*, 'the main farm/manor', a term used for both royal and noblemen's manors, appears in the sources from the fifteenth century on.
39 Ad*GH* IV.26–30(29), pp. 470–4; Adam, *Gesta*, chs 26–8, tr. Svenberg, with scholia 138–41.
40 On Uppsala in general: Hultgård (ed.) (1997); Sundqvist (2002); on Distingen: Granlund (1958); Nordberg (2006), pp. 15–22, 86–99, 107–18, 131–46. Stanzas from *Ynglingatal* are cited in *Ynglinga saga*. For the date of *Ynglingatal*, see Skre (2007) who argues for the traditional dating to around the end of the ninth century.
41 Two runestones in Scania from around 1000 (DR 279 and 295) tell of men who 'did not flee at Uppsala' but nothing more. The inscriptions probably refer to the battle of *Fýrisvellir* mentioned in Norse sources; see Snædal (1985); Strid (1993).
42 On the archaeology of Gamla Uppsala: Lindqvist (1936); Ljungkvist (2013); Ljungkvist and Frölund (2015); Sanmark (2017), pp. 60–1, 83–4, 86, 89–91, 97; Beronius Jörpeland *et al.* (eds) (2017). On crafts and exchange: Nordahl (1996), p. 63; Alström and Duczko (1996), pp. 123–5; Ljungkvist (ed.) (2000), esp. pp. 43, 98–9; Beronius Jörpeland *et al.* (2017), pp. 61–6, 153–72, 401–3. A difference from Birka and Helgö is that coins and weights are not prominent among the Gamla Uppsala finds.
43 Allerstav *et al.* (eds) (1991); Damell (1993); Björklund (2014), pp. 66–7.
44 On Valsgärde: Schönbäck (2002); Ljungkvist (2008); Gräslund and Ljungkvist (2011); on Vendel: Stolpe and Arne (1927). Two cemeteries in Uppland (Gamla Uppsala and Tuna in Alsike) contain both men and women inhumed in boats: see respectively Nordahl (2001) and Arne (1934); and a cemetery in Västmanland (Tuna in Badelunda) contains only women: Nylén and Schönbäck (1994).
45 Sawyer (1982), pp. 46–51.
46 On the *ledung*: Strauch (2001). It is described in the provincial laws of around 1300, by which time it was more or less out of date: *SL*, vol. 1, pp. 46–50; vol. 2, pp. 37–8; vol. 3, pp. 45–8. For *Rodhr*, see above, p. 319.

47 Gustavson and Selinge (1988).
48 The earlier term is preserved in the names of some *hundari* (e.g. Lagunda) and also in the names of the three *folkland* united in the thirteenth century to form Uppland: Tiundaland, Attundaland, Fjädrundaland (denoting lands consisting respectively of ten, eight and four *hund*). The term *folk* is believed to have meant 'a host': Andersson (2000, 2004, 2015, pp. 9–16). There has been a lively discussion about the *hundari* and related words, but most scholars now seem to agree that Andersson's explanation is 'the most plausible', based on 'what we know today': Brink (2013) debating with Andersson (2010, 2013).
49 *WKG*, vol. 1, figs 297–401; vol. 3.2, pp. 524, 631–4; vol. 4.2, pp. 829–71; Thunmark-Nylén (2004), p. 288; Toplak (2016).
50 On Kopparsvik: *WKG*, vol. 3.2, p. 524; in general: *WKG*, vol. 3.1, pp. 90–1; vol. 3.2, p. 653.
51 Arcini (2005); Kjellström (2014); Toplak (2016), pp. 93–105, 307–31, 337. For the strontium analyses: Arcini (2010). The only woman among the analysed individuals was a non-Gotlander buried in prone position.
52 *DKV*; *WKG*, vol. 3.2, pp. 486–90; vol. 4.2, pp. 721–7; D. Carlsson (2011), pp. 107–42; Karn (2014a, 2014b).
53 For hides and fleeces: Karlsson (2001), p. 45; *WKG*, vol. 3.2 p. 489; D. Carlsson (2011), p. 136.
54 *WKG*, vol. 3.2, p. 489; vol. 4.2, pp. 719, 726–7; D. Carlsson (2011), pp. 119–30. Two stone settings also contained unburnt human bones, and an inhumation in prone position was found near the shore: *DKV*, p. 120, fig. 19; *WKG*, vol. 3.2, p. 489.
55 *WKG*, vol. 3.2, pp. 540 (mentioning two possible boat-graves at Ire in Hellvi), 579.
56 On the beads: *WKG*, vol. 3.1, pp. 183–4.
57 Lundström (1974), p. 93; *DKV*, p. 127; *WKG*, vol. 3.2, pp. 486–8. My thanks are due to Docent Lena Thunmark-Nylén, Visby, for many Gotland discussions.
58 Jansson (1995), p. 90.
59 *DKV*, pp. 111–12, pl. 12; *WKG*, vol. 3.2, pp. 345–9; vol. 4.2, pp. 725–6. On weights in general: Gustin (2004); Steuer (2012); Ambrosiani (2013), pp. 234–6.
60 *DKV*, pp. 115–20; *WKG*, vol. 3.2, p. 490. It is disputed whether the activities had already started in the Vendel Period. Four early radiocarbon analyses made on bones have given dates in the eleventh to twelfth centuries (published uncalibrated by Lundström (1974), p. 93; *DKV*, p. 116; *WKG* as above). These dates are contradicted by the artefact finds and more recent radiocarbon analyses.
61 *MSoS*, with summaries pp. 181–92. Earlier finds of weights: *HV*, pp. 110–11. See also list of unfinished artefacts: *WKG*, vol. 3.2, pp. 384–5.
62 *WKG*, vol. 3.2, pp. 500–1, 512–14; Gustafsson and Östergren (2017); Östergren and Gustafsson (2018).
63 Broe: *WKG*, vol. 1, figs 127–49; vol. 3.1, pp. 331–2; vol. 3.2, pp. 621–3, 625–6; Slite: *WKG*, vol. 1, figs 244–61; vol. 3.2, pp. 494–7, 570–1, 625–6.
64 Luistari is the most comprehensively studied site: Lehtosalo-Hilander (1982, 2000) (on society, see Lehtosalo-Hilander (1982), vol. 3, esp. pp. 77–8).
65 Schauman-Lönnqvist (1996).
66 Mägi (2002) (on society, see pp. 139–42). The many hillforts in the eastern Baltic are another important source of information on society there (see the following section).
67 For a short but detailed survey: *WKG*, vol. 3.1, p. 30; vol. 3.2, pp. 647–55; no definitively Gotlandic finds from the early or middle Viking Age are noted on the south coast of the Baltic to the west of the river Vistula.

68 Nerman (1929) remains an indispensable survey of finds indicating contacts between Scandinavia and the eastern Baltic; von zur Mühlen (1975), written in 1937–9, gives a survey of finds in former East Prussia.

69 The material is published in two monographs: Nerman (1958); Lamm (ed.) (2009). For the arrowheads (which cannot be determined more closely than Scandinavian and Viking Age): Zabiela (1997); Lamm (ed.) (2009), pp. 28–30, 154–5, figs 27–30, 99. For Nerman's interpretations: Nerman (1934); Nerman (1958), pp. 174–200.

70 Discussions and supplementary information: Thunmark-Nylén (1983); A. Carlsson (1983), pp. 37–9; Petrenko (1990); Petrenko and Virse (1993); Jansson (1994), pp. 9–15; Petrenko and Urtāns (1995, 2012); *WKG*, vol. 3.2, p. 651 (with an important note concerning burial rites on Gotland); Bogucki (2006). See also nn. 73–8.

71 Birka: see above, p. 323. Hedeby: Kalmring and Holmquist (2018), esp. pp. 282–3, where different interpretations of the Hedeby and Birka hillforts are summarised.

72 For the Vendel Period: Høilund Nielsen (2000); for the Viking Age: Blomkvist (2011), who only uses literary sources; see above, pp. 321–2.

73 Petrenko (1991); Lamm (1991).

74 Animal-head brooches, characteristic of Gotlandic female dress, have not been found at Grobiņa but instead beak-shaped brooches (partly local variants), a type characteristic of southern Scandinavia in the early Vendel Period: Høilund Nielsen (2000), figs 3a, 4a. Only a small number of such brooches (always of true Scandinavian type) are known on Gotland. For the Grobiņa variants: Thunmark-Nylén (1983), p. 309. One such brooch (similar to those in Figure 16.4) comes from Staraia Ladoga, according to its owner (a Russian collector), a piece of information that should be treated with caution: Kirpichnikov and Sarabianov (2010), p. 152, fig. p. 151.

75 In Birka there are, however, seven cremation pits in mounds and fifty-six inhumations under flat ground: *Birka II*, pp. 58–60, 63–4.

76 Virse and Ritums (2012); Virse (2017), pp. 685–8; Guščika and Šnē (2018); Šnē and Virse (2018); Dr Andris Šnē, Riga, stresses that the ramparts are yet to be dated (personal communication). Virse (2017), p. 685, says that the hillfort according to Nerman 'was not populated during the use of Scandinavian cemeteries'. In reality, Nerman (1958), pp. 180–1, writes that the Svear constructed the fort.

77 Urtāns (1977), fig. 124 (map), pp. 129–215 (catalogue); Berga (1988), fig. 6 (map), pp. 26–31, 70 (descriptions). One hoard with only three known coins has the *tpq* 852/3; the others are dated to between 905 and the beginning of the eleventh century. On the Grobiņa grave with coins: Virse and Ritums (2012), p. 40; Virse (2017), p. 688; on scales and weights in Latvia in general: Berga (2017).

78 Cf. Bogucki (2006), p. 103 (note that the article contains misunderstandings of my Swedish papers).

79 For a summary of Pole Nowomiejskie and other remains at Elbląg: Neugebauer (1989); see also Nerman (1958), pp. 188–92; *WKG*, vol. 3.2, pp. 651–2; Jagodziński (2013), pp. 138–42. Surveys of Scandinavian/Scandinavian-like finds from the Vendel and Viking periods in the Elbląg region: Bogucki (2013); Jagodziński (2013).

80 Jagodziński (2009, 2010); Brather and Jagodziński (2012).

81 I know of only one example of what is best understood as a Gotlandic artefact type: a miscasting of two dress pins, for which the best parallels are from Gotland, including one exact parallel: Jagodziński (2010), fig. 230; Jagodziński (2017),

p. 190, pl. 29.2; cf. *WKG*, vol. 2, pl. 117.16; vol. 3.1, pp. 119–26 (type 2a2). It has been suggested that a fragment with Style III/E decoration turned into a pendant comes from a Gotlandic disc-on-bow brooch: Jagodziński (2010), p. 99, fig. 112; Brather and Jagodziński (2012), pp. 177–8, pl. 36. This may be right, but such brooches are also known from other parts of Scandinavia, e.g. Uppland: Arrhenius (1962), pp. 84–6, figs 11–12. The majority of mainland Scandinavian artefacts from Truso seem to have their background in southern Scandinavia.

82 Bogucki (2007b), pp. 167–8, figs 9–11; Jagodziński (2009, fig. 7; 2010, figs 280–1). Cf. *Birka I*, pls 95.1, 96.2–3, 96.8–10, 116–20; Jansson (1988), pp. 584–7, 610, figs 9, 21, 23.3. The possibility of direct eastern links cannot be excluded.

83 von zur Mühlen (1975), esp. pp. 14–16, 122–40; Kulakov (2005, 2012, pp. 9–31, 42–62, 123–201); Ibsen (2009), pp. 17–34, 81–144, 347–63. A plan from 1932 shows about 230 mounds.

84 von zur Mühlen (1975), graves nos 2 and 5, pp. 122–3, pls 23, 37.3, 38.1; Kulakov (2012), p. 123, fig. 56; *WKG*, vol. 3.2, pp. 651–2.

85 Nerman (1934), pp. 372–3. Ibsen (2009), p. 142, also sees a strong connection with the Mälar region.

86 For the settlements, see Ibsen (2009, pp. 145–346, 2013a); for the interpretation Ibsen (2013b). The Scandinavian artefact is a cubo-octahedral bronze 'bead', probably meant to be mounted on an iron rod: Ibsen (2009), pp. 240–1, fig. 153. Ibsen interprets it as belonging to a bridle of a type only known on Gotland, but it could also have been meant for, e.g., an iron staff like *Birka I*, pl. 125.

87 Brather (2006); Bogucki (2007a, 2012); Jagodziński (2010), pp. 133–46; Brather and Jagodziński (2012), pp. 171–4, 308–26; Steuer (2012, with an extensive survey of weights and scales in Europe); Adamczyk and Jankowiak in this volume. Lists of coins from Truso: Bogucki (2007a, 2012); Jagodziński (2017), pp. 114–30. The only later coin that I have noticed is a dirham from 901/2 turned into a pendant, found with mainland Scandinavian female jewellery in grave 184 in Kaup: Bogucki (2003), p. 20, pl. V.

88 For oval brooches found in Latvia: Jansson (1992); Spirǧis (2008), pp. 49–65, 476–8; for the late Vendel-Period brooches: Spirǧis (2008), pp. 49–50, fig. 2; and for such brooches in general: Rundkvist (2010), pp. 128–34, 189–90 (types SPL and SPU).

89 On Laukskola in general: Zariņa (2006); on the Scandinavian artefacts: Zariņa (1992). The complete set of Gotlandic brooches comes from grave 67: Zariņa (2006), p. 39, figs 139.32, 34, 185.2, 211.4; *WKG*, vol. 3.1, p. 30. On Daugmale in general and the Daugava (Western Dvina) route: Zemītis (2007); Berga (1994); Radiņš (2006); Šnē (2009), pp. 132–3.

90 A find from Huglajvs in Silte may represent a grave or a hoard belonging to a person from the eastern Baltic (*WKG*, vol. 2, pl. 297; vol. 3.2, pp. 654, 662) and a grave from Slite, with a mixture of Gotlandic and mainland Scandinavian jewellery as well as an iron amulet ring, to a woman from mainland Sweden (*WKG*, vol. 1, fig. 246; vol. 3.2, p. 654). On the bronze hoard from Spillings: *WKG*, vol. 3.2, pp. 704–6; Bliujienė (2008), pp. 170–4; *SH*, pp. 31–4, 40; Östergren in this volume. Mainland Scandinavian finds of eastern Baltic artefacts noted after Nerman (1929) include two magnificent bridles with Lithuanian parallels from Birka: *Birka I*, graves 832, 842, pls 20–1; Arwidsson (1986).

91 Jansson (1995). One of the dress pins has a design of Scandinavian character.

92 Selling (1955) is the classic study of Swedish Viking-Age pottery, which introduced the following categories: A I denotes western pottery (not including western pottery burnt at a high temperature, see Arbman (1937), pp. 90–104); A II Slavic and Slavic-inspired pottery (the latter called Baltic ware);

A III Balto-Finnic pottery; and A IV local Swedish pottery. For later studies of Birka: Ambrosiani and Arrhenius (1973); Bäck (1995, 2016); Ambrosiani (2013), p. 237; and of Helgö: Arrhenius (1964), pp. 278–90; Reisborg (1981), pp. 129–34, 161, 167. It should be noted that Gotland pottery finds from the early and middle Viking Age are not so numerous: *WKG*, vol. 3.1, pp. 351–3, 358–9.

93 Selling (1955), p. 46; *WKG*, vol. 3.1, p. 350; vol. 4.1, pp. 121–2. A stray find from the outskirts of Visby may also be of western origin and early Viking Age in date: Nerman (1941), p. 37; *WKG*, vol. 3.1, p. 359; vol. 4.2, pp. 873–4.

94 Callmer (1988), pp. 668–74; Brather (1996), pp. 161–4, 373–8. On Paviken: *DKV*, pp. 50–2, pl. 2.1; *WKG*, vol. 3.2, p. 488; on Visby: Thunmark-Nylén (2004), p. 288; *WKG*, vol. 3.2, p. 525. There is no special study of these Gotland finds. Roslund (2001, 2007) deals with Baltic ware of the late Viking and early middle ages, but discusses briefly earlier finds of A II ware; classifications of the Birka pottery made by various authors are summarised in Roslund (2001), p. 402.

95 Selling (1955), pp. 140–55; Roslund (2017), pp. 184–6, fig. 8.12; Gustin (2017), pp. 221–3. One bowl from Grobiņa is of Balto-Finnic character: Nerman (1958), p. 68, fig. 340.

96 Sundius (1955); Hulthén (1984, 2001).

97 On the animal head brooch from Staraia Ladoga: Davidan (1992), p. 27, no. 13, fig. 9; for the pseudo-penannular brooch: Pushkina (1988), pp. 162–3; for both brooches: *WKG*, vol. 3.1, pp. 30, 115; vol. 3.2, pp. 650–1 (the date of the animal head brooch type 5d is discussed in vol. 3.1, p. 49). The pseudo-penannular brooch belongs to a small group of individually shaped brooches ('type 8a') without find associations, but the date should be late in the middle Viking Age (cf. *SGW*, vol. 1, p. 74). On the Gnezdovo sword: Kirpichnikov and Kainov (2001); Thunmark-Nylén (2001); Kainov (2012), pp. 15–19. The best parallels for the decoration are found on box-shaped brooches of type 2b–3a (the date of these brooches is discussed in *WKG*, vol. 3.1, p. 85).

98 Novikova (1992); Musin (2012). For Gotland, see n. 90 above.

99 Poliakova (1996), p. 200, fig. 65.24.

100 See, e.g., peg-decorated penannular brooches: Lehtosalo-Hilander (1982), vol. 2, pp. 102–3 with distribution map; one find from Supruty on the watershed between the rivers Oka and Don could be added (State Historical Museum, Moscow, 109346, op. 2715/5, information from Dr Veronika Murasheva).

101 General surveys: Arne (1914), pp. 117–217; Jansson (1988).

102 On early oriental beads: Callmer (1990); on cornelian and rock crystal beads: Jansson (1988), pp. 584–9, 633–4; Scandinavian beads in general: Callmer (1997, 2003); Gotland beads: *WKG*, vol. 3.1, pp. 187–97 (including discussion by Callmer).

103 Jansson (1988), pp. 607–14, 640–4; Hedenstierna-Jonson and Holmquist (2006); for early finds, see n. 83; for Gotland: *WKG*, vol. 3.1, pp. 127–53 (*passim*); for Paviken and Bandlunde: *DKV*, p. 67, pl. 3.5; *MSoS*, p. 85, no. 122, figs. 72–3; *WKG*, vol. 2, pl. 142.5; vol. 3.1, pp. 141, 154; for late unfinished mounts: *WKG*, vol. 2, pl. 140.27; vol. 3.1, p. 127 nn. 7–8.

104 Callmer (1988), p. 672 n. 78; Goryunova and Plokhov (2014), p. 153; one should note that the authors refer to different vessels. Slavic-inspired Baltic ware becomes prominent on Gotland in the late Viking Age and early middle ages: Roslund (2007), pp. 334–53. One vessel of this type is understood as having been the container of a hoard of dirhams with a *tpq* in the 950s (p. 347). This *may* indicate a start for such pottery on Gotland at the end of the middle Viking Age.

105 Goryunova and Plokhov (2014), pp. 151–3; Selling (1955) placed these vessels in her group A IV (local Swedish pottery).
106 Ambrosiani and Gustin (2015), p. 231, fig. 1; found in a layer dated to the mid-tenth century.
107 Bäck (2016).
108 A 'Sino-Iranian' cup from Hemse on Gotland belongs to a collection of artefacts which obviously represent a female grave from the eleventh or twelfth century (a dirham does not contradict this). A similar cup from the Upper Volga has a comparable date. See Arne (1938); *WKG*, vol. 2, pl. 283.6; vol. 3.1, p. 353.
109 Cf. Duczko (2004), pp. 119, 168–9, 188, 191, 198, 200–1.
110 Cf. Shepard, Jankowiak and Skre in this volume.
111 Cf. the written sources presented above, and Wyatt and Brink in this volume.
112 Cf. Sawyer (1982), pp. 124–30.
113 Cf. the Norse literature, for example 'Odin's law' (*Ynglinga saga* ch. 8, *HKr*[1], vol. 1, p. 20; tr. *HKr*[3], vol. 1, p. 11), and for awareness of this on the part of Egil Skallagrimsson and his father: *Egils Saga*, ed. Bjarni Einarsson, chs 60, 87, pp. 100, 180–1; tr. Pálsson and Edwards, chs 58, 85, pp. 149–50, 236–7; Zachrisson (1998), pp. 40–54 (analysing folklore); Thunmark-Nylén (1986); Gruszczyński in this volume.
114 Cf. M. P. Malmer (1973); B. Malmer (1985), p. 190; Ambrosiani (2016b), pp. 77–8. For a detailed research history up to the 1950s, see *SGW*, vol. 1, pp. 307–20; for later years, see *inter alia* Zachrisson (1998), pp. 12–25, 198–9.
115 Ianin *et al.* (2015), pp. 63–4, fig. 9.5; Musin and Tarabardina (2019), p. 775, fig. 4.6.
116 *WKG*, vol. 2, pl. 162.1–12; vol. 3.1, pp. 198–201; for an example of a set of such pendants, see *WKG*, vol. 1, fig. 192b.

Bibliography

Primary sources

Adam of Bremen, *Gesta hammaburgensis*, Swedish tr. E. Svenberg and comm. C. F. Hallencreutz *et al.*, *Adam av Bremen, Historien om Hamburgstiftet och dess biskopar*, Stockholm (1984).

Annales Bertiniani, ed. F. Grat *et al.*, *Annales de Saint-Bertin*, Paris (1964); tr. J. L. Nelson, *The Annals of St Bertin*, Manchester; New York (1991).

Annales regni Francorum, ed. F. Kurze, *Annales regni Francorum inde ab. a. 741 usque ad a. 829, qui dicuntur Annales Laurissenses maiores et Einhardi*, MGH SRG 6, Hanover (1895); tr. B. W. Scholz and B. Rogers, *Carolingian Chronicles: Royal Frankish Annals and Nithard's Histories*, Ann Arbor, MI (1970).

Bately, J. 'Ohthere and Wulfstan in the Old English Orosius', in J. Bately and A. Englert (eds) (2007), *Ohthere's Voyages: A Late 9th-Century Account of Voyages along the Coasts of Norway and Denmark and Its Cultural Context*, Roskilde, pp. 18–58.

Bately, J. 'Wulfstan's voyage and his description of *Estland*: the text and the language of the text', in A. Englert and A. Trakadas (eds) (2009), *Wulfstan's Voyage: The Baltic Sea Region in the Early Viking Age as Seen from Shipboard*, Roskilde, pp. 14–28.

DR = *Danmarks runeindskrifter*, ed. L. Jacobsen and E. Moltke *et al.*, 2 vols, Copenhagen (1941–2).

Egils Saga, ed. Bjarni Einarsson, London (2003); tr. H. Pálsson and P. Edwards, Harmondsworth (1976).

Einhard, *Life of Charlemagne*, ed. O. Holder-Egger, *Vita Karoli magni, MGH SRG* 25, Hanover (1911); tr. L. Thorpe, *Einhard and Notker the Stammerer: Two Lives of Charlemagne*, Harmondsworth (1969).

Historia Norwegie, ed. I. Ekrem and L. B. Mortensen, tr. P. Fisher, Copenhagen (2003).

Poetry from the Kings' Sagas, vol. 1: *From Mythical Times to c. 1035*, ed. D. Whaley. Turnhout (2012).

Robinson, C. H. (tr. and comm.), *Anskar: The Apostle of the North, 801–865*, London (1921).

Samnordisk runtextdatabas, available from: www.nordiska.uu.se/forskn/samnord.htm (accessed 18 December 2019).

Vita Rimberti, ed. G. Waitz, in *MGH SRG* 55, Hanover (1884), pp. 80–100.

Secondary literature

Allerstav, A. *et al.* (eds) (1991), *Fornsigtuna: en kungsgårds historia*, Upplands-Bro.

Alström, U. and W. Duczko (1996), 'Norra gärdet: utgrävningar 1993–1994', in W. Duczko (ed.), *Arkeologi och miljögeologi i Gamla Uppsala: studier och rapporter*, Uppsala, vol. 2, pp. 115–27.

Ambrosiani, B. (2013), *Excavations in the Black Earth 1990–1995, Stratigraphy Volume 1: Part One, The Site and the Shore; Part Two, The Bronze Caster's Workshop*, Stockholm.

Ambrosiani, B. (2016a), 'Alsnöhus och den vikingatida hallen på Alsnö – rekonstruktionsförslag', *META H: historisksarkeologisk tidskrift* 2016: 7–24.

Ambrosiani, B. (2016b), *Hantverk och handel i Birka*, Stockholm.

Ambrosiani, B. and B. Arrhenius (1973), 'Keramik', in B. Ambrosiani *et al.*, *Birka. Svarta jordens hamnområde: arkeologisk undersökning 1970–1971* (RAÄ Rapport C1 1973), Stockholm, pp. 115–48.

Ambrosiani, B. and I. Gustin (2015), 'Small things and wide horizons from a Birka perspective', in L. Larsson *et al.* (eds), *Small Things, Wide Horizons: Studies in Honour of Birgitta Hårdh*, Oxford, pp. 229–36.

Andersson, T. (1998a), 'Gøtar: Namenkundliches', *RGA* 12: 278–83.

Andersson, T. (1998b), 'Goten: Namenkundliches', *RGA* 12: 402–3.

Andersson, T. (2000), 'Hundare', *RGA* 15: 233–8.

Andersson, T. (2001), 'Roden – Ruotsi', *NoB* 89: 153–4.

Andersson, T. (2004), 'Svethiudh, det svenska rikets kärna', *NoB* 92: 5–18.

Andersson, T. (2007), 'Rus' und Wikinger', *Arkiv för nordisk filologi* 122: 5–13.

Andersson, T. (2009), 'Altgermanische Ethnika', *NoB* 97: 5–39.

Andersson, T. (2010), 'Hund och hundare i Mälarlandskapen', *NoB* 98: 143–4.

Andersson, T. (2013), 'Distriktsbeteckningen *hund* än en gång', *NoB* 101: 205–6.

Andersson, T. (2015), 'Nordiska bebyggelsenamn ur språklig synvinkel', *NoB* 103: 9–34.

Arbman, H. (1937), *Schweden und das Karolingische Reich: Studien zu den Handelsverbindungen des 9. Jahrhunderts*, Stockholm.

Arcini, C. (2005), 'The Vikings bare their filed teeth', *American Journal of Physical Anthropology* 128: 727–33.

Arcini, C. (2010), 'Kopparsvik: ett märkligt gravfält från vikingatid', *GA* 82: 11–20.

Arne, T. J. (1914), *La Suède et l'Orient: études archéologiques sur les relations de la Suède et de l'Orient pendant l'âge des vikings*, Uppsala.

Arne, T. J. (1934), *Das Bootgräberfeld von Tuna in Alsike, Uppland*, Stockholm.

Arne, T. J. (1938), 'En sino–iransk kopp', *Fv* 33: 107–13.

Arrhenius, B. (1962), '"Det flammande smycket"', *Fv* 57: 79–101.

Arrhenius, B. (1964), 'Pottery', in *Helgö II*, pp. 278–90.

Arwidsson, G. (1986), "Die Kopfgestelle aus den Gräbern Bj 832 und 842", in *Birka II*, vol. 2, pp. 137–40.

Bäck, M. (1995), 'Importkeramiken i Birka', *META: medeltidsarkeologisk tidskrift* 1995 (1): 4–21.

Bäck, M. (2016), 'Birka and the archaeology of remotion: early medieval pottery from Byzantium and beyond in eastern Scandinavia', in *BVW*, pp. 255–80.

Berga, T. M. (1988), *Monety v arkheologicheskikh pamiatnikakh Latvii IX–XII vv.*, Riga.

Berga, T. M. (1994), 'Daugmales pilskalna monētas (8.–12. gs.)', *Arheoloģija un etnogrāfija* 17: 41–6.

Berga, T. M. (2017), 'The distribution and chronology of trading equipment in present-day Latvia in the tenth to thirteenth centuries', *Archaeologia Baltica* 24: 59–77.

Beronius Jörpeland, L. *et al.* (eds) (2017), *at Upsalum – människor och landskapande: Utbyggnad av Ostkustbanan genom Gamla Uppsala* (Rapport 2017:1_1, Arkeologisk undersökning), Stockholm; Uppsala.

Birka I = Arbman, H. (1943), *Die Gräber*, 2 vols, Stockholm.

Birka II = Arwidsson G. (ed.) (1984–9), *Systematische Analysen der Gräberfunde*, 3 vols, Stockholm.

Birka III = Geijer, A. (1938), *Die Textilfunde aus den Gräbern*, Uppsala.

Birka IV = Gräslund, A.-S. (1980), *The Burial Customs: A Study of the Graves on Björkö*, Stockholm.

Birka V = Duczko, W. (1985), *The Filigree and Granulation Work of the Viking Period: An Analysis of the Material from Björkö*, Stockholm.

Björklund, A. (2014), *Det medeltida Sverige*, vol. 1: *Uppland*, fasc. 10: *Håbo härad och Sigtuna stad*, Stockholm.

Bliujienė, A. (2008), 'Trade, warfare, looting and hoarding: attributes of Viking Age contacts across the Baltic Sea', in V. Muižnieks (ed.), *Pētījumi Kuršu Senatnē: Rakstu krājums*, Riga, pp. 167–79.

Blomkvist, N. (2011), 'The skattland: a concept suitable for export? The role of loosely integrated territories in the emergence of the medieval state', in S. Imsen (ed.), *Taxes, Tributes and Tributary Lands in the Making of Scandinavian Kingdoms in the Middle Ages*, Trondheim, pp. 167–88.

Bogucki, M. (2003), 'Frühmittelalterliche Silberschätze und Münzen aus dem ehemaligen Ostpreussen im Licht von Archivalien', in W. Nowakowski (ed.), *Auf der Suche nach der verlorenen Archäologie*, Warsaw, pp. 15–22.

Bogucki, M. (2006), 'Grobiņa: a sign of an early future port of trade in the Balt lands', in M. Bertašius (ed.), *Transformatio mundi: The Transition from the Late Migration Period to the Early Viking Age in the East Baltic*, Kaunas, pp. 93–106.

Bogucki, M. (2007a), 'Coin finds in the Viking-Age emporium at Janów Pomorski (*Truso*) and the "Prussian phenomenon"', in S. Suchodolski and M. Bogucki (eds), *Money Circulation in Antiquity, the Middle Ages and Modern Times: Time, Range, Intensity*, Warsaw; Cracow, pp. 79–108.

Bogucki, M. (2007b), 'Some oriental finds from the port of trade at Janów Pomorski (Truso), Poland', in U. Fransson *et al.* (eds), *Cultural Interaction between East and West: Archaeology, Artefacts and Human Contacts in Northern Europe*, SSA 44, Stockholm, pp. 164–70.

Bogucki, M. (2012), 'Numismatische Einordnung', in S. Brather and M. F. Jagodziński, *Der wikingerzeitliche Seehandelsplatz von Janów (Truso)/Nadmorska osada handlowa z okresu wikingów z Janowa (Truso)*, Bonn, pp. 160–6.

Bogucki, M. (2013), 'Before the Vikings: foreigners in the lower Vistula region during the Migration Period and the origins of Truso', in S. Moździoch *et al.* (eds), *Scandinavian Culture in Medieval Poland*, Wroclaw, pp. 81–112.

Brather, S. (1996), *Feldberger Keramik und frühe Slawen: Studien zur nordwestslawischen Keramik der Karolingerzeit*, Bonn.

Brather, S. (2006), 'Early dirham finds in the south-east Baltic: chronological problems in the light of finds from Janów Pomorski (Truso)', in M. Bertašius (ed.), *Transformatio mundi: The Transition from the Late Migration Period to the Early Viking Age in the East Baltic*, Kaunas, pp. 133–42.

Brather, S. and M. F. Jagodziński (2012), *Der wikingerzeitliche Seehandelsplatz von Janów (Truso): geophysikalische, archäopedologische und archäologische Untersuchungen 2004–2008/Nadmorska osada handlowa z okresu wikingów z Janowa (Truso): badania geofizyczne, archeo-pedologiczne i archeologiczne w latach 2004–2008*, Bonn (parallel German and Polish text).

Brink, S. (2013), '*Hund* i Mälarlandskapen', *NoB* 101: 203–4.

Brunstedt, S. (1996), *Alsnu Kungsgård. Forskningsprojekt Hovgården* (RAÄ, UV Stockholm, Rapport 1996:71/1), Stockholm.

Callmer, J. (1988), 'Slawisch-skandinavische Kontakte am Beispiel der slawischen Keramik in Skandinavien während des 8. und 9. Jahrhunderts', in M. Müller-Wille (ed.), *Oldenburg – Wolin – Staraja Ladoga – Novgorod – Kiev: Handel und Handelsverbindungen im südlichen und östlichen Ostseeraum während des frühen Mittelalters* [=Bericht der Römisch-Germanischen Kommission 69], Mainz, pp. 654–74.

Callmer, J. (1990), 'The beginning of the Easteuropean trade connections of Scandinavia and the Baltic region in the eighth and ninth centuries AD', *A Wosinsky Mór Múzeum Évkönyve* 15 (Szekszard): 19–51.

Callmer, J. (1997), 'Beads and bead production in Scandinavia and the Baltic region *c.* AD 600–1100: a general outline', in U. von Freeden and A. Wieczorek (eds), *Perlen: Archäologie, Techniken, Analysen*, Bonn, pp. 197–201.

Callmer, J. (2003), 'Beads in Scandinavia in the early and high medieval periods, ca. AD 400–1200', in I. C. Glover *et al.* (eds), *Ornaments from the Past: Bead Studies after Beck*, London, pp. 38–46.

Carlsson, A. (1983), *Djurhuvudformiga spännen och gotländsk vikingatid*, SSA 5, Stockholm.

Carlsson, D. (2011), *Vikingatidens Västergarn: en komplicerad historia*, ArkeoDok Skrifter 3, Stockholm.

Clarke, H. and K. Lamm (2017), *Helgö Revisited: A New Look at the Excavated Evidence for Helgö, Central Sweden*, Schleswig.

Damell, D. (1993), 'About royal manors from the late Iron Age in Middle Sweden', *Current Swedish Archaeology* 1: 39–47.

Davidan, O. (1992), 'Kunsthandwerkliche Gegenstände des 9. bis 10. Jahrhunderts aus Alt-Ladoga (Die Sammlung der Staatlichen Ermitage in St Petersburg)', *Zeitschrift für Archäologie des Mittelalters* 20: 5–61.

Duczko, W. (2004), *Viking Rus: Studies on the Presence of Scandinavians in Eastern Europe*, Leiden.

Dunér, J. and A. Vinberg (2008), *Barva: 2000 år vid Mälarens södra strand. E20, sträckan Eskilstuna–Arphus. Södermanland, Barva socken, Säby 4:1, RAÄ 17, RAÄ 36, RAÄ 53, RAÄ*

55–57, RAÄ 66, RAÄ 150 och RAÄ 153 (RAÄ, UV Mitt Rapport 2006:20), Stockholm.

Ekbo, S. (2000), 'Finnish *Ruotsi* and Swedish *Roslagen*: what sort of connection?', *Mediaeval Scandinavia* 13: 64–9.

Falk, K.-O. (1981), 'Einige Bemerkungen zum Namen Rusí', in R. Zeitler (ed.), *Les pays du Nord et Byzance (Scandinavie et Byzance)*, Uppsala, pp. 147–59.

Ferm, O. *et al.* (1992), *Det medeltida Sverige*, vol. 1: *Uppland*, fasc. 7: *Attundaland: Bro, Färingö, Adelsö, Sollentuna*, Stockholm.

Franklin, S. and J. Shepard (1996), *The Emergence of Rus, 750–1200*, London.

Garipzanov, I. (2006), 'The Annals of St Bertin (839) and *Chacanus* of the Rhos', *Ruthenica* 5(1): 7–11.

Goryunova, V. M. and A. V. Plokhov (2014), 'Contacts of the population of Lake Il'men' and the Volkhov River areas with peoples of the Baltic region in the 9th–10th centuries on the evidence of pottery', in P. Bauduin and A. Musin (eds), *Vers l'Orient et vers l'Occident. Regards croisés sur les dynamiques et les transferts culturels des Vikings à la Rous ancienne*, Caen, pp. 133–53.

Granlund, J. (1958), 'Disting', *KLNM* 3, cols 112–15.

Gräslund, A.-S. and J. Ljungkvist (2011), 'Valsgärde revisited', in L. Boye (ed.), *Det 61. Internationale Sachsensymposion 2010 Haderslev, Danmark*, Neumünster, pp. 123–39.

Gräslund, B. (2018), *Beowulfkvädet. Den nordiska bakgrunden*, Uppsala.

Guščika, E. and A. Šnē (2018), 'Grobiṇas pilskalna un senpilsētas arheoloģiskā izpēte', in J. Urtāns and I. L. Virse (eds), *Arheologu pētījumi Latvijā 2016/2017. gadā*, Riga, pp. 29–35.

Gustafsson, N. B. and M. Östergren (2017), 'Weights and values in the Gotlandic heartland', *Lund Archaeological Review* 23: 95–105.

Gustavson, H. and K.-G. Selinge (1988), 'Jarlabanke och hundaret: ett arkeologiskt/runologiskt bidrag till lösningen av ett historiskt tolkningsproblem', *NoB* 76: 19–83.

Gustin, I. (2004), *Mellan gåva och marknad: handel, tillit och materiell kultur under vikingatid*, Stockholm.

Gustin, I. (2017), 'Contacts, identity, and hybridity: objects from south-western Finland in the Birka graves', in *IFD*, pp. 205–58.

Hägg, I. (2016), 'Silks at Birka', in *BVW*, pp. 281–304.

Hallencreutz, C. F. and E. Odelman (1986), 'Rimbert som ärkebiskop och författare', in E. Odelman *et al.* (Swedish tr. and comm.), *Boken om Ansgar. Rimbert: Ansgars liv*, Stockholm, pp. 115–32.

Hedenstierna-Jonson, C. and L. Holmquist (2006), *The Oriental Mounts from Birka's Garrison: An Expression of Warrior Rank and Status*, Stockholm.

Hedenstierna-Jonson, C. *et al.* (2013), 'The Viking Age paradox: continuity and discontinuity of fortifications and defence works in eastern Scandinavia', in J. Baker *et al.* (eds), *Landscapes of Defence in Early Medieval Europe*, Turnhout, pp. 285–301.

Helgö II = Holmqvist, W. and B. Arrhenius (eds) (1964), *Excavations at Helgö*, vol. 2: *Report for 1957–1959*, Stockholm.

Helgö VII = Lundström, A. *et al.* (eds) (1981), *Excavations at Helgö*, vol. 7: *Glass, Iron, Clay*, Stockholm.

Helgö X = Lundström, A. and H. Clarke (eds) (1986), *Excavations at Helgö*, vol. 10: *Coins, Iron and Gold*, Stockholm.

Helgö XVIII = B. Arrhenius and U. O'Meadhra (eds) (2011), *Excavations at Helgö*, vol. 18: *Conclusions and New Aspects*, Stockholm.

Henriksen, V. (2011), 'Hallvard den Hellige', *Norsk biografisk leksikon*, vol. 3, Oslo (2001); available from: https://nbl.snl.no/Hallvard_Den_Hellige (accessed 6 November 2019).

Høilund Nielsen, K. (2000), 'The political geography of sixth- and seventh-century southern and eastern Scandinavia on the basis of material culture', *Archaeologia Baltica* 4: 161–72.

Holmquist Olausson, L. (2002), 'Patterns of settlement and defence at the proto-town of Birka, Lake Mälar, eastern Sweden', in J. Jesch (ed.), *The Scandinavians from the Vendel Period to the Tenth Century: An Ethnographic Perspective*, Woodbridge; Rochester, NY, pp. 153–75.

Hovén, B. E. (1986), 'The Sasanian and Islamic coins', in *Helgö X*, pp. 7–12.

Hultgård, A. (ed.) (1997), *Uppsala och Adam av Bremen*, Lund.

Hulthén, B. (1984), 'Keramik', in *Birka II*, vol. 1, pp. 249–62.

Hulthén, B. (2001), 'Keramiktillverkning i det tidigmedeltida Sigtuna – en ceramologisk studie', in M. Roslund, *Gäster i huset: kulturell överföring mellan slaver och skandinaver 900 till 1300*, Lund, pp. 291–307.

Ianin, V. L. *et al.* (2015), 'Raboty v Liudinom kontse Velikogo Novgoroda v 2014 g. (Troitskie raskopy: XIII–Г, Г–1 i XV)', *Novgorod i Novgorodskaia zemlia, Istoriia i arkheologiia* 29: 51–65.

Ibsen, T. (2009), '"Etwa hier die Siedlung" – Der frühmittelalterliche Fundplatz Wiskiauten/Mohovoe im Kaliningrader Gebiet im Lichte alter Dokumente und neuer Forschungen', unpublished PhD dissertation, Christian-Albrechts-Universität, Kiel.

Ibsen, T. (2013a), 'On Prussians and Vikings: new excavation results from Wiskiauten/Mohovoe', in N. A. Makarov *et al.* (eds), *Arkheologiia baltiiskogo regiona/Archaeology of the Baltic*, Moscow; St Petersburg, pp. 241–9.

Ibsen, T. (2013b), 'Wiskiauten: a trading site on the southern coast of the Baltic?', in G. Williams *et al.* (eds), *Viking*, Copenhagen, pp. 72–3.

Jagodziński, M. F. (2009), 'The settlement of Truso', in A. Englert and A. Trakadas (eds), *Wulfstan's Voyage: The Baltic Sea Region in the Early Viking Age as Seen from Shipboard*, Roskilde, pp. 182–97.

Jagodziński, M. F. (2010), *Truso: między Weonodlandem a Witlandem/Truso: Between Weonodland and Witland*, Elbląg.

Jagodziński, M. F. (2013), 'Roots of Truso', in S. Moździoch *et al.* (eds), *Scandinavian Culture in Medieval Poland*, Wroclaw, pp. 113–50.

Jagodziński, M. F. (2017), *Janów Pomorski/Truso: Struktura i zabudowa strefy portowej (badania 1982–1991)/Structure and Building Development in the Harbour Zone (Research from 1982–1991)* [= *Studia nad Truso/Truso Studies* 3.1], Elbląg.

Janson, H. (2014), 'Ansgar und die frühe Geschichte des Erzbistums Hammaburg', in R.-M. Weiss and A. Klammt (eds), *Mythos Hammaburg: Archäologische Entdeckungen zu den Anfängen Hamburgs*, Hamburg, pp. 262–79.

Jansson, I. (1981), 'Economic aspects of fine metalworking in Viking Age Scandinavia', in D. M. Wilson and M. Caygill (eds), *Economic Aspects of the Viking Age*, London, pp. 1–19.

Jansson, I. (1988), 'Wikingerzeitlicher orientalischer Import in Skandinavien', in M. Müller-Wille (ed.), *Oldenburg – Wolin – Staraja Ladoga – Novgorod – Kiev* [= *Bericht der Römisch-Germanischen Kommission* 69], Mainz, pp. 564–647.

Jansson, I. (1992), 'Scandinavian oval brooches found in Latvia', in A. Loit *et al.* (eds), *Die Kontakte zwischen Ostbaltikum und Skandinavien im frühen Mittelalter: Internationale Konferenz 23.–25. Oktober 1990, Riga*, Stockholm, pp. 61–78.

Jansson, I. (1994), 'Skandinavien, Baltikum och Rus' under vikingatiden', in K. Tønnesson and A. Loit (eds), *Det 22. nordiske historikermøte, Oslo 13.–18. august 1994: Rapporter*, vol. 1: *Norden og Baltikum*, Oslo, pp. 5–25.

Jansson, I. (1995), 'Dress pins of East Baltic type made on Gotland', in I. Jansson (ed.), *Archaeology East and West of the Baltic: Papers from the Second Estonian-Swedish Archaeological Symposium, Sigtuna, May 1991*, Stockholm, pp. 83–90.

Jonsson, K. (2011), 'The late German coin from Helgö', in *Helgö XVIII*, pp. 155–9.

Kainov, S. I. (2012), 'Swords from Gnëzdovo', *Acta Militaria Mediaevalia* 8: 7–68.

Källström, M. (2015), 'Kungen, bryten och märket: till tolkningen av runblocket U 11 vid Hovgården på Adelsö och något om runstenarnas placering', *Saga och Sed* 2015: 67–86.

Kalmring, S. and L. Holmquist (2018), 'Hedeby *Hochburg*: theories, state of research and dating', *Offa* 71/72 (2014/15): 241–91.

Karlsson, J. (2001), 'Djurbenen från Burge i Lummelunda. Osteologiska aspekter av gotländsk ekonomi och konsumtion mellan heden och kristen tid', unpublished BA thesis, Gotland University.

Karn, A. (2014a), *Paviken 2013: Rapport över 2013 års utgrävning av den vikingatida hamnplatsen Paviken, Västergarns socken*, Rapport Arendus 2014:8, Visby.

Karn, A. (2014b), *Paviken 2014: Arkeologisk undersökning, Stora Mafrids 5:12, Västergarn socken, Gotlands län*, Rapport Arendus 2014:27, Visby.

Kirpichnikov, A. N. and S. I. Kainov (2001), 'Mech s rel'efnymi ukrasheniiami rukoiati iz raskopok Gnezdovskogo mogil'nika', in V. V. Murasheva (ed.), *Arkheologicheskii sbornik: Gnezdovo, 125 let issledovaniia pamiatnika*, Moscow, pp. 68–72.

Kirpichnikov, A. N. and V. D. Sarabianov (2010), *Staraia Ladoga: drevniaia stolitsa Rusi*, St Petersburg.

Kjellström, A. (2014), 'Spatial and temporal trends in new cases of men with modified teeth from Sweden (AD 750–1100)', *European Journal of Archaeology* 17: 45–59.

Knibbs, E. (2011), *Ansgar, Rimbert and the Forged Foundations of Hamburg-Bremen*, Farnham; Burlington, VT.

Kulakov, V. I. (2005), 'Die wikingerzeitliche Siedlung und das Gräberfeld Kaup bei Wiskiauten: Bericht über die Ausgrabungen der Jahre 1956–2004', *Offa* 59/60 (2002/3): 55–79.

Kulakov, V. I. (2012), *Nemanskii iantarnyi put' v epokhu vikingov*, Kaliningrad.

Kyhlberg, O. (1980), *Vikt och värde: arkeologiska studier i värdemätning, betalningsmedel och metrologi under yngre järnålder: I Helgö, II Birka*, SSA 1, Stockholm.

Lamm, J. P. (1991), 'Ships or ducks? Comment on the picture-stone found at Grobin, Latvia', *Fv* 86: 9–10.

Lamm, J. P. (ed.) (2009), *Apuolė: Ausgrabungen und Funde 1928–1932*, Klaipeda.

Lehtosalo-Hilander, P.-L. (1982), *Luistari I–III (I: The Graves; II: The Artefacts; III: A Burial-Ground Reflecting the Finnish Viking Age Society)*, [=*Suomen muinaismuistoyhdistyksen aikakauskirja* 82(1–3)], Helsinki.

Lehtosalo-Hilander, P.-L. (2000), *Luistari IV: A History of Weapons and Ornaments*, [=*Suomen muinaismuistoyhdistyksen aikakauskirja* 107], Helsinki.

Lindqvist, S. (1936), *Uppsala högar och Ottarshögen*, Stockholm.

Ljungkvist, J. (2008), 'Valsgärde: development and change of a burial ground over 1300 years', in S. Norr (ed.), *Valsgärde Studies: The Place and Its People, Past and Present*, Uppsala, pp. 13–55.

Ljungkvist, J. (2013), 'Monumentaliseringen av Gamla Uppsala', in O. Sundqvist and P. Vikstrand (eds), *Gamla Uppsala i ny belysning*, Uppsala, pp. 33–67.

Ljungkvist, J. (ed.) (2000), *I maktens närhet: två boplatsundersökningar i Gamla Uppsala: RAÄ 285, Norra gärdet, RAÄ 547 Matsgården, Gamla Uppsala socken, Uppland* (Societas Archaeologica Upsaliensis skrifter 1), Uppsala.

Ljungkvist, J. and P. Frölund (2015), 'Gamla Uppsala: the emergence of a centre and a magnate complex', *The Journal of Archaeology and Ancient History* 16: 1–29, available at: arkeologi.uu.se/Journal (accessed 16 December 2019).

Lundström, P. (1974), 'Paviken I bei Västergarn – Hafen, Handelsplatz und Werft', in H. Jankuhn *et al.* (eds), *Vor- und frühformen der europäischen Stadt im Mittelalter: Bericht über ein Symposium in Reinhausen bei Göttingen vom 18. bis 24. April 1972*, vol. 2, Göttingen, pp. 82–93.

Mägi, M. (2002), *At the Crossroads of Space and Time: Graves, Changing Society and Ideology on Saaremaa (Ösel), 9th–13th Centuries* AD, Tallinn.

Malmer, B. (1985), 'Circulation of monetary silver in the Baltic area during the Viking Age', in S.-O. Lindquist (ed.), *Society and Trade in the Baltic during the Viking Age*, Visby, pp. 185–94.

Malmer, B. (1986), 'West European silver coins at Helgö', in *Helgö X*, pp. 127–9.

Malmer, B. (2010), *Den svenska mynthistorien: Vikingatiden ca 995–1030*, Stockholm.

Malmer, M. P. (1973), 'En korologisk aspekt på tolkningen av den gotländska järnålderns myntfynd', in P. Sarvas and A. Siiriäinen (eds), *Honos Ella Kivikoski* [= *Suomen muinaismuistoyhdistyksen aikakauskirja* 75], Helsinki, pp. 132–6.

Mel'nikova, E. A. and V. I. Petrukhin (1990–1), 'The origin and evolution of the name Rus': the Scandinavians in Eastern European ethno-political processes before the 11th century', *Tor* 23: 203–34.

Mühlen, B. von zur (1975), *Die Kultur der Wikinger in Ostpreussen*, Bonn.

Musin, A. E. (2012), 'Skandinavskoe iazychestvo na Vostoke po dannym arkheologii: obshchee i osobennoe', *Rossiiskii arkheologicheskii ezhegodnik* 2: 555–602.

Musin, A. E. and O. A. Tarabardina (2019), 'Skandinavy sredi pervoposelentsev Novgoroda po dannym arkheologii', *Vestnik Sankt-Peterburgskogo Gosudarstvennogo Universiteta, Istoriia* 64(2): 762–85, available from: https://dspace.spbu.ru/handle/11701/16353 (accessed 1 August 2020).

Nerman, B. (1929), *Die Verbindungen zwischen Skandinavien und dem Ostbaltikum in der jüngeren Eisenzeit*, Stockholm.

Nerman, B. (1934), 'Swedish Viking colonies on the Baltic', *Eurasia septentrionalis antiqua* 9: 357–80.

Nerman, B. (1941), 'En kristen mission på Gotland vid tiden omkring år 800 e. Kr.', *Fv* 36: 30–40.

Nerman, B. (1958), *Grobin–Seeburg: Ausgrabungen und Funde*, Stockholm.

Neugebauer, W. (1989), 'Elbing, II: Archäologisches', *RGA* 7: 116–27.

Nordahl, E. (1996), *… templum quod Ubsola dicitur … i arkeologisk belysning*, Uppsala.

Nordahl, E. (2001), *Båtgravar i Gamla Uppsala: spår av en vikingatida högreståndsmiljö*, Uppsala.

Nordberg, A. (2006), *Jul, disting och förkyrklig tideräkning: kalendrar och kalendariska riter i det förkristna Norden*, Uppsala.

Novikova, G. L. (1992), 'Iron neck-rings with Thor's hammers found in Eastern Europe', *Fv* 87: 73–89.

Nyberg, T. (1984), 'Stad, skrift och stift: några historiska inledningsfrågor', in E. Svenberg *et al.* (Swedish tr. and comm.), *Adam av Bremen: Historien om Hamburgstiftet och dess biskopar*, Stockholm, pp. 295–339.

Nylén, E. and B. Schönbäck (1994), *Tuna i Badelunda: guld kvinnor båtar*, 2 vols, Västerås.

Nyman, E. (2005), 'Skandinavien', *RGA* 28: 582–7.

Östergren, M. and N. B. Gustafsson (2018), 'Landets hjärta – Gutnaltinget i Roma', in C. Emdén and S. Thedéen (eds), *Spåren av det förflutna: centrala arkeologiska platser på Gotland* [= *GA* 90], Visby, pp. 60–75.

Petrenko, V. P. (1990), 'Die Hügelgräberfelder von Grobin (UdSSR)', *Das Altertum* 36 (1): 43–8.

Petrenko, V. P. (1991), 'A picture stone from Grobin (Latvia)', *Fv* 86: 1–9.

Petrenko, V. P. and J. Urtāns (1995), *The Archeological Monuments of Grobiņa*, Riga; Stockholm.

Petrenko, V. P. and J. Urtāns (2012), *Grobiņas arheoloģijas pieminekļi*, Riga.

Petrenko, V. P. and I. A. Virse (1993), 'Issledovanie mogil'nikov Grobinias Priedienes v zapadnoi Latvii', *Kratkie soobshcheniia (Rossiiskaia Akademiia Nauk, Institut arkheologii)* 208: 95–103.

Poliakova, G. F. (1996), 'Izdeliia iz tsvetnykh i dragotsennykh metallov', in G. A. Fedorov-Davydov (ed.), *Gorod Bolgar: Remeslo metallurgov, kuznetsov, liteishchikov*, Kazan, pp. 154–268.

Pushkina, T. A. (1988), 'Skandinavskie nakhodki iz okrestnostei Muroma', in M. V. Sedova (ed.), *Problemy izucheniia drevnerusskoi kul'tury (rasselenie i etnokul'turnye processy na Severo-Vostoke Rusi): Sbornik nauchnykh trudov*, Moscow, pp. 162–9.

Radiņš, A. (2006), 'Lower Daugava area in the 1st–11th century: ethnic, economic, social and political change – on the question of activity along Daugava waterway', in M. Bertašius (ed.), *Transformatio mundi: The Transition from the Late Migration Period to the Early Viking Age in the East Baltic*, Kaunas, pp. 81–92.

Reisborg, S. (1981), 'The pottery from Building Group 4'; 'The pottery from Building Group 3', in *Helgö VII*, pp. 107–34, 135–77.

Roslund, M. (2001), *Gäster i huset: kulturell överföring mellan slaver och skandinaver 900 till 1300*, Lund.

Roslund, M. (2007), *Guests in the House: Cultural Transmission between Slavs and Scandinavians 900 to 1300 AD*, Leiden.

Roslund, M. (2017), 'Bringing "the periphery" into focus: social interaction between Baltic Finns and the Svear in the Viking Age and Crusade period (*c.* 800 to 1200)', in *IFD*, pp. 168–204.

Rundkvist, M. (2010), 'Domed oblong brooches of Vendel Period Scandinavia: Ørsnes types N & O and similar brooches, including transitional types surviving into the Early Viking Age', in B. Hårdh (ed.), *Från romartida skalpeller till senvikingatida urnesspännen: nya materialstudier från Uppåkra*, Lund, pp. 127–99.

Rydh, H. (1936), *Förhistoriska undersökningar på Adelsö*, Stockholm.

Sahlén, D. (2016), 'Ceramic evidence from non-ferrous metallurgy in the Mälaren valley during the Viking Age', in P. E. Pettersson (ed.), *Prehistoric Pottery across the Baltic: Regions, Influences and Methods*, BAR IS 2785, Oxford, pp. 75–80.

Sanmark, A. (2017), *Viking Law and Order: Places and Rituals of Assembly in the Medieval North*, Edinburgh.

Sawyer, P. H. (1982), *Kings and Vikings: Scandinavia and Europe AD 700–1100*, London.

Sawyer, P. H. (2005), 'Svear: Historisch', *RGA* 30: 165–70.

Sawyer, P. H. (2007), 'Ohthere's destinations: Norway, Denmark and England', in J. Bately and A. Englert (eds), *Ohthere's Voyages: A Late 9th-Century Account of Voyages along the Coasts of Norway and Denmark and Its Cultural Context*, Roskilde, pp. 136–9.

Schauman-Lönnqvist, M. (1996), 'The Vainionmäki society', in P. Purhonen (ed.), *Vainionmäki: A Merovingian Period Cemetery in Laitila, Finland*, Helsinki, pp. 130–5.

Schönbäck, B. (2002), 'De vikingatida båtgravarna i Valsgärde: relativ kronologi', *Fv* 97: 1–8.

Schramm, G. (2002), *Altrusslands Anfang: Historische Schlüsse aus Namen, Wörtern und Texten zum 9. und 10. Jahrhundert*, Freiburg im Breisgau.

Selling, D. (1955), *Wikingerzeitliche und frühmittelalterliche Keramik in Schweden*, Stockholm.

Shepard, J. (1995), 'The Rhos guests of Louis the Pious: whence and wherefore?', *Early Medieval Europe* 4: 41–60.

Skre, D. (2007), 'The dating of *Ynglingatal*', in D. Skre (ed.), *Kaupang in Skiringssal*, Aarhus, pp. 407–29.

Snædal, T. (1985), '"Han flydde inte vid Uppsala …": slaget på Fyrisvallarna och några skånska runstenar', *Ale: Historisk tidskrift för Skåne* 1985(2): 13–23.

Snædal Brink, T. and I. Jansson (1983a), 'Gotländska runinskrifter', in *GoV*, pp. 424–37.

Snædal Brink, T. and I. Jansson (1983b), 'Runinskrifter från övriga Skandinavien', in *GoV*, pp. 438–45.

Šnē, A. (2009), 'The early town in late prehistoric Latvia', in J. Staecker (ed.), *The Reception of Medieval Europe in the Baltic Sea Region*, Visby, pp. 127–36.

Šnē, A. and I. L. Virse (2018), 'Grobiņas pilskalna vaļņa izpēte 2016. gadā', in J. Urtāns and I. L. Virse (eds), *Arheologu pētījumi Latvijā 2016/2017. gadā*, Riga, pp. 81–4.

Spirǵis, R. (2008), *Bruņrupuču saktas ar krūšu važiņrotām un lībiešu kultūras attīstība Daugavas lejtecē 10.–13. gadsimtā*, Riga.

Steuer, H. (2009), 'Principles of trade and exchange: trade goods and merchants', in A. Englert and A. Trakadas (eds), *Wulfstan's Voyage: The Baltic Sea Region in the Early Viking Age as Seen from Shipboard*, Roskilde, pp. 294–308.

Steuer, H. (2012), 'Waagen und Gewichte in Janów', in S. Brather and M. F. Jagodziński, *Der wikingerzeitliche Seehandelsplatz von Janów (Truso)/Nadmorska osada handlowa z okresu wikingów z Janowa (Truso)*, Bonn, pp. 185–280.

Stolpe, H. and T. J. Arne (1927), *La nécropole de Vendel*, Stockholm; French tr. of *Graffältet vid Vendel*, Stockholm (1912).

Strauch, D. (2001), 'Ledung', *RGA* 18: 180–91.

Strid, J. P. (1993), 'Kring Fyrisvallarna', in G. Dahlbäck (ed.), *Snorre Sturlasson och de isländska källorna till Sveriges historia. Fyra föreläsningar från ett symposium i Stockholm hösten 1988*, Stockholm, pp. 64–84.

Sundius, N. G. (1955), 'Mikroskopische Untersuchung von Keramik-Scherben aus der Wikingerzeit und dem frühen Mittelalter', in D. Selling, *Wikingerzeitliche und frühmittelalterliche Keramik in Schweden*, Stockholm, pp. 244–51.

Sundqvist, O. (2002), *Freyr's Offspring: Rulers and Religion in Ancient Svea Society*, Uppsala.

Thordeman, B. (1920), *Alsnö hus: ett svenskt medeltidspalats i sitt konsthistoriska sammanhang*, Stockholm.

Thunmark-Nylén, L. (1983), 'Gotland och Ostbaltikum', in *GoV*, pp. 306–22.

Thunmark-Nylén, L. (1986), 'Hedningar, kristna och silverskatter', *GA* 58: 23–44.

Thunmark-Nylén, L. (2001), 'Gnezdovskii mech – izdelie gotlandskogo mastera?', in V. V. Murasheva (ed.), *Arkheologicheskii sbornik: Gnezdovo, 125 let issledovaniia pamiatnika*, Moscow, pp. 73–6.

Thunmark-Nylén, L. (2004), 'Visby: ett pussel med gamla och nya pusselbitar', *Fv* 99: 285–97.

Toplak, M. S. (2016), *Das wikingerzeitliche Gräberfeld von Kopparsvik auf Gotland: Studien zu neuen Konzepten sozialer Identitäten am Übergang zum christlichen Mittelalter*, Tübingen, available from: https://publikationen.uni-tuebingen.de/xmlui/handle/10900/71537 (accessed 6 October 2019).

Urtāns, V. (1977), *Senākie depozīti Latvijā (līdz 1200 g.)*, Riga.

Virse, I. L. (2017), 'Grobiņa (Latvia): dwelling site of Scandinavians and Curonians', in B. V. Eriksen *et al.* (eds), *Interaktion ohne Grenzen: Beispiele archäologischer Forschungen am Beginn des 21. Jahrhunderts/Interaction without Borders: Exemplary Archaeological Research at the Beginning of the 21st Century*, Schleswig, vol. 2, pp. 683–9.

Virse, I. L. and R. Ritums (2012), 'The Grobiņa complex of dwelling locations and burial sites, and related questions', *Archaeologica Baltica* 17: 34–42.

Westerdahl, C. (1990), 'The maritime itinerary of the tax register of King Valdemar Sejr of Denmark (1202–1241)', *Deutsches Schiffahrtsarchiv* 13: 325–75.

Winroth, A. (2012), *The Conversion of Scandinavia: Vikings, Merchants, and Missionaries in the Remaking of Northern Europe*, New Haven, CT; London.

Zabiela, G. (1997), 'Scandinavian arrowheads in Lithuania', *Archaeologia Baltica* 2: 133–40.

Zachrisson, T. (1998), *Gård, gräns, gravfält: sammanhang kring ädelmetalldepåer och runstenar från vikingatid och tidig medeltid i Uppland och Gästrikland*, SSA 15, Stockholm.

Zariņa, A. (1992), 'Die Kontakte der Liven mit Skandinavischen Ländern nach den Schmucksachen des Gräberfeldes aus dem 10.–13. Jh. zu Salaspils Laukskola', in A. Loit *et al.* (eds), *Die Kontakte zwischen Ostbaltikum und Skandinavien im frühen Mittelalter: Internationale Konferenz 23.–25. Oktober 1990, Riga*, Stockholm, pp. 173–84.

Zariņa, A. (2006), *Salaspils Laukskolas kapulauks: 10.–13. gadsimts*, Riga.

Zemītis, G. (2007), '10th–12th century Daugmale: the earliest urban settlement along the Lower Daugava and forerunner of Riga', in U. Fransson *et al.* (eds), *Cultural Interaction between East and West: Archaeology, Artefacts and Human Contacts in Northern Europe*, SSA 44, Stockholm, pp. 279–84.

17 Silver hoarding on Bornholm and Gotland

Hoards as windows onto Viking-Age life

Gitte Tarnow Ingvardson[1]

Two islands in the Baltic, Bornholm and Gotland, are home to the largest concentrations of Viking-Age hoards in Denmark and Sweden respectively. Gotland's hoards have been subject to several comprehensive studies and make a vital contribution to research into Viking-Age life on the island. Research into Bornholm's hoards has been greatly inspired by Gotland. The fact that both islands are situated in the Baltic and display a hoard intensity that is far above average could indicate comparable development patterns, and that the hoard intensities should be seen as parallel phenomena. However, this question has not been fully addressed before. This chapter seeks to explore whether the hoarding practices of the two islands were related, and if so, how. It will compare a number of characteristic elements in the two islands' Viking-Age material culture, which differ from developments in the central parts of mainland Sweden and in Denmark. These are a lack of urbanisation, continuation of a Viking bullion economy, autonomous monetary development and intense silver hoarding.

The main focus of the chapter will be Bornholm, with Gotland serving as a comparison. As with Gotland, the focal point of Viking-Age research in Bornholm remains its silver hoards.[2] The chapter will also present the results of recent research which indicate that we should take a multi-contextual approach to interpreting why and how Viking-Age hoards were deposited. The diverse composition of the Bornholm hoards, and the varied hoarding practices on the island, are examined through case studies of six partially excavated hoard sites. Differences in hoard composition and depositional context may be related to ownership, to the hoards' functions or possibly to both. Finally, evidence from the six sites is discussed in relation to prevailing interpretations of the Gotlandic hoards.

The Bornholm hoards

Inspired by Gotland's 'Skattfyndprojektet',[3] Bornholm Museum launched a targeted research campaign in 1989 whose starting point was Georg Galster's 1980 publication of 31 hoard or grave finds and 17 single finds totalling 5,483 coins.[4] Most of the hoards described in Galster's catalogue were found in the seventeenth, eighteenth and nineteenth centuries; only seven were discovered in the twentieth century, with 1939 being the most recent find date. Information on the hoards' contexts had, in many cases, been lost over the years, or perhaps was not recorded to start with. The aim of the research campaign was to re-establish the find spots, to rescue what might be left of the hoards in the fields and to investigate the circumstances of the depositions. An important part of the projects on both Gotland and Bornholm was – in an archaeological context – the relatively newly introduced method of metal-detector survey. While on Gotland the surveys were organised and conducted by archaeologists from Gotland Museum, on Bornholm the Museum cooperated with a large, established and well-organised group of private metal-detectorists. The different legislation on metal-detector archaeology in the two countries lay behind the different approaches: Denmark allows private surveying, with permission of the landowner, while the Swedish county administrative boards (*Länsstyrelsen*) are very reluctant to give permission to private metal-detectorists – and even more so on Gotland.

The Bornholm campaign was initially organised and controlled by the museum, which undertook the archival studies that informed the private metal-detector surveys. This cooperation was a success and Galster's catalogue was revised, with the location of 23 of the hoards being determined (see Map 17.1).[5] For 11 of these sites the precise location of the hoard was established – either because part of it was still preserved in situ or because a very dense concentration of silver objects was discovered – and new surveys have added more finds to the hoards. Interest in metal-detecting on Bornholm has not faded over the years, but what started out as a museum-organised research project is now driven by private metal-detectorists. Cooperation between the two remains strong, but the museum no longer controls where surveys are conducted. Metal-detecting is widespread on Bornholm and Viking-Age silver objects such as coins, jewellery, ingots and scrap silver are constantly being found. When a large concentration of coins and hack-silver is discovered, Bornholm Museum is obliged to excavate: this is often small-scale, but necessary to determine the content and close context of the hoard, and to secure it. Thus excavation locations are selected more or less at random, in response to individual finds. This approach has its pros and cons. One downside is the difficulty of aligning these investigations with targeted research questions. But an advantage is that new hoards are sometimes found in unexpected settings. An example is the Buddegård hoard – one of the six case studies presented below – which was found in an area with no previous evidence of Viking-Age activity. Such unexpected hoards offer us surprising new evidence, which may well open up the interpretative field.

To date, Bornholm Museum has undertaken small-scale excavations triggered by finds of silver concentrations at 36 sites, seven of which are included in Galster's catalogue.[6] This has resulted in the registration of more than 8,500 coins since 1989. Based on current experience, a concentration of five or more silver objects within an area of 15m by 15m strongly indicates a disturbed hoard. At present, 46 such locations have been recorded and await further surveys, and these are likely to lead to new hoard finds (see Map 17.1).

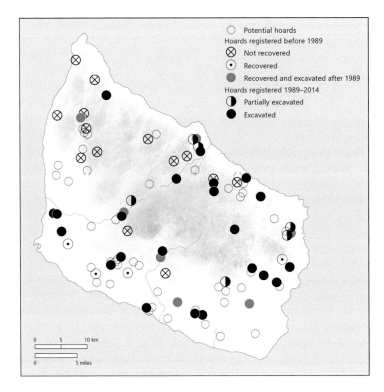

Map 17.1 Viking-Age silver hoards on Bornholm: potential hoards (a concentration of five silver objects or more within an area of 15m by 15m indicating a disturbed hoard); not recovered (subsequent metal-detecting failed to identify any new arte-facts associated with the hoard); recovered (subsequent metal-detecting has re-established the precise location of the hoard, either because part of it was still preserved in situ or because a very dense concentration of silver objects was dis-covered); recovered and excavated after 1989 (as above, but where archaeological excavations were also undertaken); partially excavated (less than 50m² excavated or the survey failed to locate the core area of the hoard); excavated (more than 200m² excavated).

Map: René Laursen.

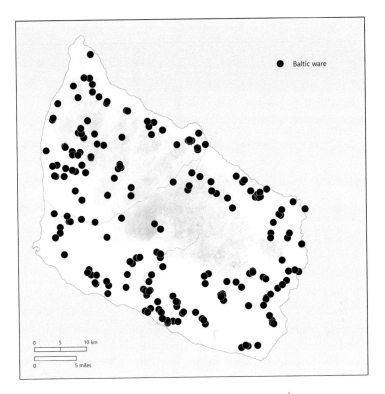

Map 17.2 The distribution of sites with Baltic ware on Bornholm.[1]

Map: J. S. Andersen

Note

1 Find sites range from a few sherds found during surveys to more extensive, excavated settlement remains; on Baltic ware, see Glossary.

Hoards and settlement

The Skovsholm hoard (*tpq* 855) is Bornholm's only hoard to be dominated by dirhams minted under the Abbasids.[7] The other dirham hoards on the island are predominantly Samanid. It is also Bornholm's only ninth-century hoard, and was deposited approximately half a century before the next oldest, the Rabækkegård hoard (*tpq* 912/13). Probably part of a burial, this hoard consists of ten complete and five fragmented dirhams (one pierced, looped Umayyad coin and 14 Samanid ones) found in a stone chamber together with some bronze pendants and 29 glass beads.[8] Tenth-century depositions are sporadic, and the second wave of Kufic coins in the Baltic area[9] only made a small impression on hoard depositions in the 960s and 970s. Hoarding was most prevalent between 990 and 1050, with 70% of the 46 dated hoards on Bornholm deposited within this 60-year period (see Figure 17.1). This increase in hoarding activity coincides with a change in hoard composition, with

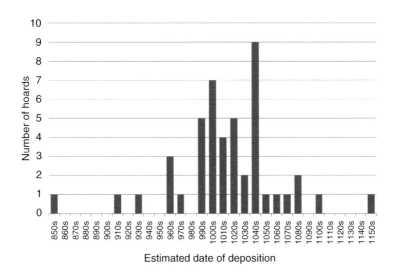

Figure 17.1 The estimated date of deposition of 46 dated Bornholm hoards.

dirhams being supplanted by western European coins. The 990s are a transitional period, when some hoards are dominated by English coins, others by Kufic, while hoards deposited in the first half of the eleventh century are dominated by German coins, although still with a number of English and, to a lesser degree, Scandinavian and Kufic coins (see Figure 17.2). At the same time there is a clear tendency towards the deposition of larger hoards. From the mid-eleventh century, Scandinavian coins make up an increasing part of hoards on Zealand, and by the end of the eleventh and early twelfth centuries, this trend spreads to Scania, Funen and Jutland. But on Bornholm, hoards continue to be dominated by foreign, mainly German, coins,[10] and it is notable that minting was never established on Bornholm – apart from counterfeiting.[11] And with the exception of Store Frigård II,[12] hoards deposited in the second half of the eleventh century are generally small.[13]

If we turn to Gotland, we see a general increase in hoarding activity from *c.* 800 to 1050 and, just as on Bornholm, the number of deposited hoards drops from the middle of the eleventh century. However, unlike Bornholm, the decline in deposited hoards is offset by a rise in the total of deposited coins, as some hoards increase considerably in size.[14] Gotland also saw a change in hoard composition, with Kufic being replaced by western European coins at the turn of the first millennium, as on Bornholm and in Scania and Zealand.[15] A distinctive element in these two islands' hoards is the continued presence of non-minted silver well into the twelfth century – indicating a bullion economy – in contrast to the central parts of mainland Sweden and Denmark, where hoards consisting purely of coins appear during the eleventh century.[16]

Towards the end of the tenth century, the dominant role of Migration-Period central sites declined. In southern Scandinavia these centres were replaced by medieval towns established in inland areas or by fjords.[17] For instance, in Zealand, the central functions moved from the manor site at Lejre to Roskilde,[18] and in Scania, Uppåkra's role as a central site diminished while Lund was founded nearby.[19] Like Uppåkra and Lejre, Bornholm's important power and trading centre, the Sorte Muld complex, gradually declined during the Viking Age, and by the late tenth and early eleventh centuries had been reduced to a few individual farmsteads.[20] Yet Bornholm lacked the processes of urbanisation seen in Zealand and Scania, and Sorte Muld was not replaced by a new town. From the end of the tenth century, Bornholm is characterised by a scattered settlement structure of individual farmsteads without a centre.[21] These late Viking-Age farmsteads have mainly been recorded using reconnaissance and metal-detector surveys, and are characterised by finds of Baltic ware, fragments of imported millstones from central Europe, whetstones from southern Norway, weights and coins.[22] The distribution of these sites is indicated by the evidence of Baltic ware (see Map 17.2). This is spread throughout the island, predominantly inland from the coast, and shows a similar distribution pattern to the island's Viking-Age silver hoards (see Map 17.1).[23] Magdalena Naum's investigations date the Baltic ware on Bornholm to between *c.* 900 and *c.* 1150. This broad timeframe does not allow for a detailed analysis, but the widespread distribution of Baltic ware seems to confirm that a decentralised settlement structure was established during the late Viking Age. However, the transitional period between the decline of Sorte Muld and the rise of the new settlement pattern is under-investigated, as excavations are almost exclusively carried out at hoard sites and ninth- and tenth-century hoards are rare.

The ninth-century Skovsholm hoard contains 170 coins minted between 611 and 855. The majority are fragmented into halves or quarters, while 22 coins are complete.[24] The site is strategically well placed near Skovsholm Bæk, a stream about 1.5km south-east of Sorte Muld on a plateau tapering towards the east coast of Bornholm. The outlet of Skovsholm Bæk into the Baltic is flanked by two natural harbours with access to fresh water from natural springs, offering a possible winter harbour. The hoard was probably deposited near a spring. However, the original deposition site was disturbed by the dismantling of a well in the area, and the coins were spread across some 30m by 15m of ploughed land. Settlement remains in the form of pits and postholes were found in the area around the hoard. Although the excavations did not give a clear picture of the buildings, a very unusual structure was revealed: a trapezoid-shaped pit house of approximately 14m by 2–3m, with a very heavy stone wall or stone foundation on its north side. Stone paving in the bottom layer slopes slightly from west to east, and a small ditch (or trench) runs parallel to the stone wall, approximately 25–30cm from the wall. Two radiocarbon datings of bones from domesticated cattle found in the bottom layer place the construction in the ninth century, and the structure may be contemporary with the hoard. Its vicinity to a natural spring, the paved sloping floor and the ditch all suggest that whatever went on in the house needed water, and a selection of bones – including cow, horse, sheep or goat and seal – indicate that it was a tannery.[25] This hypothesis is supported by the findings of a bone spike, which could have been used to affix the hides. A strategic location, proximity to the Sorte Muld complex, traces of possible trade goods – skins and hides – and the unusual early hoard all imply that Skovsholm was a key site in a changing political landscape. However, the relation between Sorte Muld and Skovsholm is still unclear.

The Skovsholm site highlights one important issue: access to the sea. The rocky coastline of northern and eastern Bornholm provides access from the sea via natural harbours, while the southern coast is characterised by long sandy beaches (see Map 17.3). The spatial distribution of silver hoards seems to show that these natural harbours to the north and east formed focal points for Viking-Age settlement, as the hoards are clustered in their hinterlands, while the southern coast is bypassed.[26] This is to some extent supported by the distribution of sites with Baltic ware. One reason could be that settlements inland from the natural harbours of the rocky north and east were easier to control and protect than the long sandy beaches of the south, where ships were able to land along the entire coast. As we have seen, Skovsholm is just such a setting, suggesting that changes in settlement structure may have started as early as the mid-ninth century.

If we turn to Gotland, Gustaf Svedjemo argues that settlement was organised in small villages and single farms from *c.* 600 and throughout the Viking Age.[27] There were a large number of harbours or landing places (around 50) on Gotland in the tenth century – a situation similar to Bornholm. It is difficult to establish the chronological sequence of the harbour sites for both islands: very few have been excavated and our knowledge mainly comes from landscape analysis and broadly dated surface finds.[28] However, the evidence does suggest that some Gotlandic harbours disappeared while others grew in size and importance during the eleventh century, implying a shift from seasonal to more permanent bases.[29] Many Viking-Age Gotlandic hoards are also clustered in the

Table 17.1 Phases of coin composition of the Bornholm hoards

Phase	tpqs	Hoard size	Coin types found
Phase 1	*c.* 855–*c.* 1000	Small	Dominated by Kufic coins
Phase 2	*c.* 1000–*c.* 1050	Generally large	German, with some English and a small number of Scandinavian and Kufic
Phase 3	*c.* 1050–*c.* 1100	Generally small	Dominated by German and English coins, some Scandinavian; almost no Kufic coins

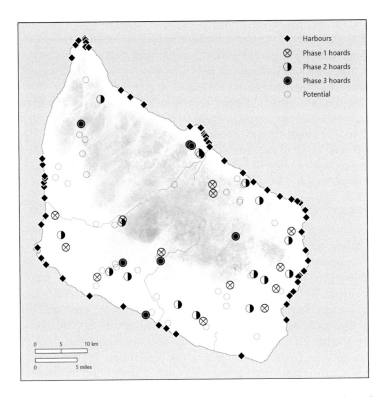

Map 17.3 The distribution of hoards in relation to natural harbours and landing places on Bornholm.[1]

After Ingvardson (2014), fig. 11 and Skaarup (2016).

Note

1 See Table 17.1 for a description of Phases 1–3; and Figure 17.2 for a more detailed break-down. Although the distribution of Viking-Age harbours or landing places has yet to be fully investigated, the historic harbours shown give an idea of where landing was possible.

hinterland of the islands' many harbour sites,[30] and display a similar distribution pattern to the Bornholm hoards. However, from the mid-eleventh century we see a clearer orientation towards the harbour areas on Gotland.[31] This change is not found on Bornholm, where the distribution pattern remains unchanged (see Map 17.3). In the twelfth century, Visby went from being one of several important harbours to being the most important and dominant harbour site; it was also the only site that developed into a city,[32] although Fröjel and Västergarn appear to have been active then, too.[33] At the same time (*c.* 1140) the introduction of Gotland's own coinage stands as a landmark in the economic development of the island.[34]

Bornholm's decentralised settlement structure was apparently mirrored by an equally decentralised organisation of its trade. As noted earlier, Bornholm did not undergo the urbanisation seen in Scania and Zealand, nor do archaeological records show evidence of new trading centres developing, as they did at the more permanent harbour sites on Gotland. However, trade-related finds such as imported goods, weights and coins can be connected to the new, decentralised settlements on Bornholm. A move from a centralised to a more decentralised trade structure is supported by the distribution pattern of weight types.[35] There is a clear difference in the distribution pattern of 'Viking-Age weight types' (such as polyhedral weights and spherical weights with flattened poles) and 'other weight types'.[36] The former are found on many sites, but with only a few per site; the latter show a similar distribution, but we also see large clusters of them at Iron-Age sites such as Sorte Muld: 28% of other weight types are concentrated at just five sites.[37] This distribution pattern implies that sites with many weights are a pre- or early Viking-Age phenomenon on Bornholm, as the Viking-Age weight types do not cluster but produce only a few weights per site.[38] Even though other weight types may also have been used to weigh silver in a bullion economy,[39] the introduction of standardised polyhedral weights and spherical weights with flattened poles signals a move towards standardising the silver trade.[40] Thus, the scattered distribution of polyhedral weights and spherical weights with flattened poles at Viking-Age sites on Bornholm indicates that trade was connected to individual farms. A similar situation is found on Gotland. Finds of tenth-century scales, weights and stray coins are limited mainly to harbour sites and a small selection of farms, yet by the eleventh century these find groups become common on individual farms, indicating a spread of trade-related activities and the regular use of scales, weights and silver on those farms.[41] The one marked difference between the two islands is the presence of harbours with permanent trading activities: these developed on Gotland but not, to the best of our knowledge, on Bornholm.

Thus, settlement on early Viking-Age Bornholm and Gotland seems to have been decentralised and based inland from the islands' many natural harbours. On Bornholm this pattern remained unchanged throughout the Viking Age, while Gotland moved towards a pattern of fewer harbours, but ones with more permanent trading activity, in the late Viking Age. Hoarding practices on the two islands display both similarities and differences. On Gotland there was a general increase in hoarding between *c.* 800 and 1050. On Bornholm it remained sporadic in the ninth and tenth centuries, only showing a marked increase from around 990. On both islands the 990s saw a transition, when western European coins replace Kufic ones in the hoards, and both show a significant decrease in hoarding activity from the mid-eleventh century. On Bornholm, fewer and smaller hoards were deposited after 1050. On Gotland, a decrease in deposited hoards was accompanied by an increase in deposited coins, as some deposited hoards grew in size.

Evidence from hoards and settlements points to very different development patterns on these two Baltic islands. Their role as stepping-stones in east–west trade routes in the early Viking Age is supported by the numerous dirham hoards on

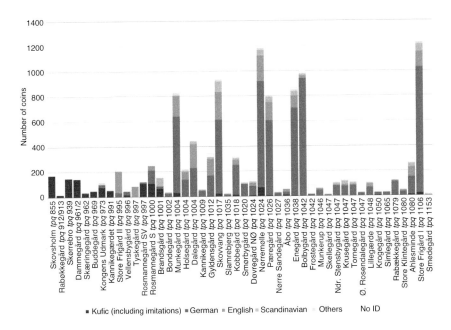

Figure 17.2 The distribution of coin types in the Bornholm hoards (*tpq* for each hoard shown after its name).

Gotland, but the same cannot be said of the few ninth- and tenth-century hoards on Bornholm. Gotland seems to have developed progressively towards a trading system that was more specialised and perhaps more controlled, which featured permanent harbours and larger hoards, and which culminated in the twelfth century with the establishment of Visby and the island's own coinage. Bornholm only seems to have become more active within the evolving trading systems around the year 1000, as shown by the switch from eastern to western coins in its hoards. For a brief period, from around 990 to 1050, the two islands seem to have experienced similar economic conditions; but whereas Gotland continued to develop into a rapidly changing medieval society, Bornholm seems to have stagnated. The evidence presented here only includes hoards and settlements, and many questions remain unanswered. For example, how did the introduction of Christianity, the integration of Bornholm into the Danish kingdom and the changing composition of merchant fleets in the Baltic influence economic development on Bornholm? These are all elements that need to be investigated further.

Raid, trade or ritual: silver hoards as windows onto Viking-Age life?

In this final section I shall move from a macro to a micro perspective and present case studies of six excavated Bornholm hoard sites. Detailed site and hoard analysis indicates a link between place of deposition and composition, and this may well register the hoard's function. Methodology and detailed analysis are presented elsewhere.[42] The six case studies outlined below will rather form the basis for discussion of hoard function in relation to general trends on Bornholm and Gotland. Equally, Gotland's vast hoard material has drawn massive scholarly attention, and this is not the place for a thorough review of publications and interpretations.[43] However, in order to contextualise the evidence from the six excavated Bornholm hoard sites, a short overview of the dominant theories is needed.

Raiding or trading is the predominant interpretation of how Gotland attained its vast silver supply. Mårten Stenberger, Majvor Östergren and Jacek Gruszczyński all emphasise Gotland's strategic position on one of the major trade routes from west to east, and argue that silver was primarily imported as the result of trade,[44] while Peter Sawyer highlights piracy as the most prevalent source of silver.[45] Mark Blackburn and Kenneth Jonsson have argued that the hoards were collected through both trading and raiding.[46] As to why so many hoards were deposited, Sture Bolin's 1926 thesis – that unrest led to an increase in hoard deposition – found many followers;[47] he suggested that the many Gotlandic hoards were deposited at times of war or when attack was feared, and were not reclaimed because of death or captivity. Östergren offers a different perspective on hoarding practices, using her analysis of hoard deposition places to argue that they were deposited under the floorboards of houses, and thus functioned as active hoards. She uses the distribution of weights, scales and single silver finds to demonstrate that silver did indeed circulate on the island, and attributes the non-retrieval of hoards to the owner's ill fortune during a journey abroad.[48] Dan Carlsson argues that hoards are primarily found in areas with workshops and suggests that they should be seen as raw material for silversmithing.[49] The ritual and symbolic aspect of hoarding has been touched upon by several researchers. Lena Thunmark-Nylén makes a distinction between hoards deposited before and after the introduction of Christianity. Hoards deposited in heathen times were made with the intention of retrieval in the afterlife, while 'Christian hoards' represent a family's savings.[50] Gruszczyński distinguishes between small hoards without containers and large hoards with containers. He argues that hoards deposited without containers were not intended for retrieval, and highlights offerings to newly broken fields and recently acquired lands as the commonest ritual behaviour when it comes to hoarding.[51] Anders Carlsson takes the ritual perspective a step further and interprets all kinds of deposits as ritual. He ascribes ritual power to all deposited coins, jewellery, silver and bronze scrap, iron bars, weights and balances and other objects. Silver hoards as well as workshop debris deposited on or near farms, harbour sites and other areas with craft activity are seen as ritual deposits, placed without any intention of retrieval.[52]

The Bornholm case studies

The six Bornholm case studies have been selected to demonstrate the diversity of the hoards. As they represent only a small part of the Bornholm hoard material, it goes without saying that similar investigations of other hoard sites may reveal different aspects and interpretations.

The Gyldensgård and Nørremølle hoards

Two of the hoards, Gyldensgård (*tpq* 1012) and Nørremølle (*tpq* 1024), were deposited during the period when hoarding activity was at its peak (*c.* 990–1050). Both are relatively large and dominated by western European coins. I interpret the hoards as deposited in the central part of a settlement area – Gyldensgård inside a house and Nørremølle just outside what may have been a Viking-Age house. They show great diversity in both coin types and non-minted silver, with a high degree of fragmentation in the latter, while most of the coins are complete. In both hoards, the majority of coins and non-minted silver had been tested for their silver content, showing signs of either test marks or bending. A further shared element is that the majority of coins were minted within a 40-year period, perhaps hinting that they were amassed during the career of one individual. Detailed analysis of where the objects in the Nørremølle hoard were made indicates that the coins were probably accumulated through trading in Scania and Zealand – to the north-west of Bornholm – while the jewellery is mainly of western Slavic origin, from the area to Bornholm's south.[53] The objects' diversity and fragmentation, and the extensive evidence of silver testing, all suggest that both hoards were built up through trade. And, following Östergren, their deposition in the central part of a settlement seems to indicate that these

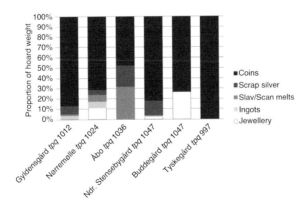

Figure 17.3 Composition by weight of the six presented hoards; after Ingvardson (2019), fig. 2.10.

were active hoards: silver that was saved, used and reused by its owner for repeated trading expeditions. The short chronological span implies that these were not long-accumulated family fortunes. Both hoards show evidence of deposition in containers: Nørremølle was partly preserved in situ within a Baltic ware vessel, and Gyldensgård was surrounded by black, organic material, believed to be the dissolved remains of a purse. This corresponds with Gruszczyński's suggestion that hoards deposited in containers were intended to be retrieved. A large number of loom weights – 31 fragments of various sizes – and quantities of hammerscale suggest craft activity at the Gyldensgård site; but there are no signs of silversmithing, and the hoard should probably not be interpreted as raw material. Both hoards were deposited in a transitional period, when Christian influences were gradually appearing alongside ancient traditions at Bornholm's burial sites.[54] The later Bornholm runestones carry a clear Christian message and testify to the gradual Christianisation of the island during the eleventh century.[55] As the two hoards were deposited at the beginning of the eleventh century, it is difficult to establish whether this was in a pre-Christian or Christian context, thus neither supporting nor contradicting Thunmark-Nylén's suggestion that 'heathen hoards' were deposited without intention of retrieval in this life. The postholes of the house near the Nørremølle hoard were filled with charcoal, large amounts of burnt wattle and daub fragments and charred grains, indicating that the house had been burnt. This, together with the discovery of an iron arrowhead at the top of one of the postholes, may indicate some sort of attack which, in turn, may have led to deposition outside the house and the hoard's non-retrieval.[56]

The Nordre (Ndr.) Stensebygård and Åbo hoards

The deposits at Ndr. Stensebygård (*tpq* 1047) and Åbo (*tpq* 1036) are later than those at Nørremølle and Gyldensgård, but still within the period of intense hoarding activity. Situated on the outskirts of settlement areas, their composition is different from that of the Nørremølle and Gyldensgård hoards. The Ndr. Stensebygård hoard had been completely dispersed by agricultural activity, but a coin cluster was found centred around a pit at the top of which lay the remains of two Baltic ware vessels, interpreted by the excavator to have been the original deposition spot. A Viking-Age silver bracelet fragment, small quantities of silver melts and pieces of a melting pot with a partially melted silver coin were found beneath the vessels.[57] Thus, the Ndr. Stensebygård hoard was probably deposited in a silversmith's pit, and the location suggests it was raw material for the workshop. This interpretation is supported by the very high proportion of scrap silver among the non-minted silver. Furthermore, the coins are heavily test marked and bent; the quasi-destructive nature of this secondary treatment indicates that the coins were considered as scrap silver at the time of deposition. The Åbo hoard was found in the posthole of a small building, whose size and location indicate some sort of workshop or storage function, and it stands out as one of the few hoards on Bornholm where the non-minted silver weighs more than the coins (see Figure 17.3). The former is almost exclusively made up of melts, with the exception of a single silver-foil bead. Of the 11 melts found at Åbo, eight are of a type indicating that they were products of cupellation, where silver was refined in hearths lined with bone-ash material, as at the Fröjel workshop on Gotland.[58] Both hoards may therefore be connected to some form of silversmithing and, following Dan Carlsson's line of argument, might have been raw material. Although no signs of a container have been found at Åbo, the single silver-foil bead may tentatively be interpreted as the remains of a purse clasp.[59] This, together with the fact that the hoard was probably deposited in a building, thus making it easy to find again, makes it possible that it was deposited with the intention of retrieval.

The Buddegård and Tyskegård hoards

The Buddegård hoard (*tpq* 969) contains Samanid coins and was deposited during the second wave of dirhams into the Baltic region, while the Tyskegård hoard (*tpq* 996) was deposited during the transitional period, when dirhams were being replaced by western European coins. Both were deposited in areas without any other archaeological finds or structures, and are of unusual composition in comparison with most Viking-Age hoards on Bornholm. The Tyskegård hoard is made up exclusively of Æthelred II's *Long Cross* pennies which show very few secondary traces such as test marking or bending. This suggests that the hoard may have been acquired over a very short period of time, probably through raiding in England,[60] and that it was deposited soon after its acquisition. The Buddegård hoard consists of a trefoil brooch, the fragment of an arm-ring and 35 dirhams. Most of the coins are complete and have been pierced or looped, indicating that they were used as jewellery, and Buddegård may fall into the group of hoards with specially selected objects of female ornamentation centred around trefoil brooches.[61] Thus, both hoards include carefully selected objects which may intentionally have been withdrawn from the economic sphere and this, together with their apparently remote deposition spots, may suggest that they were ritual deposits. No traces of containers have been found at either location, supporting Gruszczyński's theory, although it must be stressed that such traces could have been destroyed by later ploughing. In the case of Buddegård, it is more likely than not that the hoard was deposited without a container: even though nothing was discovered in situ, the finds were in a dense cluster, suggesting that the hoard had only recently been ploughed up; and it was deposited in heavy clay soil, a good medium for the preservation of organic material.[62] That the Tyskegård hoard was deposited near a very large stone perhaps also indicates some form of ritual, although not necessarily the claiming of recently occupied lands. Such stones can be significant markers in the landscape, indicating a desire to retrieve the hoard – possibly in the afterlife, as Thunmark-Nylén argues.

Conclusion

The evidence from these six case studies suggests that hoards deposited in the central parts of settlement areas, and with similar compositions to the Nørremølle and Gyldensgård hoards, should be interpreted as active hoards, amassed through trade and deposited with every intention of retrieval. Hoards deposited on the outskirts of settlement areas and with contents which suggest a connection to silversmithing – as with the high proportion of scrap silver at Ndr. Stensebygård or the melts at Åbo – may have been raw material hoards, also deposited with the intention of retrieval. However, hoards such as those at Buddegård and Tyskegård, deposited in areas devoid of other Viking-Age finds or structures and whose contents amount to careful selections of objects, may have been ritual deposits and not intended for retrieval, at least not in the present life. These functional differences may also reflect when the hoards were deposited, which in turn may register general trends in hoarding activity: the ritual hoards were deposited before the period of intense hoarding activity (*c.* 990–1050), or during the transitional period of the 990s; the active-trading hoards in the middle of the intense period; and the raw material hoards towards the end. A full picture cannot be drawn from just six hoards, and further analysis of the Bornholm hoards will hopefully give a clearer – though probably more complicated – picture of Viking-Age hoarding practices. What the survey does show is that the Viking-Age hoards were amassed, used and deposited by different people, in numerous ways and for various reasons. The diversity in hoard composition and location does not support a single interpretation and not all hoards are ritual deposits (as Anders Carlsson has suggested). The survey also suggests that the hoards' composition taken together with their archaeological settings may be viewed as windows onto Viking-Age life.

Notes

1 I would like to thank the editors and Christoph Kilger for their many helpful comments and suggestions. Any errors remain the author's own.
2 See, for example, Jensen and Kromann (1993); von Heijne (2004); Moesgaard (2006); Horsnæs (2011); Ingvardson (2012); Ingvardson (2014); Ingvardson and Nielsen (2015).
3 *SoB*; *MSoS*, pp. 11–15.
4 Galster (1980), pp. 8–9.
5 Ingvardson and Nielsen (2015).
6 Ingvardson and Nielsen (2015), table 1.
7 Horsnæs (2014); Laursen and Ingvardson (2014).
8 Galster (1980), pp. 30–1; Horsnæs *et al.* (2013), p. 26.
9 Leimus (2009), pp. 8–10.

10 Grinder-Hansen (1994), p. 106; von Heijne (2004), pp. 158–9; Jensen (2006), pp. 161–3; Ingvardson (2016), pp. 141–3.
11 Märcher and Aagaard (2014).
12 Galster (1980), pp. 135–70.
13 Horsnæs *et al.* (2013), pp. 17–22; Ingvardson (2012), p. 293; Laursen and Ingvardson (2014).
14 *MSoS*, pp. 24–5.
15 von Heijne (2004), pp. 66–72, 129–52; Jonsson (2004), pp. 27–8.
16 Hårdh (1976), p. 130; von Heijne (2004), pp. 21–75, 127–9; Ingvardson (2016), pp. 138–41.
17 Andrén (1985), pp. 71–2; Skre (2016), pp. 167–70.
18 Christensen (2015), pp. 282–6.
19 Hårdh (2000).
20 Aarsleff (2009), p. 119; Watt (2009), pp. 26–7.
21 Rasmussen (1988); Wagnkilde (1999); Nielsen (1994a); Lihammer (2007), p. 243; Christensen *et al.* (2009).
22 Aarsleff (2008), pp. 21–2; Nielsen (1994a), pp. 125–9.
23 Ingvardson (2014), pp. 330–3.
24 Horsnæs (2014); Laursen and Ingvardson (2014); Ingvardson and Nielsen (2015), pp. 29–30.
25 Excavation is ongoing and I thank Finn Ole Nielsen, Archaeologist at the Bornholm Museum, for the information presented here.
26 Majvor Östergren has suggested that silver hoards are settlement indicators; for example, *MSoS*, pp. 37–9. However, as the case studies in this chapter show, only some hoards are likely to have been deposited in the central parts of settlements. See also Svedjemo in this volume.
27 See Svedjemo in this volume.
28 Gruszczyński (2019), pp. 51–5.
29 Lundström (1983); *MSoS*, pp. 210–3; Carlsson (1999); see also Carlsson in this volume.
30 Gruszczyński (2019), pp. 51–5; see also Gruszczyński in this volume.
31 *MSoS*, fig. 13.
32 *MSoS*, pp. 212–13.
33 Carlsson (2008), pp. 131–4; Kilger *et al.* (2015).
34 Myrberg (2008), pp. 149–56.
35 Ingvardson (2014), pp. 329–36.
36 Other weight types include spherical, cylindrical, segment shaped, quadrilateral and conical or bi-conical. They have a broad chronological frame and were also used in the Viking Age.
37 The five sites are Møllegård, Agerbygård, Sandegård, Smørenge and Sorte Muld.
38 Ingvardson (2014), pp. 330–2.
39 Pedersen (2008), p. 162; Haldenby and Kershaw (2014), pp. 106–21.
40 Gustin (2004), pp. 89–108; Steuer (1987), pp. 407–9.
41 *MSoS*, pp. 184–6.
42 Ingvardson (2019).
43 The research history of the Gotlandic hoards is discussed in detail in *MSoS*, pp. 25–30 and Myrberg (2008), pp. 15–21.
44 *SGW*, vol. 1, pp. 307–19; *MSoS*, p. 244; see also Gruszczyński in this volume.
45 Sawyer (1982), pp. 144–7.
46 Blackburn and Jonsson (1981), pp. 161–84.
47 Bolin (1926) and, for example, *SGW*, vol. 1, pp. 307–13. For further references, see *MSoS*, p. 27.
48 *MSoS*.

49 See Carlsson in this volume.
50 Thunmark-Nylén (1986).
51 See Gruszczyński in this volume.
52 A. Carlsson (2015), pp. 229–44.
53 Ingvardson (2012), pp. 289–94.
54 Lihammer (2007), pp. 240–51.
55 Imer (2016), pp. 298–316.
56 Ingvardson (2012), pp. 203–5.
57 Nielsen (1994b).
58 See Ingvardson (2019) for further discussion of this Slavic/Scandinavian melt type; on the Fröjel workshop, see Gustafsson and Söderberg (2005); Gustafsson (2011), p. 26; see also Gustafsson in this volume. I am very grateful to Ny Björn Gustafsson for drawing my attention to this possible interpretation of the melt type.
59 This interpretation is put forward by Frank Pelle, the finder of the Åbo hoard.
60 For an alternative view, see Screen in this volume.
61 Kilger (2008), pp. 325–35.
62 On the preservation of containers, see Gruszczyński in this volume.

Bibliography

Aarsleff, E. (2008), 'Velstandens Ø', *Skalk* 2008(4): 18–25.

Aarsleff, E. (2009), 'Viking Age finds', in C. Adamsen *et al.* (eds), *Sorte Muld: Wealth, Power and Religion at an Iron Age Central Settlement on Bornholm*, Rønne, pp. 18–121.

Andrén, A. (1985), *Den urbana scenen. Städer och samhälle i det medeltida Danmark*, Malmö.

Blackburn, M. and K. Jonsson (1981), 'The Anglo-Saxon and Anglo-Norman element of north European coins finds', in *VACNL*, vol. 1, pp. 147–255.

Bolin, S. (1926), *Fynden av romerska mynt i det fria Germanien: studier i romersk och äldre germansk historia*, Lund.

Carlsson, A. (2015), *Tolkande arkeologi och svensk forntidshistoria: från stenålder til vikingatid*, SSA 64, Stockholm.

Carlsson, D. (1999), 'Harbours and farms on Gotland', in N. Blomkvist and S.-O. Lindquist (eds), *Europeans or Not? Local Level Strategies on the Baltic Rim 1100–1400 AD*, Visby, pp. 115–24.

Carlsson, D. (2008), '"Ridanæs": a Viking Age port of trade at Fröjel, Gotland', in *VW*, pp. 131–4.

Christensen, L. B. *et al.* (2009), 'Settlement', in C. Adamsen *et al.* (eds), *Sorte Muld: Wealth, Power and Religion at an Iron Age Central Settlement on Bornholm*, Rønne, pp. 143–55.

Christensen, T. (2015), *Lejre bag myten. De arkæologiske udgravninger*, Aarhus.

Galster, G. (1980), 'Vikingetids møntfund fra Bornholm', *NNÅ* 1977–8: 5–248.

Grinder-Hansen, K. (1994), 'Mønter som kilde til middelalderens økonomiske historie: en præsentation af et kildemateriale', *Fortid og nutid: tidsskrift for kulturhistorie og lokalhistorie* 1994(2): 101–33.

Gruszczyński, J. (2019), *Silver, Hoards and Containers: The Archaeological and Historical Context of Silver Coin Deposits in the Baltic c. 800–1050*, Abingdon.

Gustafsson, N. B. (2011), 'Beyond Wayland: thoughts on early medieval metal workshops in Scandinavia', *Historical Metallurgy* 45: 20–31.

Gustafsson, N. B. and A. Söderberg (2005), 'The tidy metalworkers of Fröjel', *Viking Heritage Magazine* 2005(3): 14–17.

Gustin, I. (2004), *Mellan gåva och marknad: handel, tillit och materiell kultur under vikingatid*, Stockholm.

Haldenby, D. and J. Kershaw (2014), 'Viking-Age lead weights from Cottam', *Yorkshire Archaeological Journal* 86: 106–23.

Hårdh, B. (1976), *Wikingerzeitliche Depotfunde aus Südschweden: Probleme und Analysen*, Lund.

Hårdh, B. (2000), 'Uppåkra: a centre in south Sweden in the 1st millennium AD', *Antiquity* 74: 640–8.

Horsnæs, H. W. (2011), 'Rosmannegård (Bornholm). to brudsølvsskatte fra omkring år 1000', *Nordisk Numismatisk Unions Medlemsblad* 2011(1): 11–14.

Horsnæs, H. W. (2014), 'Changing hands: the Skovsholm *dirham* hoard', in S. M. Sindbæk and A. Trakadas (eds), *The World in the Viking Age*, Roskilde, p. 65.

Horsnæs, H. W. et al. (2013), 'A stepping stone in the Baltic Sea: two millennia of coin finds and coin use – a case study of Vester Herred, Bornholm', *The Journal of Archæological Numismatics* 3: 1–65.

Imer, L. M. (2016), *Danmarks Runeseten: en fortælling*, Copenhagen.

Ingvardson, G. T. (2012), 'Nørremølle: the largest Viking Age silver hoard of Bornholm (Denmark)', *The Journal of Archaeological Numismatics* 2: 281–346.

Ingvardson, G. T. (2014), 'Trade and power: Bornholm in the late Viking Age', in H. C. Gulløv (ed.), *Northern Worlds: Landscapes, Interactions and Dynamics*, Odense, pp. 325–37.

Ingvardson, G. T. (2016), 'Et sted midtimellem: Svend Estridsen og 1000-tallets Mønthistorie', in L. C. A. Sonne and S. Croix (eds), *Svend Estridsen*, Odense, pp. 135–57.

Ingvardson, G. T. (2019), 'As long as it glitters: a re-evaluation of the mixed silver hoards of Bornholm, Denmark', in J. Kershaw et al. (eds), *Silver, Butter, Cloth: Monetary and Social Economies in the Viking Age*, Oxford, pp. 32–56.

Ingvardson, G. T. and F. O. S. Nielsen (2015), '100 Viking Age hoards of Bornholm: status, challenges and perspectives', in L. Larsson et al. (eds), *Small Things Wide Horizons: Studies in Honour of Birgitta Hårdh*, Oxford, pp. 27–34.

Jensen, J. S. (2006), 'The introduction and use of runic letters on Danish coins around the year 1065', in M. Stocklund et al. (eds), *Runes and Their Secrets: Studies in Runology*, Copenhagen, pp. 159–68.

Jensen, J. S. and A. Kromann (1993), 'The hoard of Lillegærde in Bornholm', in T. Hackens et al. (eds), *Actes du XIe Congrès International de Numismatique, Bruxelles, 8–13 septembre 1991*, 4 vols, Louvain-la-Neuve, vol. 3, pp. 73–80.

Jonsson, K. (2004), 'Västerländska vikingatida mynt', *GA* 76: 27–32.

Kilger, C. (2008), 'Kombinationer av föremål: de vikingatida mittspännedepåerna', in C. Prescott et al. (eds), *Facets of Archeology: Essays in Honour of Lotte Hedeager on Her 60th Birthday*, Oslo, pp. 323–38.

Kilger, C. et al. (2015), 'Mynt och bebyggelse: bebyggelseutvecklingen inom Västergarnsvallen ur ett numismatiskt perspektiv', in T. Talvio and M. Wijk (eds), *Myntstudier: Festskrift till Kenneth Jonsson*, Stockholm, pp. 141–56.

Laursen, R. and G. Ingvardson (2014), 'Skovsholm: en bornholmsk stormandsgård?', in H. Lyngstrøm and L. C. A. Sonne (eds), *Vikingetidens aristokratiske miljøer. Arkæologi på Saxo-instituttet*, Copenhagen, pp. 55–8.

Leimus, I. (2009), 'Millennium breakthrough: north goes west', in T. Tonnberg and O. Raun (eds), *Past: Special Issue on the History of Estonia* [= *Tuna: Ajalookultuuri Ajakiri Special Issue*], Tallinn, pp. 7–34.

Lihammer, A. (2007), *Bortom riksbildningen: människor, landskap och makt i sydöstra Skandinavien*, Lund.

Lundström, P. (1983), 'Gotlandshamnar', in *GoV*, pp. 99–116.

Märcher, M. and S. Aagaard (2014), 'Skattefund med falske 1100-tals mønter på store Myregård, Bornholm', *Nordisk Numismatisk Unions Medlemsblad* 2014(1): 13–17.

Moesgaard, J. C. (2006), 'The import of English coins to the Northern Lands: some remarks on coin circulation in the Viking Age based on new evidence from Denmark', in B. Cook and G. Williams (eds), *Coinage and History in the North Sea World c. 500–1250: Essays in Honour of Marion Archibald*, Leiden, pp. 389–434.

Myrberg, N. (2008), *Ett eget värde. Gotlands tidigaste myntning, ca 1140–1220*, SSA 45, Stockholm.

Naum, M. (2008), *Homelands Lost and Gained: Slavic Migration and Settlement on Bornholm in the Early Middle Ages*, Lund.

Nielsen, F. O. (1994a), 'Middelaldergårde på Bornholm', *Hikuin* 21: 125–38.

Nielsen, F. O. (1994b), *Arkæologiske Udgravninger, Ndr. Stensebygård, BMR 2151* (AUD 1994(183)), Rønne.

Pedersen, U. (2008), 'Weights and balances', in *ME*, pp. 119–79.

Rasmussen, A. H. (1988), 'Det bornholmske landbosamfund i 1700-tallet', in *Bornholms Landbrug gennem tiderne* [= *Bornholmske samlinger* 3(2)], Rønne, pp. 9–20.

Sawyer, P. H. (1982), *Kings and Vikings: Scandinavia and Europe, AD 700–1100*, London.

Skaarup, J. C. (2016), *De bornholmske kystskanser: samt bavner, magasiner, krudt- og vagthuse. Kanoner og soldater*, Rønne.

Skre, D. (2016), 'Post-substantivist production and trade: specialized sites for trade and craft production in Scandinavia AD c. 700–1000', in J. H. Barrett and S. J. Gibbon (eds), *Maritime Societies of the Viking and Medieval World*, London, pp. 156–70.

Steuer, H. (1987), 'Gewichtsgeldwirtschaften im frühgeschichtlichen Europa. Feinwaagen und Gewichte als Quellen zur Wahrungsgeschichte', in K. Düwel *et al.* (eds), *Untersuchungen zu Handel und Verkehr der vor- und frühgeschichtlichen Zeit in Mittel- und Nordeuropa*, vol. 4: *Der Handel der Karolinger- und Wikingerzeit*, Gottingen, pp. 405–527.

Thunmark-Nylén, L. (1986), 'Hedningar, kristna och silverskatter', *GA* 58: 23–44.

von Heijne, C. (2004), *Särpräglat. Vikingatida och tidigmedeltida myntfynd från Danmark, Skåne, Blekinge och Halland (ca 800–1130)*, SSA 31, Stockholm.

Wagnkilde, H. (1999), 'Slaviske træk i bornholmske grave fra tiden omkring kristendommens indførelse', *META: medeltidsarkeologisk tidskrift* 1999(2): 3–20.

Watt, M. (2009), 'Sorte Muld: past and present', in C. Adamsen *et al.* (eds), *Sorte Muld: Wealth, Power and Religion at an Iron Age Central Settlement on Bornholm*, Rønne, pp. 17–33.

18 Coins as an indicator of communications between the British Isles and Scandinavia in the Viking Age

Elina Screen

The period 790–1050 saw extensive communications between the British Isles and Scandinavia, as individuals, groups, objects, beliefs and practices all travelled between the two regions and contributed to important political, social, economic and religious changes.[1] Scandinavian raiding parties, armies and settlers reshaped Britain and Ireland politically and socially. Slaves, missionaries, merchants and occasionally experts from the British Isles reached Scandinavia, such as Godwine, the Anglo-Saxon moneyer who seems to have struck small coinages for the kings of Denmark, Norway and Sweden around the year 995.[2] Scandinavian raiding activities and tribute-taking in the British Isles and Francia contributed to increasing social stratification and intensifying royal control in Scandinavia, while Christian kings and kingdoms emerged in the late tenth and eleventh centuries. Precious metals flowed to Scandinavia along enlarged trading networks that extended from the Islamic world to York, Dublin, Iceland and beyond, with considerable economic impact.[3] Scandinavia and the Baltic thus gradually integrated into the wider political, religious and economic world of Christendom across the Viking Age.

Coins provide one window onto these processes and communications between the British Isles and Scandinavia. Coin inscriptions and types (the designs on each face of the coin) indicate the issuing authority and place of production, as well as embedding political and ideological messages. The physical characteristics of coins – metal content, weight, method of manufacture and secondary treatment (traces of use, including bending and testing) – help reveal how coins were produced and used.[4] Assemblages of coins and analysis of find distributions develop our understanding of the circumstances of coin use and loss. Study focuses in particular on individual losses (single finds or stray finds), cumulative finds (for example, assemblages discovered on a single site through metal-detecting or archaeological excavation) and hoards (simultaneous deposits of multiple coins, usually made for the safe-keeping of wealth but not recovered by their depositor, or occasionally concealed for ritual reasons without the intention of recovery). The single-find evidence, where this is plentiful through good reporting and recording of metal-detector finds, as in England and Denmark, is especially valuable for revealing what coins were being handled (and lost) day to day, and thus their economic and social roles.[5] In contrast, countries including the Republic of Ireland and Sweden prohibit metal-detecting: numismatists there have to focus on the study of excavation finds and hoards.[6] Given these significant differences in the find record, we cannot compare like with like across the British Isles and Scandinavia. Recovery biases may affect the representativeness of the extant coins, in addition to any underlying regional differences, such as distinctions between upland and lowland areas, or inland sites as against coastal or riverine sites with readier access to trade.

The use of coins and coinage in the Viking Age also differed between coin- and bullion-using economies.[7] Anglo-Saxon England, Francia, and the Byzantine and Islamic worlds were all coin-producing and coin-using economies. Rulers issued coins as part of a controlled system of coinage, enforced use of their coins in contexts such as tax payments and excluded the coins of other authorities as far as possible: the composition of English hoards and single finds confirms that Anglo-Saxon kings were largely successful in keeping out others' coins from the late eighth century.[8] Their official role gave coins a slight premium over uncoined silver. Despite the relatively high value of the silver penny, the principal denomination issued in Western Europe from the late seventh to the twelfth centuries,[9] the single-find evidence reveals that coinage was widely used in Anglo-Saxon society. While larger payments may well have been made in uncoined metal by weight, commodity money was also used alongside coins (for example, cattle, pigs, clothing and crops). Together these formed the key framework within which people reckoned value, though establishing the means of exchange actually used in transactions is more challenging.[10]

At the start of the Viking Age, the world beyond the Rhine, Scandinavia, Scotland, Wales and Ireland in contrast formed part of the bullion economy.[11] Precious metals were a key indicator of status and also played important roles in exchanges and the reckoning of value, with interesting contrasts between practices in Scandinavia and those in Scotland and Ireland before and during the Viking Age.[12] Within the bullion economy, coins had no official status and carried no innate premium; their value derived from their weight and precious metal content. Here, coins took their place alongside other forms of silver and occasionally gold, including ingots, arm-rings and other types of worked metal. Bullion was probably more important in dealings with strangers outside existing social networks, whereas commodity money was also utilised when transactions were embedded in relationships of trust.[13]

In Scandinavia, coins were part of life at Ribe and Hedeby from the eighth century, with imitative coinages produced in the early ninth century.[14] Beyond these trading centres, however, the extensive ninth-century imports of Islamic dirhams familiarised Scandinavians with silver coins and changed their use of silver. Small pieces of silver were used more and more in transactions. First hack-silver appeared in quantity. Subsequently coins, as opposed to other forms of silver, became increasingly prevalent in the hoards.[15] From the later tenth century, Scandinavian reception of the idea of coinage reached a new level with the appearance of more imitative coinages at mints including Sigtuna, Lund, Dublin and the Isle of Man.[16] In the later eleventh century, familiarity with coins enabled King Sven Estridsen of Denmark and King Harald Hardrada of Norway to introduce the first controlled royal coinages, and led to the development of a coin economy in Scandinavia. The region thus entered the wider European coin-producing and coin-using economy.[17]

Close analysis of the numismatic evidence, therefore, can reveal what coins were available in a particular region, identify changing patterns of loss or deposition of coins over time, and indicate the economic and social contexts within which coins were used, with certain caveats. The central challenge for evaluating communications through the coinage evidence is establishing the processes by which coins changed hands, when typically only the starting-point and end-point of the coin's life are known. How did coins move from their place of production, in England, Dublin, Germany or the Byzantine or Islamic world, to their ultimate point of deposition or loss, whether in the British Isles or Scandinavia? The manifold ways in which coins change hands pose a challenge to the historian and archaeologist. As with the study of objects on the move in general, prevailing assumptions about the most likely forms of communication within a particular social, economic, political and religious context tend to colour our interpretation of the processes that carried coins. The numismatic evidence for Viking-Age communications between the British Isles and Scandinavia is thus apt to be fitted into these often unspoken wider historiographical paradigms.

The communications behind the Viking-Age coin finds explored here may broadly be divided into commercial exchanges (trade), and socially embedded, non-commercial exchanges, such as gift-giving or redistribution of wealth through plunder and tribute, with differing weight placed on the two categories depending on the context.[18] For example, we presume commercial transactions were very important in the late Roman, Byzantine or Islamic worlds with their controlled coin economies and extensive coin use. In contrast, historians from the 1950s onwards tended to emphasise the role of socially embedded transfers and gift exchanges in the early medieval West, under the influence of anthropological work on the gift, and assumptions that relatively high-value coins were not widely available.[19] More recently Timothy Reuter and Nils Lund highlighted the importance of plunder and tribute to the workings of early medieval society and politics.[20] The well-known written evidence for Viking raiding and plundering, and the payment of tributes by Anglo-Saxon and Frankish rulers, therefore led to the violent redistribution of wealth being emphasised when explaining the presence of Western coins in Scandinavia. For example, the Yttergärde runestone in Uppland (U 344) records that Ulv took three gelds in England, paid by Tostig, Thorkell and Cnut. The *Anglo-Saxon Chronicle* reports the payment of increasing tributes from 991 to Cnut's massive

Danegeld of £82,500 in 1018. Thereafter, payments of ship money may have contributed to flows of coins to Scandinavia until Edward the Confessor dismissed the fleet in 1051.[21] Certainly, imports of Anglo-Saxon coins to Scandinavia and the Baltic peaked in the period *c.* 980–1050, when these payments were at their height.

In contrast, in areas with little or no written evidence for Scandinavian raiding, trade is emphasised as the main motor of coin imports. The fur and slave trades are seen as the prime movers behind the extensive finds of Islamic coins in Scandinavia and the Baltic region, supported by Arabic and Byzantine written sources such as Ibn Fadlan and the *De administrando imperio* which describe trade along the 'northern arc'.[22] The scant evidence for Scandinavian raids in Germany has also led to trade being highlighted as the principal cause for the vast numbers of German coins found in the Scandinavian and Baltic world: some 322,100 coins out of an overall total of 693,900 coins from the period *c.* 790–1200.[23] Indeed, the large-scale presence of German coins such as the *Otto-Adelheid Pfennige* in Scandinavia, together with the limited finds of these coins in Germany itself, led older numismatic scholarship to identify these German coins as *Fernhandelsdenar*, specifically produced for long-distance trade rather than local use. Increased finds of these coins within Germany have overturned this interpretation; on balance, however, the movement of coins within the Baltic area, and from Germany to Scandinavia, remains attributed to trade.[24]

Overall, today the picture is more nuanced. Thousands of metal-detected single finds have revealed that coinage was much more widely available in Western Europe than was formerly believed.[25] Ongoing study has enriched our understanding of transactions in Viking-Age Scandinavia, including the potential degree of duress involved in some superficially commercial exchanges. The fur and slave trade involved an element of redistributive exchange, as slaves were sourced through raiding in the British Isles and elsewhere, while the Norwegian chief Ohthere collected furs from tributary Sámi peoples.[26] Religious and political factors have also been addressed as potential explanations for the movement of coins, such as the impact of Frankish Christian missionary activity or rulers' desire to control trade: the *Royal Frankish Annals* recorded how in 808 the Danish king Godfrid raided Reric, an Obodrite trading place, and forcibly moved its merchants to Schleswig.[27] Since the 1970s, the development of medieval urban archaeology in the British Isles, especially in Dublin and York, and strengthened awareness of the impact of the clerical perspective of the written sources, has led to greater emphasis on the Vikings' role as traders and craftsmen, alongside their raiding and tribute-taking.[28] More recently, study of the processes of acculturation visible in areas of Scandinavian settlement, expressed in the development of place-names, language, styles of metalwork and stone sculpture drawing on both Scandinavian and local, Christian, traditions, has provided a new context for the numismatic evidence.[29] Let us turn now to the coin finds from England, Scotland and Ireland and reassess the evidence for communications, including both trading and raiding.

Changing patterns in the hoards and finds clearly communicate the arrival of the Vikings in the British Isles. In the face of Viking raiding, the local population deposited hoards such as the famous St Ninian's Isle hoard from Shetland.[30] The Viking presence, however, is also visible in assemblages that transcended previous regional distinctions, clearly deposited by the incomers. In England, Viking hoards such as the Croydon hoard typically included Anglo-Saxon, Frankish and Islamic coins together with non-numismatic silver, whereas Anglo-Saxons would have deposited English coins only.[31] The huge Cuerdale hoard deposited on the banks of the Ribble in around 905–10 included non-numismatic silver such as arm-rings and ingots, as well as hundreds of Anglo-Viking, Carolingian and Anglo-Saxon coins and around fifty dirhams.[32] In Ireland and Scotland, changes in the type of non-numismatic silver being hoarded indicated the Viking presence, including the appearance of 'ring money' and of hack-silver alongside complete ornaments and ingots, for example in the Skaill hoard from Orkney.[33] The single finds suggest coins were widely present at Scandinavian settlement sites in Scotland and in Dublin from the early tenth century onwards.[34]

Viking winter camp sites, including Repton and Torksey, have proved particularly revealing of the material being handled and lost by members of the Great Army.[35] The metal-detected finds from the Torksey winter camp in 872–3 include characteristically Scandinavian weights and gaming pieces, silver ingots and hack-silver, as well as the typical range of Islamic, Frankish and Anglo-Saxon coins.[36] The presence of weights, ingots and hack-metal indicates the active use of silver by weight on the site. This suggests that the members of the Great Army may have engaged in trading activities, with each other, with their camp followers and perhaps with the local population. Some metalworking and craft production also apparently took place on the site.[37] The written sources occasionally hint at communication between natives and the incomers: for example, the *Anglo-Saxon Chronicle* and the *Annals of Ulster* mention some Viking leaders by name.[38] The ransoming of the Codex Aureus by Ealdorman Alfred and his wife Wærburh, and St Findan's attempt to ransom his sister, also suggest that some inhabitants of the British Isles were able to negotiate and trade with the Vikings, though some degree of risk was involved.[39] It is worth recalling the sometimes narrow line between trading and raiding, however, and that the threat of force may have underpinned transactions.[40]

The numismatic evidence also communicates the social and political impact of the Viking settlers. As the Vikings became more established in Anglo-Saxon England, they began to use coinage to communicate their power. After initially imitating familiar Anglo-Saxon and Frankish coin types, from the 890s Viking rulers produced their own distinctive coins in the southern Danelaw, the towns of the Five Boroughs and York.[41] For example, the St Edmund Memorial pennies struck in East Anglia adopted the

Anglo-Saxon king killed or martyred by the Great Army in November 869 as an appropriate source of identity or religious authority for all inhabitants of the region.[42] Successive Viking rulers of York used both 'Viking' and Christian symbols and legends on their coins particularly creatively, including Thor's hammers, swords and the unique appearance of an Old Norse royal title, *Anlaf cununc* ('King Olafr'), alongside crosses and purely Christian legends, as on the *Mirabilia fecit* ('He has done marvellous works') coins.[43] The coinage evidence thus offers fascinating glimpses of the communication of ideas and the creation of new forms of representation by the Viking rulers of York and elsewhere in the Danelaw.

Socially, the differing concepts of value held by coin and bullion users led to the parallel use of coins and bullion in transactions in the Danelaw. For example, Mark Blackburn described the small Thurcaston hoard of twelve coins as the property of someone operating in a 'dual economy', equipped with Anglo-Saxon and Anglo-Viking coins for dealings with coin users, and two fragments of Islamic dirhams, for payments in silver by weight.[44] Bullion and coins continued to be used in parallel well into the tenth century in England, and recent work emphasises that multiple means of payment and silver economies could operate in parallel.[45] For example, on Gotland, hoards containing coins of different origins and silver objects continued to be deposited until the end of the Viking Age in *c.* 1145.[46] The two silver bars found with twenty-five coins (mainly English sterlings from the late twelfth to mid-thirteenth centuries) in the unusual Norrbys hoard hint at the occasional use of bullion alongside coins on Gotland at this time; so, too, may *Guta Lag*.[47] The presence in the Danelaw of coins with different silver contents after Alfred's recoinage of *c.* 875 seems to have stimulated the custom of testing coins by making nicks into the coin with a knife to gauge the softness and thus purity of the silver.[48] As the controlled royal coinage of the Wessex dynasty spread into the former areas of the Danelaw, testing died out in Anglo-Saxon England, but test or peck marks appeared in Scandinavian hoards from the 930s and 940s, and remained in use until coins became commonplace there in the mid-eleventh century.[49]

Let us now turn to the evidence offered by the coins found in Viking-Age Scandinavia. Very few Anglo-Saxon and other Western coins reached Scandinavia before *c.* 800.[50] Within the bullion economy their primary value lay in the coins' silver or gold content. Judging from their use as ornaments, however, some coins, especially rare or attractive types, may have had prestigious or high-status associations before and during the Viking Age, playing a part in what is sometimes termed a 'status' economy.[51] Ildar Garipzanov suggested that when few Carolingian coins were available in early ninth-century Norway, 'their use was mainly defined by the environment of social competition'.[52] The person or persons who assembled the Hoen hoard, deposited near Drammen, Norway in around 875, seem to have selected Western portrait pennies (coins depicting a bust or head, usually of a king), as opposed to the more prevalent Frankish and Anglo-Saxon coin types with other designs.[53] A particularly high proportion of Byzantine silver coins (up to 28%) found in Scandinavia were looped or pierced for suspension.[54] And the rare *Agnus Dei* type of Æthelred II (probably struck 1009) was clearly identified as exceptional, since ten of the eighteen specimens found in Scandinavia and the Baltic were pierced for suspension. This suggests that scarcer or more attractive coin types were recognised as such, while certain types like the *Agnus Dei* coins may have been valued as amulets or religious symbols.[55]

Exactly how coins reached Scandinavia in the early Viking Age has been much discussed. Simon Coupland has linked the hoards of Frankish coins found at Häljarp in Scania (deposited 823–40), and at Kättilstorp in Västergotland (851–60), convincingly to Viking raiding activity in Aquitaine through analysis of the mints at which the coins were struck.[56] The discovery of ever more Carolingian coins at Viking-Age trading sites such as Havsmarken on the Danish island of Ærø, however, means that trade – stimulated by the stability and economic success of the Carolingian empire from *c.* 790–820 – is now considered to have brought most of these early Western coins to Scandinavia.[57]

The low numbers of Anglo-Saxon and Frankish coins found in later ninth- and early tenth-century Scandinavia are particularly puzzling: Vikings clearly encountered coins in their raids, as finds from sites such as Torksey attest.[58] Nevertheless, very few Western coins are found in Scandinavia in this period. Prior to Alfred's recoinage of *c.* 875, the Lunettes coins of Wessex and Mercia were of poor silver, so the presumption has been that Scandinavians melted down any coins they received to form ingots or jewellery; certainly Scandinavians were familiar with the techniques involved in refining silver, as Ny Björn Gustafsson's recent work on cupellation has shown.[59] While their subjects' contributions towards tributes were clearly collected in coined money, Frankish and Anglo-Saxon kings may have made payment in bullion: Marion Archibald has suggested that ingots had 'an important, perhaps dominant, role in tribute payments of this time'.[60] Members of the Viking armies may also have engaged in trade and used coins locally, rather than taking them back to Scandinavia, especially once they began to settle in the British Isles.[61] In due course, metal analyses of the trace elements in Scandinavian ingots and silver objects may offer answers to this vexed question. Analyses of the Cuerdale ingots have certainly suggested that the silver in these was rarely derived from Arabic coins.[62] On the current evidence, it seems Anglo-Saxon coins were not always the preferred form of silver for Scandinavians. Thus in the later ninth and early tenth century, coins are not a strong marker for analysing communications between the British Isles and Scandinavia. The later example of Cnut's (1016–35) *Short Cross* coins, which are found in large numbers in English single finds, but are much scarcer in Scandinavian hoards, while the opposite is true of Cnut's earlier *Quatrefoil* and *Pointed Helmet* types, also suggests that factors beyond our present field of vision intermittently shaped both communications and the find record.[63]

In the third quarter of the tenth century, the flow of Islamic coins to Scandinavia ebbed, and Western coins appear in the finds in far greater numbers from around 980. These coins mostly came from Germany and Anglo-Saxon England, with smaller flows from Byzantium, Hungary, Bohemia and Normandy, among others. In most of Scandinavia and the Baltic countries, German coins are present in far greater numbers than those from Anglo-Saxon England; as noted above, these coins are associated with substantial trade with Ottonian and Salian Germany. The great unknown is how far trade, as opposed to the payment of tribute, was responsible for bringing Anglo-Saxon coins to Scandinavia at this time.[64] Archaeological evidence from Viking York and Dublin indicates that these towns were part of extensive trade networks. For example, Baltic amber was being worked in York.[65] The movement of some products between the British Isles and Scandinavia can be traced: Norwegian Ragstone hone stones were widely available in England from the mid-ninth century, and Anglo-Saxon Stamford ware pottery appeared in Norwegian sites in the eleventh century.[66] But how far did coins move the other way, in payment for these goods? Answers have ranged from the optimistic to the pessimistic.[67] The experience of the Irish Sea world in the tenth century suggests that complex and varied processes were at work over time. The Irish Sea was a very active trading area, which increasingly used coins (mainly drawn in from Anglo-Saxon England) in transactions from the 940s.[68] But until Sihtric Silkenbeard of Dublin began to strike his own coins in around 995, the Viking rulers of Dublin did not issue coins of their own. Thereafter, small numbers of Hiberno-Scandinavian and Hiberno-Manx coins percolated into Scandinavia.[69] The Dublin trade before the 940s is an important reminder that commercial transactions in the Viking world could be carried out successfully using silver by weight, or commodity money. Meanwhile, the parts of Ireland untouched by Scandinavian settlement retained their distinctive, largely coinless economy across the tenth century.[70] Depending on the means of payment preferred at any time, the presence or absence of coins is of variable significance in indicating communications.

The routes that coins took from the British Isles and Germany to Scandinavia have also been debated. Kenneth Jonsson's suggestion that Anglo-Saxon coins would mostly have entered Scandinavia after first circulating in the Elbe region of Germany and becoming mixed with German coins there has not been widely accepted.[71] Michael Metcalf has pointed to the differing ratios of Anglo-Saxon and German coins in the various countries, ranging from an even divide in Norway, to 60:40 in Denmark, to 80:20 or more in Finland and Estonia, which suggest that 'separate inflows, perhaps by different routes, and almost certainly to different destinations, were amalgamated through subsequent use within the northern lands'.[72] Hints in the Scandinavian hoard evidence have been particularly important in suggesting there were also some more direct contacts between the British Isles and Scandinavia. Coins that remained in Anglo-Saxon England circulated rapidly and extensively across the country, with a relatively small local bias to the coin stock.[73] Some Scandinavian hoards include identifiable groups of Anglo-Saxon coins, which appear to have travelled to Scandinavia together as 'parcels' that had not undergone much mixing or circulation in England. Hence these groups of Anglo-Saxon coins seem to have come more directly from the mint in England via a limited number of transactions in which the coins moved as a unit. Thus hoards dominated by coins of a single type, or which include groups of die-linked coins (coins struck from the same dies), suggest that direct contacts may have played a role in bringing the coins to Scandinavia. The Tyskegård hoard from Bornholm includes eighty-two coins of Æthelred II's *Long Cross* type, and has been convincingly associated with the substantial payments of tribute of Æthelred's reign.[74] The Anglo-Saxon coin stock in Finnish hoards includes an unusually high proportion of die-linked coins, perhaps indicating that a closely related group of coins arrived in Finland as a parcel, and then circulated actively.[75] Cnut's political manoeuvring and bribery of Norway's leading men may have left its mark in the Norwegian hoard record. The Årstad hoard in Rogaland (one of the areas from which Cnut recruited support for his 1028 campaign to seize Norway) in particular includes a high proportion of die-linked coins of Cnut's *Pointed Helmet* type, from mints including London, Lincoln and Newark.[76] It remains challenging, however, to interpret the specific processes of exchange behind such parcels of coins.

Further evidence for communications comes from the imitative coinages struck within Scandinavia. A few original Anglo-Saxon coin dies – and probably also moneyers – reached these imitative workshops and had a substantial afterlife within Scandinavia.[77] The Anglo-Saxon moneyers' names present in the official Danish coinages during the reigns of Cnut the Great, Harthacnut and Magnus the Good provide solid evidence for the export not only of coins and silver, but also of monetary expertise.[78] Despite their presence in generally lower numbers than the German coins, the relatively uniform Anglo-Saxon coins were clearly important in shaping Scandinavian expectations concerning the authoritative appearance of coinage, as Anglo-Saxon coin types influenced the designs adopted on Scandinavian coinages.[79]

The contrasts between the coins available in different regions within Scandinavia suggest that each area had its own particular history, and that communications were not constant. For example, Cecilia von Heijne's close analysis of the southern Scandinavian hoards indicates that Anglo-Saxon coins became less available on Bornholm after 1000.[80] Within Finland, coin use seems to have differed between the Satakunta region, where the rich cemeteries included many coins and balances but coins were not hoarded, and Finland Proper (Varsinais-Suomi/Southwest Finland) and Häme (Tavastia), where the known hoards are concentrated, and coins were most likely to have entered the country through trade.[81] And, after 1051, when

Anglo-Saxon coins were melted down together with other foreign currencies and used for national coinages in Denmark and Norway,[82] late Anglo-Saxon and early Norman coins continued to trickle into Swedish and Estonian hoards well into the twelfth century.[83] The coin evidence thus indicates the existence of active communications, and sometimes hints at changes in these communications, but unfortunately does not always speak clearly as to the quantity and quality of the relationships underlying the evidence.

The coinage evidence helps illuminate economic and political communications between Scandinavia and the British Isles, and the gradual processes by which Scandinavian ideas and expectations concerning coin use were transformed across the Viking Age. The coin finds clearly indicate the Viking presence in the British Isles. The Vikings' adoption of coinage in the Danelaw illustrates their ability to utilise Anglo-Saxon political and economic norms for their own ends. The numismatic evidence casts clear light on the start- and end-points of coins on their journeys in the Viking world, and hints at the specific processes that moved the coins between these points. The tendency to prioritise certain forms of communications, given our historiographical frameworks concerning the Viking Age, risks colouring our interpretation of the evidence, leading to an explanatory emphasis on trade with Germany, and raiding and tribute-taking in Anglo-Saxon England. Despite the huge finds of German coins in Scandinavia, the Baltic countries and Russia, these have historically been less studied than the flows of Islamic and Anglo-Saxon coins, leading to a tendency for east–west movements of coins to dominate our horizon, while north–south exchanges are perhaps underplayed in Anglophone scholarship. The role of trade in communications with the British Isles and between Scandinavia and the British Isles is less easily accessed than that of raiding, but may have been understated. Political and religious interventions likewise may have played an intermittent part in creating the pattern of numismatic finds. With further research, a more nuanced picture is emerging, of a world in which neighbouring regions of Scandinavia, indeed different individuals, might have preferential access to Anglo-Saxon coins obtained by very different means. Coins might serve as stores of wealth and indicators of status, but also took on increasingly important roles in internal Scandinavian trade as the Viking Age continued. Ever-increasing coin finds, particularly on Gotland and in Denmark and England, further study of die-linking and metal analyses of trace elements in the coinage and other precious metal objects offer good prospects for improving our understanding of how coins moved, and what they communicated to those who handled them.

Notes

1 I am very grateful to Simon Coupland, Svein H. Gullbekk, Rory Naismith and Andrew Woods for their helpful comments and references, which greatly improved the chapter. For the developments outlined in this paragraph, see e.g. *VW*.

2 Steen Jensen *et al.* (1995); Skaare (1995), vol. 1, pp. 40–1.
3 See now Horne (2014).
4 Jarrett (2009), §§ 1–17 (an excellent introduction); Grierson (1975) (numismatics in general); Ingvardson (2015) (types of secondary treatment found on Viking-Age coins).
5 Moesgaard (2006b) (different types of find); for a searchable database of finds, see PAS.
6 The *CNS* project is gradually publishing all Swedish hoards; on the Irish finds: Woods (2014); Sheehan in this volume.
7 Williams (2007), pp. 178–85, defines and discusses these terms (also distinguishing the status economy).
8 Naismith (2012), pp. 206–9; Cook (1999), pp. 232–7.
9 See Coupland (2014), pp. 283–4, on the increasing availability of halfpennies (oboles) in Francia.
10 Sawyer (2013), esp. pp. 102–7 (widespread coin use and trade in the tenth and eleventh centuries), p. 103 (references to commodity money in Ælfric's *Colloquy*). On commodity money more generally: Skre (2011); Gullbekk (2011).
11 See Williams (2007), pp. 178–85; Birgitta Hårdh's work is fundamental: e.g. Hårdh (1996).
12 Williams (2007), pp. 187–96, 202–5; on hoarding in Ireland: Sheehan (2007). Breatnach (2014) discusses Irish forms of payment including cattle and precious metal.
13 Skre (2011), pp. 77–83.
14 Malmer (2007); Feveile (2008).
15 Williams (2011b), pp. 344–50; Kilger (2007) discusses the transformative impact of hack-silver and imitative coinages on concepts of money and value. For the process in Norway: Gullbekk (2014), pp. 335–6 (use of hack-silver at Kaupang and Heimdalsjordet); Gullbekk (2009), pp. 31–5 (changing contents of the hoards).
16 Sigtuna: Kilger (2011); Hiberno-Manx, Dublin and Irish Sea imitative coinages: Bornholdt Collins *et al.* (2014), pp. 483–500. Malmer (1989, 1997) are fundamental die studies.
17 Gullbekk (2009), pp. 29–31; Ingvardson (2010), pp. 89, 98 (emphasising Sven's reign as a key turning point, but placing full monetisation and royal control in around 1150).
18 Naismith (2012), pp. 252–67 (the wider historiography); *HV*, pp. 144–50 (the older historiography for the Viking Age). For a wider view of exchanges, bringing in the human element and exploring language, see Abrams (2016).
19 See the seminal study of Grierson (1959).
20 Reuter (1985); Lund (1989).
21 E.g. *ASC*[1] s.a. 991, 1018, pp. 235, 251 (*ASC*[2] (E), p. 127, (A), p. 154); *ASC*[2] (D), p. 173. Naismith (2017), pp. 253–8, analyses the payments and how far they contributed to the Scandinavian coin finds.
22 IbnF[1]; *DAI* ch. 9, pp. 56–63, on the Rus. For discussion, see Noonan (1994).
23 Jonsson (1993); *HV*, pp. 152–7. Numbers from Talvio (2002), p. 9, Tab. 1; 61,100 Anglo-Saxon coins are recorded from the same period. German coins are particularly dominant in the finds *c.* 980–1050.
24 See Ilisch (1981), pp. 130–2; Ilisch (2016), against the *Fernhandelsdenar*. See also Kluge (ed.) (1993), esp. Blackburn (1993). *HV*, pp. 169–81, discusses merchants and the goods traded between Germany and Scandinavia.
25 E.g. Coupland (2014), pp. 258–62.
26 Ohthere's account: Lund (ed.) (1984), tr. pp. 18–22; the *Life* of St Findan provides a glimpse of the slave trade in Ireland: *VF*.

27 *ARF* s.a. 808, p. 126; von Heijne (2004), p. 163 (relates imports of English coins to political organisation); Moesgaard (2004) (suggested that missionary activity contributed to Danish finds of Louis the Pious' *Christiana religio* coins, though the author now emphasises trade).
28 On the written sources: Coupland (1991b); on Dublin: Duffy (ed.) (2000–); for York: Palliser (2014); the publications of the York Archaeological Trust including Hall *et al.* (2004).
29 Graham-Campbell *et al.* (eds) (2001); Hadley and Richards (eds) (2000).
30 Small *et al.* (1973).
31 Croydon hoard: *Checklist*, no. 67, deposited *c.* 872; for discussion: Brooks and Graham-Campbell (1986).
32 Williams (2011a) discusses the contents (pp. 42–59) and determines the *tpq* (p. 67).
33 Graham-Campbell (1995), no. 24, and pp. 34–48.
34 Williams (2006), pp. 167–9; Woods (2014), pp. 298–312.
35 Williams (2015) (comparison of British and Irish sites); on Repton: Biddle and Kjølbye-Biddle (2001); on Woodstown: Sheehan (2015).
36 Blackburn (2011); Hadley *et al.* (2016) (detailed presentation of the site and the finds).
37 Blackburn (2011), pp. 241–2 (craft production); pp. 246–7 (the Vikings' women and hangers-on); Hadley *et al.* (2016), pp. 45–54; see also Woods in this volume on potential coin production at Torksey.
38 E.g. *ASC*[1] s.a. 871, pp. 197–8 (*ASC*[2] (A), p. 70, (E), p. 71); *Annals of Ulster* s.a. 866, pp. 320–3. I owe this point to Alex Woolf.
39 'Golden Gospels of Stockholm'; *VF*, ed. Holder-Egger, p. 503; tr. Omand, p. 284; enemies of Findan's family also called on Vikings to seize him: *VF*, ed. Holder-Egger, p. 503; tr. Omand, p. 285. On the Irish slave trade: Holm (1986); for two Frankish examples of trade with Vikings: Coupland (2011), p. 123; 'Edict of Pîtres', Ch. 25, p. 321.
40 Hedeager (1994); Samson (1991).
41 Naismith (2017), pp. 278–304; Williams (2014).
42 *ASC*[1] s.a. 870, p. 197 (*ASC*[2] (A), p. 70, (E), p. 71); on St Edmund Memorial coinage: Blackburn (2001a); Williams (2014), pp. 27–8; Naismith (2017), pp. 290–2.
43 Blackburn (2004) (survey of the types); Williams (2014), pp. 28–37 and Naismith (2017), pp. 292–301 (recent finds and interpretations).
44 Blackburn (2001b); on the dual economy: Blackburn (2009), pp. 64–8.
45 Kershaw (2017); Williams (2011b) (for 'multiple economies'); Naismith (2017), pp. 18–22 (for a still wider perspective).
46 Myrberg (2008), p. 24; e.g. the Burge hoard, which included *grivna*s or standardised silver bars of Novgorod: Myrberg (2008), p. 153 and no. 4, pp. 240–1.
47 Norrbys hoard, Follingbo parish, *tpq* 1248: Rasmusson (1944); Lindblad (2007), esp. p. 6. See Gustafsson in this volume (on coin and bullion use on Gotland); *GL*, pp. 198–9 (on Gotland's medieval monetary system). *Guta Lag* reckons its payments in marks of silver (*markr silfr*), marks of coin (*markr penninga*) and marks (unspecified): see e.g. *GL*, pp. 15–20, for references to marks of silver. It is hard to distinguish between monetary referents and the actual means of payment. Coin use was well established on Gotland at this time, as coins recovered from under church floors reveal: Myrberg (2008), p. 22. Payments could also have been made in commodity money: *GL*, p. 95 (note to § 13, line 62) discusses the use of other goods including homespun cloth and cattle. See above nn. 10 and 12 on commodity money.
48 Archibald (2011), p. 64.

49 Archibald (2011), p. 61; Blackburn (2009), p. 51; Gullbekk (1992); Moesgaard (2011).
50 See Blackburn and Jonsson (1981), Tab. 2, p. 150. Islamic coins dominated until *c.* 980, with 209,500 coins known *c.* 790–1200: Talvio (2002), Tab. 1, p. 9.
51 Williams (2007), p. 178.
52 Garipzanov (2008), p. 81. On Carolingian coin finds in Scandinavia: Coupland (2011).
53 Blackburn (2006), pp. 181–2.
54 Audy (2016), p. 150.
55 Twenty-one *Agnus Dei* pennies and two mules (coins combining the *Agnus Dei* obverse with a reverse die of the next, *Last Small Cross*, type) are presently known: Keynes and Naismith (2011); Keynes and Naismith (2015). See Keynes and Naismith (2011), pp. 206–7 and Audy (2018), pp. 219–24 on the pierced coins; Audy (2018), pp. 225–31, on the varied meanings of coin pendants in Scandinavia.
56 Coupland (2011), pp. 114–15.
57 Coupland (2014), pp. 270–1; Coupland (2011), p. 125; for the finds from Havsmarken: historieinfo.dk/Fundhavsmarken.html; for the few Anglo-Saxon coins travelling with the Frankish coins: Screen (2008), pp. 98–106. See p. 380 above on possible political and religious influences.
58 Screen (2008); Coupland (1991a).
59 On the recoinage: Blackburn (2003), pp. 205–8; on cupellation: Gustafsson in this volume.
60 Archibald (2011), p. 63. The Frankish collection of tribute is best attested: Coupland (1999).
61 On trading at Torksey, see above, p. 381; see Coupland (2011), pp. 123, 126, on the Frankish evidence. See also Woods in this volume.
62 Kruse and Graham-Campbell (2011), p. 83.
63 Naismith (2017), p. 269, raises the possibility that *Short Cross* coins were issued for longer.
64 Gullbekk (2010); Naismith (2017), pp. 253–8. See above n. 23 for numbers of coins.
65 Mainman and Rogers (2004), pp. 460, 472–3; Palliser (2014), p. 69. Sawyer (1986) (on the written evidence and post-Conquest trade).
66 Screen (2008), pp. 101, 112 (with references).
67 Optimists: Blackburn and Jonsson (1981), p. 149; pessimist: Sawyer (1986), p. 195, arguing for tributes, raiding and gifts.
68 See Blackburn (2007), pp. 126–30; Blackburn (2009), pp. 58–60; Bornholdt Collins (2010); Woods (2014), p. 299; Woods (2015).
69 Blackburn (2008). Andrew Woods' important thesis on the Dublin coinage awaits publication (2013); Naismith with Woods (2017) provides an interim survey.
70 Blackburn (2007), p. 128, fig. 4; Sheehan (2007) (for a detailed breakdown of the hoards by type).
71 Jonsson (1993). On the routes taken by German coins from differing regions: *HV*, p. 163; von Heijne (2004), p. 163.
72 Metcalf (1998), p. 353; see also Metcalf (2006).
73 Naismith (2013), pp. 212–19.
74 Moesgaard (2006a), pp. 405–10; von Heijne (2004), p. 158.
75 Stewart (1981), p. 492; Talvio (2002), p. 111.
76 Screen (2017).
77 Blackburn (1985); Malmer (1997), pp. 54–5.
78 For Anglo-Saxon and Anglo-Scandinavian moneyers at Lund: Becker (1981), p. 142.

79 E.g. Malmer (1997), pp. 21–33 (on the style of the imitative types). Æthelred II's
    Long Cross type was especially important, being imitated in Scandinavia, Dublin
    and the Irish Sea: Leighton and Woods (2014), p. 515.
80 von Heijne (2004), p. 158; Ingvardson in this volume.
81 Talvio (2002), pp. 119–23.
82 Skaare (1976); Gullbekk (2009); Steen Jensen *et al.* (1995).
83 Leimus and Molvõgin (eds) (2001); Jonsson (1995), pp. 44, 56–7.

Bibliography

Primary sources

*ARF = Annales regni Francorum inde ab. a. 741 usque ad a. 829, qui dicuntur Annales Laur-
issenses maiores et Einhardi*, ed. F. Kurze, *MGH SRG* 6, Hanover (1895).

The Annals of Ulster to AD *1131*, ed. and tr. S. Mac Airt and G. Mac Niocaill, Dublin
(1983).

Checklist of Hoards from the British Isles, c. 450–1180, fitzmuseum.cam.ac.uk/dept/coins/
projects/hoards (accessed 16 December 2019).

'Edict of Pîtres', ed. A. Boretius and V. Krause, in *MGH Leges, Capitularia regum Francorum* 2, Hanover (1897), pp. 310–28.

'Golden Gospels of Stockholm', esawyer.org.uk/charter/1204a.html (accessed
16 December 2019); tr. D. Whitelock in *EHD*, no. 98, pp. 572–3.

Secondary literature

Abrams, L. (2016), 'Connections and exchange in the Viking world', in *BVW*,
pp. 37–52.

Archibald, M. (2011), 'Testing', in *CH*, pp. 51–64.

Audy, F. (2016), 'How were Byzantine coins used in Viking-Age Scandinavia?', in
BWV, pp. 141–68.

Audy, F. (2018), *Suspended Value: Using Coins as Pendants in Viking-Age Scandinavia
(c.* AD *800–1140)*, SSA 74, Stockholm.

Becker, C. J. (1981), 'The coinage of Harthacnut and Magnus the Good at Lund,
c. 1040–*c.* 1046', in C. J. Becker (ed.), *Studies in Northern Coinages of the Eleventh Century*, Copenhagen, pp. 119–74.

Biddle, M. and B. Kjølbye-Biddle (2001), 'Repton and the "great heathen army",
873–4', in J. Graham-Campbell *et al.* (eds), *Vikings and the Danelaw*, Oxford, pp.
45–96.

Blackburn, M. (1985), 'English dies used in the Scandinavian imitative coinages',
Hikuin 11: 101–24.

Blackburn, M. (1993), 'Coin circulation in Germany during the early middle ages: the
evidence of single-finds', in B. Kluge (ed.), *Fernhandel und Geldwirtschaft. Beiträge zum
deutschen Münzwesen in sächsischer und salischer Zeit*, Sigmaringen, pp. 37–54.

Blackburn, M. (2001a), 'Expansion and control: aspects of Anglo-Scandinavian minting
south of the Humber', in J. Graham-Campbell *et al.* (eds), *Vikings and the Danelaw*,
Oxford, pp. 125–44.

Blackburn, M. (2001b), 'A Viking hoard from Thurcaston, Leics.: preliminary report',
Numismatic Chronicle 161: 349–52.

Blackburn, M. (2003), 'Alfred's coinage reforms in context', in T. Reuter (ed.), *Alfred the Great*, Aldershot, pp. 199–217.

Blackburn, M. (2004), 'The coinage of Scandinavian York', in R. A. Hall *et al.* (eds), *Aspects of Anglo-Scandinavian York*, York, pp. 325–49.

Blackburn, M. (2006), 'The loops and graffiti as a guide to how and when the coins were acquired', in S. H. Fuglesang and D. M. Wilson (eds), *The Hoen Hoard: A Viking Gold Treasure of the Ninth Century*, Rome; Oslo, pp. 181–99.

Blackburn, M. (2007), 'Currency under the Vikings. Part 3: Ireland, Wales, Isle of Man and Scotland in the ninth and tenth centuries', *BNJ* 77: 119–49.

Blackburn, M. (2008), 'Currency under the Vikings. Part 4: The Dublin coinage *c.* 995–1050', *BNJ* 78: 111–37.

Blackburn, M. (2009), 'Currency under the Vikings. Part 5: The Scandinavian achievement and legacy', *BNJ* 79: 43–71.

Blackburn, M. (2011), 'The Viking winter camp at Torksey, 872–3', in *VCC*, pp. 221–64.

Blackburn, M. and K. Jonsson (1981), 'The Anglo-Saxon and Anglo-Norman element of north European coin finds', in *VACNL*, vol. 1, pp. 147–255.

Bornholdt Collins, K. (2010), 'The Dunmore Cave [2] hoard and the role of coins in the tenth-century Hiberno-Scandinavian economy', in J. Sheehan and D. Ó Corráin (eds), *The Viking Age: Ireland and the West*, Dublin, pp. 19–46.

Bornholdt Collins, K. *et al.* (2014), 'The 2003 Glenfaba hoard (*c.* 1030), Isle of Man', in R. Naismith *et al.* (eds), *Early Medieval Monetary History: Studies in Memory of Mark Blackburn*, Farnham, pp. 471–514.

Breatnach, L. (2014), 'Forms of payment in the early Irish law tracts', *Cambrian Medieval Celtic Studies* 68: 1–20.

Brooks, N. P. and J. Graham-Campbell (1986), 'Reflections on the Viking-Age silver hoard from Croydon, Surrey', in M. Blackburn (ed.), *Anglo-Saxon Monetary History: Essays in Memory of Michael Dolley*, Leicester, pp. 91–110.

Cook, B. (1999), 'Foreign coins in medieval England', in L. Travaini (ed.), *Moneta locale, moneta straniera: Italia ed Europa XI–XV secolo*, Milan, pp. 231–84.

Coupland, S. (1991a), 'Carolingian coinage and Scandinavian silver', *NNÅ* 1985–6: 11–32.

Coupland, S. (1991b), 'The Carolingian theology of the Viking invasions', *Journal of Ecclesiastical History* 42: 535–54.

Coupland, S. (1999), 'The Frankish tribute payments to the Vikings and their consequences', *Francia* 26.1: 57–75.

Coupland, S. (2011), 'Raiders, traders, worshippers and settlers: the continental perspective', in *SEMSS*, pp. 113–31.

Coupland, S. (2014), 'The use of coin in the Carolingian empire in the ninth century', in R. Naismith *et al.* (eds), *Early Medieval Monetary History: Studies in Memory of Mark Blackburn*, Farnham, pp. 257–93.

Duffy, S. (ed.) (2000–), *Medieval Dublin*, 1 vol. to date (Dublin, 2000–).

Feveile, C. (2008), 'Series X and coin circulation in Ribe', in T. Abramson (ed.), *Studies in Early Medieval Coinage*, vol. 1: *Two Decades of Discovery*, Woodbridge; London, pp. 53–67.

Garipzanov, I. (2008), 'Carolingian coins in ninth-century Scandinavia: a Norwegian perspective', *NNÅ* 2003–5: 65–92.

Graham-Campbell, J. (1995), *The Viking-Age Gold and Silver of Scotland (AD 850–1100)*, Edinburgh.

Graham-Campbell, J. *et al.* (eds) (2001), *Vikings and the Danelaw*, Oxford.

Grierson, P. (1959), 'Commerce in the Dark Ages: a critique of the evidence', *Transactions of the Royal Historical Society* 5th series 9: 123–40.

Grierson, P. (1975), *Numismatics*, Oxford.

Gullbekk, S. H. (1992), 'Some aspects of coin import to Norway and coin circulation in the late Viking Age', *NNÅ* 1991: 63–87.

Gullbekk, S. H. (2009), *Pengevesenets fremvekst og fall i Norge i middelalderen*, Copenhagen.

Gullbekk, S. H. (2010), 'Klassisk problemstilling: handel eller herjing?' *Myntstudier* 2010 (1): 28–36.

Gullbekk, S. H. (2011), 'Norway: commodity money, silver and coins', in *SEMSS*, pp. 93–112.

Gullbekk, S. H. (2014), 'Vestfold: a monetary perspective on the Viking Age', in R. Naismith *et al.* (eds), *Early Medieval Monetary History: Studies in Memory of Mark Blackburn*, Farnham, pp. 331–47.

Hadley, D. M. and J. D. Richards (eds) (2000), *Cultures in Contact: Scandinavian Settlement in England in the Ninth and Tenth Centuries*, Turnhout.

Hadley, D. M. *et al.* (2016), 'The winter camp of the Viking Great Army, AD 872–3, Torksey, Lincolnshire', *The Antiquaries Journal* 96: 23–67.

Hall, R. A. *et al.* (2004), *Aspects of Anglo-Scandinavian York*, York.

Hårdh, B. (1996), *Silver in the Viking Age: A Regional-Economic Study*, Stockholm.

Hedeager, L. (1994), 'Warrior economy and trading economy in Viking-Age Scandinavia', *Journal of European Archaeology* 2: 130–47.

Holm, P. (1986), 'The slave trade of Dublin, ninth to twelfth centuries', *Peritia* 5: 317–45.

Horne, T. J. (2014), 'The most praiseworthy journey: Scandinavian market networks in the Viking Age', unpublished PhD dissertation, University of Glasgow.

Ilisch, P. (1981), 'German Viking-Age coinage and the north', in *VACNL*, vol. 1, pp. 129–46.

Ilisch, P. (2016), 'Les monnaies du Saint-Empire du Xe et XIe siècle: exportation ou circulation interne?', *Bulletin de la Société Française de Numismatique* 71: 49–56.

Ingvardson, G. T. (2010), *Møntbrug: fra vikingetid til vendertogter*, Aarhus.

Ingvardson, G. T. (2015), 'Traces of use', in J. C. Moesgaard, *King Harold's Cross Coinage: Christian Coins for the Merchants of Haithabu and the King's Soldiers*, Copenhagen, pp. 127–38.

Jarrett, J. (2009), 'Digitizing numismatics: getting the Fitzwilliam Museum's coins to the world-wide web', *The Heroic Age* 12 (2009), heroicage.org/issues/12/foruma.php (accessed 16 December 2019).

Jonsson, K. (1993), 'The routes for the import of German and English coins to the northern lands in the Viking Age', in B. Kluge (ed.), *Fernhandel und Geldwirtschaft. Beiträge zum deutschen Münzwesen in sächsischer und salischer Zeit*, Sigmaringen, pp. 205–32.

Jonsson, K. (1995), 'Från utländsk metall til inhemskt mynt', in K. Jonsson *et al.* (eds), *Myntningen i Sverige 995–1995*, Stockholm, pp. 43–61.

Kershaw, J. (2017), 'An early medieval dual-currency economy: bullion and coin in the Danelaw', *Antiquity* 91(355): 173–90.

Keynes, S. and R. Naismith (2011), 'The *Agnus Dei* pennies of King Æthelred the Unready', *Anglo-Saxon England* 40: 175–223.

Keynes, S. and R. Naismith (2015), 'A new *Agnus Dei / Last Small Cross* mule', *Anglo-Saxon England* 44: 307–8.

Kilger, C. (2007), 'Wholeness and holiness: counting, weighing and valuing silver in the early Viking period', in *ME*, pp. 253 325.

Kilger, C. (2011), 'Hack-silver, weights and coinage: the Anglo-Scandinavian bullion coinages and their use in late Viking-Age society', in *SEMSS*, pp. 259–80.

Kluge, B. (ed.) (1993), *Fernhandel und Geldwirtschaft. Beiträge zum deutschen Münzwesen in sächsischer und salischer Zeit*, Sigmaringen.

Kruse, S. and J. Graham-Campbell (2011), 'Classification and discussion of the Cuerdale objects. Part 1: Ingots', in *CH*, pp. 73–86.

Leighton, J. and A. R. Woods (2014), 'Insular imitations of Æthelred II's *Long Cross* coinage', in R. Naismith *et al.* (eds), *Early Medieval Monetary History: Studies in Memory of Mark Blackburn*, Farnham, pp. 515–43.

Leimus, I. and A. Molvõgin (eds) (2001), *Sylloge of Coins of the British Isles*, vol. 51: *Estonian Collections*, Oxford.

Lindblad, R. (2007), 'Högmedeltida svenska fynd med engelska, franska och flamländska mynt', *Myntstudier* 2007(3): 1–12.

Lund, N. (1989), 'Allies of God or man? The Viking expansion in European perspective', *Viator* 20: 45–59.

Lund, N. (ed.) (1984), *Two Voyagers at the Court of King Alfred: The Ventures of Ohthere and Wulfstan Together with the Description of Northern Europe from the Old English Orosius*, York.

Mainman, A. and R. Rogers (2004), 'Craft and economy in Anglo-Scandinavian York', in R. A. Hall *et al.* (eds), *Aspects of Anglo-Scandinavian York*, York, pp. 459–87.

Malmer, B. (1989), *The Sigtuna Coinage, c. 995–1005*, CNS n.s. 4, Stockholm.

Malmer, B. (1997), *The Anglo-Scandinavian Coinage, c. 995–1020*, CNS n.s. 9, Stockholm.

Malmer, B. (2007), 'South Scandinavian coinage in the ninth century', in *SEVA*, pp. 13–27.

Metcalf, D. M. (1998), 'Viking-Age numismatics 4. The currency of German and Anglo-Saxon coins in the northern lands', *Numismatic Chronicle* 158: 345–71.

Metcalf, D. M. (2006), 'Inflows of Anglo-Saxon and German coins into the Northern lands, *c.* 997–1024: discerning the patterns', in B. Cook and G. Williams (eds), *Coinage and History in the North Sea World c. 500–1250: Essays in Honour of Marion Archibald*, Leiden, pp. 349–88.

Moesgaard, J. C. (2004), 'Christiana religio', *Skalk* 6: 12–17.

Moesgaard, J. C. (2006a), 'The import of English coins to the northern lands: some remarks on coin circulation in the Viking Age based on new evidence from Denmark', in B. Cook and G. Williams (eds), *Coinage and History in the North Sea World c. 500–1250: Essays in Honour of Marion Archibald*, Leiden, pp. 389–433.

Moesgaard, J. C. (2006b), 'Single finds as evidence for coin circulation in the middle ages: status and perspectives', in J. C. Moesgaard and H. Horsnæs (eds), *Single Finds: The Nordic Perspective* [= *NNÅ* 2000–2], Copenhagen, pp. 228–75.

Moesgaard, J. C. (2011), 'The Grisebjerggård hoard and the beginning of pecking in Scandinavia', in *SEMSS*, pp. 297–308.

Myrberg, N. (2008), *Ett eget värde: Gotlands tidigaste myntning, ca 1140–1220*, SSA 45, Stockholm.

Naismith, R. (2012), *Money and Power in Anglo-Saxon England: The Southern English Kingdoms, 757–865*, Cambridge.

Naismith, R. (2013), 'The English monetary economy, *c.* 973–1100: the contribution of single-finds', *Economic History Review* 66: 198–225.

Naismith, R. (2017), *Medieval European Coinage*, vol. 8: *Britain and Ireland c. 400–1066*, Cambridge.

Naismith, R. with A. Woods (2017), 'Ireland to 1170', in R. Naismith, *Medieval European Coinage*, vol. 8: *Britain and Ireland c. 400–1066*, Cambridge, pp. 323–36.

Naismith, R. *et al.* (eds) (2014), *Early Medieval Monetary History: Studies in Memory of Mark Blackburn*, Farnham.

Noonan, T. (1994), 'The Vikings in the east: coins and commerce in the Viking Age', in B. Ambrosiani and H. Clarke (eds), *Developments around the Baltic and the North Sea in the Viking Age*, Stockholm, pp. 215–36.

Palliser, D. M. (2014), *Medieval York, 600–1540*, Oxford.

Rasmusson, N. L. (1944), 'Sterlingar och barrer som betalningsmedel på Gotland under 1200-talet', *GA* 16: 29–44.

Reuter, T. (1985), 'Plunder and tribute in the Carolingian empire', *Transactions of the Royal Historical Society* 5th series 35: 75–94.

Samson, R. (1991), 'Fighting with silver: rethinking trading, raiding and hoarding', in R. Samson (ed.), *Social Approaches to Viking Studies*, Glasgow, pp. 123–33.

Sawyer, P. (1986), 'Anglo-Scandinavian trade in the Viking Age and after', in M. Blackburn (ed.), *Anglo-Saxon Monetary History: Essays in Memory of Michael Dolley*, Leicester, pp. 185–99.

Sawyer, P. (2013), *The Wealth of Anglo-Saxon England*, Oxford.

Screen, E. (2008), 'The Norwegian coin finds of the early Viking age', *NNÅ* 2003–5: 93–121.

Screen, E. (2017), 'Anglo-Saxon coin imports to late Viking-Age Norway: the die-linking evidence', in M. Caccamo Caltabiano *et al.* (eds), *XV International Numismatic Congress, Taormina, 21–25 September 2015, Proceedings*, vol. 2, Rome; Messina, pp. 1189–92.

Sheehan, J. (2007), 'The form and structure of Viking-Age silver hoards: the evidence from Ireland', in *SEVA*, pp. 149–62.

Sheehan, J. (2015), 'Fighting with silver: the Woodstown assemblage', in *VIB*, pp. 161–76.

Skaare, K. (1976), *Coins and Coinage in Viking Age Norway*, Oslo.

Skaare, K. (1995), *Norges Mynthistorie*, 2 vols, Oslo.

Skre, D. (2011), 'Commodity money, silver and coinage in Viking-Age Scandinavia', in *SEMSS*, pp. 67–91.

Small, A. *et al.* (1973), *St Ninian's Isle and Its Treasure*, Oxford.

Steen Jensen, J. *et al.* (1995), *Tusindtallets Danske Mønter fra den Kongelige Mønt- og Medaillesamling (Danish Coins from the 11th Century in the Royal Collection of Coins and Medals)*, Copenhagen.

Stewart, I. (1981), 'How did Anglo-Saxon coins reach Finland?', in *VACNL*, vol. 2, pp. 491–3.

Talvio, T. (2002), *Coins and Coin Finds in Finland AD 800–1200*, Vammala.

von Heijne, C. (2004), *Särpräglat. Vikingatida och tidigmedeltida myntfynd från Danmark, Skåne, Blekinge och Halland (ca 800–1130)*, SSA 31, Stockholm.

Williams, G. (2006), 'Monetary economy in Viking-age Scotland in the light of single finds', in J. C. Moesgaard and H. Horsnæs (eds), *Single Finds: The Nordic Perspective* [= *NNÅ* 2000–2], Copenhagen, pp. 164–72.

Williams, G. (2007), 'Kingship, Christianity and coinage: monetary and political perspectives on silver economy in the Viking Age', in *SEVA*, pp. 177–214.

Williams, G. (2011a), 'The Cuerdale coins', in *CH*, pp. 39–71.

Williams, G. (2011b), 'Silver economies, monetisation and society: an overview', in *SEMSS*, pp. 337–72.

Williams, G. (2014), 'Coins and currency in Viking England, AD 865–954', in R. Naismith *et al.* (eds), *Early Medieval Monetary History: Studies in Memory of Mark Blackburn*, Farnham, pp. 13–38.

Williams, G. (2015), 'Viking camps and the means of exchange in Britain and Ireland in the ninth century', in *VIB*, pp. 93–116.

Woods, A. R. (2013), 'Economy and authority: a study of the coinage of Hiberno-Scandinavian Dublin and Ireland', 2 vols, unpublished PhD dissertation, University of Cambridge.

Woods, A. R. (2014), 'Monetary activity in Viking-Age Ireland: the evidence of the single-finds', in R. Naismith *et al.* (eds), *Early Medieval Monetary History: Studies in Memory of Mark Blackburn*, Farnham, pp. 295–330.

Woods, A. R. (2015), 'Prelude to the Hiberno-Scandinavian coinage: the Castle Street and Werburgh Street hoards', in *VIB*, pp. 355–72.

19 Viking economies and the Great Army

Interpreting the precious metal finds from Torksey, Lincolnshire

Andrew R. Woods[1]

Scholars have recently moved away from simple narratives and embraced complexity when analysing precious metal use in Viking-Age England.[2] Clear distinctions between 'display', 'bullion' and 'coin-using' economies are increasingly being abandoned. For example, hoard analysis suggests that a silver 'dual economy', mixing hack-silver and coinage, emerged in parts of England during the ninth and tenth centuries.[3] These changing theoretical approaches have combined with many new finds, particularly those unearthed using metal detectors, to create a more dynamic view of the economies of the Viking Age. There has been growing acceptance that different practices could, and did, occur simultaneously, depending on a range of criteria such as geographical location, transaction type and who was involved in the exchange.

One key area in England where perceptions have changed is around the economy of the Viking Great Army (*micel here*). Landing in 865, the army spent 15 years campaigning and elements from it ultimately settled large swathes of eastern and northern England. It was probably of significant size, made up of various Scandinavian war-bands as well as merchants, craftsmen and possibly also women and children.[4] They over-wintered in various parts of England, but archaeological interpretations have been conditioned by discoveries made at Repton (Derbyshire), a site where the Great Army is known to have made camp in the winter of 873–4.[5] Interpreting how the economy functioned in this crucial early phase of contact and settlement has been dominated by the many hoards deposited during the 860s and 870s which can be linked to the Great Army, including two coin hoards found at Repton.[6]

Recent work has identified two further over-wintering camps – at Torksey (Lincolnshire) and Aldwark (North Yorkshire) – and these are beginning to give us an impression of the varied nature of the economies of those who made up this army.[7] The *Anglo-Saxon Chronicles* record that in the winter of 872–3 the Great Army spent the winter at Torksey in Lincolnshire, noting that 'the army went into Northumbria, and it took up winter quarters at Torksey, in Lindsey; and then the Mercians made peace with the army'.[8] Torksey has been extensively metal-detected over many decades and, more recently, has been the subject of a multi-disciplinary project which has sought to catalogue the known finds, as well as undertaking a geophysical survey, fieldwalking, environmental analysis and small-scale excavation of the site.[9]

Torksey has produced many thousands of finds and, as we shall see, the site's chronology is unusually precise,[10] in close accord with the historically attested dates of 872–3 and suggestive of a very large-scale, albeit transient, phase of activity. Taken together, these two elements mean Torksey offers a better opportunity for understanding the nature of the ninth-century economies than has been possible with most other English sites. This chapter will interpret the nature of the economies associated with the Great Army as discernible in the Torksey evidence, based primarily upon the finds assemblage.

It is important to acknowledge that the nature of recovery has influenced the known corpus of metalwork.[11] Extensive metal-detecting by a large number of individuals over many years, and the somewhat haphazard nature of earlier recording, mean that finds from the 1980s and 1990s were only sporadically reported. The current project has controlled access more tightly and recorded all finds, with locations accurately logged by GPS; it has also recorded historic collections of material accumulated during the 1990s and 2000s, where access was granted. This has produced a total of over 2,500 metal objects, almost all of which have been recovered from plough-soil (soil thrown up by ploughing).[12] While this group represents only a sample of the thousands of objects retrieved from Torksey, there is relative consistency in the types and proportions of materials found at the site by both earlier and more recent detectorists. This suggests that the recovered sample is broadly representative of the material lost on the site.

The chronology of Torksey

Connecting the Torksey material with the actions of the Great Army rests largely on interpretation of the numismatic material. The chronology of the coin finds suggests a period of very intense activity in the early 870s, which would coincide with the period when the Great Army is known to have over-wintered at Torksey. The site's chronology has been quite extensively discussed elsewhere, but it is worth briefly recapping these arguments.[13] The age profiles of the three major coin categories – English silver pennies, Islamic dirhams and Northumbrian stycas – all accord with a date of 872–3.[14]

The ninth-century English silver pennies come from the kingdoms of Mercia and Wessex, and the dates of the two show a strong correlation. These are summarised in Table 19.1, along with contemporary finds from the continent. They are clearly focused on the 860s and 870s, particularly the Lunettes type struck by Burgred, Æthelred I and the first coinage of Alfred the Great. If the finds are plotted in a chronological histogram (Figure 19.1), their concentration becomes even more apparent. There is a complete absence of any coins from the decades following the 870s: from Alfred's early types until the late tenth century. The Torksey group of silver pennies would

Table 19.1 Summary of English and Continental 'broad' silver pennies
found at Torksey

From	Ruler	Reign dates	Number found
Mercia			
	Offa	757–96	1
	Coenwulf	796–821	2
	Burgred	852–74	12
Wessex			
	Æthelberht	862–5	1
	Æthelred I	865–71	1
	Alfred	871–99	9
Continental			
	Louis the Pious	814–40	1
	Louis the Pious imitation		3
	Lothar I	840–55	1
	Total		**31**

thus appear to have been withdrawn from circulation in the 860s and 870s, during the Great Army's known period of activity.

This is reinforced by the far larger body of Islamic silver dirhams. Struck at a variety of mints across the Islamic caliphate, dirhams reached the northern lands in enormous quantities and are found in thousands of hoards around the Baltic and Scandinavia.[15] The chronology and reasons behind the movement of such huge quantities of Islamic silver to the north remain the subject of debate;[16] but it seems to have started in the years around 800 with several peaks and troughs over the following two centuries.[17] Since Islamic coins could circulate for decades or more in Scandinavia, this makes tracing the chronology of their movements a challenge.

Some 124 dirham fragments have been recovered from Torksey to date, although not all have yet been fully identified. They have a much longer age profile than the English silver pennies, as we would expect from comparison with the Scandinavian material: dirhams often circulated for hundreds of years before their deposition. The oldest Torksey dirhams date from the late seventh century and a few are Umayyad (661–750), but the majority are Abbasid coins.[18] These fluctuations in the amount of silver arriving from the Islamic lands account for the fact that there are more coins from the mid-ninth century than there are from the period immediately pre-dating the arrival of the Great Army at Torksey.[19] However, the coin age profile (Figure 19.2) resembles that from a number of sites in Scandinavia.[20] The point of divergence with these other sites is the absence of any finds postdating the activities of the Great Army at Torksey. The latest dirham from Torksey dates to 866–8 and the caesura that follows is not found at other sites in Scandinavia.[21] The concordance of the English and Islamic coins strongly suggests that the assemblage represents material to be associated with the known dates of the Great Army at Torksey.

The latest Torksey dirham from 866–8 is also of interest for the light it sheds on the Great Army. Struck several years after the force landed in England, it suggests that the 'army' was not necessarily homogenous, but was likely to have seen groups joining and leaving on a regular basis.[22] And while this coin suggests contact with Scandinavia, metalwork from across much of western Europe has also been found at the site, which would fit with the view that the Great Army was made up of a variety of groups.[23]

The chronology of the dirham assemblage also highlights the speed at which silver could travel across the continent. A date of striking in 866–8 and loss in the period 872–3 suggests somewhere between four to seven years for the coin to travel the 5,000 kilometres between the caliphate and Lincolnshire. This is of some significance when assessing the flow of Islamic silver into northern and western Europe. The later part of the ninth century, particularly the period after 875, has been characterised as one when the flow of silver between the caliphate and Scandinavia was interrupted.[24] Yet the Torksey assemblage suggests that in the years around 870, the network by which silver dirhams moved north and west was functioning very effectively. Torksey lay at one end of a communications and exchange network which saw coinage moving rapidly across the continent.

The third major group of coins, usually called 'stycas', are present in significant numbers at Torksey and are the most common type of coin found at the site. These small copper coins were struck in the northern English kingdom of Northumbria between the early years of the ninth century and the

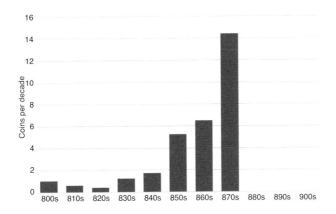

Figure 19.1 Age structure of English silver coins found at Torksey.

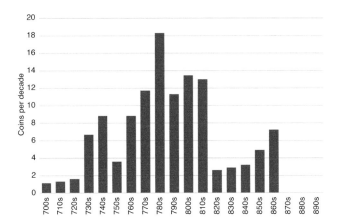

Figure 19.2 Age structure of Islamic dirhams found at Torksey.

arrival of the Great Army in the kingdom in the 860s. They are of uniform appearance, with the name of the issuing authority, usually a king; however, a minority name the archbishop of York on one face and the moneyer on the reverse. They were struck in enormous numbers, using hundreds of dies in their production.[25] They had long periods of circulation – coins struck for King Eanred in the 820s continued to circulate into the 860s – although the precise chronology of the kings and their coinage remains uncertain for lack of historical evidence.[26]

The stycas themselves cannot date Torksey precisely as it is thought that production halted with the fall of the kingdom of Northumbria to the Great Army in the 860s. However, there is some evidence that the stycas found at Torksey accord with the dating of the other types of coinage from the site. While there are stycas from almost every ninth-century issuing authority, there are significant proportions of the later types (see Table 19.2).[27] Coins that cannot be ascribed accurately to an issuer include 46 derivative series stycas (where the legends are nonsensical); 19 rendered illegible by corrosion or removal from plough-soil (recorded as 'uncertain'); and 12 whose poor condition means they cannot be attributed to either of Æthelred II's reigns.[28] However, there is no reason to think that any particular group is under-represented, other than perhaps the derivative category.

The Torksey stycas include all the kings and archbishops that would be expected from ninth-century currency, but the relative proportions suggest that most came from later reigns. Table 19.3 compares the relative proportions of different issuers found at Torksey with those from four known styca hoards.[29] Dating the hoards is slightly challenging, but they have traditionally been ascribed to either the 850s or 860s.[30] There is also variation between them, attributable to differing patterns of circulation,

Table 19.2 Summary of stycas found at Torksey

Issuer		Reign dates	Number found
Kings			
	Eanred	810–41	18
	Æthelred II (first reign)	841–4	24
	Redwulf	844	4
	Æthelred II (second reign)	844–9	31
	Æthelred II (uncertain reign)	841–9	12
	Osberht	849–67	11
	Derivative	850/60s?	46
	Double reverse		1
Archbishops of York			
	Wigmund	837–54	7
	Wulfhere	854–900	1
Uncertain			19
		Total	**174**

Table 19.3 Proportion of stycas at Torksey in comparison to hoards[1]

Issuer	Reign dates	Bolton Percy (1967)	Bolton Percy (1847)	York (1831)	York (1842)	Torksey
Kings						
Eanred	810–41	12%	19.2%	10.7%	11.2%	**11.2%**
Æthelred II (first reign)	841–4	33.7%	42.6%	39.2%	45.7%	**14.9%**
Redwulf	844	2.1%	1.6%	2.5%	1.6%	**2.5%**
Æthelred II (second reign)	844–9	9.2%	9.9%	7.8%	13.2%	**19.3%**
Osberht	849–67	4.2%	3.1%	2.8%	3.1%	**6.8%**
Derivative		22.4%	17.4%	21.2%	19.2%	**28.6%**
Archbishops of York						
Eanbald	796–808	0.2%	0.1%	0%	0.3%	**0%**
Wigmund	837–54	12%	3.5%	14%	4.8%	**4.3%**
Wulfhere	854–900	0.8%	0.6%	2.2%	0.6%	**0.6%**
Uncertain		3.2%	2.2%	0%	0%	**11.8%**

Note
1 Date in brackets after the hoard name indicates the date of discovery.

deposition, recovery and reporting. However, there are certain trends that can help us interpret the Torksey stycas. In the hoards, the relative proportion of coins from Æthelred II's two reigns is generally in the order of three to four first-reign coins to every second-reign coin. At Torksey, however, the proportion of second-reign coins is far greater. There is also a larger proportion of Osberht's coins than is found in the hoards. The Torksey Osberht coins represent a fairly sizeable group of these rare coins of Northumbria's last ruler, although their proportion is only slightly greater than would be expected in contemporary hoards. The comparison would seem to show that the Torksey assemblage is situated very late within the stycas' chronology. It is possible that the Torksey stycas represent a parcel of currency taken from Northumbria after the deposition of the four hoards. While this might have occurred either in the late 860s or early 870s, it would be entirely consistent with the coins being taken or exchanged while the Great Army was in Northumbria. They are recorded as there in 866–7, 868–9 and again in the year before they arrive at Torksey.

It has been suggested that late stycas, which display blundered nonsensical legends, may have been struck in the immediate aftermath of the Viking conquest of York.[31] The evidence from Torksey certainly suggests that stycas were in use – and retained a monetary function – into the 870s, well beyond their traditional end date.[32] It is unclear, though, whether the blundered stycas that make up over a quarter of the coins at Torksey were early Viking issues. Further work on analysing the dies used to strike these coins may reveal more, as will closer comparison with other late discoveries, such as the hoard from Bamburgh.[33]

While there may have been some activity at Torksey before 872, all the English pennies, Islamic dirhams and Northumbrian stycas could well have been brought to the site by the actions of the Great Army, only to be lost during their stay there in 872–3. The numismatic evidence suggests a group of losses within a very short period, probably in the year that the Great Army was at Torksey, rather than any longer-term forms of exchange taking place at the site. This is also supported by the fact that none of the silver from Torksey shows signs of testing – nicking or pecking – a phenomenon that began around 875.[34]

Metal–weight economies

The assemblage at Torksey is highly unusual for England as it suggests that precious metals were being routinely valued according to their weight. Before the arrival of the Great Army, English hoards usually contain whole coins, often struck in a single kingdom, in contrast to areas of Scandinavia where site finds and hoards incorporate a range of different types of silver, suggesting valuation by weight.[35] The Spillings hoard is a clear example of this and was deposited on Gotland around the very time when the Great Army was encamped at Torksey.[36] It contains 486 arm-rings, 25 finger-rings,

80 ingots and over 14,000 coins. Much of the coinage is fragmented, suggesting it was valued for its weight, while many of the arm-rings no longer serve a decorative purpose, being squashed together to form consistent units of around 200g in weight.

There is much evidence for the weighing out of precious metals at Torksey, including hack-silver, bullion weights and fragmented Islamic coinage. The non-numismatic silver from Torksey is summarised in Table 19.4. There are 15 objects whose original function can still be determined, including brooches, pins and Thor's hammers. Most are incomplete and many could perhaps be classified as hack-silver fragments. There are 65 objects that can be confidently described as hack-silver and these can be broken down into a number of form-based categories. There are also 64 droplets and melts, more readily associated with metal-working.[37] Most of the hack-silver at Torksey is undecorated, being chisel-cut sections from ingots or rods. Only 11 pieces have some sort of ornamentation or shape, suggesting that they had originally formed sections of decorative objects. A small number of pieces are tiny sections of flat plates, whose function before fragmentation is unclear.

Over 300 weights can be associated with the hack-silver and dirham fragments, interpreted as bullion weights used to weigh out precious metals.[38] There are three main types, including the cubo-octahedral weights (Figure 19.3 left) found in areas associated with the bullion use of dirhams throughout Scandinavia.[39] These outnumber the much rarer, truncated spheroid weight (Figure 19.3 centre) by around ten to one. However, lead weights are by far the most common and they take a variety of forms.[40] Some have insets into their tops which include glass, fragmentary Anglo-Saxon metalwork and a small silver bird (Figure 19.3 right). There has been considerable debate regarding weight standards and the extent to which different weight types conform to these.[41] There certainly appears to be a degree of standardisation in the cubo-octahedral and truncated spheroid weights found at Torksey, although it is difficult to be certain, since

Table 19.4 Summary of silver types found at Torksey

		Number found
Silver objects		15
Hack-silver fragments		65
Decorative	11	
Ingot	37	
Rod	10	
Other	7	
Metal-working debris		64
Total		**144**

1cm

Figure 19.3 Weights from Torksey: (left) cubo-octahedral; (centre) truncated spheroid; (right) inset lead weight.

Photos: author; courtesy of PAS.

corrosion and damage done during ploughing affect them. The various weight types have notably different average weights. The cubo-octahedral samples average 2.50g, while the other, larger types average around 14g, with a range of between 2g and 50g. Whether this reflects slightly differing functions for the weights at Torksey or the measurement of larger amounts of bullion is difficult to determine.

While the weights may represent different standards, we can be more certain that both types had their origins in the east, arriving in Scandinavia around the mid-ninth century.[42] Thus it would seem that using such standardised weight types had only recently been introduced into Scandinavia at the time of the Great Army, and its transmission to northern Britain was rapid.

The impression at Torksey is of a metal-weight valuation and exchange system similar to that employed in certain parts of Scandinavia, but alien to much of Britain. The clearest illustration of this is the presence of over 100 Islamic dirhams, comfortably the largest assemblage from anywhere in Britain.[43] Dirhams were completely alien to the pre-Viking-Age English monetary system, which used coinage of completely different form, weight and fineness. Much of the metal-weight exchange undertaken at Torksey was quite distinct from what was happening elsewhere in Anglo-Saxon England.

The exceptional aspects of Torksey are also highlighted by the degree of fragmentation found in its silver coinage. In England, dirhams are more commonly found whole, even when metal-detected from plough-soil. Rory Naismith's listing of British Islamic silver includes 20 whole single finds but only 14 fragments.[44] This contrasts with Torksey, where none of the Islamic coins is whole. The degree of fragmentation is also significant: the Torksey dirhams have an average weight of just 0.42g, and even this is slightly

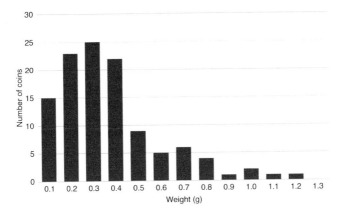

Figure 19.4 Weights of Islamic coins at Torksey.

distorted by the presence of a few large sections of more than one third of a dirham. Figure 19.4 illustrates the different weights of the Islamic coins at Torksey and indicates that the commonest weight was under 0.5g. The relatively light weight of the Torksey dirhams is reinforced when compared to other sites. At Kaupang the average is 0.6g, and the weight of many of these dirhams is thought to have been adversely affected by soil condition.[45] The Islamic coins in the vast Cuerdale hoard from Lancashire nearly all weigh more than 1g, while the small sample of 22 coins recorded with the Portable Antiquities Scheme have an average of 1.59g.[46]

The highly fragmented aspect of the Torksey silver becomes even clearer when hack–silver and ingots are included. Table 19.5 compares the levels of

Table 19.5 Proportions of weights of hack-silver and ingots at Torksey, Kaupang and Uppåkra

Weight	Torksey (England)	Kaupang (Norway)	Uppåkra (Sweden)
0–0.9g	22.2%	25.3%	28.4%
1–1.9g	36.5%	27.6%	24.6%
2–2.9g	17.5%	6.9%	18.7%
3–3.9g	7.9%	11.5%	9.7%
4–4.9g	6.3%	10.4%	9%
5–5.9g	3.2%	1.1%	2.2%
6–6.9g	3.2%	3.5%	1.5%
7–7.9g	0%	3.5%	3%
>8g	3.2%	10.2%	2.8%

fragmentation of the silver ingots and hack-silver from Torksey with two sites in Scandinavia: Kaupang and Uppåkra.[47] It has been suggested that both these sites show quite high levels of fragmentation, indicating that even relatively small-scale transactions were conducted using silver.[48] It is notable that Torksey has similar – if not slightly greater – proportions of small pieces of silver: the mean weight of non-numismatic silver is 2.48g and the median only 1.8g, with the former slightly skewed by a few large ingot sections.[49] If we include the silver dirhams, the proportion of pieces that weigh under 1g rises to 69%.[50]

We should interpret the highly fragmentary Torksey silver in the context of regular economic use. The finds are not only more fragmented than coins in British hoards, but also more than other English single finds. Indeed, they appear much closer in form to finds from some of the major economic settlements in Scandinavia than from more local areas. It would certainly suggest that similar types of activity were taking place in Torksey, necessitating the use of small pieces of silver in much the same way as in the Scandinavian central places.

The metal-weight economy at Torksey did not just involve silver: gold also played a part. Gold was relatively rare in Viking-Age England, although some recent finds, including those from Torksey, suggest that this view may need to be modified somewhat.[51] As one might expect, far less gold has been found than silver, although 12 pieces of fragmentary gold have been recovered. Just as with the silver, the majority of gold finds are small sections of ingots or rods; only two pieces – a ring and a thin appliqué – are from decorative objects. As the form of the gold found at Torksey is similar to that of the silver, there is little reason to suggest that it functioned differently. It seems very likely that it formed a high-value part of the metal-weight economy. This suggestion is reinforced by the find of a fake ingot, with a core made of copper and plated in gold.[52] Gold must have been in fairly regular use to make forging hack-gold worthwhile.

At the opposite end of the spectrum, there are a number of objects that suggest that copper alloy may also have played a low-value role in the metal-weight economy, including 15 copper-alloy ingots and fragments, three of which are whole. The largest of these has the typical form of a silver ingot, tapering from the centre with rounded ends (Figure 19.5). Many of the smaller ingot sections show signs of having been chisel-cut, again mirroring the treatment of silver ingots at the site.

Others have tentatively suggested that weighed copper alloy may have been used for exchange purposes.[53] It is difficult to tell how prevalent this might have been, since copper alloy is often assumed to have had a different function: found far less frequently in hoards than silver, it has been considered a raw material for production. However, a small but growing body of evidence suggests that it may have had an economic function. In addition to two large silver groups, the Spillings hoard has a parcel of copper-alloy material which has been interpreted as being hoarded inside a locked

1cm

Figure 19.5 Copper-alloy ingot from Torksey.
Photo: PAS.

wooden box.[54] Copper-alloy ingots, some decorated with transverse hammering such as can be seen at Torksey, have been found in England,[55] and copper-alloy stycas have been found at a small number of sites beyond its shores, most notably at Truso in the Baltic.[56] To this evidence can be added the English lead weights which have copper alloy set into them. Many of these insets are fragments of decorative copper alloy, but there are also a number with copper stycas.[57] If these insets represent something more than just a means of distinguishing one set of weights from another, the choice of copper-alloy fragments and coins may be significant. Although we cannot prove that they were used to weigh out copper – which might be termed hack-copper – it remains a possibility. It might also explain why so many stycas are set into weights compared to the relatively small number of silver coins given the same treatment.[58]

Thus the Torksey evidence suggests that metals were valued according to their weight by members of the Great Army. This is very clearly the case with silver; there are good indications that gold was being treated in much the same manner; and a case can be made for the probable economic use of hack-copper, too. The high fragmentation of the silver implies that it had a practical economic purpose and tended to be used in lower-value exchanges. These types of transaction and combination of materials were completely alien to much of England, suggesting that the Great Army brought with them a very different set of economic mentalities from those that had existed before. However, it is also important to recognise that this form of economic activity was quite unusual across much of Scandinavia in the 870s. The metal-weight economies visible at Torksey most closely mirror those of the major Scandinavian central places, which were themselves exceptional rather than typical.

Coinage

If the evidence for a metal-weight mentality at Torksey is fairly clear, it is more challenging to determine how coins were used. Although only a relatively small subset of the Torksey assemblage has been logged with precise coordinates, each of the coin types – dirhams, pennies and stycas – appears reasonably widely dispersed across the whole site. No clear clustering suggests association with a specific activity, such as metal-working,[59] and taken together with the weights, widespread exchange using these coins seems likely.

Interpreting whether they were seen purely as bullion, or whether they had a value beyond this, is tricky. Looking at how the three coin types were treated hints at the latter option, although this may reflect their differing origins and also a variety of practices at Torksey. This is most clearly shown by contrasting the English with the Islamic silver coins. There are no signs of the former being cut into smaller pieces: several whole English pennies have been found at the site, and where they are not whole, the damage appears to have occurred after deposition. Many are chipped or have jagged broken edges, in contrast to the neat cut marks on a great deal of the Islamic silver (see Figure 19.6), and much of this damage can be explained by the plough-soil recovery context and the pennies' thinner, broader shape.

While not overstating the evidence for the pennies' relative completeness, there is no sign of deliberate fragmentation, a view that is underlined by considering the coins' respective weights. Lunettes-type pennies typically weighed a little over 1g, and even amongst the partially damaged sample at Torksey, the English silver coins average 0.77g.[60] This is much greater than the weight of the dirhams at the site, which cluster below 0.5g. It is likely that at least some of the English coins would have been cut into similarly small pieces, had they held a purely bullion function. The larger and more complete English coins thus appear to have been used differently from the fragmented dirhams, probably closer to valuation based on form than on weight. The presence of various different types of people at Torksey might help to explain this: at least some of them would have valued coinage – with a face value in excess of its bullion in the kingdoms where it originated –

Figure 19.6 Silver coins from Torksey: (a) whole English penny; (b) chipped English penny; (c) cut dirham fragment.

Photos: PAS.

more highly than bullion.[61] If we accept this, the coin evidence would seem to suggest that a significant minority of transactions at Torksey were conducted using whole, English coins rather than weighed bullion.

Manufacturing

The likelihood of coinage being used as more than bullion is reinforced by the evidence of manufacturing at Torksey. There is ample evidence of metal-working on the site, with a large number of gold, silver and copper-alloy melts recovered,[62] and this appears to have included the production of coinage. Several lead trial pieces have been recorded, including two that appear to have been struck using coin dies.[63] One of the pieces is struck from dies that were used to manufacture imitative Lunettes-type silver pennies. The legends are close approximations, but without the level of literacy present on most English coins of the period. The illiterate legends on this trial piece support the notion that it was used to strike coins, as early Viking attempts elsewhere show similarly confused legends.[64] The second trial piece is for imitative gold *solidi* of Louis the Pious. It is formed from a much larger piece of lead, struck such that an impression of the whole die is visible. Mark Blackburn has surveyed finds of these coins and argues that imitations were produced in both Frisia and England.[65]

This second trial piece should be viewed alongside four gold coins also found at Torksey. One is a genuine coin of Louis the Pious, while another is a gold copy. Both are fragmentary, although the genuine coin appears to have been cut into a neat quarter. We can be more confident that the gold copy had been converted to hack-gold, losing its function as coinage and becoming closer to the 12 fragmentary gold pieces described above. Two complete imitative *solidi* have also been recovered: their copper cores and gold plating suggest that they were used as coins rather than purely as bullion. And the very production and circulation of copies indicates reasonably widespread usage.[66] Taken together, the larger lead trial piece and the four gold coins hint at a likely role for *solidi* in the economy of the Great Army – perhaps, unusually, as both bullion and as coinage. There is also the real possibility that, considering the metal-working evidence and the various trial pieces, imitative *solidi* were being produced at Torksey.

We have evidence for more decorative forms of metal-working at Torksey, too, including a die and three further trial pieces. Two of the trial pieces are formed from flat sheets with a repeated stamped decoration,[67] one in the form of three pellets in a triangle, a type very familiar on silver and gold jewellery of the ninth and tenth centuries.[68] The die – a *pressblech* one – is likely to have been used to add decoration to thin gold foil appliqués.[69] Significantly, we also have a fragmentary lead piece which mirrors the form of an Anglo-Saxon strap end.[70] This appears to be a casting, in lead, of a strap end and it is difficult to explain its presence unless strap ends were being manufactured at the site. This tallies with the numerous strap ends recovered at Torksey; over 100 to date. If we accept that the various pieces of lead represent the manufacture of different metal products at Torksey, then there is good evidence that silver jewellery of typically 'Viking' form – possibly arm-rings or the like – was being produced at Torksey, as well as copper-alloy strap ends in more traditional English form and fine gold working. This is in addition to the likely production of silver and gold imitative coinage.

Conclusion

Drawing together the diverse evidence from Torksey, the first point to make is that there was widespread use of precious metals within the Great Army's camp. Clearly some of the material may represent the spoils of war, but the finds suggest that metals were also widely in use within the Great Army as a means of exchange.[71] The Torksey assemblage represents the material remains from a single year in the ninth century, yet it points to manufacturing in a variety of metals taking place. It also points to very intense economic activity: the hundreds of finds indicate a huge number of exchange relationships within a short time span.

   Gold, silver and copper alloy all seem to have been used in an economic sense. Coins and hack-metal associated with each of the three metals have been recovered, as well as evidence for the production of imitative coins in gold and silver. This has implications for how we see the beginnings of the Viking-Age economies in England: a wide range of precious metals seem to have been used for a manner of different functions from the very outset of Scandinavian activity in England. Such variety was not something that emerged solely through contact between incomers and locals, but reflected the heterogeneous group which made up the Viking Great Army.[72]

   The Torksey finds also suggest that the economic character of the Great Army was unusual; quite distinct from other local areas, but also from much of Scandinavia. The mix of different coin types is not common in England, nor is the volume and range of hack-metal. The relatively highly fragmented nature of much of the silver, particularly the dirhams, is again unusual in an English context. Similarities in terms of the hack-silver can be found in the Scandinavian central places, but even there the presence of whole coins, and the likely production of imitative currency, would be quite exceptional. With access to a range of differing currencies, presumably representing the variety of peoples and practices, the economic experience of someone within a Great Army camp would have been almost unparalleled in contemporary north-western Europe.

Notes

1 I am grateful to Megan Gooch, Rachel Cubitt, Julian Richards and Dawn Hadley for reading and commenting on a draft of this chapter. It is improved for their comments. Errors remain my own.
2 See survey in Williams (2014); for a more general discussion of approaches see Williams (2011).
3 Graham-Campbell (2001); Blackburn (2006); Williams (2007), p. 207; Blackburn (2009); see discussion in Williams (2014), pp. 13–20.
4 Hadley *et al.* (2016), pp. 54–9.
5 Biddle and Kjølbye-Biddle (1992); Biddle and Kjølbye-Biddle (2001).
6 Brooks and Graham-Campbell (1986); Biddle *et al.* (1986a); Biddle *et al.* (1986b).
7 Hadley *et al.* (2016); Blackburn (2011); Blackburn (2002); Williams (2015), pp. 96–100.
8 ASC^2, p. 72. This is the reading from Manuscript A of the Chronicles. Manuscript E has less detail.
9 Hadley *et al.* (2016), pp. 29–31. This built upon the earlier work of Mark Blackburn who had initially catalogued the finds: Blackburn (2002); Blackburn (2011).
10 Hadley *et al.* (2016), pp. 42–5; Blackburn (2011), pp. 225–30.
11 Hadley *et al.* (2016), pp. 36–9.
12 Summarised by type in Hadley *et al.* (2016), p. 39; data available from Richards and Hadley (2016).
13 Hadley *et al.* (2016), pp. 43–5; Blackburn (2011), pp. 225–30.
14 Summaries of the English silver pennies and stycas are in Tables 19.1 and 19.2. The Islamic coinage is detailed in Blackburn (2011), pp. 253–8.
15 See discussion and maps in Kilger (2008).
16 See Blackburn (2008) contra Kilger (2008); see also Kuleshov and Jankowiak in this volume.
17 Kilger (2008), pp. 211–21; Bogucki (2010).
18 See Kuleshov in this volume.
19 For discussion of the flow of silver see Blackburn (2008); Kilger (2008); Jankowiak in this volume.
20 Blackburn (2011), pp. 229–30; Blackburn (2008), pp. 48–53.
21 Blackburn (2011), p. 230.
22 Hadley *et al.* (2016), p. 44.
23 Blackburn (2011), pp. 232–3.
24 See discussion in Kilger (2008), pp. 228–35; Gustin (2011), pp. 237–9; Jankowiak in this volume.
25 Pirie (1996).
26 Lyon (1987).
27 The table follows standard numismatic practice in dividing Æthelred II's reign into two parts, following the arrangement set out in Pirie (1996).
28 Derivative coins are often referred to as the 'blundered' series, but the term derivative is preferred here.
29 Hoard data from Pagan (1973); Pagan (1987); and Pirie (1996), with further data from the York Museums Trust computer database.
30 A digital checklist of coin hoards is maintained by the Fitzwilliam Museum, University of Cambridge: fitzmuseum.cam.ac.uk/dept/coins/projects/hoards (accessed 16 December 2019).
31 Williams (2014), p. 22.
32 Blackburn (2011), p. 225; Williams (2011), p. 354; Williams (2015), pp. 113–14.
33 Collins (2009).
34 Archibald (2011), pp. 62–4.

35 Blackburn (2009); see for example Kaupang in Norway; *ME*.
36 Östergren (2011), pp. 327–8; see also Östergren in this volume.
37 The metal-working evidence is discussed below.
38 Williams (2015), pp. 110–13.
39 Blackburn (2011), pp. 236–41.
40 The project has tried to distinguish between lead gaming pieces and weights, despite the challenges in separating the two: gaming pieces are deemed to have projections at the top or a hollow base; weights do not.
41 Blackburn (2011), pp. 236–41.
42 The chronology of this is still under discussion: Blackburn (2011), pp. 238–9.
43 Naismith (2005).
44 Naismith (2005), excluding Torksey.
45 Blackburn (2008), pp. 64–7.
46 Lowick (1976); PAS (data extracted December 2016).
47 Hårdh (2008), p. 101.
48 Hårdh (2008), p. 103.
49 Melts, silver associated with metal-working, are excluded from this analysis.
50 Of 173 pieces of silver, 120 weigh less than 1g.
51 See the gold within the late ninth-century Bedale hoard: Griffiths (2012); or a recent gold ingot find from Yorkshire: Griffiths (2014).
52 Blackburn (2011), p. 234.
53 Williams (2011), p. 354; Blackburn (2011), pp. 235–6.
54 Östergren (2011), pp. 330–2.
55 Bales (2005); Minter (2006); Rohde (2007).
56 Bogucki (2009).
57 Williams (1999).
58 Williams (1999).
59 For discussion of object distribution at Torksey see Hadley *et al.* (2016), pp. 36–42.
60 Lyons and Mackay (2008), pp. 54–6.
61 Williams (2014), p. 21.
62 Hadley *et al.* (2016), pp. 51–4.
63 For further discussion and illustrations see Hadley *et al.* (2016), pp. 50–1; Blackburn (2002).
64 Blackburn (2004), p. 338.
65 Blackburn (2007), pp. 67–73. His suggestion that this lead piece was not evidence for the production of coins at Torksey (p. 72) was made before the evidence for metal-working and the other trial pieces were known.
66 Blackburn (2007), p. 70.
67 Hadley *et al.* (2016), p. 51; Blackburn (2011), pp. 241–2.
68 See for example *CH*, plates 19–21.
69 Blackburn (2011), p. 242.
70 Hadley *et al.* (2016), p. 52.
71 See also discussion in Williams (2015), pp. 115–16.
72 Hadley *et al.* (2016), pp. 48–50.

Bibliography

Archibald, M. (2011), 'Testing', in *CH*, pp. 51–64.
Bales, E. (2005), 'NMS-C5DF38: Early medieval ingot', finds.org.uk/database/artefacts/record/id/113769 (accessed 16 December 2019).
Biddle, M. and B. Kjølbye-Biddle (1992), 'Repton and the Vikings', *Antiquity* 66: 36–51.

Biddle, M. and B. Kjølbye-Biddle (2001), 'Repton and the "great heathen army", 873–4', in J. Graham-Campbell *et al.* (eds), *Vikings and the Danelaw*, Oxford, pp. 45–96.

Biddle, M. *et al.* (1986a), 'Coins of the Anglo-Saxon period from Repton, Derbyshire', in M. Blackburn (ed.), *Anglo-Saxon Monetary History: Essays in Memory of Michael Dolley*, Leicester, pp. 111–32.

Biddle, M. *et al.* (1986b), 'Coins of the Anglo-Saxon period from Repton, Derbyshire: II', *BNJ* 56: 16–33.

Blackburn, M. (2002), 'Finds from the Anglo-Scandinavian site of Torksey, Lincolnshire', in B. Paszkiewicz (ed.), *Moneta Mediævalis*, Warsaw, pp. 89–101.

Blackburn, M. (2004), 'The coinage of Scandinavian York', in R. A. Hall *et al.*, *Aspects of Anglo-Scandinavian York*, York, pp. 325–49.

Blackburn, M. (2006), 'Currency under the Vikings. Part 2: The two Scandinavian kingdoms of the Danelaw, *c.* 895–954', *BNJ* 76: 204–26.

Blackburn, M. (2007), 'Gold in England during the "age of silver" (eighth–eleventh centuries)', in, *SEVA* pp. 55–98.

Blackburn, M. (2008), 'The coin finds', in *ME*, pp. 29–74.

Blackburn, M. (2009), 'Currency under the Vikings. Part 5: The Scandinavian achievement and legacy', *BNJ* 79: 43–71.

Blackburn, M. (2011), 'The Viking winter camp at Torksey, 872–3', in *VCC*, pp. 221–64.

Bogucki, M. (2009), 'Two Northumbrian stycas of Eanred and Æthelred II from early medieval Truso in Poland', *BNJ* 79: 34–42.

Bogucki, M. (2010), 'The beginning of the dirham import to the Baltic Sea zone and the question of the early emporia', in U. Lund Hansen and A. Bitner-Wróblewska (eds), *Worlds Apart? Contacts across the Baltic Sea in the Iron Age*, Copenhagen, pp. 351–61.

Brooks, N. P. and J. Graham-Campbell (1986), 'Reflections on the Viking-Age silver hoard from Croydon', in M. Blackburn (ed.), *Anglo-Saxon Monetary History: Essays in Memory of Michael Dolley*, Leicester, pp. 91–110.

Collins, R. (2009), 'NCL-D147A7: Early medieval hoard', finds.org.uk/database/artefacts/record/id/279980 (accessed 16 December 2019).

Graham-Campbell, J. (2001), 'The dual economy of the Danelaw: The Howard Linecar Memorial Lecture 2001', *BNJ* 71: 49–59.

Griffiths, R. (2012), 'YORYM-CEE620: Early medieval hoard', finds.org.uk/database/artefacts/record/id/504460 (accessed 16 December 2019).

Griffiths, R. (2014), 'YORYM-7706AD: Early medieval ingot', finds.org.uk/database/artefacts/record/id/646456 (accessed 16 December 2019).

Gustin, I. (2011), 'Coin stock and coin circulation in Birka', in *SEMSS*, pp. 227–44.

Hadley, D. M. *et al.* (2016), 'The winter camp of the Viking Great Army, AD 872–3, Torksey, Lincolnshire', *The Antiquaries Journal* 96: 23–67.

Hårdh, B. (2008), 'Hacksilver and ingots', in *ME*, pp. 95–119.

Kilger, C. (2008), 'Kaupang from afar: aspects of the interpretation of dirham finds in northern and eastern Europe between the late 8th and early 10th centuries', in *ME*, pp. 199–252.

Lowick, N. (1976), 'The Kufic coins from Cuerdale', *BNJ* 46: 19–28.

Lyon, C. S. S. (1987), 'Ninth-century Northumbrian chronology', in D. M. Metcalf (ed.), *Coinage in Ninth-Century Northumbria: The Tenth Oxford Symposium on Coinage and Monetary History*, Oxford, pp. 27–41.

Lyons, A. W. and W. A. Mackay (2008), 'The Lunettes coinage of Alfred the Great', *BNJ* 78: 38–110.

Minter, F. (2006), 'SF-9C5531: Early medieval ingot', finds.org.uk/database/artefacts/record/id/148444 (accessed 16 December 2019).

Naismith, R. (2005), 'Islamic coins from early medieval England', *Numismatic Chronicle* 165: 193–222.

Östergren, M. (2011), 'The Spillings hoard(s)', in *SEMSS* pp. 321–36.

Pagan, H. E. (1973), 'The Bolton Percy hoard of 1967', *BNJ* 43: 1–44.

Pagan, H. E. (1987), 'Some thoughts on the hoard evidence for the Northumbrian styca coinage', in D. M. Metcalf (ed.), *Coinage in Ninth-Century Northumbria: The Tenth Oxford Symposium on Coinage and Monetary History*, Oxford, pp. 147–58.

Pirie, E. J. (1996), *Coins of the Kingdom of Northumbria c. 700–867 in the Yorkshire Collections: The Yorkshire Museum, York, the University of Leeds, the City Museum, Leeds*, Llanfyllin.

Richards, J. D. and D. M. Hadley (2016), *Archaeological Evaluation of the Anglo-Saxon and Viking Site at Torksey, Lincolnshire* [Data-set], York, doi.10.5284/1018222 (accessed 18 December 2019).

Rohde, A. (2007), 'DENO-63EB93: Early medieval ingot', finds.org.uk/database/artefacts/record/id/204535 (accessed 16 December 2019).

Williams, G. (1999), 'Anglo-Saxon and Viking coin weights', *BNJ* 69: 19–36.

Williams, G. (2007), 'Kingship, Christianity and coinage: monetary and political perspectives on silver economy in the Viking Age', in *SEVA* pp. 177–214.

Williams, G. (2011), 'Silver economies, monetisation and society: an overview', in *SEMSS*, pp. 337–72.

Williams, G. (2014), 'Coins and currency in Viking England, AD 865–954', in R. Naismith *et al.* (eds), *Early Medieval Monetary History: Studies in Memory of Mark Blackburn*, Farnham, pp. 13–38.

Williams, G. (2015), 'Viking camps and the means of exchange in Britain and Ireland in the ninth century', in *VIB*, pp. 93–116.

20 Viking-Age bullion from southern Scandinavia and the Baltic region in Ireland

John Sheehan[1]

The presence of imported silver objects of southern Scandinavian and Baltic origin in Ireland's early Viking-Age hoards is an issue of interest if only because a limited number of examples are identifiable. This is doubtless because such imports were usually destined for the melting pot, along with imported coin, in order to supply the developing Hiberno-Scandinavian silver-working industry during the later ninth and early tenth centuries. However, some may have been kept as distinctive objects, even in hack-silver form, because of their obvious links to the important silver-supplying region in the east. The objects that, for whatever reasons, escaped the crucible show how mobile silver was during the Viking Age, a phenomenon more easily recognisable from the numismatic material. They illustrate the economic networks that connected with Ireland, as well as throwing light on the sources of the large quantities of silver used in both Hiberno-Scandinavian and native Irish silver-working. The imported material also holds the key to a better understanding of the origins of some of the Hiberno-Scandinavian ornament-types and ornamentation styles. It points towards a southern Scandinavian/Baltic influence on the development of trade and exchange in Ireland through a 'nodal market' in Dublin.[2] This chapter aims primarily to draw attention to the existence of the imported material, but the case for a southern Scandinavian/Baltic inspiration for several of the object-types that typify Hiberno-Scandinavian silver-working is strong.[3] The fact that most of the imported material occurs in hack-silver form brings up the issue of its economic role and the spread of the Scandinavian bullion economy.

There are, of course, problems in studying Ireland's limited amount of Viking-Age silver material of Scandinavian and Baltic origin. Most finds came to light either during the antiquarian era or as a result of metal-detecting in the 1970s and 1980s. Therefore, detailed information about their provenance, association or archaeological contexts is sometimes lacking. For instance, while most of the antiquarian material appears to be single finds, these could come from unrecorded hoards or assemblages – scatters of silver that were lost piecemeal from the pool of silver circulating around a settlement in the course of trade. Another problem comes from silver forms that are not culturally distinguishable and thus cannot normally be identified as either Hiberno-Scandinavian or imports, such as the ubiquitous ingot. It seems likely that some, at least, of the ingots in Ireland's early hoards originated in the southern Scandinavian/Baltic sphere, but this cannot be demonstrated at present.[4] Thus the amount of imported silver identified and discussed in this chapter is, most probably, an underestimate.

The political geography of the Viking-Age Irish Sea region should also be taken into consideration. Dublin, York, north and north-west England, and parts of Scotland were at times closely intertwined, with Dublin and York serving as the two main centres of Scandinavian power; and north-west England bore the consequences of upheaval in Scandinavian Ireland.[5] This is, of course, reflected in the circulation and hoarding patterns of imported material across the region, even if the main focus in this chapter is on the material from Ireland. Finally, given that silver objects from the southern Scandinavian and Baltic region influenced the form and ornamentation of Hiberno-Scandinavian silver-working, it is possible that some of the apparent imports are, in fact, locally produced imitative versions. Problems of identifying and separating imports from local copies should not take away from the overall significance of the imported material. Each of these issues is borne in mind in selecting the material for discussion here and, although the primary focus is on non-numismatic or bullion silver, some account will also be taken of the occurrence in Ireland of coins from the Islamic caliphates, given their links with the Baltic region.

Bullion

Fifteen non-numismatic silver objects on record from Ireland are, or may be, derived from the southern Scandinavian/Baltic silver-working tradition (Figures 20.1–20.4). All bar one are hack-silver and four different classes of objects are represented – cast band arm-rings, single-rod arm-rings of polygonal cross-section, knobbed penannular brooches and spiral rings. Seven come from three provenanced hoards, while the remaining eight apparently comprise single finds, only one of which has a rather tenuous provenance of 'Dublin?' and the others are unprovenanced. The three hoards are Loughcrew (Co. Meath), Dysart Island (Co. Westmeath)[6] and one localised only to 'Co. Dublin', with the latter two having coin-dated depositions of *c.* 910 and *c.* 935 respectively.[7] The Dysart hoard contains nineteen Islamic coin fragments, as well as other coins, and is one of only eleven Irish hoards that are recorded as featuring Islamic coins. Overall, Dysart is the Irish hoard that most closely parallels the near-contemporary Cuerdale find from north-west England (deposited *c.* 905–10), although on a much smaller scale. Containing four of the fifteen imported non-numismatic pieces and three of the four object-types under consideration here, as well as in its Islamic coin element, Dysart embodies more completely than any other Irish hoard the contacts that existed between the southern Scandinavian/Baltic region and Viking-Age Ireland.

1cm

Figure 20.1 Edge fragment of a cast band arm-ring from Dysart, Co. Westmeath.
Photo: author; copyright NMI.

Cast band arm-rings

These penannular rings, characterised by their plano-convex cross-section and the use of deep, undulating, transverse grooves in their ornamentation, are well represented in Scandinavian hoards and are particularly common in the Baltic region, as on Gotland. Mårten Stenberger regarded this, his Type Ab3, as 'the most striking of all Gotlandic arm-ring types'.[8] The only occurrence in Ireland comes from the Dysart hoard and comprises a small edge fragment which is decorated with distinctive, deep, interlocked grooves (Figure 20.1).[9] There is also a fragment of this type from Bride in the Isle of Man and another in the Cuerdale hoard (as well as two further fragments from Cuerdale that may be derived from Hiberno- or Anglo-Scandinavian copies).[10] It is possible that a gold finger-ring from High Street, Dublin,[11] which features similar undulating grooves, may have been inspired by an arm-ring of this type, as also a small number of similarly ornamented finger-rings from England.[12] A lead trial piece impressed with an S-shaped stamp of the type used to make such undulating grooves forms part of the assemblage from Torksey, Lincolnshire, a location firmly associated with the Great Army's campaign camp of 872/3.[13]

Single-rod arm-rings of polygonal cross-section

Single-rod penannular arm-rings formed of rods of octagonal or heptagonal cross-section, plain or ornamented by stamping on the outer facets, form a type that is characteristic of southern Scandinavian hoards, particularly those on Gotland.[14] Examples of this type, for instance, are well represented in the Spillings hoard, the deposition of which took place in the closing decades of the ninth century.[15] Seven rings of this type are represented amongst the material from Ireland, six of which occur in hack-silver form. The complete example, octagonal in section, and ornamented on its three outer facets with apex-to-apex triangle stamps containing pellets, is a fine example but is, unfortunately, of only unlocalised provenance to Ireland (Figure 20.2a).[16] Four of the six hack-silver fragments are provenanced: two to the Dysart hoard,[17] one to the 'Co. Dublin' hoard[18] and one to 'Dublin?'.[19] Two of these are plain, while one of the Dysart fragments, which appears to retain its original curvature and is stamped in a style comparable to the ornamentation on the complete example, has been noted by Christoph Kilger as deriving from 'a typically Gotlandic arm-ring' (Figure 20.2b).[20] The two remaining examples are a plain and a stamped specimen.[21] Some arm-rings of this type are on record from England: in the Cuerdale hoard, for instance, there is one complete example as well as about a dozen fragments;[22] two hack-silver fragments occur in the mixed hoard from Silverdale, Lancashire,[23] deposited *c.* 900–10; and one fragment forms part of a recently discovered find that is currently referred to as the 'West Coast Cumbria' hoard.[24] In addition, there is a gold fragment in the assemblage from Torksey, Lincolnshire,[25] the site of the Great Army's 872/3 winter base. The two octagonal-sectioned arm-rings that comprise a hoard provenanced only to Co. Cork, both of which feature animal-headed terminals, may be Hiberno-Scandinavian-produced variants of this Gotlandic type.[26]

Knobbed penannular brooches

This brooch type normally occurs in copper alloy and is characterised by short pins, stamped ornament and faceted-knob terminals, sometimes with hoop-knobs. Originating in Finland during the ninth century, it became the dominant type of Scandinavian/Baltic penannular brooch and may

(a)   (b)

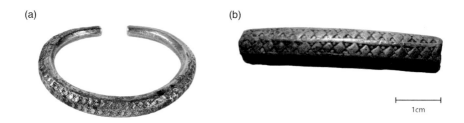

1cm

Figure 20.2 (a) Single-rod arm-ring of octagonal cross-section, provenanced to 'Ireland';
(b) fragment of the same type from the Dysart hoard, Co. Westmeath.
Photos: (a) NMI; (b) author; copyright NMI.

have been introduced (via central Sweden) to Norway, where it was copied before imitative versions were manufactured, in silver, in Ireland.[27] However, some of the examples from Ireland may be imports rather than local copies: even though in Scandinavia this type of brooch was normally manufactured in copper alloy, there is a fine hack-silver fragment in the hoard found between the parishes of Vamlingbo and Sundre in southern Gotland.[28] There are three definite and two possible silver examples on record from Ireland, and one from England, in the Cuerdale hoard,[29] all in hack-silver form. One of the examples from Ireland comes from the Loughcrew hoard, which also contains two ingots; it is a substantial hoop fragment, ornamented by stamping, with a faceted terminal knob and two hoop-knobs (Figure 20.3a).[30] The remaining two definite examples are separate unprovenanced finds: one is a fragment of a finely executed hoop bearing stamped decoration, folded out of shape, with a faceted terminal knob and a hoop-knob (Figure 20.3b);[31] the second is a straightened hoop fragment, with stamping and a single faceted hoop-knob (Figure 20.3c).[32] The two 'possible' examples survive only as terminal knobs, and

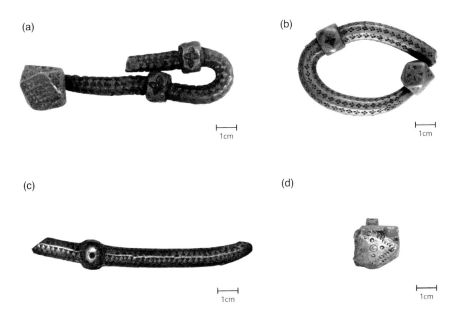

(a)

(b)

1cm

1cm

(c)

(d)

1cm

1cm

Figure 20.3 Hack-silver fragments from knobbed penannular brooches: (a) Loughcrew, Co. Meath; (b–c) unprovenanced, Ireland; (d) faceted terminal knob, Dysart, Co. Westmeath.

Photos: (a, b, d) NMI; (c) author; copyright NMI.

1cm

Figure 20.4 Terminal of spiral ring with faceted knob; unprovenanced, Ireland.
Photo: copyright NMI.

thus it is uncertain whether they derive from knobbed penannular brooches or spiral rings.[33] The first of these, unprovenanced, is a faceted knob, with stamping (Figure 20.3d),[34] while the second, from the Dysart hoard, is a small fragment with only part of two of its original faces surviving.[35]

Spiral rings

Spiral (or Permian) rings are one of the most characteristic Viking-Age object-types known from southern Scandinavian and Baltic silver hoards.[36] Of central or northern Russian origin and dating from the ninth/early tenth centuries, these rings were probably made from melted-down Islamic coins. They are formed of long rods with continuous spiral grooving, resulting in a rifled or corded effect, with one end terminating in a faceted knob and the other forming a simple loop. Some lighter variants, found mainly on Gotland and Öland and in Denmark, are of local manufacture and have been referred to by Egon Wamers as 'Baltic ring-money'.[37] The type is rarely encountered in Norway.

Two hack-silver fragments of spiral rings are known from Ireland. The first is one of the non-numismatic components of the hoard provenanced to 'Co. Dublin' and deposited *c.* 935,[38] while the second is an unprovenanced terminal portion complete with a faceted knob (Figure 20.4).[39] The latter's form indicates that it may have been a Permian import, rather than a southern Scandinavian/Baltic copy, while the former's thickness may suggest the same. In addition, there are the two fragments noted above: terminal knobs from either penannular brooches or spiral rings, one of which is from the Dysart hoard. Fragments of spiral rings are found in nine hoards or assemblages from Britain: five mixed hoards – Croydon, Surrey, *c.* 872;[40] Silverdale, Lancashire, *c.* 900–10;[41] Cuerdale, Lancashire, *c.* 905–10;[42] Vale of York, Yorkshire, *c.* 927/8;[43] and Storr Rock, Skye, *c.* 935–40[44] – and two coinless finds, those from Bedale, Yorkshire,[45] and the 'West Coast Cumbria' hoard.[46] Examples are also recorded from the assemblage from Torksey, Lincolnshire,[47] and the settlement at Llanbedrgoch, Anglesey, Wales.[48] The odd ones out chronologically are the Croydon hoard and the Torksey assemblage, both from the early 870s and both locations firmly associated with the Great Army's campaign.[49] When these are excluded, it appears reasonable to suggest that hack-silver fragments of spiral rings were generally in circulation in Britain and Ireland during the late ninth century and the opening decades of the tenth.

In summary, examples of these four Viking-Age imported object-types – cast band arm-rings, single-rod arm-rings of polygonal cross-section, knobbed penannular brooches and spiral rings – are represented at least once in three Irish hoards, as well as by a number of apparent single finds. The greatest representation is in the Dysart hoard, where three or four of the types are found. In Britain at least one of the types is present in nine hoards or assemblages (Map 20.1), with all four types occurring in the Cuerdale hoard. This find also contains a fifth category of imported object, a fragment of a *Gusskuchen*-type ingot[50] – a distinctive form that is otherwise not found in Britain or Ireland but is characteristic of finds of a later date on Gotland and Bornholm, as well as in Poland and southern Sweden.[51] The clear link between the imported non-numismatic elements of the Cuerdale and Dysart hoards may simply be a product of the near contemporaneity of their deposition dates, *c.* 905–10 and *c.* 910 respectively. But they share other elements of composition, notably silver of Irish and Hiberno-Scandinavian character and Islamic coins. These are also characteristics of some of the other mixed hoards from Britain – those from Silverdale, the Vale of York and Storr Rock – while the coinless hoards from Bedale and 'West Coast Cumbria', as well as the assemblage from Llanbedrgoch, also feature items of Hiberno-Scandinavian character. Given that much of the identifiable non-numismatic material in the Cuerdale hoard is of Hiberno-Scandinavian character,[52] and may have been assembled in Ireland, this could also have been the immediate source of the hoard's southern Scandinavian/Baltic silver components. The same argument can be made for the imported bullion from Silverdale, the Vale of York, Storr Rock, 'West Coast Cumbria' and Llanbedrgoch. Thus, on the present non-numismatic evidence, it seems likely that some of the imported southern Scandinavian/ Baltic silver in the west may have gone directly to Ireland, particularly to the Dublin region; from there, some of it may have been redistributed across the Irish Sea to north and north-west England, areas that were, at times, closely politically

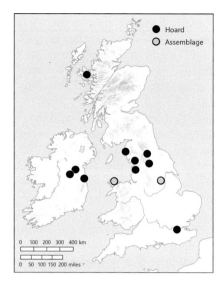

Map 20.1 Location of hoards and assemblages from Britain and Ireland with southern Scan-
dinavian/Baltic non-numismatic material.
Map: author/Nick Hogan.

linked with Dublin. It is, of course, probable that this type of material also entered
England directly from Scandinavia, through the Danelaw, and travelled westwards
through York. It is interesting to note, however, that there are indications in the
numismatic evidence that the Dublin region may have had close and, perhaps,
direct connections with southern Scandinavia and the Baltic area.

Islamic coins

Islamic coins are recorded as forming part of twenty-seven silver hoards
from Britain and Ireland, all of which were deposited during the period
between *c.* 870 and *c.* 970. The majority of these are found either in the
Dublin region and its hinterlands or, directly across the Irish Sea, in north-
west England (Map 20.2 and Table 20.1).[53] These are also the two regions
from which nearly all hoards containing silver bullion of southern
Scandinavian/Baltic origin are found, suggesting that Islamic coins generally
circulated in tandem with this type of silver. The Dublin region features
eight hoards with Islamic coins, equally divided between coin-only and
mixed hoards. There are four times as many coin-only hoards with an
Islamic element in the Dublin region than in north-west England, where
mixed hoards are the norm, based on current evidence.

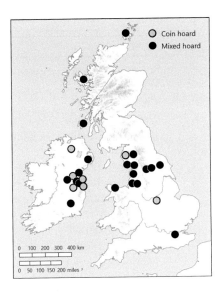

Map 20.2 Location of hoards from Britain and Ireland with Islamic coins.
Map: author/Nick Hogan.

The inflow of Islamic coins to the Baltic region starts to pick up pace from the beginning of the tenth century, culminating in the 950s. While the deposition date of all British and Irish hoards with such coins spans almost a century, 70% of the total can be dated to between *c.* 900 and *c.* 930. This raises the question of the route by which these coins travelled to the west. In Scandinavia during this period, the greatest number of Islamic coins is found on Gotland,[54] followed by mainland southern Scandinavia, with Norway producing significantly smaller totals. This pattern suggests that the finds from Britain and Ireland are unlikely to have passed through Norway, which remained economically less developed than the dynamic southern Scandinavian zone,[55] even though new economic practices started to spread in the Viking Age via the *Norðweg*, the sailing way to the north.[56] The distribution patterns of southern Scandinavian and Baltic-type bullion material, including the object-types discussed above, reinforce this suggestion, given their rather limited occurrence in Norway.[57]

The period when most of the British and Irish hoards containing Islamic coins were deposited (900–30) overlaps to a significant degree with Kilger's Phase IVb (890–920), the period when Samanid dirhams first start to flow into Scandinavia.[58] They travelled from Central Asia and through the territory of the Volga Bulgars, from where spiral rings had earlier reached Scandinavia and the Baltic alongside Abbasid dirhams.[59] In Scandinavia the

Table 20.1 Ninth- and tenth-century hoards from Britain and Ireland containing Islamic coins, showing approximate date of deposit (see n. 53 for sources)

Hoard	Region	Approximate date of deposit
Croydon	South-east England	*c.* 872
Near Dublin	Ireland	early tenth century
Millockstown	Co. Louth, Ireland	*c.* 905
Cuerdale	North-west England	*c.* 905–10
Drogheda	Co. Louth, Ireland	*c.* 905
Dysart Island (No. 4) [Dysart]	Co. Westmeath, Ireland	*c.* 910
Silverdale	North-west England	*c.* 900–10
Dean	North-west England	*c.* 915
Harkirk	North-west England	*c.* 910
Co. Derry	Ireland	*c.* 910 (?)
Magheralagan	Co. Down, Ireland	*c.* 910 (?)
Leggagh	Co. Meath, Ireland	*c.* 920
Goldsborough	North-east England	*c.* 925
Warton	North-west England	*c.* 925
Bangor	North Wales	*c.* 925
Thurcaston	Midlands, England	*c.* 925
Flusco Pike 2	North-west England	*c.* 925
Bossall/Flaxton	North-east England	*c.* 927
Glasnevin	Dublin, Ireland	*c.* 927
Vale of York	North-east England	*c.* 927–8
Dunmore Cave	Co. Kilkenny, Ireland	*c.* 928
Co. Kildare	Ireland	*c.* 935
Storr Rock	West Scotland	*c.* 940
Furness	North-west England	*c.* 955
Skaill	North Scotland	*c.* 950–70
Co. Meath	Ireland	*c.* 970
Machrie	West Scotland	*c.* 970

earliest Samanid coins are found largely on Gotland, where they feature in about twenty-five hoards, and on Öland; only two hoards containing them are recorded from mainland Sweden and Denmark, and it is not until *c.* 915/20 that these coins start to become familiar on mainland Scandinavia. The strongly Gotland-focused distribution pattern of early Samanid coins is of particular interest, since these dirhams also occur in a small number of hoards from the Irish Sea region. Anton Amlé demonstrates that they were minted during a very specific period, between 905 and 914, and that some of them were deposited in hoards in Ireland before the type became common on mainland Scandinavia and at its 'central' sites, such as Kaupang and Birka.[60] Thus, on the present evidence, these dirhams seem most likely to have been imported directly into the Irish Sea region from Gotland, presumably to Dublin and through southern Scandinavia,[61] strongly hinting at a formative southern Scandinavian influence behind the establishment of Dublin as a Hiberno-Scandinavian interpretation of Danish-style market sites like Hedeby and Kaupang.[62]

One of the three Irish hoards to feature these early Samanid dirhams is Dysart, deposited *c.* 910. As noted above, this hack-silver hoard closely parallels the near-contemporary Cuerdale find, albeit on a much smaller scale. Also significant is the high degree of silver fragmentation in the Dysart hoard, which is best paralleled in Ireland not in a hoard, but in the assemblage from the ninth-century *longphort* at Woodstown, Co. Waterford.[63] As we have seen, Dysart contains four of the fifteen identifiable imported bullion pieces from Ireland, together representing three of the four object-types. These alone signify contact between Ireland and the general southern Scandinavian/ Baltic region. But when Dysart's early Samanid dirhams are also taken into consideration, these interactions may be more firmly focused on Gotland. It is worth recalling that among the Dysart bullion is the only Irish example of a cast band arm-ring fragment, a type described as 'the most striking of all Gotlandic arm-ring types';[64] a fragment of a single-rod arm-ring, described as 'typically Gotlandic';[65] and a fragment of a faceted knob derived from either a spiral ring or a knobbed penannular brooch, neither of which would be out of place on Gotland. It seems reasonable to suggest that these hack-silver pieces may, along with the early Samanid dirhams, represent a discrete parcel of Gotlandic origin in the Dysart hoard.

The second Irish hoard that contains an early Samanid dirham is a small, mixed find from Millockstown, Co. Louth (*tpq* 905), which also features two ingot fragments.[66] The third is a mixed hoard from Leggagh, Co. Meath, deposited *c.* 920, which included an unknown number of ingots.[67] In addition to these finds, Amlé has drawn attention to a further important hoard that contained, in Michael Dolley's opinion, early Samanid dirhams.[68] This is the large find from near Drogheda, Co. Louth, now unfortunately lost, which was deposited *c.* 905 and may have featured as many as 5,000 coins. In Britain, such coins also form part of the numismatic element of three mixed hoards, all deposited during the 920s, each of which has strong connections with Ireland in their bullion contents. These are two hoards from Yorkshire (Goldsborough, deposited *c.* 925;[69] Bossall/Flaxton, deposited *c.* 927[70]) and one from north Wales (Bangor, deposited *c.* 925).[71] The Goldsborough find is of particular interest given that most of its culturally diagnostic bullion content is Irish or Hiberno-Scandinavian, its numismatic content is almost completely Islamic and, despite its provenance close to York, it contains no Danelaw coins. As James Graham-Campbell has suggested, this hoard could only have been assembled in Ireland.[72]

Silver and politics

When the Irish hoards containing early Samanid dirhams are plotted on a map alongside those containing silver bullion of southern Scandinavian/Baltic type, the six find spots are all in the area to the north and west of Dublin (Map 20.3). The only provenanced single find of imported bullion of this type, a polygonal-sectioned rod arm-ring fragment, is also from this area. Given that the 130 or so ninth- and tenth-century hoards recorded from Ireland are fairly widely distributed across the island, this loose concentration is unlikely to be coincidental and probably reflects a hoarding horizon.[73] It is significant that all six hoards in this horizon are located within Southern Uí Néill, one of six over-kingdoms in early medieval Ireland. There are sometimes discernible correlations between groupings of specific types of hoards and the kingdoms of Ireland's dominant dynasties,[74] as would appear to be the case with this one. The tendency for many of Ireland's hoards to derive from Irish settlements would imply that a great many of these finds were in Irish ownership on deposition.[75] This hoarding horizon is no different: three of the six, those from Dysart, Loughcrew and Millockstown, are recorded as having been found on crannógs and ringforts.

Silver of Scandinavian character begins to appear in Ireland during the mid-ninth century, around the same time as the Vikings' fortified *longphuirt*

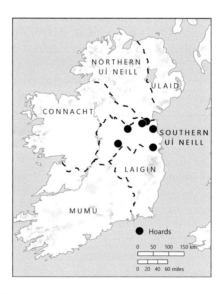

Map 20.3 Location of hoards from Ireland with early Samanid coins and/or southern Scandinavian/Baltic bullion, showing the boundaries of the province-kingdoms *c.* 900
Map: author/Nick Hogan.

settlements start to develop.[76] However, the military potential of these sites was kept in check by the Irish kings and the Scandinavians, unlike in England, generally remained landless. Unable to use Ireland's basic unit of wealth – cattle – in economic transactions, the Scandinavians introduced a new exchange system to the country based on silver, although other commodities probably also had a role to play.[77] A significant proportion of the coinless Irish hoards are now understood to belong to the second half of the ninth century, the main era of the *longphuirt*.[78] Recent excavations of the *longphort* at Woodstown have shown that silver and ingot production were important facets of its economy,[79] and the site has yielded a furnace for working silver as well as copper alloy, together with crucibles, silver assaying cupels and numerous lead weights.[80] These finds would suggest a major Scandinavian innovation in Ireland at this time: the introduction of a silver-based system of exchange.

Irish acquisition of silver is usually attributed to trade with the Scandinavians, although other potential mechanisms for silver exchange should be considered, such as the formation of political alliances, the practice of gift exchange, the conventions of ransoming and, perhaps most importantly in the Irish context, the exercise of tribute. The sources mention both intermarriage and the establishment of Irish-Scandinavian military alliances from the mid-ninth century onwards. Indeed, the first recorded military pact of this type was in 842, within one year of the foundation of the first *longphort*.[81] Rather than the traditional interpretation of *longphuirt* as glorified raiding bases, they could be seen as a product of cooperation between the Scandinavian leaders and some Irish kings. For example, it has been suggested that the foundation of the early *longphort* at Rossnaree, only a short distance from the royal centre of Knowth, may have been established with the consent of the local kingship.[82] It seems that the appearance of the *longphuirt* marked the arrival of the Scandinavians on the Irish political scene, and that trading and other economic functions were developed from these power bases using silver and other media. It is hardly surprising, therefore, that during the following century Ireland's first towns developed in the same locations as some of the *longphuirt*.[83]

Southern Uí Néill, Brega and Clann Cholmáin

As we have seen, Southern Uí Néill is the over-kingdom in which all of the provenanced hoards containing early Samanid dirhams and silver bullion of southern Scandinavian/Baltic type are located. It is also the over-kingdom with the highest number of individual Viking-Age hoards in Ireland, numbering almost fifty, and with by far the greatest overall bullion value. The great silver wealth of this kingdom is unquestionable, and it is clear that the majority of these hoards represent wealth in Irish rather than Scandinavian hands, even if it was the existence of Viking Dublin on its border zone that made the silver obtainable.[84] Southern Uí Néill was the most powerful polity in ninth- and tenth-century Ireland, and the most significant of its three main groupings (septs) was Clann Cholmáin.[85] Over 60% of the hoards in Southern Uí Néill are from Clann Cholmáin's kingdom of Mide, by far the greatest number from a single kingdom in Viking-Age Ireland. In bullion terms, however, most of this silver derives from a number of finds from around Lough Ennell, Co. Westmeath, the location of Clann Cholmáin's royal centre.

Two of the Clann Cholmáin kings – Máelsechlainn and his son, Flann Sinna – held the high-kingship of Ireland. The seventy years of their joint kingships (846–916) is also the formative period when *longphuirt* and noteworthy quantities of silver first appear in Viking-Age Ireland. The sources show that these kings allied with the Dublin Vikings on occasion, sometimes through intermarriage, even if relations were often hostile.[86] The size and nature of the hoards deposited within Clann Cholmáin territory, particularly at the royal centre of Lough Ennell, shed light on this relationship: eight hoards in all and an impressive amount of Viking-Age silver.[87] Largely characterised by ingots and hack-silver rather than ornaments, the size and quantity of these hoards compensate for their apparent ordinariness. The sheer amount of wealth that the Lough Ennell silver represents is paralleled in only a few other locations in the Viking world, such as Cuerdale and Spillings. The hoards total a little over 50kg of silver – over half the total weight of Ireland's Viking-Age hoards. One of them is the Dysart hoard which, as noted above, contains a selection of bullion hack-silver and early Samanid dirhams that may represent a distinct parcel of Gotlandic origin.

The second most important kingdom in Southern Uí Néill was Northern Brega. Although it had a tradition of enmity with Viking Dublin, it occasionally used the Scandinavians as allies in its power plays with Clann Cholmáin, its over-kings. Some of the six hoards that contain early Samanid dirhams and/or silver bullion of southern Scandinavian/Baltic type are from Northern Brega, including those from Drogheda, Millockstown and Leggagh. These three hoards were deposited between *c.* 905 and *c.* 920, fairly closely mirroring the years when Dublin's ruling elite were in exile in England (902–17) following the 902 attack. The king of Northern Brega played a leading role in this attack, and it has been suggested that his over-king, Flann Sinna of Clann Cholmáin, may have assumed the overlordship of Dublin during the period that followed.[88] However, it is clear from the deposition dates of the Northern Brega hoards, and of the important Dysart hoard from neighbouring Mide (*c.* 910), that Scandinavian economic activity continued apace in Dublin, even if its military elite were absent. Indeed, excavations at Temple Bar West demonstrate that there was no break in Dublin's occupation following the events of 902.[89]

The apparent connection between these Southern Uí Néill mixed hoards – to which might be added the coinless hoard from Loughcrew in Mide – and the period when Dublin's Scandinavian rulers were in exile is intriguing. Most of the dated contexts for hoards containing silver bullion of southern Scandinavian/ Baltic type or early Samanid dirhams (which on current evidence are also closely linked to Gotland) suggest that these materials arrived in Dublin around the time of this exile or during the period of upheaval immediately preceding it. Could some southern Scandinavian have seized the opportunity of a power vacuum in Dublin to develop a new trade network, perhaps in the knowledge that a powerful Irish king, presumably Flann Sinna, was now the overlord? This may not have been without precedent. Were the tangible links between Dublin and the southern Scandinavian/Baltic region in the early tenth century a repetition of the 840s, when ambitious 'Danes', perhaps operating out of Kaupang, may have exploited disruption among the Dublin Scandinavians to establish a trading site in their own image?

Notes

1 The author wishes to thank James Graham-Campbell and Tom Horne for their comments on a draft of this chapter; Maeve Sikora of the National Museum of Ireland (NMI), for providing some of the photographs; and Nick Hogan of University College Cork for producing the maps.
2 Suggested by Tom Horne (personal communication).
3 See Sheehan (2001), pp. 54–9; Sheehan (2011), pp. 98–9.
4 X-ray fluorescence (XRF) and lead isotope analyses may determine this in the future. Analyses of some of Scotland's hoards, including ones with strong Hiberno-Scandinavian elements such as that from Skaill, Orkney, have revealed a few ingots that may have used Islamic coins as their main silver source: Kruse and Tate (1992), pp. 74–5.
5 Griffiths (2010), pp. 39–45.
6 This is the Dysart Island (no. 4) hoard, and it is referred to in this chapter as the Dysart hoard.
7 For Loughcrew: Sheehan (1998), p. 189 and fig. 6.8; Graham-Campbell and Sheehan (2009), p. 85 and fig. 7; for Dysart no. 4: Ryan *et al.* (1984), pp. 339–56 and pls 6–12; for 'Co. Dublin': Graham-Campbell (1976), pp. 49, 62, 66 and pl. 2.
8 *SGW*, vol. 1, p. 109.
9 Ryan *et al.* (1984), pp. 341, 344 (no. 95) and pl. 9.25; Sheehan (1998), pp. 184–5 and fig. 6.2.
10 *CH*, pp. 91–2.
11 Ó Ríordáin (1973), p. 25 (no. 11).
12 *CH*, p. 106.
13 *CH*, p. 106; Blackburn (2011), p. 242, fig. 11b; Woods in this volume.
14 *SGW*, vol. 1, pp. 104–7.
15 *SH*, p. 16; Östergren in this volume.
16 Unpublished. NMI registration number 1997:41.
17 Ryan *et al.* (1984), p. 341 (no. 96) and pl. 9.24; p. 365 (no. 21) (where it is misidentified as an ingot fragment); Sheehan (1998), p. 184 and fig. 6.2.
18 Graham-Campbell (1976), pl. 2, bottom right.
19 Unpublished. NMI registration number X4576.
20 Kilger (2008), p. 237.
21 Bøe (1940), pp. 108 (W16), 113 (W61).
22 *CH*, p. 102.
23 Broughton (2011), nos 29, 166.

24 Noon (2014), no. 9.
25 Blackburn (2011), pp. 234, 259 (appendix 3 and pl. 4 [no. 1]).
26 Sheehan (1990), pp. 50–2.
27 *CH*, p. 119.
28 *SGW*, vol. 2, pp. 211–12 (no. 525) and pl. 55.3.
29 *CH*, p. 119.
30 Sheehan (1998), p. 189 and fig. 6.8; Graham-Campbell and Sheehan (2009), p. 85 and fig. 7.
31 Bøe (1940), pp. 122–4 and fig. 85.
32 Bøe (1940), p. 113 (W60).
33 *CH*, p. 109 n. 6, 119, 131 n. 18.
34 Bøe (1940), p. 124.
35 Ryan *et al.* (1984), pp. 341–2 (no. 111) and pl. 9.6.
36 Hårdh (2016).
37 Wamers (2011), p. 309.
38 Along with an ingot and a fragment of an octagonal-sectioned ring: Graham-Campbell (1976), p. 49 and pl. 2.
39 Bøe (1940), pp. 112–13 (W59) and fig. 75.
40 Brooks and Graham-Campbell (1986), pp. 95–6 and fig. 6.1.
41 Broughton (2011), no. 32.
42 *CH*, pp. 88–9, figs 5.2–3.
43 Downes (2007), no. 17.
44 Graham-Campbell (1995), p. 144.
45 Griffiths (2012), no. 37.
46 Noon (2014), no. 15.
47 Blackburn (2011), p. 259 and pl. 4.4.
48 Redknap (2004), p. 157.
49 Brooks and Graham-Campbell (1986), pp. 105–10; Hadley *et al.* (2016).
50 *CH*, pp. 75, 73–4 (on the shape and manufacture of *Gusskuchen* ingots).
51 *SGW*, vol. 1, p. 231.
52 See also Williams (2011), pp. 70–1.
53 The data for Map 20.2 and Table 20.1 is derived from the Fitzwilliam Museum's online 'Checklist of Coin Hoards from the British Isles', with the addition of the hoards from Silverdale, the Vale of York and Furness. In some cases the deposition dates of hoards have been adjusted in line with proposals made by Williams (2011).
54 Blackburn (2008), p. 41.
55 Skre (2008).
56 Sindbæk (2011), pp. 57–9.
57 Sheehan (1998), pp. 184–92.
58 Kilger (2008), pp. 235–40 and fig. 7.21; see also Jankowiak in this volume.
59 Hårdh (2007), p. 135.
60 Amlé (2015), pp. 28–9.
61 Kilger (2008), p. 237.
62 Horne (personal communication).
63 Sheehan (2014), pp. 210, 216.
64 *SGW*, vol. 1, p. 109.
65 Kilger (2008), p. 237.
66 Kenny (1994).
67 Dolley (1972).
68 Dolley (1966), pp. 26–7.
69 Graham-Campbell (1993).
70 Graham-Campbell (2001), pp. 212–17.
71 Boon (1986), pp. 92–7.

72 Graham-Campbell (1993), p. 83.
73 A hoarding horizon may be broadly defined as a group of hoards that exhibits enough consistent patterns of composition and/or other types of recurring linkages to one another to suggest that they represent a deposition trend that may relate to a particular phase or phenomenon, or even to a specific event.
74 Purcell and Sheehan (2013), pp. 37–41; Sheehan (2015).
75 Kenny (1987), pp. 512–15; Sheehan (1998), pp. 173–6.
76 Sheehan (2008), pp. 290–3; Williams (2015), pp. 108–14.
77 Williams (2015), pp. 104–8.
78 Sheehan (2014), pp. 210–11.
79 Sheehan (2014), pp. 195–6.
80 Wallace (2014).
81 Purcell and Sheehan (2013), p. 41.
82 Downham (2003–4), p. 238.
83 Kelly (2015), pp. 91–2.
84 Kenny (1987), p. 512.
85 Downham (2003–4).
86 Purcell and Sheehan (2013), pp. 37–41 and *passim*.
87 Ryan *et al.* (1984); Maas (2015).
88 Purcell and Sheehan (2013), pp. 45–6.
89 Simpson (2010), pp. 420–1.

Bibliography

Amlé, A. (2015), 'Western silver from the east: Hiberno-Norse and Gotlandic contacts in the Viking Age', unpublished MA thesis, Uppsala University.

Blackburn, M. (2008), 'The coin-finds', in *ME*, pp. 29–74.

Blackburn, M. (2011), 'The Viking winter camp at Torksey, 872–3', in *VCC*, pp. 221–64.

Bøe, J. (1940), *Norse Antiquities in Ireland* [= H. Shetelig (ed.), *Viking Antiquities in Great Britain and Ireland*, vol. 3], Oslo.

Boon, G. C. (1986), *Welsh Hoards 1979–1981*, Cardiff.

Brooks, N. P. and J. Graham-Campbell (1986), 'Reflections on the Viking-Age silver hoard from Croydon, Surrey', in M. Blackburn (ed.), *Anglo-Saxon Monetary History: Essays in Memory of Michael Dolley*, Leicester, pp. 91–110; rev. ed. in N. Brooks, *Communities and Warfare, 700–1400*, London, pp. 69–92.

Broughton, D. (2011), 'LANCUM-65C1B4: Early medieval hoard', finds.org.uk/database/artefacts/record/id/462949 (accessed 15 December 2019).

Dolley, R. H. M. (1966), *The Hiberno-Norse Coins in the British Museum*, London.

Dolley, R. H. M. (1972), 'The *c.* 1843 Leggagh (Nobber) coin-hoard reconsidered', *Ríocht Na Mídhe: Records of the Meath Archaeological and Historical Society* 5: 14–21.

Downes, A. (2007), 'SWYOR-AECB53: Early medieval hoard', finds.org.uk/database/artefacts/record/id/198978 (accessed 15 December 2019).

Downham, C. (2003–4), 'The Vikings in Southern Uí Néill to 1014', *Peritia* 17–18: 233–55.

Graham-Campbell, J. (1976), 'The Viking-Age silver hoards of Ireland', in B. Almqvist and D. Greene (eds), *Proceedings of the Seventh Viking Congress, Dublin, 15–21 August 1973*, Dublin, pp. 39–74.

Graham-Campbell, J. (1993), 'A "vital" Yorkshire Viking hoard revisited', in M. Carver (ed.), *In Search of Cult: Archaeological Investigations in Honour of Philip Rahtz*, Woodbridge, pp. 79–84.

Graham-Campbell, J. (1995), *The Viking-Age Gold and Silver of Scotland (AD 850–1100)*, Edinburgh.

Graham-Campbell, J. (2001), 'The northern hoards: from Cuerdale to Bossall/Flaxton', in N. J. Higham and D. H. Hill (eds), *Edward the Elder 899–924*, London, pp. 212–29.

Graham-Campbell, J. and J. Sheehan (2009), 'Viking Age gold and silver from Irish crannogs and other watery places', *Journal of Irish Archaeology* 18: 77–93.

Griffiths, D. (2010), *Vikings of the Irish Sea: Conflict and Assimilation AD 790–1050*, Stroud.

Griffiths, R. (2012) 'YORYM-CEE620: Early medieval hoard', https://finds.org.uk/database/artefacts/record/id/504460 (accessed 15 December 2019).

Hadley, D. M. *et al.* (2016), 'The winter camp of the Viking Great Army, AD 872–3, Torksey, Lincolnshire', *The Antiquaries Journal* 96: 23–67.

Hårdh, B. (2007), 'Oriental-Scandinavian contacts on the Volga, as manifested by silver rings and weight systems', in *SEVA*, pp. 135–47.

Hårdh, B. (2016), *The Perm'/Glazov Rings: Contacts and Economy in the Viking Age between Russia and the Baltic Region*, Lund.

Kelly, E. P. (2015), 'The *longphort* in Viking-Age Ireland: the archaeological evidence', in *VIB*, pp. 55–92.

Kenny, M. (1987), 'The geographical distribution of Irish Viking-age coin hoards', *Proceedings of the Royal Irish Academy* 87c: 507–25.

Kenny, M. (1994), 'An early tenth century Samanid half dirham from Millockstown, Co. Louth', *Spinks Numismatic Circular* 102: 156.

Kilger, C. (2008), 'Kaupang from afar: aspects of the interpretation of dirham finds in northern and eastern Europe between the late 8th and early 10th centuries', in *ME*, pp. 199–252.

Kruse, S. E. and J. Tate (1992), 'XRF analysis of Viking Age silver ingots', *Proceedings of the Society of Antiquaries of Scotland* 122: 295–328.

Maas, J. (2015), 'The Viking events of AD 902–19 and the Lough Ennell hoards', in E. Purcell *et al.* (eds), *Clerics, Kings and Vikings: Essays on Medieval Ireland in Honour of Donnchadh Ó Corráin*, Dublin, pp. 251–62.

Noon, S. (2014) 'LANCUM-FA14C8: Early medieval hoard', finds.org.uk/database/artefacts/record/id/630959 (accessed 15 December 2019).

Ó Ríordáin, B. (1973), *Viking and Medieval Dublin, National Museum Excavations, 1962–1973: Catalogue of Exhibition*, Dublin.

Purcell, E. and J. Sheehan (2013), 'Viking Dublin: enmities, alliances and the cold gleam of silver', in D. M. Hadley and L. Ten Harkel (eds), *Everyday Life in Viking-Age Towns: Social Approaches to Towns in England and Ireland, c. 800–1100*, Oxford, pp. 35–60.

Redknap, M. (2004), 'Viking-Age settlement in Wales and the evidence from Llanbedrgoch', in J. Hines *et al.* (eds), *Land, Sea and Home*, Leeds, pp. 139–75.

Ryan, M. *et al.* (1984), 'Six silver finds of the Viking period from the vicinity of Lough Ennell, Co. Westmeath', *Peritia* 3: 334–81.

Sheehan, J. (1990), 'A pair of Viking-Age animal-headed arm-rings from County Cork', *Journal of the Cork Historical and Archaeological Society* 95: 41–54.

Sheehan, J. (1998), 'Early Viking-age silver hoards from Ireland and their Scandinavian elements', in H. B. Clarke *et al.* (eds), *Scandinavia and Ireland in the Early Viking Age*, Dublin, pp. 166–202.

Sheehan, J. (2001), 'Ireland's Viking-age hoards: sources and contacts', in A.-C. Larsen (ed.), *The Vikings in Ireland*, Roskilde, pp. 51–9.

Sheehan, J. (2008), 'The *longphort* in Viking Age Ireland', *Acta Archaeologica* 79: 282–95.

Sheehan, J. (2011), 'Hiberno-Scandinavian broad-band arm-rings', in *CH*, pp. 94–100.

Sheehan, J. (2014), 'Silver', in I. Russell and M. Hurley (eds), *Woodstown: A Viking-Age Settlement in Co. Waterford*, Dublin, pp. 194–222.

Sheehan, J. (2015), 'Fighting with silver: the Woodstown assemblage', in *VIB*, pp. 161–76.

Simpson, L. (2010), 'The first phase of Viking activity in Ireland: archaeological evidence from Dublin', in J. Sheehan and D. Ó Corráin (eds), *The Viking Age: Ireland and the West*, Dublin, pp. 418–29.

Sindbæk, S. (2011), 'Silver economies and social ties: long-distance interaction, long-term investments – and why the Viking Age happened', in *SEMSS*, pp. 41–65.

Skre, D. (2008), 'Post-substantivist towns and trade AD 600–1000', in *ME*, pp. 327–41.

Wallace, P. F. (2014), 'Weights', in I. Russell and M. Hurley (eds), *Woodstown: A Viking-Age Settlement in Co. Waterford*, Dublin, pp. 222–55.

Wamers, E. (2011), 'The Duesminde hoard', in *SEMSS*, pp. 309–20.

Williams, G. (2011), 'The Cuerdale coins', in *CH*, pp. 39–71.

Williams, G. (2015), 'Viking camps and the means of exchange in Britain and Ireland in the ninth century', in *VIB*, pp. 93–116.

Part V

Conclusions

21 Some reflections on Gotland

Slavery, slave-traders and slave-takers

Dagfinn Skre[1]

Slavery in the early medieval period is an utterly elusive phenomenon, particularly in societies that have left few or no contemporary written records; for instance, Iron- and Viking-Age Scandinavia. Although significant insights into the keeping of slaves in Scandinavia have been obtained on the basis of place names together with archaeological evidence, sagas and law codes,[2] many questions remain unanswered. Assessments of the economic and social significance of slavery at different times in the first millennium AD, including my own,[3] remain conjectural.

Even more elusive is the Scandinavian involvement in overseas slave-taking and -trading. A few sources do testify to Viking involvement in such activities, but the lack of well-founded estimates of the volume, extent and chronology is a constant frustration for scholars of the late eighth to eleventh centuries. Given the current state of research, we cannot be sure whether slave-taking and -trading was a (if not *the*) central motive for hostile Viking activities overseas, or secondary to other objectives; whether it was routine, or undertaken by only a few. The best means of clarifying these issues would be a broad, interdisciplinary research programme devoted to careful analysis of all the indirect and circumstantial evidence, aiming to reveal any imprints left by slavery there. Yet even then a clear picture is unlikely to emerge, although some contours of slave-taking and -trading might appear eventually.

The magnitude and complexity of such an undertaking is awe-inspiring. In the first place, scholars of disparate disciplines would need to find common ground for discussion, as well as reaching agreement on the project's objectives – difficulties commonly encountered by interdisciplinary projects, especially in the publication phase.

These factors were probably among the main obstacles to organising a concerted research effort addressing Viking slave-taking and -trading until 2011, when the *Dirhams for Slaves* project was launched. My first impressions of the project left me hopeful that significant results would be produced.[4] The project's research design appeared solid; focusing on the import of dirhams to Scandinavia in the ninth and tenth centuries supplied common ground for the historians, numismatists and archaeologists on the project team.

Not only did the project have the courage to address one of the most problematic research themes in Viking scholarship, but it was also boldly named after the team's main hypothesis. Any concerns that the project name pre-empts the conclusion and lapses into confirmation bias are effectively laid to rest by this volume: the judicious inclusion of a variety of scholars allows a multitude of voices and opinions to be heard.

The editors have invited me to provide some concluding comments to this book, leaving it up to me to decide the scope and nature of my remarks. Rather than attempting to synthesise the many and diverse contributions, I will reflect upon two issues where the contributions have inspired my own thinking: the holding of slaves in Scandinavia; and the possibility that Gotlanders were involved in the slave trade in the ninth and tenth centuries.

Slaves and slavery in Scandinavia

Exploring the 'trade system that connected northern Europe and the Islamic world in the ninth and tenth centuries AD' was the project's main aim,[5] its central hypothesis being that the thousands of Islamic dirhams found in northern Europe are a residue of this system, and that slaves were the most prominent commodity brought into it by Scandinavians. The project also addressed several questions regarding the drivers in the trade system, as well as its ramifications in Scandinavia; given its suggested magnitude and duration, these ramifications are potentially massive and varied. For instance, was the slave trade a main driver behind the Scandinavian monetisation boom in the late ninth and tenth centuries?

Understandably, such wider ramifications in Scandinavia are beyond the scope of this volume, but I hope that future publications will address these issues. The book is intended to explore 'the Scandinavian end' of the trade system. Based on evidence primarily from Gotland, and to a lesser extent from the rest of Scandinavia, the Baltic coast, the British Isles and Ireland, the editors have quite successfully built a case for understanding the bulk of Islamic silver found there as payment for slaves.

David Wyatt's contribution on Britain and Ireland and Stefan Brink's on Scandinavia do touch upon one of the wider ramifications:[6] slavery in Scandinavia and in some of the lands settled by Scandinavians. It is fruitful to compare their respective approaches, which show some profound similarities. Both draw on Orlando Patterson's seminal work,[7] whose cultural and social perspectives on slavery have tended to displace the formerly dominant economic approach. Yet while both embrace this, they make quite different uses of it.

Illustrative of this difference is Wyatt's extensive use of one of Patterson's main points:[8] the connection between slaveholding and honorific culture. Patterson holds that honour is a prominent hallmark of slaveholding societies, some of which valued the enhancement of the slave-owner's honour as the sole reason for keeping slaves. This perspective forms the basis of Wyatt's analysis of slavery in Britain and Ireland, whereas Brink devotes far less of his discussion to it.

Perhaps Wyatt overstates the significance of slaveholders' honour as motivation for slaveholding. By contrast, Brink's decision to omit honour as a factor when assessing the character and volume of slaveholding in Scandinavia is surprising, in light of his commitment to social and cultural perspectives on slavery.[9] Brink uses these perspectives to a different end. In his reading of the evidence on the rights and obligations of the thrall (*þræll*), he considers these to be similar to those of most other people: a difference of degree, rather than of kind. Brink suggests that while thralls were positioned at the lower end of two scales (unfree–free and low–high social prestige), there were no sharp distinctions between thralls and non-thralls in Viking-Age Scandinavia, and that the relation between the slaveholder and his thrall was not outright ownership, but rather a patron–client relationship characterised by dependency and fidelity. Only as the church gained a foothold were social categories more firmly defined and social mobility reduced; in his view, before then Scandinavian societies lacked economic complexity, and slaveholding was small-scale and practised mainly by the elite.[10]

Some aspects of Brink's argument may be challenged. Firstly, the features of Scandinavian culture and society that lead him to blur the distinction between free and unfree, for instance the fact that some slaves held high positions,[11] are widespread in slaveholding societies.[12] Brink seems to apply a modern meaning of the term 'free', evaluating levels of freedom based on how far an individual could decide where to live, whom to marry and so on. However, in written evidence the term 'free' does not imply individual autonomy; it is limited to meaning that one is not a slave – and thus protected by the law and other concomitant privileges.[13] Igor Kopytoff's statement on freedom as opposed to slavery is certainly valid for early medieval Scandinavia:

> But freedom is a notoriously ethnocentric concept [...]. Ethnographic-ally, the opposite of slavery in most societies [...] is some notion not of autonomy but of citizenship, of civic belongingness, of attachment to structure rather than detachment from it.[14]

In light of my own research, I find it difficult to agree with Brink that the agrarian economy of Viking-Age Scandinavia had little need for slave labour. As indicated in the paragraph from the *Older Frostathing Law* cited at the start of his chapter in this volume, fairly average farms could have slaves, at least in some regions. Furthermore, production was not limited to subsistence, as Brink seems to suggest. A farm needed to produce a surplus in order to acquire necessities that were not produced on the spot, such as iron, cooking vessels, flax, wool, hides, whetstones and horses. Some of this surplus came from the farm proper, some from woodlands, coast and mountains, and production increased between around 800 and the eleventh century. The small-scale production and distribution of the seventh and eighth centuries was expanded, reorganised and developed by means of new techniques into large-scale commodity production for long-distance trade, some of which was distributed at the towns and markets established in the period.[15] In western Scandinavia, this included commodities like whetstones, soapstone vessels, iron, quern-stones and reindeer antler.

Thus, the Scandinavian economy can hardly be characterised as less complex than contemporary societies with extensive slaveholding. The sharp increase in production around 800, and again at the turn of the millennium, would have needed considerable manpower. In addition, the overseas raiding and settlement of the Viking period would have drained manpower from the homelands: forced labour may have been necessary for the period's economic boom.

Although understanding what is meant by 'free' in the written sources and assessing economic complexity in Scandinavian societies are key issues when considering Viking-Age slavery in Scandinavia, my main reservation remains Brink's choice not to include honour as a factor. The evidence is clear that honour held profound significance in Scandinavian society and culture, and was intimately connected to warrior identity. From the Roman Iron Age on, most male aristocratic graves display the man's warrior identity. In his contribution to this volume, Ingmar Jansson describes the centralisation of power in *Sviþjoð* starting in the late sixth to seventh centuries, culminating in the formation of the Swedish kingdom in the late Viking Age. Evidently, this power was held by a warrior elite. The grave finds, for instance in Vendel and Valsgärde, as well as the written evidence, for instance the skaldic poem *Ynglingatal*, leave little doubt as to the martial identity and activities of the ruling stratum.

This warrior identity, which in the Roman Iron Age was limited to the ruling elite, became increasingly common among the male population, with some leaps and regional variations. In the Viking Age, male graves without weapons are hard to find in many parts of Scandinavia. As early as the Migration Period, the probable introduction of wergild suggests that assessment of honour was widely practised in Scandinavia.[16] Using William Ian Miller's concept of a talionic culture, the early Germanic law codes' price-ranges of lives and limbs can be read as evidence in favour of just this. 'Talionic cultures tended to be honor cultures', writes Miller. 'The entire moral and social order involved sizing people up; that's what honor was, and still is, all about'.[17]

It was not only a matter of warrior identity and wergild: honour came to permeate all levels of society. Thus, as Wyatt notes in his chapter, most northern European societies had strict honour codes at this time, for instance in the establishment and maintenance of social ties through gift-giving, and mutual loyalty through various patron–client relationships (e.g. landowner–tenant and commander–warrior) as well as between equals (e.g. *félags*-men, kinsmen and members of warrior bands). The main glue in these relationships was honour. Breaking the obligations embedded in these bonds put one's honour in jeopardy – a great hazard in a society in which honour was the basis of one's social standing on which all relations and possessions rested.[18]

Slaves were an integral part of this honour culture, since keeping these honourless people served to enhance their master's honour. But there is more to it than that: the very idea that if a person had none of these social relations, he or she possessed no rights, even to life itself, reflects the acknowledgement of one's own and all other free men and women's dependence on being socially connected.

As we have noted, these elements in Scandinavian culture date from the Roman and Migration Periods at the latest, becoming widespread thereafter and intensifying during the Viking Age. In his chapter, Brink argues that slaveholding was restricted to the elite, based on the paucity of burials containing slaves who had been killed to follow their master into the grave, and the tendency of such graves to be particularly richly furnished. However, a survey I conducted in 1998 suggests that slaves were given as grave goods in both richly and modestly furnished graves.[19] I identified nineteen inhumation graves containing more than one individual and indications that one of these individuals had been killed immediately before burial. One of the reasons for the paucity of such graves is that cremations were predominant in most parts of Iron- and Viking-Age Scandinavia, making it hard to decide whether the cause of death was violent. Some indications may be found, though. From analyses of the 1,082 cremations kept in the Museum of Cultural History in Oslo, Per Holck found that forty-eight graves (4.4%) contained more than one individual, roughly the same proportion as is found elsewhere in Scandinavia.[20] Based on gender and the much higher frequency of pathological features in these graves (29.2% against the normal 6.4%), he concluded that, probably, a slave had been killed and buried in many of these graves.[21]

Thus, there is good reason to believe that slaveholding existed across most of the social spectrum and that it was more widespread in Iron- and Viking-Age Scandinavia than Brink suggests. The fact that much of the Vikings' activity overseas took place among strangers may have reduced any qualms about, or restrictions on, taking slaves. Patterson[22] and others emphasise that ethnic differences stimulate slave-taking – it makes the captives outsiders in every sense. If slaves were an essential commodity in an extensive trade system, and if slave-taking and -trading was a prominent Viking activity, it becomes hard to imagine that this had no influence on the volume of slaveholding in Scandinavia. This is especially so because of the economic expansion in Viking-Age Scandinavia and the leeching of manpower in the same period; both would have contributed to an increased demand for slaves. Mats Roslund's conclusions on slaveholding accord better with these developments. By analysing the distribution and development of Slavic-type vessels retrieved in Sweden and produced in local clays, Roslund suggests that Slavic slaves were held on Gotland and elsewhere in Sweden from the tenth century onwards.[23]

Why Gotland?

The bulk of this book is dedicated to Gotland and the variety of factors that may help explain the abundance of Islamic silver hoarded there. The contributions offer diverse opinions on where to look for explanations. It seems clear to me that the silver wealth on Gotland does not imply that Gotlanders acquired significantly more silver than the other Scandinavians who were raiding and trading overseas. After all, according to Frankish sources, Vikings extorted some 20,000kg of silver and 340kg of gold from the Carolingians in the mid- to late ninth century,[24] in addition to the vast payments they received from the British Isles. What distinguishes Gotland from other parts of Scandinavia is the extent to which the island's inhabitants brought the silver back home and buried it. Why did they not keep and spend their wealth in the diaspora, as the marauders of Francia and Britain appear to have done? I will suggest an answer to this question below.

None of the contributions to this book mentions what, to me, seems a significant factor for explaining Gotland's apparently special character among Scandinavian regions in the Viking Age: a connection between the vast quantities of dirhams deposited there from *c.* 800 on and the vast quantities of gold buried on the same island only 250–400 years previously. Migration-Period gold finds on Gotland amount to 3.95kg, some 294 gold *solidi* weighing 1.27kg and a further 2.68kg of gold objects.[25] The majority of the latter are rough rods, bars, rings and spirals intended to be cut up and used for payment. Other Swedish regions have produced a total of *c.* 41kg of gold of the Migration Period, with the neighbouring island of Öland having the highest quantity (some 308 *solidi* and a total of 7.52kg of gold objects).[26]

Only these two islands have such a high proportion of *solidi*, suggesting that they were where much of the Roman and Byzantine gold first arrived in Scandinavia; that they were gateway communities. When connections to the south were abruptly broken off in the mid-sixth century,[27] the Gotlanders already had more than 150, possibly more than 500 years' worth of experience in travelling and obtaining wealth in distant lands. This proficiency may have been sustained in the intervening 250 years by journeys to less distant regions, giving them an advantage when opportunities to reach far to the south opened up again in the decades around 800.

Turning to the Viking Age: did Islamic silver circulate on Gotland, or is it possible that the hoards were buried capital, obtained on long-distance expeditions and safeguarded for spending on similar voyages in the future?[28] There now seems to be firm evidence that silver really was used for payment on Gotland itself. Several contributions in this volume point to the recent finds at Roma, the ancient assembly place of the *Althing*, which are typical of Viking-Age market sites. Majvor Östergren reports the finds in detail.[29] They were retrieved through metal-detecting and seem to be concentrated in five neighbouring sites, probably post-Viking-Age farms, although some may date back to the Roman Iron Age. One of them, Guldåkern ('The Gold Field'), has produced the highest number of finds with the greatest time depth, dating back to the early Roman Iron Age, including 220 coins, mostly cut dirham fragments, and 370 weights, predominantly from the ninth and tenth centuries. Östergren's identification of Guldåkern as a market connected to the *Allthing* seems well founded. Notably, *solidi* have also been found there.

Not only does the early use of silver for payment distinguish Gotland from other regions with market sites, since elsewhere in ninth-century Scandinavia this was restricted to towns:[30] its property structure was different, too. Whereas landed estates with landlords and peasants are typical of densely settled, fertile regions elsewhere in Scandinavia, Gotlandic farmers seem mainly to have been freeholders with farms of fairly equal size. Thus, any social hierarchy on Gotland will have been built on footings other than control of land, tenants and agrarian produce.

As Jacek Gruszczyński and Gustaf Svedjemo note, freeholders dominate on Viking-Age Gotland, and this seems relevant for the inhabitants' opportunity to engage in trade. Olof Holm was the first to identify the correlation between freeholding and trade in Jämtland, central Sweden, primarily datable to the tenth and eleventh centuries.[31] Similar patterns have since been identified in two neighbouring communities in the Upper Setesdal Valley of southern Norway: Valle and Bygland.[32] Both there and in Jämtland, weights, scales and hack-silver are found in a high proportion of graves. On Gotland the evidence for trade comes mainly from hoards, but the correlations appear to be identical: in some Viking-Age communities, where freeholders dominated and where thus a land-owning aristocracy was lacking, trade was open to popular participation. Future studies will surely identify other regions where a similar correlation between property structure and trade indicators can be found – Holm mentions some candidates.[33]

Enterprising Gotland?

Much like any other commodity, slaves were produced, traded and consumed; this volume addresses mainly the second of these economic spheres. Significant for discussing the slave trade is the fact that normally, slave-takers – the producers – were not the ones who brought them to market. In general, most externally sourced slaves (i.e. those not born into slavery) were captured in the course of various types of military operation.[34] For large armies as for small raiding bands, proficiency, equipment, numbers, organisation, supplies, mobility and access to information could mean the difference between life and death. Securing and transporting captives of war or victims of kidnapping placed demands on their captors. Choosing to enslave rather than to ransom, kill or release a captive required a commitment of time and resources from the slave-taker in preventing their escape and keeping them well fed and healthy during what could be a long journey to the slave market. Otherwise the value of the commodity would diminish. Most of the demands on organisation and equipment posed by the feeding, transport and sale of slaves went against the qualities that the commander of an army or war band would have sought to cultivate in his unit. The first two in particular would have depleted supplies, reduced mobility and diverted some of his men to guard- and supply-duty, exposing the army or war band as a whole to great danger, particularly in hostile terrain. Thus, because slave-taking and -trading demanded different types of organisation, resources and skill, the two were rarely parts of one and the same enterprise. According to Patterson, the optimal course of action for slave-takers was to sell their captives to traders as soon as possible.[35]

Reconsidering Gotland in light of these discussions and some of the contributions to this volume, we may well suspect that the islanders were specialised traders dealing primarily in slaves, but possibly in other commodities, too; and that the eastern and southern Baltic coasts and inland waterways towards the Caspian and Black Seas were where they bought, transported and sold their goods. Gotlanders may have forged links with more or less well-established polities, aristocrats or warrior bands which specialised in kidnapping and warfare but had little or no organisation for selling off captives and other kinds of loot.

The slave-takers may have been settled or semi-settled groups of Scandinavians and others along the Baltic coast and inland, probably paid in silver by the slave-traders, with much of this silver being kept or spent in the region – as happened with the Scandinavian diaspora in the west. The slave-traders, on the other hand, would have brought their silver back to the homelands where they were based. Settling in the diaspora would have led to involvement in local hierarchies which might threaten their independence.

To undertake such an enterprise, the Gotlanders would have had to form groups with the necessary size, skills, equipment and networks to negotiate deals with slave-takers; to transport slaves and to control, feed and lodge them while en route; to negotiate deals with buyers; and finally to protect their proceeds on their return home. This would have required specialised equipment, different from that of an army or war band: shackles to restrain the movements of their captives, as well as weapons designed to coerce, scare and inflict pain without wounding and killing (the cinematic and literary cliché is the whip, but there were surely alternatives). They would also have needed the skills and equipment to defend their stock and their profits. Such an enterprise may have developed from trade in other commodities in the east, for instance furs,[36] and these probably continued to constitute a proportion of the Gotlandic traders' business.

In such an enterprise, precious-metal money would have been the preferred means of payment. While trade in Viking-Age Scandinavia would not normally involve such money, except in towns,[37] this light and easily divisible currency would have been ideal for traders who travelled long distances between their base, the area where they acquired commodities and the market. Most likely, they would have preferred to deal in a type of currency that was generally accepted by those from whom they bought and by those to whom they sold their merchandise. The currency of their primary customers, the silver dirhams of the Muslim slave merchants, was ideally suited. Because investments in new stock were made before proceeds were obtained, Gotlanders needed to store sufficient funds in their homeland base while preparing for the next expedition.

Thus Gotland?

An enterprise of the type sketched above would be rather meaningless if the proceeds had little or no use in the homelands other than as dead capital buried in the ground. As discussed in the contribution by Christoph Kilger and several others in this volume, silver may have been used in the homelands for a variety of purposes – not least metalwork, given the indigenous character of Gotlandic ornaments.

The recent evidence from Roma, however, seems to indicate that silver could have been used as payment on Gotland as early as the ninth century, just as it was in the few Scandinavian towns then in existence. In Birka, for example, silver appears to have been used as a means of payment on a modest scale around the time when hoarding started on Gotland, and then on a much larger scale in the tenth century;[38] Hedeby saw a parallel development, and market sites along the southern and eastern Baltic coasts will have followed suit. Gotlandic traders may have found good use for their silver in these markets, not least to buy goods for their own consumption, but possibly also for sale elsewhere. Such practices will have carried silver brought to the north by Gotlanders into the Scandinavian networks that extended to Ireland[39] and to the camps of the Great Army in England.[40]

Why was there no 'Gotland' in western Scandinavia, a region rich in deposited Frankish and British coinage and silver? Why was a similar enterprise not set up to facilitate the sale of commodities – human or otherwise – from trade, tributes, warfare and raiding in the western Viking diaspora? A possible answer might be that the slave trade in the west was already well established by the time Scandinavians started roaming along its coasts and waterways.[41] There may have been no demand for a new enterprise and little room for establishing one there.

One element in the stark divergence between the character of the Swedes' homeland and that of the Gotlanders, discussed by Ingmar Jansson in this volume, may have been that the former were slave-takers while the latter were slave-traders. The clearly martial, hierarchical culture of the Swedes and the distinct apartness of Gotlandic dress and ornament throughout the Viking Age may express these conspicuously different identities.

Although some answers to the question 'Why Gotland?' have been suggested above, one significant point remains. Although Jämtland and Upper Setesdal apparently display some parallel developments, the first evidence of trading activity on Viking-Age Gotland predates these by more than a century. Nor do we find any indications of trading activity in the vast majority of Scandinavian regions which were dominated by freeholders on farms of fairly equal size. There must, therefore, be something other than freeholding that distinguishes Gotland, Jämtland and Upper Setesdal, and there must be a reason why Gotlandic trade predates the other two by a century.

Although Gotland is an island and the other two are inland regions, this is not the key issue. More important is the position of the two mainland regions: between a commodity-producing area and a region where that commodity was in high demand. Holm mentions products from the vast woodland areas in Jämtland, such as furs and antler, and identifies the town of Birka in Uppland as the most likely main market – probably the place where Jämtlanders obtained silver and weighing implements.[42] Traders from Upper Setesdal may have acquired bog iron produced in the mountain plain around the valley's northern end and brought it to coastal market sites – one potential site is identified in Fjære in the county of Aust-Agder.[43] In both cases it seems that the traders were not selling their own products, but were merchants proper; that is, they bought commodities with the aim of reselling them at a profit elsewhere.

While the Gotlanders specialised in trading slaves and possibly other commodities, operating mainly between the Baltic in the north and the Black and Caspian Seas in the south, they were not positioned between production areas and markets in the manner of the Jämtlanders and the Setesdøls. Instead, as noted above, it is possible that they had plied the networks in those areas from ancient times, especially towards the Black Sea, and as a result had a longstanding culture of travel and trade. And this is where we may find an explanation as to why Gotlanders appear to have been the first in Viking-Age Scandinavia to position themselves as merchants in a long-distance trading system.

Notes

1 I am grateful for valuable comments to preliminary versions of this chapter from Professors Jonathan Shepard, Neil Price and Mats Roslund. Language revision has been conducted by Anthony Zannino and Jonathan Shepard. This paper was written under the auspices of the Avaldsnes Royal Manor Project, funded by Avaldsnes Municipality and the Norwegian Ministry of Education and Research: khm.uio.no/english/research/projects/avaldsnes (accessed 18 December 2019).
2 Iversen (1997); Brink (2012).
3 Skre (1998, 2001, 2002).
4 Based on Jankowiak (2012), DfS-organised presentations at the Leeds International Medieval Congress 2015 and the project's website (see DfS in the Abbreviations and notes on bibliography).
5 DfS, 'Description of the project'.
6 Based on their respective monographs: Wyatt (2009); Brink (2012).
7 Patterson (1982).
8 Wyatt (2009), pp. 61–171; Patterson (1982), pp. 77–101.
9 Brink (2012), pp. 15–18.
10 Brink (2012), pp. 263–9; see also Brink in this volume.
11 See Brink in this volume.
12 E.g. Kopytoff (1982); Patterson (1982).

13 Skre (2014).
14 Kopytoff (1982), pp. 220–1.
15 Skre (2017a).
16 Skre (2017c).
17 Miller (2006), p. x (preface).
18 Meulengracht Sørensen (1995).
19 Skre (1998), pp. 47–50.
20 Holck (1986), pp. 164–7.
21 Holck (1986), pp. 167, 218.
22 Patterson (1982), pp. 117–18, 178.
23 See, e.g., Roslund (2007), pp. 472–3, 505–15; Roslund (2021 forthcoming); Roslund (forthcoming).
24 Sawyer (1971), pp. 100–1.
25 Klang (2013).
26 Herschend (1980), pp. 9, 244.
27 Ljungkvist (2009), pp. 44–7.
28 Skre (2012), p. 61.
29 Östergren (2016).
30 Skre (2017b).
31 Holm (2012, 2015, 2017).
32 Glørstad and Wenn (2017); Skre (2017a), p. 17.
33 Holm (2015), p. 104.
34 Patterson (1982), pp. 105–31.
35 Patterson (1982), p. 106.
36 See Howard-Johnston in this volume.
37 Skre (2011).
38 Gustin (1998).
39 See Sheehan in this volume.
40 See Woods in this volume.
41 Verlinden (1979); McCormick (2001), pp. 733–77.
42 Holm (2015), pp. 85, 92, 100.
43 Skre (2017a), p. 17.

Bibliography

Brink, S. (2012), *Vikingarnas slavar. Den nordiska trädomen under yngre järnålder och äldsta medeltid*, Stockholm.

Glørstad, Z. T. and C. C. Wenn (2017), 'A view from the valley: Langeid in Setesdal, South Norway – a Viking-Age trade station along a mercantile highway', in Z. T. Glørstad and K. Loftsgarden (eds), *Viking Age Transformations: Trade, Craft and Resources in Western Scandinavia*, Abingdon, pp. 191–211.

Gustin, I. (1998), 'Means of payment and the use of coins in the Viking Age town of Birka in Sweden: preliminary results', *Current Swedish Archaeology* 6: 73–83.

Herschend, F. (1980), *Myntat och omyntat guld. Två studier i öländska guldfynd*, Uppsala.

Holck, P. (1986), *Cremated Bones: A Medical-Anthropological Study of an Archaeological Material on Cremation Burials*, Oslo.

Holm, O. (2012), *Självägarområdenas egenart. Jämtland och andra områden i Skandinavien med småskaligt jordägande 900–1500*, Stockholm.

Holm, O. (2015), 'Trading in Viking-period Scandinavia: a business only for a few? The Jämtland case', *Viking and Medieval Scandinavia* 11: 79–126.

Holm, O. (2017), 'The use of silver as a medium of exchange in Jämtland, *c.* 875–1050', in Z. T. Glørstad and K. Loftsgarden (eds), *Viking Age Transformations: Trade, Craft and Resources in Western Scandinavia*, Abingdon, pp. 42–58.

Iversen, T. (1997), *Trelldommen. Norsk slaveri i middelalderen*, vol. 1, Bergen.

Jankowiak, M. (2012), 'Dirhams for slaves: investigating the Slavic slave trade in the tenth century', Oxford Medieval Seminar, All Souls College (27 February 2012), available at: academia.edu/1764468/Dirhams_for_slaves._Investigating_the_Slavic_slave_trade_in_the_tenth_century (accessed 16 December 2019).

Klang, A. (2013), 'Guldfynd på Gotland. En jämnförande studie av guldfynden från folkvandringstiden', unpublished BA thesis, Stockholm University.

Kopytoff, I. (1982), 'Slavery', *Annual Review of Anthropology* 11: 207–30.

Ljungkvist, J. (2009), 'Continental imports to Scandinavia: patterns and changes between AD 400 and 800', in D. Quast (ed), *Foreigners in Early Medieval Europe*, Mainz, pp. 27–49.

McCormick, M. (2001), *Origins of the European Economy: Communications and Commerce AD 300–900*, Cambridge.

Meulengracht Sørensen, P. (1995), *Fortælling og ære. Studier i islændingesagaerne*, Oslo.

Miller, W. I. (2006), *Eye for an Eye*, Cambridge.

Östergren, M. (2016), '"Rudera efter Steenhuus och andra Monumenter". Om Roma som central ort för landet Gotland', in E. Sehlin and C. Emdén (eds), *Roma kloster och cistercienserna*, Visby, pp. 39–64.

Patterson, O. (1982), *Slavery and Social Death: A Comparative Study*, Cambridge, MA.

Roslund, M. (2007), *Guests in the House: Cultural Transmission between Slavs and Scandinavians 900 to 1300 AD*, Leiden.

Roslund, M. (2021 forthcoming), 'Legacy of the disowned: finding *ambátt*s in high medieval Scania and Östergötland through ceramic production', in *IC*.

Roslund, M. (forthcoming), 'Tacit knowing of thralls: style negotiation among the unfree in eleventh- and twelfth-century Sweden', in M. Brittain and T. Clack (eds), *Archaeologies of Contact and Hybridity*, Oxford.

Sawyer, P. (1971), *The Age of the Vikings*, London.

Skre, D. (1998), *Herredømmet. Bosetning og besittelse på Romerike 200–1350 e. Kr.*, Oslo.

Skre, D. (2001), 'The social context of settlement in Norway in the first millennium AD', *Norwegian Archaeological Review* 34: 1–12.

Skre, D. (2002), 'The role of slavery in agrarian production in Norway 200–1100 AD', in P. Hernæs and T. Iversen (eds), *Slavery across Time and Space: Studies in Slavery in Medieval Europe and Africa*, Trondheim, pp. 147–58.

Skre, D. (2011), 'Commodity money, silver and coinage in Viking-Age Scandinavia', in *SEMSS*, pp. 67–91.

Skre, D. (2012), 'Markets, towns and currencies in Scandinavia c. AD 200–1000', in R. Hodges and S. Gelichi (eds), *From One Sea to Another: Trading Places in the European and Mediterranean Early Middle Ages*, Turnhout, pp. 47–63.

Skre, D. (2014), 'Fri er den "som fri kommer til verden". Om frihet i vikingtiden', in S. H. Gullbekk (ed.), *Ja, vi elsker frihet*, Oslo, pp. 172–9.

Skre, D. (2017a), 'Viking-age economic transformations: the west Scandinavian case', in Z. T. Glørstad and K. Loftsgarden (eds), *Viking Age Transformations: Trade, Craft and Resources in Western Scandinavia*, Abingdon, pp. 1–27.

Skre, D. (2017b), 'Monetary practices in early medieval western Scandinavia (5th–10th centuries AD)', *Medieval Archaeology* 61: 277–99.

Skre, D. (2017c), 'Scandinavian monetisation in the first millennium AD: practices and institutions', in J. Mitchell *et al.* (eds), *Encounters, Excavations and Argosies: Essays for Richard Hodges*, Oxford, pp. 291–9.

Verlinden, C. (1979), 'Ist mittelalterliche Sklaverei ein bedeutsamer demographischer Faktor gewesen?' *Vierteljahrschrift Für Sozial- Und Wirtschaftsgeschichte* 66: 153–73.

Wyatt, D. (2009), *Slaves and Warriors in Medieval Britain and Ireland, 800–1200*, Leiden.

Appendix

No.	Site	Parish	Feature	Sample ID	Uncalibrated (years BP)	Calibrated (years calAD)		
						Probability		Highest peak
						68.2%	95.4%	
1	Kanonen	Visby		St 2349	980±10	1021–1037	1017–1146	1017–1045 (83.7%)
2	Apoteket	Visby		St 4605	855±150	1030–1274	880–1410	1030–1274 (68.2%)
3	Apoteket	Visby		St 4606	1020±100	896–1154	776–1216	941–1059 (37.0%)
4	Kalvskinnet	Visby		St 4607	920±110	1022–1216	894–1281	1022–1216 (68.2%)
5	Kalvskinnet	Visby		St 4608	955±100	995–1185	890–1265	995–1185 (68.2%)
6	Hamburgergränd	Visby		St 5542	1285±120	650–881	543–995	650–881 (68.2%)
7	Apoteket	Visby		St 5544	1290±95	652–865	591–969	652–778 (50.7%)
8	Strandgatan	Visby		St 5546	1030±90	894–1151	776–1202	938–1050 (41.4%)
9	Apoteket	Visby		St 5547	990±95	909–1164	778–1256	696–1164 (67.4%)
10	Kaplanen	Visby		St 5548	870±85	1046–1247	1018–1279	1147–1247 (41.5%)
11	Kompaniet	Visby		St 8345	1215±85	690–891	661–982	761–891 (48.3%)
12	Kompaniet	Visby		St 8346	1055±80	885–1118	776–1155	885–1044 (64.9%)
13	Novisen	Visby		St 9777	1090±150	730–1147	661–1217	769–1045 (62.6%)

No.	Site	Parish	Feature	Sample ID	Uncalibrated (years BP)	Calibrated (years calAD)		Highest peak
						Probability		
						68.2%	95.4%	
14	A7	Visby	Hearth	Ua-37774	1165±35	777–941	771–970	802–896 (50.9%)
15	A7	Visby	Building 1, post	Ua-37775	1165±35	777–941	771–970	802–896 (50.9%)
16	A7	Visby	Hearth	Ua-37776	1165±35	777–941	771–970	802–896 (50.9%)
17	A7	Visby	Hearth	Ua-37777	1105±35	895–983	779–1019	940–983 (38.3%)
18	Bandlunde	Burs		St 9517	1170±115	721–981	646–1147	767–981 (63.2%)
19	Bandlunde	Burs		St 9518	1030±115	890–1154	720–1242	890–1154 (68.2%)
20	Fröjel	Bottarve	Smithy	Ua-18941	1000±75	975–1154	889–1210	975–1059 (36.1%)
21	Fröjel	Bottarve	Christian churchyard	Ua-16696	870±70	1046–1244	1029–1265	1147–1225 (37.9%)
22	Fröjel	Bottarve	Christian churchyard	Ua-16697	865±80	1049–1250	1026–1274	1150–1250 (47.1%)
23	Fröjel	Bottarve	Christian churchyard	Ua-16698	695±75	1256–1392	1190–1413	1256–1321 (42.7%)
24	Fröjel	Bottarve	Christian churchyard	Ua-16698	775±75	1170–1287	1044–1389	1182–1287 (65.8%)
25	Fröjel	Bottarve	Christian churchyard	Ua-16700	935±60	1034–1155	995–1219	1034–1155 (68.2%)
26	Fröjel	Bottarve	Christian churchyard	Ua-16701	1120±65	778–994	724–1025	865–994 (61.0%)
27	Fröjel	Bottarve	Christian churchyard	Ua-16702	700±65	1256–1389	1214–1405	1256–1316 (45.7%)
28	Fröjel	Bottarve	Christian churchyard	Ua-16703	670±70	1272–1392	1224–1413	1272–1322 (36.3%)
29	Fröjel	Bottarve	Christian churchyard	Ua-16704	690±70	1260–1391	1215–1410	1260–1320 (42.0%)
30	Spillings	Othem	Wood shavings	Beta-147554	940±70	1025–1160	982–1246	1025–1160 (68.2%)
31	Spillings	Othem	Post	Beta-147555	1220±80	691–888	662–973	761–888 (47.8%)
32	Spillings	Othem	Post	Beta-147556	1450±40	581–645	545–656	581–645 (68.2%)

(*Continued*)

No.	Site	Parish	Feature	Sample ID	Uncalibrated (years BP)	Calibrated (years calAD)		
						Probability		Highest peak
						68.2%	95.4%	
33	Spillings	Othem	Beam	Beta-147557	1550±70	425–569	382–645	425–569 (68.2%)
34	Paviken	Västergarn	Post	Ua-49284	1431±33	603–649	569–659	603–649 (68.2%)
35	Paviken	Västergarn	Hearth	Ua-49285	1318±35	658–764	650–770	650–710 (70.4%)
36	Paviken	Västergarn	Post	Ua-49286	1220±32	725–872	690–889	789–872 (52.6%)
37	Paviken	Västergarn	Post (southern building)	Ua-49287	1089±33	899–991	892–1016	945–991 (44.3%)
38	Gannarve	Hall	Post 3	St 9280	1015±70	905–1151	881–1205	967–1051 (42.5%)
39	Gannarve	Hall	Post 19	St 9281	1030±140	779–1165	695–1256	871–1165 (66.7%)
40	Gannarve	Hall	Hearth 8	St 9278	855±70	1051–1258	1035–1270	1151–1258 (53.1%)
41	Gannarve	Hall	Hearth 8	St 9279	1130±85	777–989	682–1033	855–989 (49.9%)
42	Fjäle	Ala	Building 2	Fjäle 1	755±85	1169–1380	1045–1399	1169–1299 (64.8%)
43	Fjäle	Ala	Building 2	Fjäle 2	795±85	1154–1288	1032–1385	1154–1288 (68.2%)
44	Fjäle	Ala	Building 2	Fjäle 3	845±85	1050–1265	1023–1284	1151–1265 (52.8%)
45	Fjäle	Ala	Building 3	Fjäle 4	900±85	1040–1209	994–1269	1040–1209 (68.2%)
46	Fjäle	Ala	Building 4	Fjäle 5	570±150	1261–1485	1055–1655	1261–1485 (68.2%)
47	Fjäle	Ala	Building 4	Fjäle 6	810±100	1050–1284	1020–1389	1151–1284 (56.6%)
48	Fjäle	Ala	Building 4	Fjäle 7	990±85	981–1158	879–1244	981–1158 (68.2%)
49	Fjäle	Ala	Building 4	Fjäle 8	1025±85	897–1151	777–1206	943–1050 (42.0%)
50	Fjäle	Ala	Building 4	Fjäle 9	1085±75	780–1025	727–1151	876–1025 (66.6%)
51	Fjäle	Ala	Building 4	Fjäle 10	1275±110	658–876	575–988	658–780 (43.1%)

Appendix (Cont.)

No.	Site	Parish	Feature	Sample ID	Uncalibrated (years BP)	Calibrated (years calAD)		Highest peak
						Probability		
						68.2%	95.4%	
52	Fjäle	Ala	Building 5	Fjäle 11	870±85	1046–1247	1018–1279	1147–1247 (41.5%)
53	Fjäle	Ala	Building 5	Fjäle 12	970±100	984–1184	780–1267	984–1184 (68.2%)
54	Fjäle	Ala	Building 5	Fjäle 13	1000±85	972–1156	778–1223	972–1156 (68.2%)
55	Fjäle	Ala	Building 5	Fjäle 14	1010±85	904–1154	778–1218	966–1059 (36.1%)
56	Burge	Lummelunda	'Hoard' building, post	Burge 1	1175±100	726–971	664–1021	768–971 (64.8%)
57	Norra Gnisvärd	Tofta	Floor	Norra Gnisvärd 1	1075±70	887–1025	772–1151	887–1025 (68.2%)
58	Norra Gnisvärd	Tofta	Floor	Norra Gnisvärd 2	1095±48	893–993	778–1024	893–993 (68.2%)
59	Norra Gnisvärd	Tofta	Trench A	Norra Gnisvärd 3	1240±75	687–870	655–967	655–905 (88.6%)
60	Norra Gnisvärd	Tofta	Area K	Norra Gnisvärd 4	620±110	1281–1414	1163–1485	1281–1414 (68.2%)
61	Norra Gnisvärd	Tofta	Area M	Norra Gnisvärd 5	1145±70	777–974	695–1019	857–974 (47.8%)
62	Norrgårde	Sanda	Hearth	St 11377	1370±255	411–961	87–1165	411–902 (64.3%)
63	Norrgårde	Sanda	Pit	St 11378	1145±70	778–972	729–995	864–972 (56.9%)
64	Norrgårde	Sanda	Pit	St 11379	1185±70	724–950	684–984	768–900 (54.8%)
65	Norrgårde	Sanda	Pit	St 11386	630±295	1040–1631	777–1910	1116–1542 (54.3%)

* All calibrations undertaken with OxCal v4.3.2 Bronk Ramsey (2017); r:5; IntCal13 atmospheric curve (Reimer *et al.*, 2013).
** Dates for Fjäle were published in Carlsson (1984) as dates AD corrected with the use of an early linear calibration method devised by Damon *et al.* (1974). The uncalibrated BP dates and uncertainty intervals presented in the table are approximations reverse-calculated with the use of the same method.

Bibliography

Bronk Ramsey, C. (2017). 'Methods for summarizing radiocarbon datasets', *Radiocarbon* 59(2): 1809–33.

Carlsson, D. (1984). 'Change and continuity in the iron age settlement of Gotland', in K. Kristiansen (ed.), *Settlement and Economy in Later Scandinavian Prehistory*, Oxford, pp. 129–53.

Damon, P. E. *et al.* (1974). 'Dendrochronologic calibration of the radiocarbon time scale', *American Antiquity* 39: 350–66.

Reimer, P. J. *et al.* (2013). 'IntCal13 and MARINE13 radiocarbon age calibration curves 0–50,000 years cal BP', *Radiocarbon* 55(4): 1869–87.

Glossary

A: Arabic; G: Greek; IR: Irish; L: Latin; ON: Old Norse; OS: Old Slavonic; SW: Swedish

^{14}C *see* radiocarbon dating

allodial lands   held outright, without acknowledgement of any superior; tenure not conditional upon any obligation to a lord

Althing   assembling of free men (from *þing*, ON) which took place regularly in early Scandinavian society; on Gotland, this may have taken place at Roma and was also known as the *Landsting*, or *Gutnalthing* (i.e. the *Althing* of the Gotlanders)

Baltic Prussia   region inhabited by the Baltic-speaking people known as Prussians

Baltic ware   a style of pottery introduced into Bornholm and other Baltic-facing Danish territories from *c.* 1000 onwards; believed to be of Slavic origin, highly decorated and wheel-thrown (in contrast to the island's earlier, hand-made pottery), it was soon adopted and adapted to local tastes[1]

bullion   gold or silver in a lump, rather than in the form of coin or manufactured articles

bullion economy   where transactions depend on silver weight and any silver (whether coin, ornament, hack-silver or ingot) was valid; in contrast, a coined-money economy gives coin a fixed buying power, despite variations in weight or purity, and presupposes a strong government, able to exclude foreign currency or other bullion[2]

crannóg   [IR] a (normally circular) artificial dwelling island, built on a lake bed, mudbank or islet, characteristic of early medieval Ireland

cropmark   variation in the colour and physical appearance of growing crops caused by differences in the underlying soil, alerting an observer to archaeological features under the surface

cupellation   the process of fire assaying or refining precious metals in a cupel[3]

dar al-Islam   [A] ('home of Islam') at its fullest extent under the Umayyads and early Abbasids, the *dar al-Islam* included much of the former Byzantine and Sasanian (Persian) empires, stretching from Afghanistan and the borders of

China to North Africa and the Iberian peninsula, with raiding into central France and Italy

debt slavery [debt bondage or bonded labour] self-sale or the temporary pledging of free status in exchange for a loan[4]

denier (from L: *denarius*) silver and billon coin current throughout western Europe from the Merovingians onwards; under Charlemagne's reforms of the monetary system, 240 deniers were struck from one pound of silver, with the denier valued at one twelfth of the gold *solidus*; sometimes called a silver penny

diagnostic in archaeology, an artefact or some other aspect of a site known to be associated with a particular time period

die the stamp used for striking coins: the obverse die was attached to the moneyer's workbench, a blank placed on top of it and the reverse die hammered down onto it

die-identical [die duplicate] coins struck from the same pair of obverse and reverse dies

die linked coins struck using the same obverse die but a different reverse die, or vice versa

dinar [A] (from G: *denarion*; L: *denarius*) standard Islamic gold coin, first issued in the later seventh century, initially weighing 4.25g

dirham [A] (from G: *drachma*) standard Islamic silver coin, first issued in the later seventh century and usually weighing between 2.97g and 3g, although both weight and size underwent many variations

Edda two thirteenth-century Icelandic books which are our main source of knowledge about Scandinavian mythology; can refer to either the *Prose (Younger) Edda*, a handbook of Icelandic poetry written *c*. 1230, or the *Poetic (Elder) Edda*, a handbook of Icelandic poetry attributable to Snorri Sturluson

Fernhandelsdenar modern German term for long-distance trading deniers: German coins produced mainly for export to the north and east[5]

FMIS (RAÄ Archaeological Sites Information System) Sweden's very comprehensive, compared to most other countries, GIS database of archaeological sites and monuments; created for planning purposes and developed since the 1930s via nationwide surveys, it contains information on some 1.7 million remains in around 700,000 locations – although new sites are added daily[6]

garþr [ON] farmstead; originally the word for a fence, then the area thereby enclosed, it came to include all the buildings within a farm's fence, both working and residential[7]

geld Germanic term for money in general; payment or tribute; tax paid to the crown by English landholders before the Conquest, and continuing under the Norman kings

GIS (Geographic Information System) database/mapping system which captures, stores and manipulates geographic data; used by archaeologists to plot and analyse site distributions against environmental and other background information gained from remote sensing, digitised maps and other sources

GM1700   database project using the large-scale cadastral maps of Gotland drawn between 1693 and 1705; used to denote this corpus of 1:8,000 maps of Gotland

Götar   one of the two main Swedish groupings (along with the Svear), who lived in Östergötland, Västergötland and Småland

GPS   (Global Positioning System) a radio-navigation system using satellites in space to broadcast highly accurate navigation pulses to users on earth

Guta Lag   ('law of Gotland') one of the earliest laws of Scandinavia, probably written between 1207 and *c.* 1220[8]

Gutar   inhabitants of the island of Gotland

Guta Saga   legendary history of Gotland, probably written between 1220 and 1275, and forming a 2,000-word appendix to one of the main *Guta Lag* manuscripts (B 64)

Gutnalthing   *see Althing*

Gutnish   the language of Gotland

hack-silver   cut or hacked fragments of silver plate, jewellery or other items, treated as bullion or used as currency by weight; frequently found in Viking hoards

haimfylgi   [ON] dowry

hammerscale   oxide coating which forms on red-hot iron and can be separated by hammering

Heimskringla   collection of sixteen Old Norse kings' sagas, attributed to the Icelandic author Snorri Sturluson (d. 1241), recounting the history of Norway to 1177[9]

Hiberno-Scandinavian   term to describe the hybrid culture of Vikings settled in Ireland that has both Irish and Scandinavian elements

hoard   assemblage of items deliberately deposited in the ground; may consist entirely or partially of coins, or of objects other than coins that were held in esteem by the depositor(s); the minimum number of coins deemed to constitute a hoard varies, with some favouring five or more, others only two[10]

hogback   distinctive, rectangular stone with a pitched top, put over tenth-century graves in the north of England and southern Scotland; the upper surfaces usually have interlaced decoration, possibly imitating a house

infield   a farm's land which lies around or near the homestead; land regularly manured and cropped, hence arable land as opposed to pasture

ingot   a mass of cast metal, usually oblong or brick-shaped, whose weight is generally related to portability; ingots of a particular metal, when of standard size and weight, can be used as currency for trade

kämpgrav   (pl. *kämpgravar*) [SW] ('giant's grave') traditional term denoting the substantial, low stone walls of houses characteristic of the Roman Iron Age and Migration Period on Gotland[11]

kernel density estimation   a non-parametric method for estimating the probability density of a random variable; a data smoothing technique which can help visualise temporal and spatial distributions, including clustering and spread

Kufic   [A] of or pertaining to Kufa, near Babylon; used of various forms of Arabic writing; early Islamic coins were inscribed in the Kufic script

jarl   [ON] ('chieftain') Scandinavian under-king; equivalent to the Anglo-Saxon term 'earl'

Länsstyrelsen   Swedish county administrative board; regional government

legend   the words or letters on a coin; where a coin's inscription is distorted or illiterate, it is said to be 'blundered'

Long Cross   a cross having limbs extending to the outer circle on a coin, appearing on the coinage of Æthelred II (978–1013, 1014–16)

longhouse   domestic building including living-quarters, stabling and byres all under one roof, but with access via a single entry-passage

longphort (s.), *longphuirt* (pl.)   [IR] ninth- and tenth-century Viking fortified bases, built to protect fleets and to facilitate raiding and trading[12]

Lunettes coins   late ninth-century pennies and half-pennies from Wessex and Mercia, where the moneyer's name appears on the reverse between two half-moon shapes

manumission   formal release from slavery or servitude

mark   measure of weight, mainly for gold and silver, used throughout western Europe and usually worth 226.8g (although with considerable variations); monetary unit originally based on the value of a mark weight of pure silver

metal-weight economy   *see* bullion economy

miliaresion (s.), *miliaresia* (pl.)   [G] the basic Byzantine silver coin, introduced by Leo III (717–41) and characteristic of the eighth to eleventh centuries; worth 12 to the *nomisma* (*solidus*)

nicking   *see* test marks

obverse   the side of a coin that bears the more important device or inscription; the other side is called the reverse

öre   unit of medieval currency in Sweden, equal to one-eighth of a mark

Otto-Adelheid Pfennig   regional penny from the Harz area, minted between the late tenth and mid-eleventh centuries, bearing the name of Otto III (983–1002) and his grandmother, Adelheid of Burgundy

outfield   a farm's outlying land, generally unenclosed pasture

pecking   *see* test marks

penannular   in the form of a ring but missing a small section of the circumference

penannular brooch   used to fasten clothes, featuring a large pin attached to an incomplete circle

Permian ring   thick round silver rod, decorated with spiral grooves, typically with a hook at one end and a faceted knob at the other; probably designed as neck-rings and, alongside dirhams, acquired by Scandinavian merchants in Russia; named after the region of the Perm in the Kama river basin[13]

phosphate mapping   systematic collection of soil samples from a site analysed to determine their phosphate content; used to detect past human activity, since phosphates are released when organic matter decomposes and certain activities associated with settlement generate phosphate levels that are distinguishable from natural ones[14]

plano-convex   object with one flat and one outwardly curved surface

polyhedral weights both spherical (round) and polyhedral (many-sided) weights, together with balances, appear in the Baltic region towards the end of the ninth century, probably having crossed the lands of Rus from Khazaria and the Islamic world[15]

pressblech embossed metal used to decorate objects such as helmets, drinking horns and cups

Quatrefoil design used on Cnut's coinage, having four leaves radiating out at right angles

RAÄ (abbr. for Riksantikvareämbetet, the Swedish National Heritage Board) government agency for heritage and the historic environment; RAÄ site references give both parish name and serial number (e.g. Roma 85:1)

radiocarbon dating technique for determining the absolute date of organic matter: all living organisms contain a small but constant proportion of the radioactive isotope of carbon (^{14}C); upon death, ^{14}C ceases to be replenished from the environment and what is present decays at a constant rate; by measuring the radioactivity of the carbon remaining in a specimen, its age can be calculated and then calibrated, using curves derived from tree-ring chronologies, to give calendar dates[16]

Ragstone hone stones whetstones used to give a fine edge to cutting tools; between the ninth and fifteenth centuries, their use and trade between Scandinavia and England was dominated by two main types – Norwegian Ragstone and purple Phyllite – both found abundantly throughout the Viking world[17]

regression in statistics, the relationship between the estimated value of a dependent variable and the corresponding values of one or more independent variables; the process of determining such a relationship from observed data

Saqaliba [A] (s. *Saqlab*; from G: *Sklavos*, 'Slav') an ethnonym used by Arab geographers to refer to the Slavs, and sometimes more broadly to other northern people

sceat (also sceatta) small early medieval silver coin minted in England, Frisia and Jutland[18]

siettungar [ON] literally 'sixths'; administrative divisions of Gotland

skeppssättning [SW] ('stone ship') typical early Scandinavian form of burial surrounded by stones in the outline of a ship; also found in northern Germany and to the east of the Baltic

slag waste matter separated from metals during smelting

slipskårestenar [SW] stones carved with parallel grooves, common to north-western Scania, Gotland and Östergötland; believed to be grinding stones

solidus (s.), *solidi* (pl.) [L] gold coin struck in Byzantium at 72 to the pound of gold

spit originally a spade's depth of earth; in archaeology, the thickness of deposit (around 1–10cm) removed as a single operation

Stamford ware one of the earliest forms of lead-glazed earthenware from England, manufactured in Stamford, Lincolnshire from the ninth to thirteenth centuries

strap end   metal fastening on a strap, often highly decorated

stratigraphic association   relationship between objects or structural elements found within the same layer of archaeological remains

styca   name traditionally given to the small copper coin current in Northumbria between the seventh and ninth centuries

Svear   one of the two main Swedish groupings (along with the Götar), based around Lake Mälar

technical ceramics   moulds for producing weights and other metal objects

terminus post quem (*tpq*)   [L] the date after which a hoard must have been deposited, based on determination of the date of the latest coin in the find

test marks   coins, ingots and hack-silver often bear test marks, as users in a bullion economy would seek to verify silver quality by assessing how soft it was: dirhams were characteristically tested by nicking (scratches on the face of the coin, near the edge) in the early and mid-ninth centuries, and by notching (cuts made into the edge of the coin) from the mid-ninth to tenth centuries; in the later Viking Age, coins were tested with the point of a knife, leaving peck marks (small indentations) on their faces, a practice that seems to have emerged in the Danelaw in the last quarter of the ninth century, spreading to Scandinavia by the 930s, but dying out in the mid-eleventh century as coins became more familiar. Older coins in hoards tend to have more test marks and the presence of multiple test marks can indicate that coins were in circulation for some time before their deposition. Analysing test marks and other kinds of secondary treatment on coins (including bending, graffiti, piercing, looping and mounting) thus helps reveal how coins were used[19]

Thing   (*þing*) [ON] an assembly of free men in Scandinavian society

Thor's hammers   miniature hammers, worn as pendants of distinct amuletic character, sometimes threaded onto neck-rings; the powerful Norse god, Thor, would throw his hammer when battling against giants, thus producing thunder and lightning[20]

thrall   (s. *þræll*, pl. *þrælar*) [ON] one who is in bondage to a lord or master; one of the more common, generic terms for a (male) slave in medieval Scandinavia and which was absorbed into English

toft   a homestead, the site of a house and its outbuildings

tradition   series of archaeological phases that share cultural similarities

tredingar   [ON] literally 'thirds'; the equivalent of the English ridings; one of the three administrative divisions of Gotland in the early middle ages

wattle and daub   interwoven twigs plastered with clay or mud used as a building material for huts

wergild   (man price) the value placed on people or property; when an individual was injured or killed, or property stolen, the offender had to pay wergild at the appropriate tariff in recompense to the victim's family or the property's owner

Notes

1 Naum (2016), pp. 85–7; see now Roslund (2021 forthcoming).
2 Kruse (1988).
3 See Gustafsson in this volume.
4 Rio (2017), pp. 42–74 ('Self-sale, debt slavery, and penal enslavement').
5 Steuer (2004), p. 112.
6 Baumert (2016).
7 *GL*, pp. 105–6.
8 *GL*, p. xxxix; Myrberg (2008), p, 164; see also Wyatt in this volume.
9 *Hkr³*, vol. 1, pp. vii–xiii.
10 See Gruszczyński in this volume (n. 2).
11 See Svedjemo in this volume.
12 Kelly (2015).
13 Hårdh (2007), p. 135.
14 Matthews *et al.* (1997).
15 Hårdh (2007), p. 140.
16 See 'radiocarbon dating', in Darvill (ed.) (2002).
17 Crosby and Mitchell (1987).
18 See Howard-Johnston in this volume.
19 Ingvardson (2015), pp. 131–2; see also Screen in this volume.
20 *VW*, pp. 220–1, 253–4.

Bibliography

Baumert, A. (2016), *Riksantikvarieämbetets fornminnesinformationssystem (FMIS)* (RAÄ PM [Memorandum], 7 July 2016).

Crosby, D. D. B. and J. G. Mitchell (1987), 'A survey of British metamorphic hone stones of the 9th to 15th centuries AD in the light of potassium–argon and natural remanent magnetization studies', *Journal of Archaeological Science* 14: 483–506.

Darvill, T. (ed.) (2002), *The Concise Oxford Dictionary of Archaeology*, Oxford.

Hårdh, B. (2007), 'Oriental-Scandinavian contacts on the Volga, as manifested by silver rings and weight systems', in *SEVA*, pp. 135–47.

Ingvardson, G. T. (2015), 'Traces of use', in J. C. Moesgaard, *King Harold's Cross Coinage: Christian Coins for the Merchants of Haithabu and the King's Soldiers*, Copenhagen, pp. 127–38.

Kelly, E. P. (2015), 'The *longphort* in Viking-Age Ireland: the archaeological evidence', in *VIB*, pp. 55–92.

Kruse, S. E. (1988), 'Ingots and weight units in Viking Age silver hoards', *World Archaeology* 20: 285–301.

Matthews, W. *et al.* (1997), 'Microstratigraphic traces of site formation processes and human activities', *World Archaeology* 29: 281–308.

Myrberg, N. (2008), *Ett eget värde: Gotlands tidigaste myntning, ca 1140–1220*, SSA 45, Stockholm.

Naum, M. (2016), 'Viking Age Bornholm: an island on the crossways', in J. H. Barrett and S. J. Gibbon (eds), *Maritime Societies of the Viking and Medieval World*, Oxford, pp. 69–87.

Rio, A. (2017), *Slavery after Rome, 500–1100*, Oxford.

Roslund, M. (2021 forthcoming), 'Legacy of the disowned: finding *ambátt*s in high medieval Scania and Östergötland through ceramic production', in *IC*.

Steuer, H. (2004), 'Minting, silver routes and mining in Europe: economic expansion and technological innovation', in J. Heitzman and W. Schenkluhn (eds), *The World in the Year 1000*, Lanham, MD, pp. 105–17.

Index

Page numbers in *italics* refer to maps, figures, tables, or the Appendix and Glossary at the end of the volume. References to footnotes are given where the index item is not mentioned in the main text or where substantive material is added. Personal names are generally listed by first name followed by family name (for example, Snorri Sturluson and not Sturluson, Snorri). Entries for frequently occurring first names are sequenced in alphabetical order. The letters Æ, Å, Ä and Ö have been alphabetised under A and O (*pace* our Scandinavian colleagues).